AN IRISH FLORA

AN IRISH FLORA

BY

D. A. WEBB, J. PARNELL and D. DOOGUE

With drawings by
HOLLY NIXON

1996
DUNDALGAN PRESS (W. TEMPEST) LTD.
DUNDALK

First published 1943
Seventh Revised Edition 1996

ISBN 0-85221-131-7

PREFACE

The aim of this book is to provide the student or keen amateur with a clear and reliable means of identifying those higher plants which grow wild in Ireland, and to provide it in a format which fits the pocket and at a price which is reasonable. The descriptions have, therefore, been made as brief as is consistent with clarity, and as untechnical as is consistent with brevity.

Brief notes on common cultivated plants are given at the beginning of the account of the family or genus to which they belong; it is hoped that this may encourage the student to bring into closer relation than usual knowledge of wild and cultivated plants.

The keys are designed solely to lead the enquirer as quickly and as painlessly as possible to a decision as to the identity of a plant. They use, therefore, visible characters rather than those of classificatory importance. They have been constructed largely with species which occur in Ireland in view, and they will give misleading results if applied to other plants.

The drawings are intended to illustrate specific structural points or general items of gross morphology. Though based on real material, drawings in the latter category represent more than a single, particular species. The provision of a drawing of every species, for which readers naturally clamour, is still, unfortunately, quite impossible in a low-priced book with a limited market.

The present edition has been completely revised throughout, not only to accommodate the changes in the flora and our knowledge of it over the past twenty years, but also to make other improvements. All the keys have been rewritten, and nearly all of the descriptions modified. A number of newly discovered or recently naturalised species have been added, and a few others, mainly weeds, which appear to be extinct in Ireland, have been omitted. Widely planted species are also included for the first time.

The order of families, genera and species now follows, with a few exceptions, that of the *Census Catalogue*, which itself is based on *Flora Europaea*. Adherence to this scheme has the unfortunate effect of splitting up a few families or genera present in the last edition into idiosyncratic and somewhat ill-defined units - a good example is that of the fern family, the Polypodiaceae. However we hope that this change in layout will satisfy those colleagues who have requested a more up-to-date ordering of the families, whilst not alienating those used to earlier editions. Our adherence to the *Census Catalogue* is not, in fact, absolutely rigid, for we have not admitted all of the species in that work, preferring to omit, for example, species likely to be extinct and those which are rare aliens. On the other hand, we have included some widely naturalised species which are not listed in the *Census Catalogue*. Perhaps our most notable departure from the structure of the *Census Catalogue* is in the Liliaceae which, following current, probably correct schemes, we have split-up.

Much the same story applies to nomenclature. Following the practice of previous editions we have had no hesitation in omitting the 'authorities' - that is the abbreviated authors' names following the Latin name of the plant. In a work of primary taxonomic reference these are essential, but they are of little use unless completed by a bibliographic citation, and their use in secondary works such as this is, in our opinion, a pure superstition, in deference to which erroneously cited authorities are carefully copied from one book to another for half a century or more. The elementary student gains nothing by seeing (L.) P. Beauv. ex J.S. & C. Presl. appended to the name *Arrhenatherum elatius*, and is likely to be repelled by its technical complexity. In general the names of species we use are those which appear in the *Census*

v

Catalogue. However, we have used some new names not in the *Census Catalogue* where we believe there is good reason to do so. The number of synonyms has been increased, as compared to previous editions, so as to facilitate comparison with other works. The general scope of the book has also been increased so as to allow mention of many more subspecies, and, where necessary, varieties and hybrids.

The drawings, which are all new, were executed by Holly Nixon based on examination of both fresh material and herbarium specimens; the latter taken from the herbarium in Trinity College Dublin. Those drawings intended to illustrate specific structural points are placed, as appropriate, within the main body of the book; whereas those which are illustrative of general points of morphology are now placed in the glossary.

The glossary of technical terms has been contracted and illustrations added. Contraction has been achieved by avoiding unnecessary technical terms, which can be easily replaced by conventional English words; for example glabrous, glaucous and sessile are no longer used. We have also included a second glossary which gives the meaning of many of the specific epithets in use in the Irish flora. The concept of such a glossary will be familiar to owners of the first edition of this book, the only one up until now to contain something similar.

We are grateful to several colleagues and students for pointing out errors in the previous edition and for suggesting improvements. If we have rejected the latter it is because they would have further added to the size, complexity and cost of the book, or because they would have involved technicalities which might frighten off the beginner. For this book does not set out to be an authoritative treatise; its aim is merely to present the basic facts of Irish botany with accuracy, simplicity and clarity. We are particularly grateful to Drs. M. Jebb and S. Waldren whose reading of an early draft of the book highlighted a number of inconsistencies.

We have pleasure in acknowledging the financial assistance given by the Provost of Trinity College Dublin, through his development fund, which covered most of the costs of the illustrations.

David Webb, the sole author of the first six editions of this book, was killed in a car accident before he was able to see the complete text of the present edition. Nevertheless, David was, as ever, highly organised and he had left the parts of this edition which he himself wrote and comments on his co-authors work in perfect condition. We hope that any changes we have made subsequent to his death are fully in accord with his wishes.

Herbarium,
School of Botany,
Trinity College Dublin,
November, 1995.

CONTENTS

HOW TO USE THIS BOOK

To identify an unknown plant two distinct parts of this book should be used: the descriptions and the analytical keys.

The keys are devices to enable you to find your way as quickly as possible to the description that applies to the plant which is under consideration. They consist of a series of statements arranged in pairs, the statements of each pair being mutually contradictory, so that, as descriptions of a given plant, one of them must be true and the other false. When you have decided which is true for the plant you are trying to identify, note the number that appears at the right-hand margin, and look for the next pair of statements that bear this number in the left-hand margin. After repeating this process a number of times, you will eventually find in the right-hand margin a name, which should be that of the family, genus or species of your plant.

Suppose that you have a specimen of the Foxglove (*Digitalis purpurea*) and want to identify it by this method. Turn to the general key on page xxi and, as it is obviously a seed-plant, and not a pteridophyte (Fern or Fern ally), start with the pair of statements bearing the number 1. The Foxglove is terrestrial, not aquatic, so you turn next to the pair of statements numbered 2. It is a herb, not a tree or shrub, which leads you to 3; sepals and petals are both clearly visible thus leading you to 4; and as the petals are united into a tubular corolla your plant must be a member of Group B. You therefore start again on page xxiii and since the ovary is superior you proceed to 2 in this part of the key. The green leaves lead you to 23, the simple leaves to 24, the 4 stamens to 26, and so through to 28. Here the fact that the fruit is a capsule tells you that your plant is a member of the Scrophulariaceae which is family number XCVI. Refer, therefore, to the index to find this family or flick through the book until you find the correct page. First read the general diagnosis of the family, checking each point to see that it agrees with your plant. If it does, go on to the generic key which immediately follows the diagnosis. By using it in the same way you should be led to the genus *Digitalis*. On turning up this genus, you will find that it is represented in Ireland only by a single species, so that your quest is at an end. All that remains now is to go through the description carefully and make sure that it tallies with your plant before you accept your identification as correct.

It is very important that the descriptions of the individual species should be read together with the descriptions of the family and genus in which they are included, and that the specific descriptions be interpreted in the light of the information already given in the others. For example, in the descriptions of the various species of *Veronica* no mention is made of the stamens. This is because all the essential information has already been given in the description of the genus (when their number is stated to be 2) and that of the family Scrophulariaceae (where they are stated to be attached to the corolla).

It must be realised that these generic and family descriptions are meant to cover only such Irish species as are included in the genus or family in question. Foreign species may have very different characteristics; but by ignoring them and concentrating on the native ones, it is possible to make such descriptions much shorter, more detailed and more precise.

For the proper examination of flowers a good hand-lens is necessary. It should give a magnification of x10; lenses of less power are of very little use, whilst those which are more powerful often have too small a field of view and too shallow a depth of field.

NOTES ON THE TEXT

The description of each species consists of the following parts:

(1) The Latin name of the plant, printed in bold-faced type, preceeded, in certain cases, by conventional signs indicating that the plant has been introduced to Ireland (whether deliberately or accidentally) by human agency.

* indicates certainly introduced.

† indicates probably or possibly introduced.

Species bearing neither mark are native to Ireland.

(2) The other Latin names (if any) under which the same plant has been known. These are printed in italic type, in parentheses. They include not only genuine synonyms, but also names which have been erroneously applied to Irish plants.

(3) The English name, in bold-faced type, and the Irish name, in italics, if such names exist. With regard to English names, only those which have some currency in speech have been given: book-names invented by nineteenth- or twentieth-century authors have been mostly omitted, and it is far better in these cases to refer to the plant by its Latin name. We, therefore, have decided not to adopt the more formalised structure for English names advocated by a number of UK authors and ridiculed by others. Irish names present a difficult problem. The predominance of the spoken over the written language for centuries, coupled with the fact that the Irish have been, and possibly still are, more interested in words and people than in material objects, has made the application of popular plant names in Ireland extremely fluctuating and obscure. Very many names are applied indifferently to a wide variety of plants: and these, though of interest to the student of folk-lore, have no place in a Flora. The names given in this book are those which seem to have a fairly constant reference to a particular species or genus.

(4) The time of flowering, indicated, in bold faced type, by figures which represent the months in numerical order. Thus 6-8 is printed for a plant that normally flowers from June to August. There is, of course, much variation in the period of flowering according to the weather and latitude; furthermore many plants in Ireland flower intermittently throughout a mild winter.

(5) The description. This, it should be remembered, applies to a normal plant, and every kind of aberration from it may be expected in occasional, abnormal, individuals. In particular, it should be noted that when measurements are given that they represent the average, and that considerable deviations can be expected from them in stunted or luxurient plants. For convenience a scale has been printed on both the end-papers of this book.

(6) A summary, printed in italics, of the type of ground in which the plant grows, and its distribution throughout the country. Frequency is indicated by the following terms, in ascending order: very rare, rare, occasional, frequent, very frequent, abundant. They must be interpreted subject to the information on habitat which preceeds them: *Salt marshes; very frequent* means that in any given salt-marsh you will usually find the plant, and often in considerable quantity, but, as salt-marshes are rather few and far between, the plant is rare over the country as a whole.

Geographical distribution is very briefly summarised: for further information reference should be made to Praeger's *Botanist in Ireland*, the *Atlas of the British Flora* by Perring & Walters and its supplement by Perring and Sell and the *Census Catalogue* of Scannell & Synnott. The terms North half and South half are indicative of areas separated, roughly, by a line from Galway to Balbriggan; East half and West half of areas bounded by a line from Londonderry to Youghal. Finally we have indicated the native range of those species certainly introduced to Ireland which are also not native to Britain.

Of the 1341 species, species groups and hybrids included in this book, 1251 are printed in bold-face type and are accounted for in the keys. The remaining 90 species and hybrids, which are mostly difficult to discriminate or are imperfectly naturalised, are printed in italics and are not taken account of in the keys, but are appended to the full description of that species to which they are most closely allied.

The figures in the main body of the text bear Roman numerals followed by a lower-case letter. The Roman numerals are those of the appropriate family to which the figure applies whilst the lower-case letter allows within family identification. For example the figures for family III - the Isoetaceae - are numbered Fig. IIIa and Fig. IIIb whilst those for family number XCIII - the Labiatae - are numbered Fig. XCIIIa, Fig. XCIIIb etc. Figures in the Glossary are coded as Gloss. Fig. 1, Gloss. Fig. 2. etc.

HOW AND WHERE TO LOOK FOR PLANTS

The best way for the beginner to learn how to find interesting plants and how to identify them is to go out on field excursions with a more expert friend. There are a large number of recognition-points which are almost impossible to explain in books, but which can be taught in five minutes with the plants in one's hand. Similarly 'a nose' for good localities is best aquired by imitation. There are a number of associations or groups which meet regularly and which run field-excursions which are led by experts. Three such groups are the Irish Wildlife Conservancy, the Belfast Naturalists' Field Club and the Dublin Naturalists' Field Club. As this book, however, is partly written to enable those who have not the good fortune to find such a mentor to work out the identification for themselves, a few hints on how and where to look for plants may not be out of place. The beginner may walk for miles over moorland or pastureland, disappointed in the monotony of the flora, but passing constantly within a few metres of places which would yield exciting novelties.

Every species has a certain tolerance of conditions of soil, climate, *etc.*: for some the range is very narrow, for others wide. Those with a wide range constitute most of our common plants; their tolerance is sufficient to allow them to grow in most types of community, and they are, in consequence, widespread and familiar. Species with a narrow range of tolerance are as a rule rare, unless it happens that the conditions they demand occur over large area, as in a raised bog or salt-marsh. It follows, therefore, that extreme and specialised environments offer the best chance of finding the rarer species or unusual forms of common species. Go for the driest spots and the wettest, the sunniest and the shadiest, the mountain-tops and the sea-shore (in both these habitats many interesting, often dwarfed forms of common species occur), the acid bog and the limestone scree. If you are in pastureland look for a marshy corner to a field or a dry, gravelly ridge; it will certainly yield something new. If you are on limestone look for siliceous rock or peat, and also *vice versa*; new species will come tumbling in by dozens. If you are on a mountain the best patches will be cliffs, or at any rate broken, rocky ground; and cliffs facing North or North-east are most likely to be most fruitful. On a dry gravel-ridge, on the other hand, it is likely to be the South slope that yields the rarities. In a bog the best places are usually in the wettest places, and remember Praeger's comment on naturalists who do not realise how much they miss by having, according to their code, to keep reasonably clean and dry, instead of poking their enquiring noses, like terriers, into every hole, be it wet or dry.

A few regions of Ireland are famous for their rare plants - the Burren, Killarney, Roundstone, Ben Bulben - but the visitors who confine their attentions to these regions are missing a great deal, and there are other districts, without great rarities but with an abundance and variety of not-so-common species, which are not visited so often as they deserve. A list of these regions, classified by province and county, is given below.

MUNSTER

Kerry. Clonee Lakes (South-west of Kenmare); Derrynane; Glencar; Killarney Lakes (especially around Muckross and Upper Lakes); Brandon Mountain; Castlegregory; marshes around Lixnaw; Coast between Fenit and Ballyheigue.

Cork. Glengarriff; Roaring Water Bay; Adrigole; Gouganebarra and thence down the Lee valley to Macroom; coast near Glandore and Castletownsend; suburbs of Cork city; Cork harbour; Kinsale; Youghal; Blackwater valley.

Waterford. Blackwater River around Lismore; Comeragh Mountains; Tramore.

Tipperary. Galtee Mountains (North side); Lough Gur; Shannon near Limerick; Askeaton.

Clare. Burren district (Northwards frrom Corrofin and Lisdoonvarna to Galway Bay); Aran Islands*; Lough Derg near Scarriff; Fergus estuary.

LEINSTER

Kilkenny. Nore valley, from Kilkenny downstream; lower Barrow valley.

Wexford. New Ross; Lady's Island Lake; Tacumshin lagoon; Rosslare; Curracloe; Bunclody.

Carlow. Barrow valley.

Leix. Bogs and moraines near Clonaslee; water-meadows northwards from Stradbally.

Offaly. Raised bogs throughout; eskers near Clonmacnoise.

Kildare. Fen North of the Curragh; raised bogs in the North-west; Barrow valley; middle Liffey valley.

Wicklow. Dargle and Glencree; Devil's Glen; Lugnaquilla; Vale of Clara; coastal marshes from Wicklow to Newcastle; Brittas Bay.

Dublin. Hill of Howth; Killiney; North Bull Island; Glenasmole; Canals; Slade valley.

Meath. Boyne valley from Trim to Slane; coast.

Westmeath. Lough Ree; Inny valley; lakes near Mullingar.

Longford. Lough Ree, and Shannon north of it; Lough Gowna.

Louth. Carlingford Mountain; Clogher Head; Boyne estuary; Braganstown bog.

CONNAUGHT

Galway. Roundstone; Twelve Bens; Lissoughter (near Recess); Kylemore; Leenane; Shores of Lough Corrib; district between Tuam and Headford; Oranmore; Westwards from Gort and Kinvarra; shores of Lough Derg near Portumna.

Roscommon. Eskers near Athlone; shores of Lough Key; Boyle district.

Mayo. Lough Carra; Ballinrobe region; South-west shore of Lough Mask; Mweelrea; Achill Island; Mulranny; Pontoon.

Sligo. Ben Bulben range; Knocknaree; Lough Gill; Lough Arrow and adjoining hills.

Leitrim. Glenade Mountain; Lough Melvin; Shannon below Lough Allen.

ULSTER.

Cavan. Erne valley; Lough Sheelin; Virginia.

Monaghan. Lakes and marshes, especially in the South-eastern half; Scotstown area.

Fermanagh. Lower Lough Erne and mountains South of it; Upper Lough Erne.

Donegal. Mountains of Inishowen; Dunlewy; the Rosses; Maas; Slieve League; Lough Eske; Ballyshannon district.

---

* The Aran Islands, though administratively part of County Galway, are always included in County Clare for biological purposes.

Tyrone.   Shores of Lough Neagh; Strabane and lower Foyle valley.

Armagh.   Shores of Lough Neagh and adjoining fens; Newry river.

Down.   Mourne Mountains; Newcastle-Downpatrick-Ardglass district (especially Dundrum Bay & Lecale); Ards peninsula.

Antrim.   Shore of Lough Neagh; coast, especially from the Giant's Causeway to Cushendun; moorland above Garron Point; hills above Belfast.

Londonderry.   Benevenagh; Magilligan strand; Foyle estuary; Portstewart.

BIBLIOGRAPHY

For students who wish to extend their knowledge of the Irish Flora the following books may be useful. Nearly all cover not only Ireland but also Britain, and in some cases a large portion of continental Europe. These latter works therefore include a large number of species which one will never find, except perhaps in specialist collections in gardens, in Ireland. A number of the works cited do not contain keys, but instead rely on 'matching by eye'. Although satisfactory in many cases this procedure is not sufficiently precise for accurate identification in many genera. We have restricted ourselves to books which are currently and easily available. We have omitted specialist works which cannot, by members of the public, be easily purchased. It should be borne in mind that detailed regional accounts of the Flora, familiar to students of British Botany, are scarce in Ireland. Indeed most areas - *e.g.* Sligo, Mayo, Tipperary, Meath, Cavan, Longford, Waterford, *etc.* still await their first county flora. Many of those for which an account has been published are either out of print - *e.g.* Connemara & the Burren, Inner Dublin and Carlow, or are both out of print and out of date - *e.g.* the floras of Cork, Dublin, Kerry and Wicklow are all about 100 years old.

<u>General works:</u>

CLAPHAM, A.R., TUTIN, T.G. & Moore, D.M. (1989). *Flora of the British Isles*. Third Edition (with corrections). Cambridge University Press. 688pp. Available in paperback. Clear and authoritative and still the most comprehensive work available. Rather too bulky for field use, but should be consulted indoors whenever opportunity offers. All Irish plants are fully described, though their distribution is, in many cases, inadequately summarised. References are given to monographic treatments of the difficult genera. An abbreviated version, entitled *Excursion Flora of the British Isles*, by Clapham, A.R., Tutin, T.G. & Warburg, E.F. is available only in soft covers. Though reprinted in 1993 this work was last fully revised in 1981 and is therefore somewhat out-of-date. Despite being 499 pages in length this tall, narrow book, still fits, after a bit of shoving, into one's pocket.

CURTIS, T.G.F. & MCGOUGH, H.N. (1988). *The Irish Red Data Book*. 1 Vascular Plants. Wildlife Service, Stationary Office. Dublin. A summary of the current state of knowledge of rare and threatened Irish higher-plants.

FITTER, R., FITTER, A. & BLAMEY, M. (1974). *The Illustrated Flora of Britain and Northern Europe*. Collins, London. 544pp. This is a large book, useful for consultation indoors, which has attractive and generally accurate colour illustrations of most Irish species. An abbreviated version, *The wild flowers of Britain and Northern Europe* is pocket-size and has reasonable, if sometimes rather small, illustrations.

HACKNEY, P. (Editor) (1992). *Stewart & Corry's Flora of the North-east of Ireland*. Institute of Irish Studies, Queen's University of Belfast. 419pp. An excellent regional flora, now in its 3rd edition; it covers the Counties of Down, Antrim and Londonderry.

PERRING, F. & WALTERS, S.M. (Editors) (1976). *Atlas of the British Flora*. Botanical Society of the British Isles. 432pp. Contains over 1,600 maps, giving details of distribution in Britain and Ireland of all but a few critical species. These latter are mostly difficult to identify and are mostly dealt with, together with hybrids and sub-species, in the *Critical Supplement to the Atlas of the British Flora* edited by F. Perring & P.D. Sell, re-published in 1978. The maps in both these books are almost 30 years old and substantial changes have occurred in the distributions of certain species since they were published. In fact the maps were never as accurate for Ireland as they were for Britain, the Irish data being less complete, but this is as much the fault of Irish botanists as of the editors.

SCANNELL, M.J.P. & SYNNOTT, D.M. (1987). *Census Catalogue of the Flora of Ireland*. Stationary Office, Dublin. 171pp. Available from the National Botanic Gardens, Glasnevin. A modern check-list of Irish plants, with the distributions of each given in terms of the biological vice-counties. It replaces the census catalogue in *Praeger's The Botanist in Ireland* which is out-of-print and unavailable. This latter work contains information not available elsewhere and is worth looking-out for on the second-hand book market.

STACE, C.A. (1991). *New Flora of the British Isles*. Cambridge University Press. 1226pp. This soft-cover book allows one to key-out almost any higher plant, whether native, naturalised or alien which one is likely to find in Britain or Ireland. Its scope is far broader than that of Clapham, Tutin & Moore and necessarily there is a loss of detail in the descriptions of the species which are highly abbreviated. The keys are comprehensive, if sometimes structurally rather complex; most of the illustrations are clear. Like Clapham's, this book is too large to fit in all but the most capacious pocket.

Works relating to particular groups of plants:

THE BOTANICAL SOCIETY OF THE BRITISH ISLES (BSBI) produce a series of small paperback books of similar style which are principally designed to allow easy identification of difficult, native or naturalised plant groups. The guides, most of which are listed below, all contain keys and numerous line drawings and are low priced.

BUTTLER, K.P. (1991). *Field guide to Orchids of Britain and Europe*. Crowood Press, Swindon. 288pp. A very comprehensive guide with every species illustrated by at least one, usually excellent, colour photograph which accompanies a very full description. There are keys to the larger genera.

GRAHAM, G.G. & PRIMAVESI, A.L. (1993). *Roses of Great Britain and Ireland*. BSBI Handbook No. 7. Botanical Society of the British Isles, London. 208pp.

JERMY, C. & CAMUS, J. (1991). *The Illustrated Filed Guide to Ferns and Allied Plants of the British Isles*. Natural History Museum, London. 194pp. The best available small guide to this group, containing good line drawings, silhouettes and helpful field hints. Hybrids are not dealt with.

JERMY, A.C. CHATER, A.O. & DAVID, R.W. (1982). *Sedges of the British Isles*. BSBI Handbook No. 1. Botanical Society of the British Isles, London. 269pp.

HUBBARD, C.E. (1984). *Grasses*. 3rd Edition revised by J.C.E. Hubbard. Penguin Books. 476pp. The best guide to this difficult family, combining a good key with numerous line drawings, one for each species. The author, now deceased, was recognised as the world authority on this group. Unfortunately many species names in the grasses have been changed recently and do not correspond to those in this book.

LOUSLEY, J.E. & KENT, D.H. (1981). *Docks and Knotweeds of the British Isles*. BSBI Handbook No. 3. Botanical Society of the British Isles, London. 205pp.

MEIKLE, R.D. (1984). *Willows and Poplars of Great Britain and Ireland*. BSBI Handbook No. 4. Botanical Society of the British Isles, London. 198pp.

MITCHELL, A. (1974). *A Field Guide to the Trees of Britain and Northern Europe*. Collins, London. 415pp. This book contains authoritative descriptions and many illustrations of the native, naturalised and planted trees of Ireland.

PAGE, C.N. (1982). *The Ferns of Britain and Ireland*. Cambridge University Press. 447pp. More comprehensive than Jermy & Camus but not so easily obtained and rather more expensive.

PHILLIPS, R. (1980). *Grasses, Ferns, Mosses & Lichens of Great Britain and Ireland*. Pan. London. 191pp. A reasonably priced photographic guide which lacks keys.

PRESTON, C. D. (1995). *Pondweeds of Great Britain and Ireland*. BSBI Handbook No. 8. Botanical Society of the British Isles, London. 352pp.

RICH, T.G. (1991). *Crucifers of Great Britain and Ireland*. BSBI Handbook No. 6. Botanical Society of the British Isles, London. 336pp.

TUTIN, T.G. (1980). *Umbellifers of the British Isles*. BSBI Handbook No. 2. Botanical Society of the British Isles, London. 197pp.

GENERAL KEY TO FAMILIES OR GENERA

(1) SEED PLANTS*

1. Aquatic plant, with leaves almost all submerged or floating (though flowers may be raised above the water) .. .. **Group F**
   Terrestrial plant, or, if aquatic, with many of the leaves raised above the surface 2
2. Tree or shrub, or climber with woody stem .. .. **Group E**
   Herbaceous plant, or low, creeping shrub less than 15 cm high 3
3. Sepals and petals both present and clearly differentiated from each other 4
   Perianth absent, or apparently consisting of either calyx or corolla, but not both **5**
4. Petals free, or very slightly united at the extreme base .. **Group A**
   Petals united .. .. **Group B**
5. Perianth corolla-like in colour and texture .. .. **Group C**
   Perianth calyx-like in colour and texture, or absent .. .. **Group D**

GROUP A

(Herbs or dwarf shrubs with calyx, and corolla of free petals)

1. Flowers regular 2
   Flowers irregular 39
2. Stamens indefinite in number, usually more than 12 3
   Stamens definite in number, usually 12 or fewer 13
3. Leaves in the form of a hollow cone, with a lid-like flap at the mouth .. .. **Sarracenia (XLIV)**
   Leaves not in the form of a hollow cone 4
4. Latex present .. .. **Papaveraceae (XL)**
   Latex absent 5
5. Ovary inferior 6
   Ovary superior 7
6. Petals numerous .. .. .. **Aizoaceae (XXXII)**
   Petals not more than 6 .. .. .. **Rosaceae (LI)**
7. Pistil consisting of several free carpels 8
   Carpels united in flower, though sometimes separating in fruit .. 10
8. Petals 3; some of the leaves sagittate .. .. **Sagittaria (CV)**
   Petals 4 or more; none of the leaves sagittate 9
9. Stipules usually present; sepals united at the base .. **Rosaceae (LI)**
   Stipules usually absent; sepals quite free .. **Ranunculaceae (XXXVIII)**
10. Upper petals deeply lobed .. .. .. **Resedaceae (XLIII)**
    Petals all unlobed 11
11. Stamens united to form a tube surrounding the styles .. **Malvaceae (LXIV)**
    Stamens free, or united only at the base, and not forming a tube .. 12

* For key to Pteridophytes (ferns and their allies) see p.

12. Style 1   ..   ..   **Cistaceae (LXIX)**
    Styles 3-5   ..   ..   **Guttiferae (LXVI)**

13. Plant without green colour; leaves reduced to brownish-yellow
    scales   ..   ..   **Monotropa (LXXX)**
    Plant green in parts   14

14. Petals 6-8   ..   ..   ·   ..   15
    Petals 3-5   16

15. Petals purple   ..   ..   **Lythrum (LXXI)**
    Petals yellow   ..   ..   **Sedum (XLVI)**

16. Leaves alternate or basal   17
    Leaves opposite or whorled   32

17. Ovary superior   18
    Ovary inferior or partly inferior   30

18. Leaves divided or lobed   19
    Leaves undivided   21

19. Petals 4   ..   ..   **Cruciferae (XLII)**
    Petals 5   20

20. Leaves with 3 undivided, heart-shaped leaflets   ..   **Oxalidaceae (LIII)**
    Leaves variously lobed or divided, but never with 3 undivided
    leaflets   ..   ..   **Geraniaceae (LIV)**

21. Carpels unfused   22
    Carpels fused   23

22. Petals 3   ..   ..   **Alismataceae (CV)**
    Petals 5   ..   ..   **Crassulaceae (XLVI)**

23. Leaves covered in red, glandular hairs   ..   ..   **Drosera (XLV)**
    Leaves without red, glandular hairs   24

24. Stamens 10   ..   ..   ·   25
    Stamens 2-6   26

25. Styles 2; anthers opening by splitting down the side   .. **Saxifragaceae (XLVII)**
    Style 1; anthers opening by terminal pores   ..   **Ericaceae (LXXX)**

26. Stamens 6   ..   ..   **Cruciferae (XLII)**
    Stamens 2-5   27

27. Leaves pinnate ..   ..   **Cruciferae (XLII)**
    Leaves entire   28

28. Petals white   ..   ..   **Parnassia (XLVIII)**
    Petals pink, lilac or blue   29

29. Leaves all basal ..   ..   ..   **Plumbaginaceae (LXXXIII)**
    Some leaves on stem   ..   ..   ..   **Linum (LV)**

30. Petals 4   ..   ..   **Vaccinium (LXXX)**
    Petals 5   31

31. Stamens 10   ..   .. **Saxifragaceae (XLVII)**
    Stamens 5   ..   .. **Umbelliferae (LXXIX)**

32. Ovary inferior   33
    Ovary superior   34

33. Stamens 8   ..   .. **Onagraceae (LXXIII)**
    Stamens 10   ..   .. **Saxifraga (XLVII)**

34. Petals yellow   ..   .. **Lysimachia (LXXXII)**
    Petals not yellow   35

35. Stems prostrate, woody; leaves in whorls of 3   ..   **Empetrum (LXXXI)**
     Stems usually erect, not woody; leaves in opposite pairs   ..   36
36. Capsule 1-seeded   ..   ..   ..   **Claytonia (XXXIII)**
     Capsule with several seeds   37
37. Sepals 2, free   ..   ..   ..   **Montia (XXXIII)**
     Sepals 4-5, free or united   38
38. Stigmas round; ovary 5-celled   ..   ..   **Linum (LV)**
     Stigmas linear-oblong; ovary 1-celled   ..   **Caryophyllaceae (XXXIV)**
39. Stamens 5; filaments free, but anthers more or less united round the
     style   ..   ..   **Viola (LXVII)**
     Stamens 6-10; anthers free, but filaments united, at least towards the
     base   40
40. Sepals united at the base to form a tubular calyx   ..   **Leguminosae (LII)**
     Sepals free   41
41. Leaves simple ..   ..   **Polygala (LVII)**
     Leaves compound   ..   ..   ..   **Fumariaceae (XLI)**

GROUP B

(Herbs or dwarf shrubs with evident calyx and corolla of united petals)

1. Ovary superior   2
     Ovary inferior   32
2. Plant without green colour; leaves absent or reduced to scales   ..   3
     Plant green in parts   4
3. Stems slender, twining; plant without roots   ..   **Cuscuta (LXXXVIII)**
     Stems erect, stout; plant with roots   ..   **Scrophulariaceae (XCVI)**
4. Flowers regular   5
     Flowers irregular   23
5. Stamens more than 5   6
     Stamens 5 or fewer   8
6. Flowers bright yellow; corolla with 6-8 lobes   ..   **Blackstonia (LXXXV)**
     Flowers not yellow; corolla with 4-5 lobes   7
7. Leaves fleshy, peltate   ..   ..   **Umbilicus (XLVI)**
     Leaves neither fleshy nor peltate   ..   **Ericaceae (LXXX)**
8. Leaves opposite or whorled   9
     Leaves alternate or basal   15
9. Flowers in whorls or compact ovoid or globular heads   **Labiatae (XCIII)**
     Flowers not in whorls or compact heads   10
10. Stamens 2   ..   ..   ..   **Veronica (XCVI)**
     Stamens 4 or 5   11
11. Flowers 3-6 mm in diameter   12
     Flowers at least 8 mm in diameter   13
12. Corolla yellow; calyx of 4 united sepals   ..   **Cicendia (LXXXV)**
     Corolla white; sepals 2, free ..   ..   **Montia (XXXIII)**
13. Calyx tubular   ..   ..   **Gentianaceae (LXXXV)**
     Sepals united only at the base   14
14. Flowers 25-50 mm across   ..   ..   **Vinca (LXXXVII)**
     Flowers not more than 15 mm across   ..   **Anagallis (LXXXII)**

15. Stamens 2 .. .. **Veronica (XCVI)**
    Stamens 4-5 16

16. Stamens 4 17
    Stamens 5 18

17. Minute annual; leaves 3 mm long .. .. **Anagallis (LXXXII)**
    Leaves at least 10 mm long .. .. **Plantaginaceae (XCVIII)**

18. Leaves all basal 19
    Some leaves present on the stem 20

19. Leaves divided, with 3 leaflets .. **Menyanthes (LXXXVI)**
    Leaves undivided .. .. .. **Primula (LXXXII)**

20 Corolla with entire margin, not lobed .. **Convolvulaceae (LXXXVIII)**
    Corolla distinctly lobed 21

21. Ovary 4-lobed .. .. **Boraginaceae (XL)**
    Ovary not 4-lobed 22

22. Corolla bright yellow; leaves woolly .. .. **Verbascum (XLVI)**
    Corolla purple, white or dull yellow; leaves not woolly **Solanaceae (XCIV)**

23. Leaves with 3 more or less equal leaflets .. .. **Trifolium (LII)**
    Leaves simple, or pinnately divided, with more than 3 leaflets .. 24

24. Stamens 6-8, united by their filaments into 1 or 2 bundles .. 25
    Stamens 2-5, free 26

25. Leaves simple, entire .. .. .. **Polygala (LVII)**
    Leaves compound, pinnate .. .. .. **Fumariaceae (XLI)**

26. Leaves all basal, sticky .. .. **Pinguicula (XCVII)**
    Some leaves present on stem 27

27. Stamens 2-4 28
    Stamens 5 30

28. Fruit a capsule .. .. .. **Scrophulariaceae (XCVI)**
    Fruit of 4 separate nutlets 29

29. Ovary at flowering time scarcely lobed .. .. **Verbenaceae (XCI)**
    Ovary at flowering time deeply 4-lobed .. .. **Labiatae (XCIII)**

30. Flowers blue (pink in bud) .. .. .. **Echium (XC)**
    Flowers yellow 31

31. Corolla funnel- or bell-shaped, dull yellow, veined with
    purple .. .. **Hyoscyamus (XCIV)**
    Corolla with short tube and spreading lobes, bright yellow **Verbascum (XCVI)**

32. Flowers in compact heads, each surrounded by an involucre of
    bracts 33
    Flowers not in compact heads 36

33. Stamens united by their anthers, forming a tube around the style .. 34
    Anthers quite free 35

34. Florets stalkless, with ovary attached directly to the common
    receptacle .. .. **Compositae (CIV)**
    Florets attached to the common receptacle by short stalks **Jasione (CIII)**

35. Flowering stem with at least one pair of opposite leaves **Dipsacaceae (CII)**
    Flowering stems leafless .. .. .. **Armeria (LXXXIII)**

36. Leaves alternate or basal 37
    Leaves opposite or whorled 39

37.	Flowers blue	..	..	.. **Campanulaceae (CIII)**
	Flowers not blue	..	..	.. 38
38.	Stamens 8-10	..	..	.. **Vaccinium (LXXX)**
	Stamens 5	..	..	.. **Samolus (LXXXII)**
39.	Leaves pinnate	..	..	.. **Sambucus (XCIX)**
	Leaves simple	..	..	**Rubiaceae (LXXXVIII)**

GROUP C

(Herbs or dwarf shrubs with evident corolla but apparently no calyx)

1. Flowers in compact heads, each surrounded by an involucre of
   bracts   ..   .. **Compositae (CIV)**
   Flowers not in compact heads   2
2. Flowers regular 3
   Flowers irregular   20
3. Stamens indefinite in number   .. **Ranunculaceae (XXXVIII)**
   Stamens not more than 10   4
4. Leaves opposite or whorled 5
   Leaves alternate or basal   8
5. Stamens 1-3   ..   .. **Valerianaceae (CI)**
   Stamens 4-5   6
6. Ovary inferior ..   ..   .. **Rubiaceae (LXXXVIII)**
   Ovary superior 7
7. Dwarf shrub; leaves 3 mm long, crowded, overlapping and closely
   appressed to the stem   ..   ..   .. **Calluna (LXXX)**
   Herb; leaves 6-10 mm long, not overlapping and not appressed to
   the stem   ..   .. **Glaux (LXXXIII)**
8. Ovary inferior 9
   Ovary superior 11
9. Stamens 3   ..   .. **Iridaceae (CXXIII)**
   Stamens 5-6   10
10. Stamens 5   ..   ..   .. **Umbelliferae (LXXIX)**
    Stamens 6   ..   ..   .. **Amaryllidaceae (LXXI)**
11. Petals 5   12
    Petals 6   13
12. Leaves all basal ..   .. **Plumbaginaceae (LXXXIII)**
    Leaves alternate, on the stem   ..   .. **Polygonaceae (XXIX)**
13. Stamens 9   ..   .. **Butomus (CVI)**
    Stamens 6   14
14. Leaves small and scale-like, replaced by numerous short, needle-
    like branches ..   ..   .. **Asparagaceae (CXX)**
    Leaves normal, at least 25 mm long   15
15. Flowers solitary, arising from ground-level   .. **Colchicaceae (CXVI)**
    Flowers in a panicle, raceme, corymb or umbel   16
16. Flowers in an umbel   ..   ..   .. **Alliaceae (CXVIII)**
    Flowers in a raceme, corymb or panicle 17
17. Leaves stiff and fibrous, sword-shaped, at least 100 cm
    long   ..   .. **Phormiaceae (CXIX)**
    Leaves soft, not fibrous, not more than 35 cm long   18

18. Flowers blue; rootstock a bulb   .. **Hyacinthaceae (CXVII)**
    Flowers white or yellow; rootstock slender, not a bulb   ..   19

19. Flowers yellow, in a compact, spike-like raceme   .. **Melanthiaceae (CXIV)**
    Flowers white, in a lax panicle   ..   .. **Asphodelaceae (CXV)**

20. Leaves all opposite   21
    Upper leaves alternate, or leaves all basal   ..   22

21. Stamens 1-3; perianth-segments united at the base into a fairly long
        tube   ..   .. **Valerianaceae (CI)**
    Stamens 5; perianth-segments free, the largest sac-like, with a short
        spur   ..   .. **Impatiens (LX)**

22. Ovary superior   23
    Ovary inferior   24

23. Leaves compound   ..   ..   .. **Fumariaceae (XLI)**
    Leaves simple, entire   ..   ..   .. **Polygalaceae (LVII)**

24. Leaves usually compound; stamens 5   ..   .. **Umbelliferae (LXXIX)**
    Leaves simple; stamens 1-3   25

25. Stamens 3, free ..   .. **Crocosmia (LXXIII)**
    Stamens 1, united to the style   ..   ..**Orchidaceae (CXXXII)**

GROUP D

(Herbs or dwarf shrubs, with perianth entirely calyx-like, or absent)

1. Leaves apparently absent   2
   Leaves easily seen   4

2. Plant with fleshy, jointed stem   ..   **Chenopodiaceae (XXXI)**
   Stems neither fleshy nor jointed   3

3. Inflorescence lateral; perianth present, of 6 sepal-like segments **Juncus (CXIV)**
   Inflorescence terminal; perianth absent, or represented by
       bristles   ..   .. **Cyperaceae (CXXXI)**

4. Leaves all opposite or whorled   5
   Leaves partly or wholly alternate, or mostly basal   ..   14

5. Stems woody; leaves needle-like, in whorls of 3   6
   Stems not woody   7

6. Leaves blunt, without resinous smell   ..   .. **Empetrum (LXXXI)**
   Leaves pointed, with resinous smell   ..   .. **Juniperus (XIX)**

7. Leaves in whorls of about 10   ..   .. **Hippuris (LXXVI)**
   Leaves opposite..   8

8. Leaves linear   9
   Leaves at least half as broad as long   10

9. Styles 2   ..   .. **Scleranthus (XXXIV)**
   Styles 4-5   ..   .. **Sagina (XXXIV)**

10. Stem twining ..   .. **Humulus (XXVII)**
    Stem not twining   11

11. Stem erect   12
    Stem creeping or spreading   13

12. Leaves sharply toothed, with stinging hairs   ..   **Urtica (XXVIII)**
    Leaves bluntly toothed, without stinging hairs   ..   **Mercurialis (LVI)**

13. Flowers greenish-yellow, in terminal cymes   **Chrysosplenium (XLVII)**
     Flowers green or purple, solitary in leaf-axils   ..   **Lythrum (LXXI)**

14. Leaves compound   15
     Leaves undivided or lobed, sometimes deeply, but not truly compound   17

15. Leaves simply palmate or pinnate, with stipules   ..   **Rosaceae (LI)**
     Leaves bipinnate or biternate, without stipules   16

16. Leaves twice or thrice pinnate; flowers in a raceme or
     panicle   ..   .. **Thalictrum (XXXVIII)**
     Leaves biternate; flowers in a globular head   ..   ..   **Adoxa (C)**

17. Leaves grass-like, rush-like or sword-shaped (long, narrow and
     entire, with parallel veins)   18
     Leaves relatively broad, often lobed, not rush- or grass-like   ..   25

18. Flowers with regular perianth   19
     Flowers surrounded by bristles or scales, but without regular perianth   22

19. Flowers in clusters or panicles, rarely solitary   ..   **Juncaceae (CXIV)**
     Flowers in racemes or spikes   20

20. Stamens 4   ..   ..   ..   **Plantaginaceae (XCVIII)**
     Stamens 6   21

21. Leaves not more than 4 mm wide   ..   ..   **Triglochin (CVIII)**
     Leaves at least 12 mm wide ..   ..   ..   **Acorus (CXXVII)**

22. Flowers in globular heads   ..   ..   ..   **Sparganium (CXXIX)**
     Flowers in spikes, racemes or panicles   23

23. Flowers in a dense spike, surrounded by hairs, but without
     glumes   ..   ..   ..   **Typha (CXXX)**
     Flowers in the axils of glumes (small, chaffy bracts)   24

24. Stems usually solid, often 3-angled, not swollen at the nodes.
     Sheaths of leaves not split down the side   ..   **Cyperaceae (CXXXI)**
     Stems cylindrical, hollow, with swollen nodes; sheaths of leaves.
     Sheaths often split down the side, opposite the blade   **Gramineae (CXXVI)**

25. Latex present   ..   ..   **Euphorbia (LVI)**
     Latex absent

26. Flowers unisexual, without perianth   27
     Flowers with perianth, usually hermaphrodite   28

27. Stems woody; flowers in small catkins   ..   ..   **Salix (XXI)**
     Stems not woody; flowers in a spike surrounded by a large
     bract   ..   ..   **Arum (CXXVII)**

28. Sepals 2-4   29
     Sepals 5-6   36

29. Leaves very large, with spiny stalks   ..   ..   **Gunnera (LXXIV)**
     Leaves of moderate size; stalks not spiny   30

30. Leaves all basal, or nearly so   31
     Some leaves present on upper part of stem   32

31. Leaves round or kidney-shaped; flowers in a panicle   ..   **Oxyria (XXIX)**
     Leaves linear to oval; flowers in dense, cylindrical spikes   **Plantago (XCVII)**

32. Leaves neither toothed or lobed   ..   ..   **Parietaria (XXVIII)**
     Leaves toothed or lobed   33

33. Stipules present   ..   ..   ..   **Rosaceae (LI)**
     Stipules absent   34

34. Leaves deeply pinnatifid .. .. .. **Coronopus (XLII)**
    Leaves not deeply lobed 35

35. Rhizome stout; stamens 8 .. .. .. **Rhodiola (XLVI)**
    Rhizome absent; stamens 2-5 .. **Chenopodiaceae (XXXI)**

36. Leaves pinnately lobed .. .. .. **Erodium (LIV)**
    Leaves undivided, hastate or palmately lobed 37

37. Translucent, papery stipules present .. **Polygonaceae (XXIX)**
    Stipules absent 38

38. Flowers in umbels .. .. .. **Hedera (LXXVIII)**
    Flowers not in umbels 39

39. Fruit a berry .. .. **Frangula (LXIII)**
    Fruit dry .. .. .. **Chenopodiaceae (XXXI)**

GROUP E

(Trees, shrubs and woody climbers)

1. Leaves linear, not more than 3 mm wide, sometimes reduced to
   thorns or scales 2
   Larger leaves at least 4 mm wide 6

2. Very thorny shrub; corolla bright yellow .. .. .. **Ulex (LII)**
   Thorns few or absent 3

3. Leaves opposite, or in whorls of 3-5 4
   Leaves alternate, or grouped in pairs or larger groups on short shoots 5

4. Corolla absent .. .. **Juniperus (XIX)**
   Corolla present, pink or purple .. .. **Ericaceae (LXXX)**

5. Winter buds green; plant without resin; seeds solitary, not in cones **Taxus (XX)**
   Winter buds brown; resin present in leaves and wood; seeds in
   cones .. .. **Pinaceae (XVIII)**

6. Leaves opposite (on mature shoots) 7
   Leaves alternate (on mature shoots) 26

7. Leaves compound 8
   Leaves lobed or unlobed but not divided 11

8. Climber .. .. **Clematis (XXXVIII)**
   Tree 9

9. Leaves palmate .. .. **Aesculus (LIX)**
   Leaves pinnate 10

10. Flowers white; leaf-buds purplish .. .. **Sambucus (XCIX)**
    Flowers blackish-green; leaf-buds black .. .. **Fraxinus (LXXXIV)**

11. Leaves palmately lobed 12
    Leaves not lobed 13

12. Corolla white; fruit a berry .. .. **Viburnum (XCIX)**
    Flowers greenish; fruit dry, winged .. .. **Acer (LVIII)**

13. Leaves untoothed 14
    Leaves toothed 23

14. Climber .. .. **Lonicera (XCIX)**
    Shrub or tree 15

15. Leaves strongly aromatic; corolla white and stamens
    numerous .. .. **Amomyrtus (LXXII)**
    Leaves not strongly aromatic; stamens few (if numerous then
    corolla yellow not white) 16

16. Corolla yellow; stamens numerous .. .. **Hypericum (LXVI)**
    Corolla not yellow; stamens not more than 5 17

17. Flowers unisexual .. .. .. **Salix (XXI)**
    Flowers hermaphrodite 18

18. Most leaves not more than 12 mm long; flowers usually
    absent .. .. **Lonicera (XCIX)**
    Larger leaves at least 25 mm long 19

19. Flowers greenish; corolla absent .. .. **Halimione (XXXI)**
    Corolla white, purple or pinkish 20

20. Stamens 5 .. .. **Caprifoliaceae (XCIX)**
    Stamens 2 or 4 21

21. Stamens 4 .. .. **Cornus (LXXVII)**
    Stamens 2 22

22. Flowers in axillary spikes; fruit a capsule .. **Hebe (XCVI)**
    Flowers in terminal panicles; fruit a berry .. **Ligustrum (LXXXIV)**

23. Flowers solitary, axillary, hanging; calyx bright red .. **Fuchsia (LXXIII)**
    Flowers in panicles or corymbs; not hanging; calyx green .. 24

24. Twigs 4-angled; ovary (and fruit) 4-lobed .. **Euonymus (LXII)**
    Twigs rounded, not 4-angled; ovary and fruit not 4-lobed .. 25

25. Stamens 4; flowers in long, conical panicles .. **Buddleja (XCV)**
    Stamens 5; flowers in flat-topped corymbs .. **Viburnum (XCIX)**

26. Leaves compound 27
    Leaves undivided 32

27. Leaflets not toothed or lobed 28
    Leaflets toothed or lobed 30

28. Stem climbing or straggling; corolla purple or white .. **Solanum (XCIV)**
    Stem erect; corolla yellow 29

29. Leaflets 3; flowers irregular .. .. .. **Leguminosae (LII)**
    Leaflets 5, at least on lower leaves; flowers regular .. **Potentilla (LI)**

30. Stems prickly .. .. **Rosaceae (LI)**
    Stems not prickly 31

31. Undershrub; leaves irregularly dissected, with narrow, jagged
    segments .. .. **Artemisia (CIV)**
    Tree; leaves pinnate .. .. .. **Sorbus (LI)**

32. Leaves not toothed or lobed 33
    Leaves toothed or lobed 44

33. Flowers with coloured corolla 34
    Corolla calyx-like or minute or absent 37

34. Flowers white 35
    Flowers pink or purple 36

35. Leaves with wavy, and usually spiny margins .. .. **Ilex (LXI)**
    Leaves flat, not spiny .. .. .. **Rosaceae (LI)**

36. Stamens 8-10 .. .. **Ericaceae (LXXX)**
    Stamens 5 .. .. **Solanum (XCIV)**

37. Climber 38
    Erect tree or shrub 39

38. Stems angled; mature leaves heart-shaped not palmately lobed **Tamus (CXXII)**
    Stems rounded; mature leaves palmately lobed .. **Hedera (LXXVIII)**

39. Leaves hairless, but covered with silvery scales, especially
       beneath .. .. **Hippophae (LV)**
    Leaves without silvery scales, often with some hairs, at least when
       young 40

40. Leaves fragrant 41
    Leaves not fragrant 42

41. Tall tree, usually in or near plantations or gardens .. **Eucalyptus (LXXII)**
    Small shrub about 1 m tall, not in or near plantations or
       gardens .. .. **Myrica (XXII)**

42. Tree; buds narrowly cylindrical, 15-20 mm long .. **Fagus (XXV)**
    Shrub; buds ovoid, not more than 6 mm long .. 43

43. Mature leaves hairless; fruit berry-like, dark purple .. **Frangula (LXIII)**
    Mature leaves hairy beneath; fruit a small capsule, discharging
       seeds clothed with silky hairs .. .. **Salix (XXI)**

44. Evergreen, with glossy, dark green leaves 45
    Deciduous; leaves seldom very dark green or glossy 51

45. Some leaves with spiny margins 46
    Leaves toothed, but not spiny 48

46. Corolla white 47
    Corolla orange .. .. .. **Berberis (XXXIX)**

47. Corolla fused for most of its length, urn-shaped, with 5
       lobes .. .. **Gaultheria (LXXX)**
    Corolla not urn-shaped, free for most of its length, with 4 lobes **Ilex (LXI)**

48. Climber; some of the leaves palmately lobed .. **Hedera (LXXVIII)**
    Erect tree or shrub; leaves not lobed 49

49. Petals united to form an urn-shaped corolla .. **Ericaceae (LXXX)**
    Petals free 50

50. Petals red .. .. .. **Escallonia (XLIX)**
    Petals white .. .. .. **Prunus (LI)**

51. Leaves palmately lobed 52
    Leaves undivided or pinnately lobed 53

52. Flowers large, purple .. .. .. **Lavatera (LXIV)**
    Flowers small, greenish .. .. .. **Ribes (L)**

53. Corolla conspicuous 54
    Corolla minute or absent 56

54. Petals free 55
    Petals united into an urn-shaped corolla .. **Vaccinium (LXXX)**

55. Petals yellow; stamens 6 .. .. **Berberis (XXXIX)**
    Petals white or pink; stamens numerous .. **Rosaceae (LI)**

56. Leaves fragrant .. .. .. **Myrica (XXII)**
    Leaves not fragrant 57

57. Flowers unisexual 58
    Flowers hermaphrodite 61

58. Fruit 1-seeded   59
    Fruit a small capsule, releasing a number of seeds clothed with silky
      hairs   ..   ..   ..   **Salix (XXI)**
59. Fruit small and seed-like   ..   ..   **Betulaceae (XXIII)**
    Fruit a nut, large, with easily seen 'kernel' (seed)   ..   60
60. Nut surrounded by or arising from an involucre of woody
      bracts   ..   **Fagaceae (XXV)**
    Nut surrounded by an involucre of green, leafy bracts   **Corylaceae (XXIV)**
61. Shrub; fruit a black, berry-like drupe   ..   **Rhamnus (LXIII)**
    Tree; fruit a green, winged achene   ..   **Ulmus (XXVI)**

GROUP F

(Submerged or floating aquatics)

1. Minute plants, without distinct leaves or stem   **Lemnaceae (CXXVIII)**
    [Check also the fern family ..   ..   **Azollaceae (XVII)**]
    Stem, and usually leaves, distinct   2
2. Leaves reduced to inconspicuous sheaths   ..   **Eleocharis (CXXXI)**
    Leaves with well-developed blades   3
3. Some of the leaves dissected into narrow segments   ..   4
    Leaves undivided   9
4. Leaves alternate   5
    Leaves opposite or whorled   7
5. Small bladders present on leaves or stems   ..   **Utricularia (XCVII)**
    Bladders absent   6
6. Flowers in umbels; petals 1-3 mm   ..   **Apium (LXXIX)**
    Flowers solitary in leaf-axils; petals at least 5 mm
      long   ..   ..   **Ranunculus (XXXVIII)**
7. Petals at least 10 mm long   ..   ..   **Hottonia (CXXXII)**
    Petals absent, or not more than 3 mm long   8
8. Leaves pinnate; flowers in a spike usually borne above the
      water   ..   ..   **Myriophyllum (LXXV)**
    Leaves repeatedly forked; flowers submerged,
      axillary   ..   ..   **Ceratophyllum (XXXVII)**
9. Flowers inconspicuous, with petals absent or not more than 3 mm long   10
    Flowers conspicuous, with petals at least 5 mm long   ..   32
10. Leaves all basal   11
    [Note the fern family **Marsileaceae (XVI)**, with young leaves
    coiled, could key-out here]
    Some leaves present on the stem   13
11. Flowers in compact, button-like heads   ..   **Eriocaulon (CXXV)**
    Flowers solitary, or in racemes   12
12. Plants solitary; flowers in a raceme; filaments shorter than
      perianth   ..   ..   **Subularia (XLII)**
    Plants emitting stolons, so as to form mats; flowers solitary;
      filaments longer than perianth   ..   **Littorella (XCVIII)**
13. Leaves alternate   14
    Leaves opposite or whorled   20

14. Flowers in compact, globular heads, solitary in the axils of the
upper leaves .. .. **Sparganium (CXXIX)**
Flowers not so arranged 15

15. Regular perianth present, of 4 or 6 segments 16
Perianth absent 17

16. Flowers in spikes; perianth segments 4, obtuse .. **Potamogeton (CIX)**
Flowers in compact clusters; perianth-segments 6, acute **Juncus (CXIV)**

17. All leaves submerged; in brackish or salt-water 18
Some leaves floating; in fresh-water 19

18. Flowers unisexual, in a spike enclosed in a leaf-sheath **Zostera (CXI)**
Flowers hermaphrodite, in pairs in leaf-axils, not enclosed in a
sheath .. .. **Ruppia (CX)**

19. Flowers in spikelets 2-4 mm long, solitary on long stalks in the
leaf-axils .. .. .. **Eleogiton (CXXI)**
Flowers in spikelets 15-30 mm long, arranged in a raceme or
narrow panicle .. .. .. **Glyceria (CXXVI)**

20. Leaves in whorls of about 10 .. .. **Hippuris (LXXVI)**
Leaves opposite, or in whorls of 3-5 21

21. Largest leaves not more than 3 mm wide 22
Some leaves at least 6 mm wide 31

22. Leaves toothed (sometimes very minutely, visible only under a lens) 23
Leaves quite untoothed, though sometimes notched at the tip .. 26

23. Leaves mostly opposite; flowers stalkless .. **Najas (CXIII)**
Leaves mostly in whorls of 3-5; flowers long-stalked 24

24. Leaves dark green, obtuse .. .. .. **Elodea (CVII)**
Leaves light green, acute 25

25. Minute scales at base of leaf with their margin undivided; leaves in
whorls of 3, rarely 4 .. .. .. **Elodea (CVII)**
Minute scales at base of leaf strongly fringed; leaves in whorls
of 3-6 .. .. **Hydrilla (CVII)**

26. Flowers with calyx, and usually corolla 27
Flowers without perianth 29

27. Petals, if present, purple; often absent .. .. **Lythrum (LXXI)**
Petals always present, white or pink 28

28. Sepals 2; petals 5 .. .. .. **Montia (XXXIII)**
Sepals 3-4; petals 3-4 .. .. .. **Elatine (LXX)**

29. Fruits stalkless 30
Fruits on long, slender stalks .. .. **Ruppia (CX)**

30. Leaves more or less obtuse, notched at the tip .. **Callitriche (XCII)**
Leaves tapered to a fine point, not notched .. **Zannichellia (CXII)**

31. Leaves flat, seldom more than 12 mm long, some of them usually
floating .. .. **Callitriche (XCII)**
Leaves somewhat wavy, about 25 mm long, all submerged **Groenlandia (CIX)**

32. Petals numerous, free .. .. **Nymphaeaceae (XXXVI)**
Petals united, or, if free, not more than 5 33

33. Leaves spinous-toothed .. .. .. **Stratiotes (CVII)**
Leaves entire or bluntly lobed 34

34. Leaves lobed .. .. .. **Ranunculus (XXXVIII)**
Leaves entire 35

35. Petals united to form an irregular corolla with two lips .. **Lobelia (CIII)**
Petals free or united at the base to form a regular corolla .. 36

36. Flowers bright pink .. .. .. **Polygonum (XXIX)**
Flowers white or pale lilac 37

37. Ovary inferior .. .. **Hydrocharis (CVII)**
Ovary superior 38

38. All leaves acute .. .. **Baldellia (CV)**
Floating leaves obtuse .. .. .. **Luronium (CV)**

(2) PTERIDOPHYTA (FERNS AND RELATED PLANTS)

1. Stems conspicuously jointed .. .. **Equisteum (IV)**
Stems not jointed 2

2. Floating plant .. .. .. **Azolla (XVII)**
Plant rooted, not floating 3

3. Leaves numerous and crowded, small in relation to the stem .. 4
Leaves not crowded, fairly large in relation to the stem .. 7

4. Leaves cylindrical 5
Leaves flattened 6

5. Leaves in clusters .. .. .. **Isoetes (III)**
Leaves arising singly along a creeping rhizome .. **Pilularia (XVI)**

6. Sporangia all similar, with numerous small spores .. **Lycopodiaceae (I)**
Sporangia of 2 kinds, some containing 4 large spores .. **Selaginellaceae (II)**

7. Leaves very delicate in texture, dark translucent
green .. .. .. **Hymenophyllaceae (VIII)**
Leaves not delicate or translucent 8

8. Leaves of 2 very different types; those bearing sporangia lacking a
distinct leaf-like blade 9
Leaves all more or less the same; those bearing sporangia little
different from those which do not 13

9. Plant with a single (or at most 2) normal looking leaves
(sometimes this leaf is small and often it is fleshy) .. **Ophioglossaceae (V)**
Plant with a many more than one normal looking leaf 10

10. Leaves more than twice pinnate 11
Leaves once or twice pinnate only 12

11. Fertile leaves about half the length of the sterile .. **Matteucia (XIII)**
Fertile leaves longer than the sterile .. .. **Cryptogramma (VII)**

12. Plant large; leaves twice pinnate, at least 60 cm long .. **Osmunda (VI)**
Plant of moderate size; leaves once pinnate, no more than
50 cm long .. .. .. **Blechnum (XV)**

13. Sporangia linear or j-shaped 14
Sporangia round or oval, not linear 17

14. Sporangia without an indusium .. .. **Adiantaceae (VII)**
Sporangia with an indusium, this sometimes concealed by the
leaf-margin 15

15. Sporangia j-shaped .. .. .. **Athyrium (XIII)**
Sporangia linear, not j-shaped 16

16. Fronds arising singly from an underground rhizome; plants at least
    80 cm tall, with divided leaves   ..   ..   **Pteridium (X)**
    Fronds arising in clusters; plants small or moderately sized, less
    than 80 cm tall   ..   ..   ..   **Aspleniaceae (XII)**

17. Indusium absent or rudimentary   18
    Indusium present   20

18. Leaves once pinnate   ..   ..   ..   **Polypodium (IX)**
    Leaves twice or more pinnate   19

19. Leaves thrice pinnate, at least at the base ..   .. **Gymnocarpium (XIII)**
    Leaves once to twice pinnate   ..   .. **Thelypteridaceae (XI)**

20. Sori kidney-shaped   ..   ..   ..   **Dryopteris (XIV)**
    Sori more or less circular   21

21. Ultimate leaf segments entire   ..   ..   **Thelypteris (XI)**
    Ultimate leaf segments toothed or lobed   22

22. Teeth usually rounded; leaf-stalk very slender and brittle   **Cystopteris (XIII)**
    Teeth acute; leaf-stalk robust   ..   ..   **Polystichum (XIV)**

PTERIDOPHYTA

Plants without flowers, reproducing by spores, not seeds. The spores are usually all similar, but in the Marsileaceae, Azollaceae, Selaginellaceae and Isoetaceae they are differentiated into large megaspores and much smaller microspores, both borne on the same plant.

I. LYCOPODIACEAE. Club-moss

Plants of somewhat moss-like habit, but more robust. Leaves numerous, small, undivided. Sporangia borne singly in leaf-axils, all alike, with small spores.

1. Stems all erect, usually forked. Sporangia in the axils of ordinary
   leaves, not in cones .. .. **3. Huperzia**
   Stems prostrate, at least in basal part. Sporangia in cones, in which the leaves
   are different in size, shape or arrangement from those on the rest of the stem 2
2. Leaves pale bluish-green; branches flattened, often arranged so as to
   resemble a fan .. .. .. **4. Diphasiastrum**
   Leaves not pale bluish-green; branches not flattened .. 3
3. Leaves ending in a white, hair-like point. Cones borne at the tip of
   a slender stalk, usually in pairs .. .. **1. Lycopodium**
   Leaves ending in a short, acute, but not hair-like point. Cones borne
   at the tip of an ordinary stem, usually solitary .. **2. Lycopodiella**

1. Lycopodium
Lycopodium clavatum. 6-9. Stems prostrate, rooting, up to 50 cm long, sparingly branched; branches short, erect, many of them ending in cones. Leaves linear-oblong, with a white, hair-like tip, numerous, crowded except in the region below the cones, where they are sparse and widely spaced. *Heaths and grassy mountain slopes; rare and declining.*

2. Lycopodiella
Lycopodiella inundata (*Lycopodium inundatum*). **6-8.** Stems short, sparingly branched, prostrate at the base but erect at the tip; some branches bearing terminal, erect, poorly defined cones. Leaves linear-lanceolate, shortly pointed, those of the cones broader at the base. *Lake-margins and wet bogs. Occasional locally in West Galway; very rare elsewhere.*

3. Huperzia
Huperzia selago (*Lycopodium selago*). Crúibíní sionnaigh. **6-8.** Stem sturdy, erect, 5-12 cm high, forked 1-2, rarely more, times. Leaves all alike, 5-7 mm long, oval-lanceolate. Sporangia situated in leaf-axils here and there, not aggregated into distinct cones. Bud-like bulbils are often present in the leaf-axils in place of sporangia; these become detached and serve for vegetative reproduction. *Moorlands and heaths, mostly above 300 m, but sometimes on lowland bogs; frequent but local.*

4. Diphasiastrum
Diphasiastrum alpinum (*Diphasium alpinum, Lycopodium alpinum*). **6-8.** Main stem prostrate, often buried, with widely spaced alternate leaves; from this, branches arise which themselves are repeatedly branched, forming fan-shaped structures, bearing pale bluish-green, lanceolate, acutely pointed leaves arranged in 4 longitudinal rows. Cones terminal, not very clearly differentiated. *Mossy heaths or bare peat on mountain ridges and summits, from Wicklow and Galway northwards; formerly in Kerry but apparently extinct there; rare.*

II. SELAGINELLACEAE

Selaginella

Plants of somewhat moss-like habit, with numerous small leaves. Sporangia of two kinds, both situated in the leaf-axils of rather ill-defined terminal cones; some (megasporangia) containing 4 large spores, others (microsporangia) containing numerous small spores.

1. Branches not flattened; leaves on vegetative parts all alike   **1. S. selaginoides**
    Branches flattened; leaves in 4 rows, those on the upper and lower
        surfaces of the shoot much smaller than those at the sides   **2. S. kraussiana**

1. Selaginella selaginoides. 6-8. Stem erect, from a creeping base, 2-10 cm high. Leaves alternate, lanceolate, acute, finely toothed, sometimes tinged with pinkish-buff; those in the cones a little larger than the others, but otherwise similar. Megasporangia situated at the base of the cone, more numerous than the microsporangia higher up. *Marshes, fens, damp hollows in sand-hills and mountain ledges; frequent in the North, occasional in the Centre, rare in the South.*

2. * S. kraussiana. 7-9. Stems creeping, bearing flattened sprays of foliage; leaves arranged in 4 longitudinal rows, those at the sides of the stem 2 mm long, oval lanceolate, acute, those on the top and beneath only half as long. Cones rarely produced, short, 4-angled, with oval, abruptly pointed, keeled leaves. *Cultivated in greenhouses, and occasionally naturalised on lawns, paths and roadside banks, mainly in the South and West.* Native of the Azores and Africa.

III. ISOETACEAE

Isoetes

Submerged, aquatic perennials. Leaves linear, pointed, arranged in a dense rosette, each leaf swollen at the base and traversed inside by 4 longitudinal air-canals. Sporangia situated in a pouch at the base of some of the leaves, covered by a membrane, those on some leaves containing a few large megaspores, on others containing numerous small microspores [Fig. IIIa].

1. Leaves stiff, tapered rather suddenly near the tip to a fine point; mega-
        spores greyish-white, ornamented with low ridges [Fig. IIIb]   **1. I. lacustris**
    Leaves soft and limp, tapered uniformly from near the base; mega-
        spores chalky white, ornamented with spines [Fig. IIIc]   **2. I. echinospora**

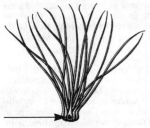

Fig. IIIa   Fig. IIIb   Fig. IIIc

1. Isoetes lacustris. 6-9. Leaves 10-25 cm long (rarely more), fairly stiff and brittle, dark green, tapering rather suddenly near the tip to a fine point. Megaspores greyish-white, marked with a fine pattern of ridges, but without spines. *In shallow or fairly deep water at the margins of non-calcareous lakes, mainly in the North and West; occasional.*

2. I. echinospora (*I. setacea*). **6-9.** Like *I. lacustris*, but leaves rather shorter, soft and flexible, tapering uniformly from base to tip. Megaspores chalky white, covered with small spines. *Shallow water in non-calcareous lakes; occasional near the West coast, unknown elsewhere.*

IV.   EQUISETACEAE

Equisetum. Horsetail. *Gliogán*

Perennials, with creeping, underground rhizome. Stems usually erect, unbranched or branched, longitudinally ridged, impregnated with silica, and thus usually rather harsh to the touch. Leaves small, whorled, united at the base to form a tubular sheath which surrounds the stem or branch and ends in acute teeth which are usually brown, black or white. Spores all alike; sporangia borne on small, mushroom-shaped structures grouped to form a terminal cone.

1.	Stems white or brownish, unbranched, with a cone at the tip ..	2
	Stems and branches green, with or without a terminal cone	3
2.	Leaf-sheaths with at least 20 teeth; cone at least 4 cm long	**11. E. telmateia**
	Leaf-sheaths with fewer than 20 teeth; cone less than 4 cm long	**7. E. arvense**
3.	Branches bearing regular whorls of secondary branches	**9. E. sylvaticum**
	Branches without or with very few secondary branches ..	4
4.	Stems thin-walled, with the central cavity occupying about 4/5 of the total diameter [Fig. IVa]	**5. E. fluviatile**
	Stems fairly thick-walled, with the central cavity occupying not more than half the diameter	5
5.	Internodes of main stem white, c. 10 mm in diameter, with at least 20 ridges and grooves [Fig. IVb]	**11. E. telmateia**
	Internodes of main stem green, not more than 6 mm in diameter, with less than 20 ridges and grooves	6

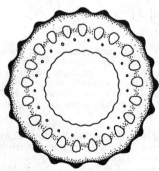

Fig. IVa   Fig. IVb

6. Stem unbranched, more than 3 mm across, with 12 or more ridges and
grooves   7
Stem branched or unbranched, not more than 3 mm across, with fewer
than 10 ridges and grooves   8

7. Stem 5-6 mm in diameter   ..   ..   ..   **1. E. hyemale**
Stem 3-4 mm in diameter   ..   ..   ..   **2. E. x moorei**

8. Cone narrowed at the tip to a short, sharp point   9
Cone rounded at the tip   10

9. Leaf-sheaths on main stem consisting of a broad black band c. 5 mm
long; teeth long and slender, usually falling early [Fig. IVc] **4. E. x trachyodon**
Leaf-sheaths on main stem forming a very narrow black band, not
more than 2 mm long; teeth squat, persistent, with a narrow black
midrib and broad translucent margins [Fig. IVd] ..   **3. E. variegatum**

10. Branches slender (not more than 1 mm in diameter), flexuous,
horizontal or drooping, mostly 3-angled   ..   **8. E. pratense**
Branches fairly stout, stiff, pointing obliquely upwards, at least at first,
mostly 4- or 5- angled   11

11. Stem with central hollow occupying about half the total diameter,
compressible between finger and thumb   ..   **6. E. x litorale**
Stem with central hollow occupying not more than a third of the
total diameter, not easily compressible between finger and thumb   12

12. Sheaths on stem with entirely black teeth; sheaths on branches
with green, divergent teeth [Fig. IVe]   ..   **7. E. arvense**
Sheaths on stem with black teeth with a conspicuous white margin;
sheaths on branches with brown, close-fitting teeth [Fig. IVf] **10. E. palustre**

  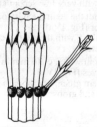 

Fig. IVc   Fig. IVd   Fig. IVe   Fig. IVf

1. Equisetum hyemale. 7-8. Stems all alike, some bearing cones, erect, rough,
unbranched, fairly thin-walled, with about 20 conspicuous ridges and grooves,
evergreen, 35-100 cm high, 5-6 mm in diameter. Sheaths 4-6 mm long, close-fitting,
whitish, with a narrow black band at the top and another at the bottom which
broadens with age so as almost to join the upper band; teeth soon disappearing. Cone
with a short sharp point. *Damp, open woods and river-banks, mainly in the East;
rather rare.*

2. E. x moorei. 7-8. Similar to *E. hyemale*, but the stems are less robust and only
3-5 mm in diameter; they are less reliably evergreen and tend to die back, at least at
the tips, in winter, and usually a few slender teeth persist on the leaf-sheaths. Cones
are rare and the spores abortive. *Sandhills and clay banks by the sea; locally
frequent on the East coast in Wicklow and Wexford; unknown elsewhere.*

A supposed hybrid between *E. hyemale* and another species; the second parent is said on cytological grounds to be *E. ramosissimum*, but as this has never been recorded for Ireland, and even in Britain is only a rare alien, the parentage must be considered doubtful.

3. E. variegatum. 7-8. Very variable. Stems erect or prostrate, slender, usually not more than 3 mm in diameter and often less, unbranched, or with a few long, wiry branches from near the base; some bearing cones, all hard, thick-walled (with central cavity occupying about $1/3$ of the total diameter), with 6-8 ridges and grooves. Leaf-sheaths with a conspicuous black band at the top and sometimes also at the base, and persistent teeth with broad, translucent margins and a thin black midrib [Fig. IVd]. Cone sharply pointed. *By lakes and canals, in fens, and damp hollows in sandhills; occasional in the Centre, rather rare elsewhere.*

4. E. x trachyodon. 6-8. Like *E. variegatum*, but stems usually erect, up to 5 mm in diameter, with 8-12 ridges and grooves; leaf-sheaths mainly black, with impersistent, slender, mainly black teeth [Fig. IVc]. Spores abortive. *Riversides, calcareous lake-shores and wet woods, mainly in the North and West; widespread but rare.*

A hybrid between *E. hyemale* and *E. variegatum*, but often found in the absence of both parents.

5. E. fluviatile (*E. limosum*). **6-7.** Stems all alike, erect, unbranched or with a few branches irregularly disposed, more rarely with regular whorls of branches, smooth and fairly soft, with 10-25 very low and inconspicuous ridges, very thin-walled, with the central cavity occupying at least $4/5$ of the total diameter [Fig. IVa]. Leaf-sheaths green, with persistent, acute, black teeth. Cones rounded at the tip. *Ditches, wet marshes and shallow water at the margins of lakes and canals; very frequent.*

6. E. x litorale. 6-8. A hybrid between *E. arvense* and *E. fluviatile*, but sometimes found in the absence of both parents. It is in most features intermediate between the parents, with erect stems up to 100 cm high and 1.5-3 mm in diameter, usually with regular whorls of branches in the middle part, but unbranched above and below; ridges and grooves 8-10, moderately well-marked. Central hollow occupying about half the diameter; this means that when compressed between finger and thumb it yields, but springs back when the pressure is released. Branches 4- or 5-angled; their leaf-sheaths loose-fitting. Sheaths of main stems green, with persistent, acute, black teeth. Cones short, rounded; spores abortive. *Ditches and rocky lake-shores; frequent in most districts.*

7. E. arvense. 4-5. Fertile stems appearing in Spring, unbranched, white or pale brown, with terminal cone 2-3.5 cm long; leaf-sheaths very loose-fitting, with 10-18 slender, brown teeth. Vegetative stems appearing about a month later, green, with regular whorls of branches which are at first directed obliquely upwards, with about 12 fairly prominent ridges and grooves, thick-walled, with the central cavity occupying less than a third of the total diameter. Branches 4-angled with entirely green, rather loose-fitting sheaths, their lowest internode usually much longer than the adjacent sheath on the main stem. *Roadsides, waste places, railway tracks and other bare ground, usually in drier habitats than other species of the genus; also as a persistent garden weed; abundant.*

8. E. pratense. 5. Stems eventually all alike, but the fertile stems (which are rarely produced) are at first unbranched. Vegetative stems 10-35 cm high, rough, 2-3 mm wide, with the central cavity occupying at least half the total diameter, regularly branched. Branches very slender, 3-angled, flexuous, horizontal or drooping. Leaf-sheaths of the main stems green; teeth persistent, with translucent margins and a narrow, dark brown midrib. *Damp, shady places, from Fermanagh northwards; occasional.*

9. E. sylvaticum. 5. Fertile stems at first unbranched, later branching and coming to resemble vegetative stems, which are up to 50 cm high and 2-4 mm wide, with the central cavity occupying one third or less of the total diameter. They bear 3- or 4-angled branches in regular whorls; these in turn all bear a few secondary branches. Leaf-sheaths on the main stems long, with persistent, rather broad brown teeth, which usually adhere by their edges into groups. *Streamsides and damp woods, mainly in mountain districts; frequent in the North, occasional elsewhere.*

10. E. palustre. 6-7. Stems all alike, resembling in general appearance the vegetative stems of *E. arvense*, but with only 5-9 ridges and grooves and a very small central hollow; teeth of leaf-sheath obtuse, with the margin translucent and sharply contrasting with the black, central, area of the teeth; branches rather fewer, 4- or 5-angled, more or less erect, their lowest internode shorter than or equalling the sheath on the main stem. *Ditches, marshes and damp grassland; abundant in the North, frequent elsewhere.*

11. E. telmateia (*E. maximum*). **4.** Fertile shoots unbranched, white, up to 25 cm, dying away as soon as spores have been shed; cone 5-8 cm long. Vegetative shoots appearing about a month later, up to 150 cm high and 6-9 mm wide, white, with 18-30 low ridges and grooves, with numerous green whorled, slender, drooping, branches up to 15 cm long, each with 4-5 double ridges. Leaf sheaths on main stem greenish, with a brown band at the top and numerous acute, brown teeth. *Damp hedgerows and banks; frequent but local.*

V.   OPHIOGLOSSACEAE

Small ferns with an underground stem, which lacks scales, and, usually, with only one leaf at a time; this is divided into two quite distinct portions - an ordinary, leaf-like blade, and a fertile spike, bearing sporangia, which stands-up in front of the leaf-like portion.

1. Blade of mature leaf divided and spike branched   ..   **1. Botrychium**
    Blade of mature leaf undivided and spike unbranched   **2. Ophioglossum**

1. Botrychium
Botrychium lunaria. Moonwort. 6-8. Blade of leaf 3-8 cm long, deeply pinnately divided, with about 6 pairs of fan-shaped segments. Fertile spike usually taller, and irregularly branched. Sporangia prominent, not sunken. *Grassland and mountain ledges; widespread but rare.*

2. Ophioglossum. Adder's tongue
Blade of leaf entire; spike unbranched; sporangia sunken.
1. Blade of leaf usually more than 4 cm long by 2 cm wide; spike
    with 10-40 sporangia on each side   ..   ..   **1. O. vulgatum**
    Blade of leaf usually less than 4 cm long by 2 cm wide; spike
    with 6-14 sporangia on each side   ..   ..   **2. O. azoricum**

1. Ophioglossum vulgatum. 5-8. Leaves usually single. Blade of leaf oval, more or less erect, 4-15 cm long; fertile spike slender, nearly cylindrical, with a row of 10-40 sporangia on each side. *Pastures, meadows and rocky ground; occasional.*

2. O. azoricum. 5-8. Differing from *O. vulgatum* in its more slender habit with the leaves somewhat spreading and often produced in pairs; the blade narrow, often lanceolate, 3-3.5 cm long and in the fertile spike with only 6-14 sporangia on each side. *Dune-slacks and coastal grassland in the West only; rare and local.*

VI. OSMUNDACEAE

Osmunda regalis. Royal fern. 6-8. Stem short, erect, stout. Leaves large, 60-100 cm long, twice-pinnate; young stalks covered in golden-brown hairs which soon fall off. The outer leaves are entirely green and leaf-like with parallel-sided, obtuse segments, about 3 times as long as broad, entire or lobed at the base. The lower segments of the inner leaves are similar but the upper segments are reduced to clustered masses of brown sporangia, without any leafy tissue. *Ditches, bog-margins, damp woods and river-banks; very frequent in most of the West half, much rarer in the East.*

VII. ADIANTACEAE

Moderately sized ferns with linear sporangia, which lack a true indusium, but are protected by the rolled-under margins of the leaves.

1. Fertile leaves taller and obviously different to sterile leaves; ultimate
   leaf segments not fan or wedge shaped . . **1. Cryptogramma**
   Leaves all similar; ultimate leaf-segments fan or wedge-shaped **2. Adiantum**

1. Cryptogramma
Cryptogramma crispa. Parsley fern. 6-8. Stem short; leaves tufted, 7-25 cm long. Stem and bases of leaf-stalk clothed with light brown scales; leaves of two kinds, both irregularly tripinnate with numerous small segments; sterile leaves small, with the ultimate segments broad and overlapping; fertile leaves larger, with the ultimate segments linear-oblong with turned-over margins, not overlapping. Sori small, oval but running together so as to form linear sporangia, near to and covered by the turned-over, lower margin of the leaf. *Rocky and stony places, almost exclusively in the mountains of the North and East (largely in the Mourne Mountains); extremely rare.*

2. Adiantum
Adiantum capillus-veneris. Maidenhair fern. *Dubh-chosach.* **6-9.** Stem shortly creeping, covered with dark brown scales. Leaves pale green, usually bipinnate, 7-30 cm long; leaf-stalk long, shining black, hairless in the upper parts, with scales at the base. Ultimate segments of leaf fan-shaped, with straight sides and a curved outer margin, which may be entire or deeply cut; all on slender, shining black stalks. Sori linear, covered by small, brown flaps of tissue arising from the outer margins of the leaf on the lower side. *Rock-crevices and damp rock-faces from Clare to Donegal; locally frequent in the Aran Islands and the Burren district of Clare, very rare elsewhere.*

VIII. HYMENOPHYLLACEAE

Smallish, evergreen ferns with slender, creeping, black rhizomes and deeply divided leaves which are very thin and of a dark, translucent green. Sori marginal.

1. Leaves seldom over 7 cm long; rhizome thread-like, almost hairless
                                                    1. Hymenophyllum
    Leaves usually over 7 cm long; rhizome cord-like, hairy   **2. Trichomanes**

1. Hymenophyllum. Filmy fern

Small plants, moss-like in habit. Rhizome thread-like; almost hairless. Ultimate divisions of leaves with small, distinct teeth. Indusium consisting of two, nearly circular flaps, united only in their lower half. Sorus short, not projecting beyond indusium.

1.Veins ending just short of leaf-margin; tip of indusium toothed [Fig. VIIIa]
                                                    1. H. tunbridgense
    Veins reaching leaf-margin; tip of indusium without teeth [Fig. VIIIb] **2. H. wilsonii**

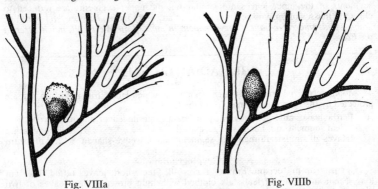

Fig. VIIIa   Fig. VIIIb

1. Hymenophyllum tunbridgense. 6-7. Leaves 2-6 cm long, dark, somewhat pale bluish-green green; blade flat, at least half as broad as long, irregularly divided into oblong segments. Veins stopping just short of the margin. Flaps of indusium circular, irregularly toothed at the tip [Fig. VIIIa]. *Boulders and tree-stumps in moist woods, sheltered crevices mainly in mountain areas, and similar places in the lowlands; occasional in the South-west, rare elsewhere.*

2. H. wilsonii. 6-7. Similar but with the leaf a pure, deep green, the leaf tip and margins slightly recurved so as to make the surface somewhat convex above; the blade of the leaf at most a quarter as broad as long, with the veins reaching the margin and the tip of the indusium without teeth [Fig. VIIIb]. *Similar situations, but more frequent, and on higher ground.*

2. Trichomanes

Trichomanes speciosum (*T. radicans*). **Killarney fern. 6-8.** Rhizome covered with black hairs, bearing leaves at wide intervals. Leaves 8-25 cm long, with a long wiry stalk, winged in its upper part. Blade oval-lanceolate in outline, irregularly and repeatedly divided; margins of the ultimate segments entire. Sori cylindrical, borne around a bristle-like receptacle, projecting beyond the margins of the flask-shaped indusium; the sporangia eventually fall off, leaving the receptacle as a persistent bristle. *Beside waterfalls, in crevices between boulders, under overhanging rocks, and in similar damp, dark, sheltered situations. Formerly widespread, and fairly frequent in the South-west; now almost exterminated by collectors and very rare and* *scattered, from Donegal and Fermanagh south and westwards to Mayo and Kerry with isolated populations in the Centre and eastern counties. Possibly more widespread.*

Plants form sterile, filamentous gametophytes which produce gemmae; these have established themselves over a wider range than is presently seen in the sporophyte.

IX. POLYPODIACEAE

Polypodium

Small to medium sized ferns. Rhizome stout, usually above ground, covered with brown scales. Leaves borne singly along the rhizome, evergreen, once pinnate with linear-oblong, entire or toothed segments. Sori large and conspicuous, round to oval, some distance from the margin, without an indusium.

The three species present in Ireland can only be distinguished with certainty after microscopic examination of the rhizome scales, sori and sporangia. However, with some experience, most specimens can be named with a fair degree of confidence.

1. Leaves broadly oval to triangular with the segments often toothed
                                                            3. P. cambricum
    Leaves narrowly oval to narrowly oblong with the segments more or less
        untoothed   2
2. Sori usually oval; rhizome with scales at least 4 times as long as broad
                                                            2. P. interjectum
    Sori usually round; rhizome with scales about 3 times as long as broad
                                                            1. P. vulgare

1. Polypodium vulgare. 8-3. Leaves mostly 3-3.5 times as long as broad, more or less parallel-sided; segments not toothed and with a rounded tip. New leaves produced in early summer. Young sori round. Rhizome scales 3-6 mm long, about 3 times as long as broad, narrowly triangular. *Rocks, walls and trees; very frequent.*

2. P. interjectum. 9-2. Similar to *P. vulgare* but with the leaves mostly 2-2.5 times as long as broad and ovate-lanceolate and the segments not toothed and with a rounded tip. New leaves produced in mid-summer. Young sori oval. Rhizome scales 3-11 mm long, at least 4 times as long as broad, narrowly triangular, with a long, pointed, but not hair-like, tip. *Similar situations; frequent in the South and West, rarer elsewhere.*

Hybrids (*P. x mantonii*) between this and the preceeding species occur in eastern areas; they are often of larger size and may be distinguished by their colourless sporangia and abortive spores.

3. P. cambricum (*P. australe*). **11-5.** Leaves mostly less than twice as long as broad, triangular, sometimes narrowing at the base; segments often toothed with an acute tip. New leaves produced in autumn. Young sori oval. Rhizome scales 5-16 mm long, narrowly triangular, with a hair-like tip. *Rocks and walls, often on limestone; locally frequent in the South half, rare elsewhere.*

X. HYPOLEPIDACEAE

Pteridium aquilinum (*Pteris aquilina*). **Bracken.** *Raithneach.* **7-8.** Rhizome underground, extensively creeping. Leaves 50-200 cm high, or even more, with erect stalks and somewhat recurved, oval-triangular blades, thrice pinnate. Young leaves densely hairy when young; mature leaves only hairy underneath. Ultimate segments of leaf narrow-oblong, entire, numerous and parallel sided. Sporangia forming continuous sori, just below the leaf-margin, protected by the recurved margin and by an inner membranous indusium. *Open woods, mountain slopes, neglected pastures and sandhills; abundant.*

XI. THELYPTERIDACEAE

Small to medium sized ferns with sparsely hairy leaves.

1. Leaf smelling strongly of lemon when crushed   ..   **3. Oreopteris**
    Leaf not smelling strongly of lemon when crushed   2
2. Rachis without evident hairs; lowest segments of leaf borne at the same
    angle as the others; indusium present   ..   **1. Thelypteris**
    Rachis clearly hairy; lowest segments borne at a different angle from
    the others; indusium absent   ..   ..   **2. Phegopteris**

1. Thelypteris

Thelypteris palustris (*T. thelypteroides, Lastraea thelypteris*). **Marsh fern. 7-8.** Rhizome long, creeping, underground. Scales on upper part of the rachis few or none. Leaves arising singly, 30-60 cm long, long-stalked; leaf-blade slightly hairy underneath, oblong in outline, the lower pinnae being slightly shorter or about the same length as those half-way up the leaf; fertile fronds usually longer than the sterile, with narrower ultimate segments. Ultimate segments oblong, tip pointed, sometimes weakly crenate, with the margin somewhat inrolled. Sori circular, eventually merging together; indusium present. *Marshes; rare and decreasing due to increased drainage.*

2. Phegopteris

Phegopteris connectilis (*P. polypodioides, Thelypteris phegopteris*). **Beech fern. 6-8.** Rhizome long, creeping, slender, underground. Scales clearly visible on the upper part of the rachis. Leaves arising singly, 15-50 cm long, long-stalked, hairy underneath, pale green, thin, triangular-oval in outline, the lowest 2 pairs of pinnae the longest, the lowest pair usually not lying in the same plane as the rest of the frond. Ultimate segments oblong, tip rounded, sometimes weakly crenate, with the margin flat. Sori circular, very close to the margin; indusium absent. *Damp, rocky places in mountains; occasional in the North (though locally abundant in the Mourne Mountains); rare in the South.*

3. Oreopteris

Oreopteris limbosperma (*Thelypteris limbosperma, Thelypteris oreopteris, Lastraea montana*). **Mountain fern, Lemon-scented fern. 7-8.** Stem short and stout, erect. Leaves tufted, 30-90 cm long, short-stalked, oval in outline, the longest pinnae being near the middle and those at the base much shorter. Ultimate segments oblong, blunt-tipped, weakly crenate, with the margin flat, covered on the lower side with minute yellow glands which release a strong lemon-like smell when crushed. Sori circular, very close to the margin; indusium absent or rudimentary. *Mountain slopes, stream or ditch-sides and open woods; rather rare.*

Easily confused with *Dryopteris filix-mas* or *D. affinis*, the leaves of which, however lack scented glands and sporangia of which have an obvious indusium.

XII. ASPLENIACEAE

Asplenium. Spleenwort

Small to medium sized ferns with short stems and tufted leaves, bearing elongated sori on their underside, protected by a linear, membranous or whitish indusium attached along one side. Stem and lower part of leaf-stalks clothed with narrow, blackish-brown scales; upper part of leaf-stalk usually bare.

1. Leaves undivided, entire ..   ..   ..   **1. A. scolopendrium**
   Leaves divided   2

2. Back of leaf densely scaly ..   ..   ..   **10. A. ceterach**
   Back of leaf not densely scaly   3

3. Leaves forked or once pinnate   4
   Leaves twice or more pinnate or trifoliate   7

4. Leaves deeply forked   ..   ..   ..   **5. A septentrionale**
   Leaves once pinnate   5

5. Leaf distinctly glossy on the upper surface, rather thick and leathery;
   pinnae usually more than twice as long as wide ..   **7. A. marinum**
   Leaf not distinctly glossy above, nor thick and leathery; pinnae less
   than twice as long as wide   6

6. Leaf-stalk blackish or reddish-brown ..   ..   **8. A. trichomanes**
   Leaf-stalk green throughout   ..   ..   **9. A. viride**

7. Leaf-stalk green (except at the very base); ultimate segments fan-
   shaped ..   ..   **6. A. ruta-muraria**
   Leaf-stalk blackish or reddish-brown; ultimate segments not fan-shaped   8

8. Longest pinnae in the middle of the leaf   ..   **4. A. obovatum**
   Longest pinnae clearly at the base of the leaf   9

9. Apex of leaves and pinnae narrowly lanceolate with a long, sharp tip; pinnae
   often swept-up towards the tip of the leaf   ..   **3. A. onopteris**
   Apex of leaves and pinnae acute, without a long, sharp tip; pinnae spreading, not
   swept up towards the leaf-tip   ..   ..   **2. A. adiantum-nigrum**

1. Asplenium scolopendrium (*Phyllitis scolopendrium*). **Hart's tongue.** *Creamh muice fiadh.* **7-8.** Leaves 20-70 cm long, occasionally more, evergreen, rather firm and leathery, oblong, undivided, bright green; leaf-stalk brownish-purple. Sori lying obliquely (over a vein), in pairs on the underside of the leaves, the members of each pair merging so as to look like one sorus, but each with its own indusium. *Woods, hedge-banks, wet areas on walls, and rocky places; very frequent, especially in limestone districts.*

2. A. adiantum-nigrum. 6-10. Leaves evergreen, dark shining green above, paler underneath, 10-35 cm long, twice to thrice pinnate, triangular in outline; leaf-stalk blackish. Ultimate segments oval or lanceolate, often toothed. Sori about 2 mm long, often merging together. Spores about 0.4 mm across or more.*Walls, hedge-banks and shady places; frequent in the South, local elsewhere.*

Plants growing on serpentine in Connemara have been referred to *A. cuneifolium* or *A. cuneatum*, a species known from mainland Europe, but are in fact variants of *A. adiantum-nigrum.*

3. A. onopteris. Similar to *A. adiantum-nigrum* but with the pinnae narrowly lanceolate and often swept-up towards the tip of the leaf, the ultimate segments with a very narrowly lanceolate tip and smaller spores (about 0.3 mm across). *Dry, sunny earth-banks and rock-faces, near the sea; rare, in the South and South-west (mainly in Kerry and Cork).*

4. A. obovatum (*A. billotii, A. lanceolatum*). **6-9.** Leaves 10-30 cm long, twice pinnate, sometimes approaching thrice pinnate. Lowest pinnae somewhat shorter than those higher up. Leaf-stalk dark brown. Ultimate segments oval, toothed. Sori about 2 mm long. *Banks and walls near the South and East coasts; very rare.*

5. A septentrionale. 6-10. Leaves evergreen, dull darkish green, 2-7 cm long, forked once or twice; segments parallel-sided, very narrow. Leaf-stalk brown at base, green higher up. Sori about 3 mm long, merging to cover almost the whole of the undersurface of the frond. *Vertical sides of volcanic rocks near Roundstone, Co. Galway; very rare.*

6. A. ruta-muraria. Wall-rue. 6-10. Leaves evergreen, dull darkish green, rather thick, 2-10 cm long, twice or thrice pinnate, with the lowest ultimate segments the largest. Ultimate segments rather few, fan-shaped or oval, tapered to stalks. Leaf-stalk mostly green. Sori about 2 mm long, merging to cover most of the undersurface of the frond. *Walls and rock crevices; very frequent.*

7. A. marinum. 6-9. Leaves 7-30 cm long, occasionally more, glossy green on the upper surface, rather leathery, once pinnate. Leaf-stalk brownish-purple. Pinnae about 25 mm long, oblong, usually crenate and sometimes irregularly lobed, asymmetrical at the base, largest in the middle of the leaf. Sori about 4 mm long. *Rocks by the sea, especially in crevices; occasional and local.*

8. A. trichomanes. 5-10. Leaves 5-20 cm long, narrow, once pinnate; leaf-stalk and rachis black. Pinnae 3-8 mm long, nearly equal in size, except at the apex of the leaf, broadly oval or oblong, or nearly round, bluntly toothed, but not lobed, eventually falling away and leaving the rachis bare. Sori about 2 mm long. *Walls and rocks; very frequent.*
Three rather indistinct sub-species are recognised:
    old collections from Co. Clare of subsp. *pachyrachis*, which has lobed pinnae usually minutely hairy underneath and with a basal projection, require re-finding
    subsp. *trichomanes* has leaf-stalks persistent after the pinnae are shed and is known only from silicous rocks in Co. Down
    subsp. *quadrivalens,* the common subspecies, lacks persistent leaf-stalks.

9. A. viride (*A. trichomanes-ramosum, A. ramosum*). **6-9.** Very similar to *A. trichomanes*, differing principally in the green rachis and leaf-stalk; also in the rounder, more delicate, fresher green pinnae, which are serrate and do not fall away from the rachis. *Crevices in mountain cliffs in the West half; rather rare.*

10. A. ceterach (*Ceterach officinarum*). **Rusty-back. 4-10.** Leaves 5-20 cm long, evergreen, pinnately lobed or once pinnate, with short, broad, obtuse, alternate pinnae, which are entire or crenate, dark green above and covered beneath with numerous scales, which are silvery at first and later rusty brown. Sori hidden by the scales, about 2-3 mm long, eventually almost merging together. *Limestone rocks and mortared walls; frequent in most districts but decreasing northwards.*

XIII. WOODSIACEAE

Small to medium sized, rather delicate.

1. Leaves borne in tufts   2
   Leaf borne singly   3
2. Leaves of two distinct kinds, the inner smaller and fertile, the outer
       larger and sterile   . .   . . **1. Matteucia**
   Leaves all fairly similar . .   . . **2. Athyrium**

3. Leaf broadly triangular in outline; indusium absent .. **3. Gymnocarpium**
   Leaf elliptic or lanceolate in outline; indusium present but often
   inconspicuous .. .. .. **4. Cystopteris**

1. Matteucia

* Matteucia struthiopteris. Ostrich fern. 7-9. Plant with both long-creeping stolons and an erect, short stem, which often forms a miniature "trunk", producing a crown of leaves at the top. Leaves of two types. Outer leaves sterile, large (up to 1.5 m long) rather like those of *Dryopteris filix-mas*. Inner leaves smaller (20-40 cm), narrow, once pinnate, pinnae broadly linear, crenate, green at first, later covered with sporangia and entirely brown, with the margin strongly inrolled. *Naturalised in marshy ground by Lough Neagh; also in Leitrim.* Native of Eurasia.

2. Athyrium

Athyrium filix-femina. Lady fern. 7-8. Stem stout, short, erect, covered with dark brown scales which ascend for some distance up the leaf-stalks. Leaves 30-100 cm long, erect or somewhat spreading, soft and rather limp, pale green, twice pinnate, oval in outline, rachis usually reddish. Ultimate segments oblong-lanceolate, usually somewhat pinnately lobed. Sori rather elongated with a j-shaped or linear indusium attached along one side. *Woods, shady banks and streamsides; very frequent except in the Centre.*

3. Gymnocarpium

Small ferns with long, slender, creeping rhizome and thrice divided leaves. Sori very small, close to the margin; indusium absent.

1. Young leaves rolled into 3 separate balls; leaf blade not mealy, without
   glands .. .. **1. G. dryopteris**
   Young leaves rolled into a single ball; leaf blade appearing mealy due
   to the presence of minute glands .. .. **2. G. robertianum**

1. Gymnocarpium dryopteris (*Thelypteris dryopteris, Phegopteris dryopteris*). **Oak fern. 7-8.** Leaves 10-30 cm long, long-stalked, hairless, bright green, broadly triangular in outline, the lowest pair of pinnae being very much the largest, each almost as big as the rest of the leaf, which therefore appears almost ternate. Ultimate segments oblong, bluntly toothed. Young leaves rolled-up into 3 distinct balls. *Shady rocks in the mountains of Antrim; very rare.*

2. G. robertianum (*Thelypteris robertiana, Phegopteris robertiana*). **7-8.** Similar to *G. dryopteris* but with dull green leaves, with minute glands underneath, and the lowest pair of pinnae, though the largest, are not so disproportionate to the others. Young leaves rolled-up into a single ball. *Known only from rocky ground on one hill near Headford, on the Galway-Mayo border.*

4. Cystopteris

Cystopteris fragilis. 7-8. Stem short but creeping, covered with pale yellowish-brown scales; leaf-stalk with some scales at the base but none higher up. Leaves delicate, 6-25 cm long, oval-lanceolate in outline, bipinnate, with the lowest one or two pairs of pinnae distinctly shorter than those immediately above. Ultimate segments rather irregularly shaped, oval or oblong, lobed or toothed. Sori small, circular, protected by a delicate indusium which soon becomes folded back and inconspicuous. *Damp rocks crevices, limestone pavement and occasionally on walls; fairly frequent in the North and West, rare in the South and East; possibly declining.*

XIV. DRYOPTERIDACEAE

Large or medium sized ferns with short, stout erect stems and pinnate leaves, of which the leaf-stalks and the lower part of the rachis bear fairly numerous scales. Sori small, round.

1. Indusium circular; teeth on ultimate leaf-segments with a bristle-like
    tip   ..   ..   **1. Polystichum**
    Indusium kidney-shaped; teeth on ultimate leaf-segments without a
    bristle-like tip   ..   ..   ..   **2. Dryopteris**

1. Polystichum

Leaves dark green, short-stalked, often rather leathery, the ultimate segments with sharp, bristle-like teeth, and some or all of them markedly asymmetrical at the base, the side nearest the tip of the leaf or pinna being drawn out into a distinct lobe. Sori circular, protected by a circular induisum attached to the leaf by a central stalk; usually confined to the upper half of the leaf. Scales on leaf-stalk and rachis pale brown, rather numerous.

1. Leaves once pinnate   ..   ..   ..   **1. P. lonchitis**
    Leaves twice or more pinnate   2
2. Ultimate segments from the middle of the leaf mostly more or less
    symmetrical at their base   ..   ..   **2. P. aculeatum**
    Ultimate segments above the middle of the pinna markedly
    asymmetrical at their base   ..   ..   **3. P. setiferum**

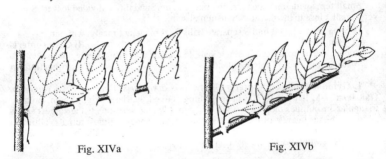

Fig. XIVa   Fig. XIVb

1. Polystichum lonchitis. Holly fern. 6-8. Leaves 15-45 cm long, narrow, once pinnate, with the longest pinnae about the middle, evergreen, dark green and stiff and leathery. Pinnae all asymmetrical at the base (this is most marked in the middle ones), short, oval toothed with straight spiny teeth. *Mountain cliffs in the West; very rare.*

2. P. aculeatum (*P. lobatum*). **7-8.** Leaves 30-100 cm long, twice pinnate, lance-olate, evergreen, slightly stiff and leathery and with the margin weakly spiny; ultimate segments in the middle of the leaf more or less symmetrical at their base, except for the upper basal segment of each pinna which is both much larger than the rest and usually asymmetric at the base [Fig. XIVa]. *Shady banks and rocky places; widespread but not frequent.*

3. P. setiferum (*P. angulare*). **7-8.** Similar to *P. aculeatum* but with leaves softer, usually withering in winter and the margins with bristle-like teeth but scarcely spiny;

ultimate segments in the middle of the leaf highly asymmetrical at their base, the upper basal segment of each pinna slightly larger than the rest [Fig. XIVb]. *Woods, hedge-banks and other shady places; frequent in the South-east, frequent in most other areas except the West where it is rare.*

Hybrids (*P. x bicknellii*) between this species and *P. aculeatum* are frequent, especially in eastern areas. They are intermediate in form and are mostly sterile.

2. Dryopteris

Leaves mid to dark green, short-stalked, twice or thrice pinnate. Sori circular, protected by a kidney-shaped indusium; usually confined to the upper half of the leaf. Scales on leaf-stalk and rachis pale to dark brown, numerous.

1. Leaves appearing twice pinnate; ultimate divisions not or scarcely
   narrowed at the base 2
   Leaves appearing thrice or more pinnate; ultimate divisions narrowed
   or stalked at the base 4

Fig. XIVc   Fig. XIVd

2. Scales on rachis dense, orange-brown; ultimate segments often square
   at the tip [Fig. XIVc] .. .. .. **3. D. affinis**
   Scales on rachis moderately sparse, pale brown or straw-coloured;
   ultimate segments rounded to acute at tip .. 3
3. Leaves usually 50-120 cm long; tips of ultimate segments with distinct,
   usually acute teeth; widespread and frequent [Fig. XIVd]   **1. D. filix-mas**
   Leaves usually 40-50 cm long; tips of ultimate segments with
   blunt teeth or feebly crenate; very rare .. **2. D. oreades**
4. Scales on leaf-stalk with a dark central stripe .. **6. D. dilatata**
   Scales on leaf-stalk uniform light brown .. 5
5. Scales on leaf-stalk narrowly triangular, about 5-6 times as long as
   broad; leaf concave above, glandular .. **4. D. aemula**
   Scales on leaf-stalk broadly triangular to rounded almost as broad as
   long; leaf flat, without glands .. .. **5. D. carthusiana**

1. Dryopteris filix-mas (*Lastraea filix-mas*). **Male fern. 7-8.** Leaves 50-120 cm long, usually withered by mid-winter, rather short stalked, narrowly oval in outline. Leaf-stalk and rachis clothed with few or moderately numerous, straw-coloured scales. Ultimate segments undivided, oblong, acute or rounded at the tip, more or less toothed on the sides and at the tip [Fig. XIVd]. Sori 3-6 on each ultimate segment. Scales narrowly triangular [Fig. XIVd]. *Woods, hedges, streamsides and mountain glens; widespread and abundant.*

2. D. oreades (*D. abbreviata*). **8-10.** Similar to *D. filix-mas* but smaller in all its parts, with the ultimate segments with blunt teeth, each ultimate segment bearing only 1-2 sori, the indusia of which have glandular, tucked under margins. *Mountain rocks; known only from Eagle Mountain in Down, where it may now be extinct, and from one site in Kerry and one in West Cork.*

3. D. affinis (*D. pseudomas, D. borreri*). **7-8.** Also similar to *D. filix-mas*. Leaves 50-150 cm long, sometimes even longer; usually persisting till spring, short stalked, oval in outline. Leaf-stalk and rachis clothed with numerous orange-brown scales, and often with a blackish patch at the junction of pinna and rachis. Ultimate segments undivided, with the tip cut off square or rounded [Fig. XIVc]. Scales narrowly triangular [Fig. XIVc]. *Woods, hedges, stramsides and mountain glens; very frequent in the West half, frequent, but more local in the East.*

A very variable, usually apomictic species within which a number of ill-defined sub-species or 'morphotypes' have been recognised; their status in Ireland awaits investigation. Hybrids between *D. affinis* and *D. filix-mas*, have been recorded from a number of localities in Ireland; they are intermediate in most characters but are larger with a number of sterile spores.

4. D. aemula. 7-9. Leaves 15-40 cm long, long-stalked, thrice pinnate; blade triangular in outline, the lowest pinna being distinctly the longest, fresh, pale green. Ultimate segments oblong, coarsely toothed; margins upturned, giving the whole leaf, when fresh, a somewhat crimped appearance; lower surface with minute glands which give the leaf a sweet scent when drying. Scales uniformly coloured, very narrowly triangular, numerous. Indusium with stalkless glands on the jagged margin. *Woods, shady banks and by mountain streams; frequent in the West, occasional in the East, very rare in the Centre.*

5. D. carthusiana (*D. lanceolata-cristata, D. spinulosa, Lastraea spinulosa*). **7-9.** Leaves 40-80 cm long, long-stalked, thrice pinnate, more or less flat; lanceolate to triangular-lanceolate in outline, with the pinnae in the lower half all about the same length, pale yellowish-green. Leaf-stalk and rachis with sparse, uniformly pale brown scales, which are almost as wide as they are long. Ultimate segments oblong, with sharp and shortly spiny teeth. Indusium entire, eglandular. *Damp woods and cutaway bogs; occasional, throughout but much less frequent in the South.*

6. D. dilatata (*D. austriaca, Lastraea aristata*). **7-9.** Similar to *D. carthusiana*, differing mainly in its more triangular leaf, which is of a darker green, and clearly convex above, at least when young, its oval-triangular scales which are pale brown at the edges but have a dark stripe in the centre, and its indusium which has an irregular margin, which sometimes bears small, stalked glands. *Woods, banks, heaths and moorland; very frequent, especially in upland areas.*

XV. BLECHNACEAE

Blechnum spicant. Hard fern. 6-8. Stem short, covered, like the base of the leaf-stalks, with darkish-brown scales. Leaves tufted, erect, 15-50 cm long, short-stalked, simply pinnate, of two kinds; sterile with flat, oblong, slightly curved segments about 12 mm long and 4 mm broad, set close together; and fertile, usually longer, with longer, narrower and more widely spaced segments, of which almost the whole of the lower surface is occupied by the elongated sori. *Woods, heaths, turf-banks; moorland and mountain slopes; very frequent.*

XVI. MARSILEACEAE

Pilularia globulifera. Pillwort. 6-9. Rhizome slender, creeping in the mud or on its surface. Leaves narrow, cylindrical, pointed, about 5 cm long, borne singly or in small tufts, curled at the tip when young. Sporangia borne in spherical bodies 3 mm across at the base of the leaves. *Margins of lakes, pools and slow-moving rivers; very rare and largely confined to the North (possibly extinct around Lough Neagh) and West.*

XVII. AZOLLACEAE

* Azolla filiculoides. 6-9. A small, floating fern of moss-like habit, with branched stems about 2.5 cm long and slender, unbranched roots. Leaves very small and scale-like, closely overlapping, greenish in summer (especially when shaded), bright red in winter; surface unwettable. Sporangia borne in small spherical structures amongst the leaves. *Garden ponds; naturalised in a few places (West Cork, Dublin & Wicklow).* Native of tropical and subtropical America.

GYMNOSPERMS

XVIII. PINACEAE

Trees, with resin-canals in leaves and wood. Leaves linear, needle-like, borne alternately, or in groups or clusters on short shoots. Monoecious. Male cones small. Seeds borne on scales grouped into cones, which become woody as the seeds ripen.

1. Leaves in clusters of more than 5, light green, deciduous .. **4. Larix**
    Leaves solitary or in pairs, dark green; evergreen 2
2. All leaves alternate, not in pairs 3
    Leaves borne in pairs on short shoots .. .. .. **5. Pinus**
3. Leaf-scars round, flat or very slightly raised 4
    Twigs rough after leaf-fall, on account of 'pegs' left by the base of the
    leaves .. .. **3. Picea**
4. Cones hanging, falling whole, with 3-lobed bracts protruding beyond the seed
    scales [Fig. XVIIIa] .. .. .. **2. Pseudotsuga**
    Cones erect, shedding seeds and scales while still on the tree; bracts
    not 3-lobed [Fig. XVIIIb] .. .. .. **1. Abies**

1. Abies. Fir
Leaves usually blunt, alternate, evergreen. Leaf-scars circular, not raised above the surface of the twig. Seed-cones erect, shedding the scales while still on the tree.

1. Leaves dark green on upper side, diverging to the sides so as to leave
    a clear 'parting' on the upper side of the twig .. .. **1. A. alba**
    Leaves grey-green or pale bluish-green on upper side, pointing
    forwards and upwards but not sideways, and not leaving a 'parting'
    on the upper side of the twig .. .. **2. A. procera**

1. * Abies alba. Silver fir. A large tree, up to 45 m. Twigs downy. Leaves 15-30 mm, dark green above, with 2 white stripes on lower side, diverging laterally so as to leave a 'parting' on upper side of twig. Cones 101-105 mm; bracts protruding beyond

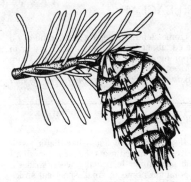

Fig. XVIIIa

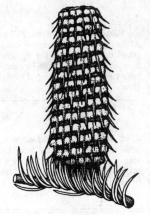

Fig. XVIIIb

Fig. XVIIIc

Fig. XVIIId

Fig. XVIIIe

seed-scales, acutely pointed, with the tip turned downwards [Fig. XVIIIb]. *Formerly planted for forestry fairly widely, less often today.* Native of Central and southern Europe.

2. * A. procera (*A. nobilis*). A large tree, but seldom seen fully grown. Leaves greyish- pale bluish-green on upper side, pointing upwards and forwards, and not leaving a 'parting' on the upper side of the twig. Cones as in *A. alba. Planted increasingly, mainly for Christmas trees.* Native of western North America.

2. Pseudotsuga

* Pseudotsuga menziesii (*P. douglasii, P. taxifolia*). **Douglas fir.** A tall tree, up to 45 m. Leaves evergreen, dark green, alternate, subacute, fragrant when bruised; leaf-scars circular, very slightly raised above the surface of the twig. Leaves directed sideways, so as to leave a fairly distinct 'parting' on the upper side of the shoot. Winter buds narrow, conical. Cones hanging, 7-10 cm long, falling entire; bracts protruding beyond the seed-scales, 3-lobed [Fig. XVIIIa]. *Planted fairly frequently for forestry.* Native of western North America.

3. Picea. Spruce

Leaves acute, evergreen, those on the upper side of the shoot pointing forwards, alternate; twigs rough with peg-like projections which are left by the leaves when they fall. Seed-cones hanging, remaining for some time on the tree after the seeds have fallen, but eventually falling whole. Bracts small, not protruding beyond the seed-scales.

1. Leaves flat, about twice as broad as thick, with very acute, spinous
    points, standing out all round the twig. Cones usually less than
    10 cm long [Fig. XVIIIc] .. .. **2. P. sitchensis**
   Leaves quadrangular, at least as thick as wide, with an acute, but not
    spinous point, those on the upper side of the twig point forward,
    those on the lower side pointing sideways. Cones usually more
    than 10 cm long .. .. **1. P. abies**

1. * Picea abies. Norway spruce. A tall but rather slender tree. Leaves quadrangular, with acute, but not spinous tip, lying more or less flat along the twig. Twigs reddish brown, sometimes minutely downy. Cones 10-15 cm long. *Formerly widely planted for forestry; now largely replaced by* P. sitchensis. Native of North and Central Europe.

2. * P. sitchensis. Sitka spruce. Like *P. abies*, but more thickly furnished with leaves, which are darker green, furnished with very acute, spinous points, and stand out on all sides of the twig. Twigs pale brown, hairless. Cones 5-10 cm long. *Very widely planted for forestry.* Native of western North America.

4. Larix. Larch

Leaves obtuse or subacute, light green, soft, deciduous, borne alternately on the long shoots and also in tufts of about 30-50 on short shoots, which persist as short, rounded projections after they have ceased to produce leaves. Cones 2.5-4 cm long, erect, persisting long after the seeds have been shed; bracts at first longer than seed-scales, but at maturity slightly shorter.

1. Twigs greyish-brown; cone-scales erect, not bent back at tip
    [Fig. XVIIId] .. .. .. **1. L. decidua**
   Twigs reddish; cone-scales bent outwards and downwards at tip
    [Fig. XVIIIe] .. .. .. **2. L. leptolepis**

1. * Larix decidua (*L. europaea*). Up to 40 m high. Twigs not pale bluish-green, greyish-brown. Leaves up to 3 cm long, light green, not pale bluish-green. Young cones bright red. Scales of mature cone erect, not curved outwards at the tip [Fig. XVIIId]. *Formerly planted for forestry and shelter; now largely replaced by* L. leptolepis *or the hybrid*. Native of Central Europe.

2. * L. leptolepis. Japanese larch. Like *L. decidua*, but with twigs slightly pale bluish-green at first and reddish in their second year, leaves slightly broader, somewhat pale bluish-green, and cone-scales curved outwards and downwards at the tip [Fig. XVIIIe]. *Fairly widely planted for forestry*. Native of Japan.

A hybrid between the two species above, *L.* x *eurolepis*, is planted almost as widely as either of the parents. It is intermediate in all characters.

5. Pinus. Pine

Leaves evergreen, dark green, acute, stiff, borne in pairs (in some other species in groups of 3 or 5) on short shoots in the axils of scale-leaves; at the base of each pair is a thin, papery sheath. Cones requiring at least two years to mature, green at first but eventually brown and woody; falling whole, but sometimes remaining for many years on the tree.

1. Cone-scales without a sharp point on the outer face; leaves pale
         bluish-green   ..   ..   ..   **1. P. sylvestris**
    Cone-scales with a sharp point on the outer face; leaves fairly bright
         green, not pale bluish-green   ..   ..   **2. P. contorta**

1. * Pinus sylvestris. Scots pine. *Giuis*. **6.** Up to 30 m high, with a regular conical outline when young, but older trees have a bare trunk surmounted by a flat crown of foliage. Bark of older trunks orange-red in upper part. Leaves 4-7 cm long, pale bluish-green. Cones 4-7 cm long; scales without a spine on outer face. *Native in the post-glacial period, but apparently becoming extinct early in the Christian era; re-introduced two or three hundred years ago; now widely planted and naturalised in several places, mainly in the West half.*

Some authors believe that the species did not become completely extinct, but persisted as very small populations through the Middle Ages.

2. * P. contorta. Lodgepole pine. Differs from *P. sylvestris* in preserving its conical outline, in the absence of orange-red colour on old trunks, in the dark but rich green leaves, not pale bluish-green, and in having a sharp spine on the outer face of the cone-scales. *Widely planted for forestry*. Native of western North America.

XIX.   CUPRESSACEAE

(In addition to the species described below, several others are planted for forestry on a small scale or as windbreaks. Of these *X Cupressocyparis leylandii* (Leyland cypress) and *Chamaecyparis lawsonii* (Lawson's cypress) are the most frequently encountered).

Trees or shrubs with resin in leaves and wood; leaves opposite or whorled. Cone-scales becoming succulent and uniting together, so as to form a berry-like structure in which the seeds are retained until it is dispersed.

Juniperus communis. Juniper. 5. A shrub, very variable in habit, from erect to prostrate. Bark reddish-brown, flaking. Leaves 1-2.5 cm long, rather pale bluish-green, needle-like. Cones pale bluish-green-green at first, later bluish-black. *Rocky ground, mountain heaths and lake-shores, mainly in the North and West; occasional*.

Divisible into two fairly well-marked sub-species, though intermediates can be found:

Subsp. *communis*. Erect or prostrate. Leaves spreading, sharply pointed, so that branches are prickly, *Mainly on limestone rocks.*

Subsp. *alpina* (subsp. *nana, J. sibirica*). Always prostrate. Leaves pointing forwards and incurved, subobtuse, so that branches are not prickly. *Mainly on siliceous rocks.*

XX. TAXACEAE

Trees or shrubs without resin. Leaves linear, but not needle-like. Seeds solitary, not in cones.

Taxus baccata. Yew. *Iúr*. **3.** A shrub or small tree with the bark peeling off in scales. Leaves flat, soft, dark green, 1-4 cm long, alternate, but usually arranged in two ranks in a flattened spray. Male cones small, globular, with about 10 stamens. Female flowers consisting of a single ovule with small scales at the base. Seed green, surrounded by a scarlet, fleshy, cup-shaped aril. *Woods, lake-islands, cliffs and rocky ground in the West and North; rather rare. Occasionally bird-sown from gardens elsewhere.*

Widely planted in graveyards. Often used as a 'Palm' on Palm Sunday.

ANGIOSPERMAE

DICOTYLEDONS

XXI. SALICACEAE

Dioecious trees, shrubs or undershrubs. Leaves simple, nearly always alternate; stipules usually present, but often falling early. Flowers many, in erect, spreading or pendulous catkins, each single in the bract axils. Perianth minute or absent; stamens 2 or more; ovary 1-celled, style short, stigmas 2. Fruit a small capsule containing numerous minute seeds, each with a tuft of white silky hairs.

1. Petioles short. Buds protected by a single scale-leaf. Catkins usually
       erect or spreading   ..   ..   **1. Salix**
    Petioles long. Buds protected by several scale-leaves. Catkins pendulous.
                                                                          2. Populus

1. Salix. Willow. *Saileach*

Petioles short. Buds protected by a single leaf-scale. Catkins stalkless or shortly stalked, erect, spreading or rarely somewhat pendulous; catkin-scales (bract-scales) small, undivided, usually hairy. Perianth absent. Stamens 2-5 (rarely more); filaments long; anthers usually yellow.

The identification of willows is often difficult, complicated chiefly by the frequency of hybrids, which possess characteristics intermediate in various degrees between those of the parent species. It is important to examine the leaves of the crown growth since those of the lower suckering shoots are often very different in shape.

18 hybrids have been recorded in Ireland, and others probably occur. Some, especially those between the native species, appear to have arisen spontaneously and

often share characteristics of both putative parents, but not necessarily in equal measure. Others have been propogated by cuttings, as hedging or for basketwork, and may therefore be found in the absence of one or both parents. Triple hybrids are also known but it is even more difficult to determine their parentage.

1. Tree or shrub more than 1 m high 2
    Small spreading shrub or creeping undershrub less than 1 m high 14

2. Leaves more than three times as long as wide; tip pointed .. 3
    Leaves less than three times as broad as long; tip not pointed .. 9

3. Leaf-margins finely toothed 4
    Leaf-margins entire 6

4. Stipules persistent, large; bark smooth, peeling in large flakes **4. S. triandra**
    Stipules absent or falling early; bark furrowed 5

5. Underside of mature leaves covered in fine white silky hairs **3. S. alba**
    Underside of mature leaves hairless or with a few hairs .. **2. S. fragilis**

6. Leaves hairless, even when young. Leaves mostly opposite. Stamens 2,
    with fused filaments, thus appearing like a single stamen with 2 anthers
                                                            10. S. purpurea
    Mature leaves downy or hairy, especially on undersides .. 7

7. Leaves at least five times as long as wide, with their sides parallel for
    most of their length .. .. .. **12. S. viminalis**
    Leaves less than five times as long as wide, broadest below the middle 8

8. Mature leaves densely hairy below, with prominent veins. Under-bark
    wood smooth .. .. .. **13. S. x sericans**
    Mature leaves slightly hairy below, with less-prominent veins. Under-bark
    wood longitudinally ridged .. .. **14. S. x smithiana**

9. Leaves hairless on undersides 10
    Leaves hairy on undersides, at least on veins 11

10 Leaf-margins finely toothed with gland-tipped points; leaf-stalks
    glandular; stamens 5; ovary and capsule hairless .. **1. S. pentandra**
    Leaf-margins entire or slightly toothed, glandless; leaf-stalks glandless;
    stamens 2; ovary and capsule hairy .. **6. S. phylicifolia**

11 Leaves blackening when bruised or dried, thinly pubescent below,
    the pubescence often restricted to the veins (*rare*) **7. S. myrsinifolia**
    Leaves not blackening when bruised or dried, usually hairy below,
    or if thinly pubescent, then bluish-green 12

12. Upper surface of mature leaves dull grey-green and strongly wrinkled
                                                            9. S. aurita
    Upper surface of mature leaves slightly shining and smooth .. 13

13. Leaves sparsely downy and slightly glaucous beneath, more than twice
    as long as broad, usually with some rusty-brown hairs evident in
    summer .. .. **8. S. cinerea**
    Leaves densely downy and whitish beneath, less than twice as long
    as broad .. .. **11. S. caprea**

14. Dense woody undershrub; leaf-margins entire, silvery on the underside
                                                            15. S. repens
    Dwarf mountain undershrub; leaves round or oval, leaf-margins finely
    toothed, conspicuously veined on underside .. **5. S. herbacea**

1. Salix pentandra. Bay willow. 5-6. A large shrub or small tree with shining, brown, hairless twigs. Bud-scales shining, sticky. Leaves slightly fragrant, oval or broadly lanceolate, 1.5-3 times as long as broad, finely glandular-toothed, hairless, thick and leathery, dark shining green above, paler and duller beneath, up to 10 cm long but often smaller. Petiole less than 1 cm, glandular. Stipules small, oval, falling early. Catkins 2-5 cm long, slender, appearing after the leaves, on leafy side-shoots 2-5 cm long. Catkin-scales yellowish-green. Stamens usually 5. Capsule very shortly stalked, hairless. *Riversides, thickets and hedges; frequent in North, rare in South and usually only where planted.*

2. * S. fragilis. Crack willow. 4-5. A tall tree to 20 m, but often pollarded. Bark deeply fissured. Branches widely spreading; twigs smooth, yellowish brown, easily snapped off at base. Leaves lanceolate, about 5 times as long as broad, toothed, hairless at maturity, dark glossy green above, slightly bluish-green beneath, 7-10 cm long. Stipules lanceolate, usually falling early. Catkins long and rather loose, often drooping, appearing with the leaves, on leafy side-shoots 1-2 cm long. Catkin-scales yellowish. Stamens 2. Capsule shortly stalked, hairless. The commonest form is var. *russelliana* which is always female, with brown or olive-brown twigs and long narrow leaves that are finely silken-haired only when young, and up to 6 times as long as broad. Var. *decipiens* is usually smaller, with paler young twigs and shorter and broader, shining hairless leaves, even when young. *Riversides and hedges in marshy areas; locally frequent.*

3. * S. alba. White willow. 4-5. Similar in build to *S. fragilis*, but with more erect branches and young twigs which are not easily snapped off. Leaves lanceolate, covered with persistent white silky hairs, especially on the undersides. Catkins shorter and less drooping; capsule hairless, stalkless. Var. *vitellina* is usually smaller, with young twigs yellow or orange, conspicuous in winter. *Hedges, riversides and damp places; frequent.*

* *S. x rubens* (*S. alba* x *S. fragilis*) is likely to be mistaken for *S. fragilis* from which it differs in its leaves which are dull green above and which become hairless on the upper side though retaining some silky hairs on the undersides at maturity.

4. S. triandra. 4-5. A tall shrub or small tree with smooth bark peeling off in large flakes; twigs hairless, pale brown, not easily snapped off. Leaves slightly fragrant, narrow-oblong or oblong lanceolate, 3.5-5 times as long as broad, finely toothed, hairless, dark green above, paler beneath, about 7 cm long. Stipules conspicuous, broad, usually persistent. Male catkins 3-5 cm long; female shorter; both appearing with or slightly before the leaves on short side shoots with a few leaves at the base. Catkin-scales yellowish. Stamens usually 3. Capsule distinctly stalked, hairless. *Thickets and hedges in wet areas, mainly in South-east; rare.*

5. S. herbacea. 6. A dwarf shrub with prostrate or semi-erect, weak twigs, seldom over 7 cm long, arising from a creeping, woody, underground rhizome. Leaves round or broadly oval, finely toothed, hairless with a conspicuous network of fine veins, 12-15 mm long. Stipules minute or absent. Catkins very small and few-flowered, shortly stalked, appearing after the leaves. Catkin-scales yellowish green, with or without hairs. Stamens 2. Capsule hairless, shortly stalked. *Mountain-ridges and summits, in rock crevices or on bare ground; widespread but rare.*

6. S. phylicifolia (*S. hibernica*). **4-5.** A small, bushy shrub; twigs hairless and shining. Leaves oval-oblong, usually 2-3.5 times as long as broad, somewhat leathery, shining green above, bluish-green beneath, hairless. Stipules small, falling early. Catkins ovoid, erect, on short leafy twigs, appearing with the leaves. Catkin-scales black-tipped. Stamens 2. Capsule shortly stalked, downy. *Mountain cliffs and rocky ground in North-west (Ben Bulben range); very rare.*

7. S. myrsinifolia (*S. nigricans*). **4-5.** Similar to *S. phylicifolia*, but has pubescent twigs, thinner more shining leaves that are somewhat downy beneath and which blacken on drying, persistent stipules and a hairless capsule. *Native in the North and North-east and naturalised by a few lakes and rivers in the Centre.*

8. S. cinerea. Sally. 3-4. A large shrub or small tree, with dark, downy, reddish-brown young twigs, becoming hairless later. Wood of peeled twigs with longditudinal striae. Leaves 4-8 cm long, oval to lanceolate, 2-3.5 times as long as broad, blunt or shortly pointed, dull green and slightly downy but not wrinkled above; bluish-green and slightly downy below, usually also developing rusty brown hairs which become much more obvious in late summer; margin slightly rolled back, weakly crenate. Stipules small, falling early. Catkins ovoid, erect, stalkless, about 2-3 cm long, appearing before the leaves. Catkin-scales black-tipped. Stamens 2. Capsule stalked, downy. *Hedges, thickets and damp woods; very frequent.*

The above description relates to subsp. *oleifolia*, the widespread Irish plant. Recently, subsp. *cinerea* has been recognised from a number of locations in the Centre and North-east. Its younger twigs remain downy often into the second year, its mature leaves are duller and hairier on the upperside and densely pubescent on the lowerside and its stipules are larger and more persistent.

9. S. aurita. Eared willow. 3-4. A small, bushy shrub, 60-200 cm high, with spreading, angular, reddish brown, hairless branches. Wood of peeled branches with many conspicuous longditudinal striae. Leaves oblong, oval or nearly round, 1.5-3 times as long as broad, obtuse, very wrinkled, slightly downy above, very downy and grey beneath, strongly veined, 2-4 cm long, often with a distinct twist at the tip. Stipules large, leafy, ear-shaped, persistent, usually toothed. Catkins ovoid, erect, stalkless or slightly stalked, 15-25 mm long, appearing just before the leaves. Catkin-scales dark at the tip. Stamens 2. Capsule stalked, downy. *Damp thickets, moors, bog-margins and by mountain streams; frequent in most districts.*

S. x *multinervis* (*S. aurita* x *cinerea*). **4-5.** A tall much-branched shrub intermediate in growth form between both putative parents. Under-bark wood conspicuously striate. Leaves oblong or obovate, 1.5-2 cm long, wrinkled, dull green above, undersides persistently grey-pubescent with some rusty-hairs. Leaf tip often with a twist, edges wavy. Stipules often conspicuous and persistent, ear-shaped. Catkins appearing before the leaves. *Widespread and possibly overlooked on bog-margins and hedged drains on acid soils.*

10. S. purpurea. Purple osier. 4-5. A large, spreading shrub, with very bitter bark. Twigs straight and slender, hairless, often purple-brown. Leaves often opposite, especially towards the tips of the branches, shortly stalked, parallel for most of their length, 4-6 times as long as broad, entire or slightly toothed, hairless at maturity, bluish-green, especially beneath, 5-10 cm long. Stipules narrow, falling very early. Catkins erect, nearly stalkless, with a few small leaves at the base, 2-4 cm long, appearing before the leaves. Catkin-scales tipped with black. Stamens 2, but with the filaments fused together, appearing as a single stamen with a double anther. Anthers red or purple. Capsule broad, downy, stalkless. *Hedges, ditches, bog-margins and river-sides; frequent.*

11. S. caprea. Goat willow. 3-4. A large shrub or small tree, with brownish twigs, downy in spring, later hairless. Wood of peeled twigs lacking longditudinal striae. Leaves oval-oblong or nearly round, up to 10 cm long, even larger on coppiced shoots, 1.25 times as long as broad, usually with a short point, dark green, smooth and nearly hairless above, wrinkled and covered with grey down beneath, prominently veined. Catkins as in *S. cinerea*, but larger, stouter and appearing earlier. *Woodland margins and hedges; fairly frequent.*

S. x *reichardtii* (*S. caprea* x *cinerea*). *3-4.* Resembles *S. caprea*, in growth form, leaf-shape and sub-foliar tomentum. It resembles *S. cinerea* in its downy reddish-brown twigs, whose under-bark wood has some longditudinal striae. The distinctive rusty-brown hairs of *S. cinerea* ssp. *oleifolia* are sometimes evident among the sub-foliar tomentum, especially in late summer.

12. * S. viminalis. Osier. 4-5. A tall shrub 3-4 m high, with very long, straight, slender, strong, flexible twigs, downy when young, smooth and shining later. Leaves linear, 8-20 times as long as broad, dull green and hairless above, white with silky hairs beneath, up to 20 cm long; margin usually rolled back and slightly wavy. Stipules very narrow, sickle-shaped. Catkins ovoid or shortly cylindrical, 12-25 mm long, stalkless, erect, appearing before the leaves. Catkin-scales brown, tipped with black. Stamens 2. Capsule downy, stalkless. *Roadsides, ditches and river-banks; frequent and often planted.*

13. * S. x sericans (*S. caprea* x *S. viminalis*). **4-5.** A tall shrub or small tree, with pale yellowish twigs at first downy, later almost hairless and with the under-bark wood smooth; leaves about 4-5 times as long as broad, tapered to an acute apex, densely felted and prominently net-veined on the underside. *Frequent throughout the lowlands, often as a relic of cultivation but also apparently arising spontaneously.*

14. * S. x smithiana (*S. cinerea* x *S. viminalis*). **4-5.** Similar to *S. x sericans* but differs in its persistently downy reddish-brown twigs, striations under the peeled bark, slightly narrower leaves (about 4-5 times as long as broad, tapered to a less acute apex, whose undersides are less persistently downy and less strongly-veined). *Hedges and riversides; occasional.*

* *S.* x *rubra* (*S. viminalis* x *purpurea*) has leaves 5-12 times as long as broad, green and nearly hairless beneath. It is frequently planted, especially in the North.

15. S. repens. 4-5. An undershrub, seldom 125 cm high and often much less, with creeping rhizomes and erect, wiry, spreading or prostrate woody stems, more or less downy when young. Leaves very variable; oval to linear-lanceolate, 2-5 times as long as broad, more or less silvery with silky hairs, at least when young, 5-40 mm long; margin entire, rolled back. Stipules lanceolate or absent. Catkins ovoid, up to 25 mm long, usually nearly stalkless, less often on short, leafy side-shoots appearing before the leaves. Catkin-scales dark at the tip. Stamens 2. Capsule stalked, hairless or silky. *Sandy, peaty or rocky ground; locally frequent near the coast; rare in the Centre.*

S. x *ambigua* (*S. repens* x *aurita*). *3-4.* A shrub with the low growth-form of *S. repens*, leaves dark green on the undersides with flat silky hairs and with persistent broad stipules is occasionally found in regions where both parents occur.

2. Populus. Poplar

Trees with broad, alternate, long-stalked leaves. Stipules small and falling early. Buds protected by several scale-leaves. Catkins long and slender, appearing before the leaves, pendulous. Catkin-scales irregularly fringed or toothed. Perianth small, cup shaped. Stamens 8 or more; filaments very short; anthers reddish.

The White poplar, *P. alba*, with more broadly lobed leaves, snowy felted-white beneath, is occasionally planted but is scarcely naturalised. The Lombardy poplar, with erect branches and very narrow outline, is a cultivated variant of *P. nigra*.

1. Bark (except on old trunks) grey and fairly smooth. Leaves lobed or
    irregularly toothed 2
    Bark soon becoming dark and furrowed. Leaves finely and regularly
    toothed or crenate 3

2. Buds, young and mature leaves hairless   ..   **1. P. tremula**
    Buds, young twigs and leaves downy ..   ..   **2. P. x canescens**
3. Branches erect, trunk not burred, leaf-margins distinctly toothed
                                                                3. P. x canadensis
    Branches drooping, trunk burred, leaf margins shallowly lobed or
      bluntly toothed   ..   ..   ..   **4. P. nigra**

1. Populus tremula. Aspen. 3-4. A shrub or fair-sized tree, usually with numerous suckers. Bark grey, fairly smooth. Buds hairless but not sticky. Leaves on the main branches broadly oval or nearly round, coarsely and irregularly tothed, hairless, rather pale green, 3-5 cm across, with very flattened petioles, and hence trembling in the slightest breeze. Leaves of the sucker shoots slightly hairy, pointed and more regularly toothed. Catkins 5-8 cm long; bract scales very hairy. Stamens about 12. *Fairly frequent as a native in glens and other wild or rocky places in West and North; rarer in hedges in East and South-east, and sometimes planted.*

2. * P. x canescens (*P. alba* x *P. tremula*). **Grey poplar. 3-4.** Differs from *P. tremula* chiefly in the somewhat palmately lobed leaves and the grey hairs on the buds, young twigs and lower side of the leaves. *Often planted in woods and hedges and spreading by suckers.*

3. * P. x canadensis (*P. serotina*). **Black Italian poplar. 4.** A hybrid (*P. deltoides* x *P. nigra*), propagated by cuttings, only male plants being known. A very tall tree (25-30m) with dark, fissured bark and branches which curve upwards, to form a fan-like crown. Buds long, hairless, sticky. Leaves hairless, shining green, broadly triangular, pointed, regularly and bluntly toothed, usually 7-10 cm across; often with a few reddish glands near the top of the petiole. Catkins 8 cm long; stamens 20-30. *Hedges, roadsides and river-banks; frequent but always planted.*

4. P. nigra. Black poplar. 4. A tall tree (c. 20-25 m) with a rounded crown and large burrs on the stems; branches curving downwards, often bearing large, corky bosses. Leaves very pointed, somewhat rhombic, seldom over 5 cm across, without glands; *Planted or possibly native in the South and Centre in similar situations; occasional.*

XXII.   MYRICACEAE

Myrica gale. Bog myrtle. *Railleóg.* **4-5.** A small, bushy, sparsely hairy shrub, seldom more than 100 cm high, with twiggy, dark brown branches. Leaves 2-4 cm long, oblong, broadest near the tip, entire or shortly toothed in the upper half, gland-dotted and very fragrant. Dioecious, but apparently the sex of a plant can change. Flowers in catkins, borne on branches distinct from those bearing leaves. Male catkins 15 mm long; stamens 4 together in the axil of a broad, entire bract; filaments very short. Female catkins 6 mm long, with 2 flowers in the axil of each bract. Fruit a nut surrounded by enlarged bracteoles. *Bogs and lake-shores; frequent in the West half; rather rare in the East.*

XXIII.   BETULACEAE

Trees with alternate, undivided, stalked leaves; stipules falling early. Flowers monoecious, in catkins. Male catkins long, pendulous, consisting of broad, entire bracts each with about 12 stamens in its axil; filaments very short. Female catkins shorter; bracts lobed, each with 2 or 3 flowers in its axil, consisting of an ovary with 2 styles; perianth rudimentary or absent. Fruit a small, seed-like achene, sometimes winged.

1. Flowers appearing with the leaves. Bracts of female catkins papery, falling
     with the fruits   ..   ..   ..   **1. Betula**
   Flowers appearing before the leaves. Bracts of female catkins persisting
     after seeds have been shed and becoming woody and forming a
     cone-like structure   ..   ..   ..   **2. Alnus**

1. Betula. Birch. *Beith*

Small to medium-sized trees with slender twigs and peeling bark. Catkins appearing with the leaves. Bracts of female catkins 3-lobed, not woody, falling singly with the fruits. Achenes with a broad, membranous wing.

1. Twigs hairless, with raised, whitish glands. Leaves drawn out to a slender
     point   ..   ..   **1. B. pendula**
   Twigs usually downy, often with small, brown glands. Leaves triangular
     without a slender point   ..   ..   ..   **2. B. pubescens**

1. Betula pendula. Silver birch. 4-5. A tall but slender tree, usually with drooping twigs. Young shoots and leaves hairless, covered to a variable extent with round, raised, whitish glands. Leaves triangular or diamond-shaped, 2-4 cm long, tapered at the tip to a long, fairly slender point; margin sharply toothed, with every second to fourth tooth much longer than the others. Lateral lobes of bracts of female catkins directed obliquely upwards. *Stony lake-shores, margins of raised bogs, and locally in woods; occasional.*

Although undoubtedly native in some stations, some trees in woods seem to be derived from planted specimens in adjacent parks or demesnes.

2. B. pubescens. Common birch. 4-5. A rather bushy tree; twigs not drooping. Young shoots, leaf-stalks and bases of leaf-blades usually covered with downy hairs, and without pale, raised glands; some trees, however, mainly in the West, have no hairs, but instead have on the twigs fairly numerous brown glands, much smaller than those of *B. pendula*. Leaves triangular, without the long, slender point seen in *B. pendula*; margin irregularly toothed. Lateral lobes of bracts of female catkins often curved somewhat downwards, towards the base of the bract. *Woods, especially on acid soils, and scrub in mountain glens; very frequent and locally abundant.*

Variation in this species is not fully understood; there are probably two subspecies present in Ireland, but they cannot be named with confidence. Hybrids with *B. pubescens* occur occasionally; they have a sparse covering both of down and of large, pale glands.

2. Alnus. Alder. *Fearnóg*

Medium-sized trees; bark not peeling. Winter-buds stalked, reddish-brown. Catkins appearing before the leaves. Bracts of female catkins turning woody, and persisting, for some months after seeds have been shed, appearing like a small pine-cone. Achenes very narrowly winged.

1. Leaves obtuse, about the same colour on both sides; twigs hairless
                                                          1. A. glutinosa
   Leaves pointed, distinctly paler on lower side; twigs downy   **2. A. incana**

1. Alnus glutinosa. Common alder. 3-4. Bark dark brown, fissured on older trees. Leaves hairless, dark green on both sides, broadly oval, broadest above the middle, obtuse, irregularly and bluntly toothed, 4-6 cm across. Twigs hairless.

Catkins stalked, in small panicles, the male slender and pendulous, the female shorter, erect. *River-banks, lake-shores and damp woods; abundant.*

2. * A. incana. Grey alder. 2-3. Bark grey, remaining smooth even on old trees. Leaves oval, broadest near the middle, pointed, sharply toothed; lower surface much paler than the upper. Twigs downy. Catkins as in *A. glutinosa,* but appearing earlier. *Planted for shelter and timber, and naturalised in several places.* Native of Eurasia.

XXIV. CORYLACEAE

Shrubs or trees with undivided, alternate, deciduous leaves; stipules falling early. Flowers monoecious, in catkins; perianth inconspicuous or absent. Fruit a nut, surrounded by leafy bracts.

1. Leaves downy or rather harshly hairy, nearly round .. .. **1. Corylus**
    Leaves hairless or with silky hairs, nearly twice as long as wide   **2. Carpinus**

1. Corylus
Corylus avellana. Hazel. *Coll.* **2-4.** A large shrub with smooth, pale brown bark and downy twigs; winter buds stalkless, short, rounded, greenish-brown. Leaves shortly stalked, round or broadly oval, obtuse or shortly pointed, roughly hairy on both sides, toothed, 6-10 cm across. Catkins appearing before the leaves, the male long, slender, pendulous; bracts downy, each with a single flower in its axil consisting of 8 stamens. Female catkins stalkless, very small and bud-like; bracts fringed with hairs, each with 2 flowers in its axil; stigmas 2, bright red. Fruit a nut 15 mm long, surrounded by ragged, leafy bracts. *Woods and scrub, rocky places and hedges; locally abundant.*

2. Carpinus
* Carpinus betulus. Hornbeam. 4-5. A tree with fluted trunk, but more often seen as a shrub. Bark smooth, grey; winter buds small, stalkless, pointed. Leaves oval, acute, hairless or with a few silky hairs, sharply toothed. Male and female catkins both pendulous. Bracts of male catkins rounded, with a single flower in its axil; bracts of female catkin 3-lobed, enlarging greatly in fruit (up to 4 cm). Nut round, 7 mm long, not winged. *Occasionally planted in demesne woods and possibly naturalised in several places.*

XXV. FAGACEAE

Large, deciduous trees with undivided, alternate leaves; stipules falling early. Flowers monoecious, the male in pendulous catkins, the female solitary or in small clusters, surrounded by an involucre of bracts which become woody in fruit. Stamens 6-12; filaments long. Styles 3. Fruit a nut.

1. Leaves pinnately lobed. Nut rounded, without angles .. **3. Quercus**
    Leaves entire or toothed, but not lobed. Nut 3-angled .. 2

2. Leaves entire or very bluntly toothed, fringed with silky hairs .. **1. Fagus**
    Leaves sharply toothed, hairless .. .. .. **2. Castanea**

1. Fagus
* Fagus sylvatica. Beech. *Fea.* **4-5.** Bark grey, smooth, even on old trunks. Winter buds long, slender, pointed, reddish-brown. Twigs slender, erect. Leaves broadly oval, shortly stalked, entire or bluntly toothed, with silky hairs on the

margins and the veins when young. Male catkins globular, on long peduncles, each with about 12 flowers; stamens 12 in each flower. Female flowers 2 or 3 together, surrounded by bracts, on short, hairy stalks. Fruit a 3-angled nut, of which 2 or 3 are enclosed together in an involucre of 4 woody, spiny bracts. Pericarp shining outside, hairy inside. *Woods and hedges; frequent.*

Although well naturalised in Ireland and freely self-sown, all specimens are ultimately derived from planted trees.

2. Castanea
* **Castanea sativa. Spanish chestnut. 6-7.** Bark ridged, the ridges often showing a spiral twist. Twigs fairly stout; winter buds short, stalkless, greenish-brown. Leaves up to 15 cm long, oblong, hairless, coarsely and sharply toothed. Male catkins 12-18 cm long, slender, whitish. Stamens 10-20. Female flowers in groups of 3; styles 7-9. Nuts brown, enclosed in a capule of united, spiny bracts, which splits open irregularly. *Frequently planted, and naturalised in some estate woods.* Native of the Mediterranean.

3. Quercus. Oak. *Dair*
Leaves pinnately lobed. Winter buds stalkless, ovoid, brown, clustered together near the tip of the twig. Male catkins slender; flowers numerous with 6-12 stamens. Female catkins small, few flowered; each flower with an involucre of numerous small bracts which become woody in fruit and form a cup surrounding the base of the large, smooth nut.

1.   Acorns stalkless, or borne on a peduncle less than 2 cm long; leaf-stalk
      at least 12 mm long [Fig. XXVa]   ..   ..   **1. Q. petraea**
    Acorns borne on a peduncle over 2 cm long; leaf-stalk not more than
      5 mm long [Fig. XXVb]   ..   ..   **2. Q. robur**

1. Quercus petraea (*Q. sessiliflora*). **5.** A tall tree with relatively slender outline. Leaves oblong, usually broadest above the middle, pinnately lobed, with 5-6 obtuse lobes on each side, somewhat hairy beneath when young, and with persistent tufts of hairs at the base of each lateral vein; leaf-stalk at least 12 mm long; adjacent margin of blade flat, not rolled back to form auricles. Acorns 2-4 together, stalkless or on a very short peduncle [Fig. XXVa]. *Woods and hedges; most commonly on acid soils and in mountain districts; very frequent in suitable habitats.*

        Fig. XXVa   Fig. XXVb

2. Q. robur (*Q. pedunculata*). **5.** Very like *Q. petraea*, but usually with more spreading branches and a wider outline; leaves usually hairless, and with 3-5 lobes on each side; leaf-stalk very short, the blade-margin beside it rolled back to form two small auricles; acorns on a peduncle at least 1.5 cm long [Fig. XXVb]. *Woods and hedges, chiefly in the lowlands and on the richer soils; very frequent.*

Doubtless native in some regions, but extensively planted and seeding itself freely.

Hybrids between these two species are frequent; they are intermediate in most characteristics. Backcrosses between some hybrids and the parents often occur. This gives rise to trees which possess most of the features of either parent species but also a few features of the other species.

XXVI. ULMACEAE

Ulmus. Elm. *Leamhán*

Trees with alternate, undivided leaves, asymmetric at the base. Flowers small, green, regular, appearing before the leaves, in stalkless clusters. Corolla absent; calyx bell-shaped, with 4-7 lobes; stamens as many; ovary superior, 2-celled; styles 2. Fruit 1-seeded, surrounded by a broad, flat, leafy wing with a small notch at the apex.

Dutch elm disease has decimated elms throughout Ireland. Many of those that survive do so as suckers and are almost impossible to identify with any certainty.

1. Petiole less than 3.5 mm long. Buds with rust coloured hairs   .. **1. U. glabra**
    Petiole more than 5 mm long. Buds without rust coloured hairs ..   2

2. Leaves broadly oval, at least 3/4 as wide as long, usually rough on upper
    side   ..   ..   **2. U. procera**
    Leaves oval or oblong, less than 3/4 as wide as long, usually smooth on
    upper side ..   .. **3. U. minor**

1. Ulmus glabra (*U. montana*). **Wych elm. 3-4.** A large tree with spreading branches; usually not suckering. Young twigs hairy with rust-coloured hairs. Leaves broadly oval, pointed, coarsely toothed, very asymmetrical at the base, rough on the upper surface, hairy beneath, usually 10-12 cm long with 12-18 pairs of lateral veins; petiole very short and partly obscured by the base of the leaf. *Rare as a native, chiefly in mountain glens in the North-west; planted frequently in most districts.*

U. x *hollandica*, Dutch elm, is occasionally found in hedges. It differs from *U. glabra* in it having very few rust-coloured hairs which are confined to the buds and leaves which are smooth on the upper surface, with 10-14 pairs of lateral veins.

2. * U. procera (*U. campestris*). **English elm. 3-4.** A tall tree, often oblong in outline and suckering with very rough and furrowed bark, and downy, often corky twigs. Leaves as in *U. glabra*, but smaller (seldom 9 cm long), with 10-12 pairs of lateral viens, with longer petioles most of which are clearly visible. *Hedges and roadsides; frequent, but always planted.*

3. * U. minor (*U. carpinifolia*). **3-4.** A large tree, of very varied form. Leaves usually less than 8 (rarely 10) cm long, smooth on the upper surface, oblong or narrowly oval, less than 3/4 as long as wide with long petioles not obscured by the base of the leaves, and with 8-12 pairs of lateral veins. *Hedges and roadsides; less frequent than* U. procera, *always planted.*

XXVII. CANNABACEAE

Herbs. Leaves opposite or alternate, palmately lobed. Flowers small, dioecious; male flowers with perianth segments and stamens 5; female flowers with a fused perianth and a single ovary. Fruit a small achene.

1. Leaves lobed virtually to the base; leaflets lanceolate .. **1. Cannabis**
   Leaves lobed to about $^3/4$; leaflets broadly triangular .. **2. Humulus**

1. Cannabis

* **Cannabis sativa. Cannabis. Hemp. 7-9.** Erect annual, with distinctive short, hooked hairs. Usually unbranched, up to 2.5 m tall. Leaves deeply palmately divided, to the base, into 3-9 shallowly toothed lobes. Flowers in drooping axillary clusters, about 8 mm across; often not forming. *Fairly frequent casual of waste-areas and railway-banks and roadsides; mainly in cities. Occasionally illicitly planted.* Native of Europe.

2. Humulus

* **Humulus lupulus. Hop. 7.** A roughly hairy, almost prickly perennial with long twining stems several metres long. Leaves palmately lobed to about $^3/4$, with 3-4 broadly triangular lobes. Male flowers 6 mm across. Female flowers in drooping, ovoid, cone-like catkins, made up of numerous, overlapping, broadly oval bracts, whose base is covered in orange glands, and with 2 stalkless flowers in its axils; each flower with 2 purple styles. *Hedges, roadsides, and near houses, mainly in the South and Centre; rare and declining.*

XXVIII. URTICACEAE

Herbs with undivided leaves. Flowers small, green, unisexual. Calyx 4-lobed; corolla absent; stamens 4; ovary superior, 1-celled, with a single seed. Fruit an achene.

1. Leaves opposite, with stinging hairs ..   ..   .. **1. Urtica**
   Leaves alternate, with soft downy hairs 2
2. Stems rooting at the nodes; leaves about 5 mm long ..   .. **2. Soleirolia**
   Stems not rooting at the nodes; leaves about 10 mm long .. **3. Parietaria**

1. Urtica. Nettle. *Neanntóg*

Leaves opposite, covered with stinging hairs, with stipules. Calyx deeply 4-cleft; lobes spreading, equal in male flowers; in female flowers one pair bigger than the other, especially in fruit. Seed ovoid, pale, flattened, slightly shining or dull.

1. Plant either with male or female flowers; leaf stalk no more than $^1/2$ as
   long as blade   ..   .. **1. U. dioica**
   Plants with both male and female flowers; leaf stalk $^2/3$rds as long as
   leaf-blade ..   .. **2. U. urens**

1. Urtica dioica. 6-9. A dark green perennial 60-100 cm high, with oval, pointed, strongly toothed leaves, 5-10 cm long; the leaf stalk no more than half as long as the blade. Dioecious; flowers in long, branched, axillary spikes, up to 10 cm long. *Roadsides, pastures, thickets, waste places, ruins etc; abundant.*

2. † U. urens. 6-9. Very similar but annual, less hairy, lighter green and only 20-60 cm high. Leaves more deeply and sharply toothed with longer stalks. Monoecious; male and female flowers together in short, unbranched, axillary spikes, up to 1 cm long. *Waste places and tilled fields; occasional.*

2. Soleirolia

* **Soleirolia soleirolii** (*Helixine soleirolii*). **5-10.** A creeping perennial, rooting at the nodes. Stems up to 20 cm long. Leaves usually distinctly stalked, sometimes stalkless, without stipules; blade almost round, about 5 mm across, shining. Flowers minute, axillary. Seeds, ovoid, light brown, shining *An escape from cultivation, formerly established largely in the West, now also in the North and East (Dublin).* Native of the Mediterranean.

3. Parietaria

Parietaria judaica (*P. diffusa, P. ramiflora, P. officinalis*). **Pellitory. 6-9.** A downy perennial, with branched, rather spreading stems 20-40 cm long, not rooting at the nodes. Leaves alternate, without stipules, oval to lanceolate, entire, tapered at both ends. Flowers small, green, in nearly stalkless, often branched, axillary clusters; mostly hermaphrodite, but a few unisexual. Calyx persisting in fruit; in hermaphrodite flowers long and tubular, with short lobes; in male flowers shorter and more deeply cleft. Seed ovoid, black, shining. *Old walls, and occasionally on rocks or shingle beaches; frequent in the South; occasional elsewhere.*

XXIX. POLYGONACEAE

Herbs, mostly hairless, with alternate or basal, undivided leaves. Stipules membranous, whitish or brown, united to form a sheath (*ochrea*) surrounding the stem or leaf-stalk. Flowers small, in spikes, panicles or axillary clusters. Sepals 4-6, sometimes red, pink or white and more or less petal-like. Petals absent. Stamens 5-8. Ovary superior, 1-celled. Fruit a small nut, often enclosed in the persistent calyx. The rhubarb (*Rheum*) belongs to this family.

1. Leaves round or kidney-shaped; sepals 4   ..   ..   **4. Oxyria**
    Leaves not round or kidney-shaped; sepals 5 or 6   2
2. Sepals 6, the 3 inner much larger than the outer, especially in fruit   **5. Rumex**
    Sepals 5, more or less equal, or the outer larger   3
3. Sepals winged or keeled, at least in fruit   4
    Sepals not winged or keeled   ..   ..   **1. Polygonum**
4. Annual, with twining stem   ..   ..   ..   **2. Fallopia**
    Perennial, with stout, erect stems   ..   ..   **3. Reynoutria**

1. Polygonum

Sepals 5, usually united at the base, equal, not winged or keeled. Stamens 8 (rarely fewer). Styles 2, more rarely 3.

1. Flowers solitary or in small clusters in the leaf-axils, forming a loose,
    leafy spike ..   2
    Flowers in terminal or axillary spikes or panicles, in which leaf-like
    bracts are absent or inconspicuous   5
2. Stipules very conspicuous, those in the upper half of the stem as long
    as the internode   ..   ..   ..   **1. P. maritimum**
    Stipules not very conspicuous; much shorter than the internodes in all
    parts of the stem except the extreme tip   3
3. Leaves usually pale bluish-green, with margins slightly rolled downwards;
    nut 5 mm, smooth and shiny, protruding from the perianth for about a
    third of its length   ..   ..   **2. P. oxyspermum**
    Leaves not pale bluish-green; margins flat; nut 3.5-4 mm, finely striated,
    not shiny, enclosed in the perianth or only slightly protruding ..   4

4. Leaves all about the same size; tube of perianth at least half as long as the
    lobes   ..   ..   **4. P. arenastrum**
    Leaves on main stem (sometimes falling early) much larger than those
      on the branches; tube of perianth not more than a quarter as long as
      the lobes   ..   ..   ..   **3. P. aviculare**

5. Flowers in panicles   6
    Flowers in unbranched spikes   7

6. Panicle fairly compact; flowers tinged with bright pink; perianth bell-shaped
                                                 15. P. campanulatum
    Panicle diffuse; sepals white, free   ..   ..   **14. P. polystachyum**

7. Spike lax and slender, 3-5 mm wide   8
    Spike dense and stout, 7-10 mm wide   10

8. Leaves with a strong peppery taste; solitary flowers present in the axils
      of many of the lower leaves   ..   ..   **7. P. hydropiper**
    Leaves without a peppery taste; flowers confined to the spikes   ..   9

9. Leaves linear-oblong, usually not more than 8 mm wide; nut not more
      than 2.5 mm   ..   ..   ..   **5. P. minus**
    Leaves lanceolate, usually at least 10 mm wide; nut 2.8-4 mm   ..   **6. P. mite**

10. Flowers in lower part of spike replaced by brown or purple bulbils
                                                   12. P. viviparum
    Spike without bulbils   11

11. Stalks of lower leaves broadly winged in their upper part   **11. P. bistorta**
    Leaf-stalks not winged   12

12. Upper leaves clasping the stem   ..   ..   **13. P. amplexicaule**
    No leaves clasping the stem   13

13. Pedicels with raised, yellow glands; flowers greenish-white or dull pink
                                                   9. P. lapathifolium
    Pedicels without raised, yellow glands; flowers clear pink or white   14

14. Perennial, with long, creeping rhizome; leaves rounded or truncate at the
      base; stalk of lower leaves at least 2 cm long   ..   **10. P. amphibium**
    Annual; leaves tapered at the base; leaf-stalk short or absent   **8. P. persicaria**

1. Polygonum maritimum. 7-9. Perennial, with a stout, woody rootstock. Stems prostrate, branched, stout, up to 40 cm long. Leaves 10-20 mm, narrowly oval, acute, pale bluish-green, often blackening on drying; margins rolled downwards. Stipules conspicuous, brown at the base, whitish above, with brown veins, at least as long as the internodes on the middle and upper parts of the stem. Flowers pink or white, solitary or 2-3 together in the leaf-axils. Nut 3.5-5 mm, glossy, equalling the perianth or slightly longer. *Sandy sea-shore at Tramore, Co. Waterford, and possibly elsewhere; intermittent in its appearances and possibly extinct.*

2. P. oxyspermum (*P. raii*). **8-9.** Annual; stems prostrate, rather woody, up to 100 cm long. Leaves widely spaced, lanceolate to oval, rather pale bluish-green and thick, with margins slightly rolled downwards. Stipules silvery, shorter than internodes except at the extreme tip of the stem. Flowers pink or greenish-white, in small axillary clusters. Nut 5-6 mm, dark brown, shiny, protruding from the perianth for about a third of its length. *Sandy seashores; widespread but local, and apparently diminishing.*

3. P. aviculare (*P. heterophyllum*). **6-10.** Annual, with slender, branched leafy stems, erect or prostrate, up to 70 cm long. Larger leaves on the main stem (which often drop off early) up to 4 x 2 cm; those on the side-branches much smaller.

Stipules silvery, not very conspicuous. Flowers almost stalkless, in small axillary clusters. Sepals green, edged with pink or white, broad and overlapping, shortly united at the base to form a tube about a quarter the length of the free lobes. Nut 3 mm, finely striated, not shiny, enclosed in the persistent calyx. *Roadsides, waste places and arable ground; abundant.*
Very variable, but no satisfactory classification of the variants has been devised.

4. P. arenastrum (*P. aequale*). **6-10.** Like *P. aviculare*, but with stems always prostrate; leaves mostly 7-15 x 3-8 mm, all more or less equal in size; lobes of calyx narrower, 1.5-2 times as long as the tube; nut slightly smaller. *Paths, roadsides and trampled ground; frequent.*

5. P. minus (*Persicaria minor*). **8-9.** Annual; stems usually straggling or nearly prostrate, but occasionally erect. Larger leaves 20-75 mm long, at least 5 times as long as wide, oblong-lanceolate, broadest near the base. Flowers in small, erect, slender, lax spikes. Sepals deep reddish-pink, without glands. Nut about 2 mm long, enclosed in the calyx, black, shiny. *Lake-shores, turloughs and other grounds subject to intermittent flooding; frequent in the North half, occasional in the South.*

6. † P. mite (*P. laxiflorum, Persicaria laxiflora*). **7-9.** Like *P. minus*, but stems usually more or less erect; leaves 3-4.5 times as long as wide, narrowly elliptic, broadest near the middle; sepals pale pink, usually with a few flat glands; nut about 3 mm long. *Lake-shores and river-banks; locally abundant round Lough Neagh and by the lower River Bann; possibly by the river at Limerick; records from elsewhere are erroneous.*

7. P. hydropiper (*Persicaria hydropiper*). **Water-pepper.** *Glúineach the.* **7-9.** Annual, with erect, branched stems up to 75 cm high. Leaves lanceolate, very shortly stalked, up to 80 mm long, with a strong peppery taste. Flowers in slender, terminal and axillary spikes, which are usually slightly nodding; solitary flowers are also present in the axils of most of the lower leaves. Calyx greenish, dotted with numerous glands, which are dark green and flat when fresh, but when dried become raised, brown and much more conspicuous. Stamens usually 6. Nut dull black, not shiny, about 3.25 mm long, enclosed in the calyx. *Ditches, damp ground and edges of lakes; abundant except in parts of the Centre, where it is rather rare.*

8. P. persicaria (*Persicaria maculosa*). **Redshank.** *Glúineach dhearg.* **6-9.** Annual; stems usually erect but sometimes straggling and nearly prostrate, up to 50 cm high. Leaves 7-10 cm long, oval-lanceolate, very shortly stalked, downy beneath, often with a dark blotch on the upper side. Flowers in several compact, fairly stout, erect spikes. Sepals bright pink, rarely white, without glands. Stamens 5-8. Nut 3 mm, black, shiny, enclosed by calyx. *Arable ground, roadsides and damp waste places; abundant.*

9. P. lapathifolium (*P. nodosum, Persicaria lapathifolia*). **7-9.** Like *P. persicaria*, but often larger and coarser, with leaves up to 15 cm long; flowers dingy pink or greenish-white; and with numerous raised, yellow glands on the peduncles, and sometimes also on the pedicels and calyx. *Arable fields, damp waste places and river-gravels; locally frequent.*

10. P. amphibium (*Persicaria amphibia*). **7-9.** Perennial, with long rhizome, often rooting at the nodes. Leaves sometimes floating, triangular-lanceolate, stalked, rounded or truncate at the base, up to 15 cm long. Flowers in erect, dense terminal spikes 2-4 cm long. Stamens 5; styles 2. *In pools, canals and slow-flowing rivers; also on damp ground on river-banks; frequent.*

11. * **P. bistorta** (*Persicaria bistorta*). **6-9.** A nearly hairless perennial with short, stout rhizome. Lower leaves up to 15 cm, broadly oval, obtuse, long-stalked, with stalks broadly winged in upper part; upper leaves much smaller, triangular, with stalks sheathing the stem. Flowers in a dense, stout, terminal spike, bright pink. Stamens 8; styles 3. Nut 5 mm, brown. *Damp meadows and pastures; rare and declining.*

12. P. viviparum (*Persicaria vivipara*). **6-8.** Perennial, with short, compact stock. Stems erect, unbranched, up to 25 cm. Leaves oblong to linear-lanceolate, the lower ones stalked. Flowers in a slender, terminal spike, in the lower part of which the flowers are replaced by brown or purple bulbils, from which leaf-rudiments sometimes protrude. Calyx white. Stamens 8; styles 3. Nut rarely, if ever, developed. *Mountain ridges and summits in Kerry and the North-west; very rare.*

13. * **P. amplexicaule** (*Persicaria amplexicaulis*). **7-8.** Perennial, with erect stems up to 100 cm high and shortly creeping rhizome, forming dense clumps. Leaves oval, acute, the lower stalked, 15-20 cm long, the upper smaller, clasping the stem. Flowers crimson, in dense, cylindrical, terminal spikes. Stamens 8; styles 3. *Roadsides and waste ground, mainly in the West; rather rare.* Native of Himalaya.

14. * **P. polystachyum** (*Persicaria wallichii*). **6-8.** Perennial with creeping rhizome and stout, erect stems up to 120 cm high, forming extensive clumps. Leaves oval-lanceolate, acute, shortly stalked, up to 25 cm long. Flowers white, in a diffuse, freely branched leafy panicle. Sepals free. *Roadsides and waste ground; occasional.* Native of Himalaya and Afghanistan.

15. * **P. campanulatum** (*Persicaria campanulata*). **7-8.** A downy perennial, spreading by stolons to form small clumps. Leaves oval, pointed, 7-10 cm long, shortly stalked; hairs whitish on the upper surface, usually buff beneath; midrib red. Flowers stalkless, in short spikes which are grouped into small, compact, usually leafy panicles. Calyx bell-shaped, with tube rather longer than the lobes, white in lower part, variably flushed with bright pink on the lobes. Stamens 8; styles 3. *Naturalised from gardens on damp roadsides or in open woods in a few places in the West.* Native of Himalaya.

2. Fallopia

† **Fallopia convolvulus** (*Bilderdykia convolvulus, Polygonum convolvulus*). **Black bindweed. 7-9.** A twinning annual, with slender, angular stems up to 80 cm long. Leaves triangular-sagittate, pointed, stalked; stalks and lower part of blade rough with very short, stiff hairs. Flowers greenish-white or pink, in slender axillary spikes. Sepals 5, the 3 outer larger and keeled. Stamens 8. Fruit 4 mm long, dull black, minutely pitted. *Arable fields, roadsides and hedges; very frequent.*

3. Reynoutria

Stout, erect, rhizomatous perennials. Leaves triangular, stalked. Flowers imperfectly dioecious, in small, axillary panicles. Sepals 5, the 3 outer keeled or winged. Stamens 8; styles 3; stigmas fringed.

1. Leaves mostly 8-10 cm long, suddenly narrowed at the tip to a slender
   point; flowers white, in long, interrupted panicles **1. R. japonica**
   Leaves up to 12-18 cm long, rounded or gradually narrowed at the tip;
   flowers yellowish-green, in short, compact panicles **2. R. sachalinensis**

1. * **Reynoutria japonica** (*Polygonum cuspidatum, Fallopia japonica*). **7-10.** Stems 150-200 cm high. Leaves mostly 8-10 cm long, broadly oval, with truncate base, narrowed suddenly at the tip to a slender point. Flowers imperfectly dioecious (most commonly female) in long, diffuse, lax panicles. Sepals 5, free, white; styles 3. *Roadsides, waste places and tips; frequent and increasing.* Native of Japan.

2. * R. sachalinensis (*Fallopia sachalinensis*). **7-10.** Like *R. japonica*, but with stouter stems up to 3 m high; leaves cordate at the base and rounded or gradually narrowed at the tip, usually 12-18 cm long; flowers yellowish green, in fairly compact panicles, usually shorter than or equalling the adjacent leaf-stalk. *Roadsides; occasional.* Native of eastern Siberia.

4. Oxyria

Oxyria digyna. Mountain sorrel. 7-8. A small, hairless perennial. Leaves nearly all basal, round or kidney-shaped with wavy margins, long-stalked, with acid taste. Flowers greenish, in a terminal panicle. Sepals 4, the two inner enlarging in fruit. Sepals 6; stigmas 2, feathery. Fruit flat, broadly winged. *Wet mountain cliffs and screes in the West and the Galtee Mountains; rare.*

5. Rumex. Dock. *Copóg*

Erect, hairless perennials. Flowers green or reddish, stalked, in whorl-like clusters arranged in a raceme or panicle. Sepals 6, the inner three larger than the outer, and enlarging further in fruit, the outer often bearing small swellings (tubercles). Stamens 6; styles 3; stigmas feathery. Fruit a 3-angled nut, enclosed in the inner calyx-segments.

1. Leaves hastate or sagittate, with acid taste; fruiting sepals without tubercles   2
    Leaves without basal lobes, not hastate or sagittate; at least one of the
        fruiting sepals bearing a rounded tubercle   3

2. Leaves 5-10 cm long, sagittate, with basal lobes incurved or parallel to the
        leaf-stalk   ..   .. **2. R. acetosa**
    Leaves 1-4 cm long, hastate, with basal lobes sharply diverging
                                                               1. R. acetosella

3. Fruiting sepals strongly toothed   4
    Fruiting sepals entire or crenate   6

4. Teeth of fruiting sepals at least 2 mm long, almost equalling the breadth
        of the sepal ..   .. **9. R. maritimus**
    Teeth of fruiting sepals not more than 1 mm long, much less than the
        breadth of the sepal   5

5. Some of the leaves narrowed in the middle, so as to be violin-shaped;
        some branches of the panicle diverging almost at right angles   **7. R. pulcher**
    None of the leaves narrowed in the middle; all branches of the panicle
        directed obliquely upwards   ..   .. **8. R. obtusifolius**

6. Panicles slender and sparse, the whorls of flowers being distinct and
        separated by substantial gaps; fruiting sepals not more than 3 mm long   7
    Panicles stout and dense, with the whorls of flowers not separated by
        any large gaps; fruiting sepals 4-6 mm long   ..   8

7. All three fruiting sepals bearing a well-developed tubercle; panicle leafy,
        at least throughout its lower half   ..   .. **5. R. conglomeratus**
    One fruiting sepal bearing a well-developed tubercle, the other two with
        a very small tubercle or none; panicle leafy only at the extreme base
                                                               6. R. sanguineus

8. Leaves not more than 20 cm long, with very wavy margins   .. **4. R. crispus**
    Larger leaves 25-50 cm long, with flat or very finely wavy margins
                                                               3. R. hydrolapathum

1. Rumex acetosella (incl. *R. tenuifolius* and *R. angiocarpus*). **Sheep's sorrel.** *Samhadh caorach.* **6-8.** Stems 7-30 cm high, erect from a slender, creeping rhizome. Leaves up to 4 cm long, hastate, with two divergent, acute basal lobes, acid to the taste. Dioecious; flowers in slender, interrupted panicles. Inner sepals only slightly enlarged in fruit, shorter than the nut. *Heaths and sandy, stony or peaty ground; abundant in mountain districts, occasional to frequent elsewhere.*

2. R. acetosa. Sorrel. *Samhadh.* **6-8.** Stems erect, 35-80 cm high, sparingly branched. Leaves 3-12 cm long, with two basal lobes parallel to the stalk, acid to the taste. Dioecious; flowers in usually fairly dense panicles. Fruiting sepals red, strongly keeled, 3-4 mm long, enclosing the narrow nut. *Meadows and pastures; abundant.*

Variants found on sand-dunes by the West coast are distinguished as subsp. *hibernicus.* They have short stems and short, compact inflorescences; the leaves are rather fleshy and scabrid with stiff, very short hairs.

3. R. hydrolapathum. Water dock. 7-8. Stems stout, 100-180 cm high, with long, erect branches. Leaves lanceolate, tapered at both ends, 40-65 cm long; margin flat or very finely waved. Panicle large, fairly dense, somewhat leafy at the base. Fruiting sepals triangular, 6-7 mm long, each with an oblong tubercle. *Ditches, marshes and shallow water; occasional.*

4. R. crispus. 6-8. Stems 50-200 cm high, with short, suberect branches. Leaves narrowly lanceolate; margins usually strongly waved. Panicle rather dense, leafy at the base. Fruiting sepals 4-5 mm, broadly oval, usually all with a tubercle, but often one larger than the other two. *Roadsides, fields, waste places and seashores; abundant.*

Very tall plants, usually found on estuarine mud, with a large fruit (at least 2.5 mm) and a panicle rather lax in fruit, are distinguished as subsp. *uliginosus.*

5. R. conglomeratus. 6-8. Rather slender; stem 60-80 cm high, branched from the base. Leaves oblong-lanceolate, entire, with slightly wavy margin. Panicle slender and sparse, with whorls of flowers clearly separated; all its branches leafy in the lower half. Fruiting sepals oblong, entire, 2.5-3 mm long, each with a well-developed tubercle. *Damp, bare or grassy places, especially where trampled; abundant except in parts of the North, where it is local.*

6. R. sanguineus (*R. nemorosus, R. condylodes*). **6-8.** Like *R. conglomeratus*, but with the panicle-branches leafless except at the extreme base, and only one of the fruiting sepals with a well-developed tubercle. *Hedges, wood-margins and other damp, shady places; very frequent to abundant.*

7. † R. pulcher. Fiddle dock. 6-7. Stems somewhat straggling, up to 40 cm long. Leaves oval-oblong, many of them narrowed in the middle, so as to be violin-shaped. Panicle diffuse, with slender branches diverging almost at right angles from the main axis, furnished with small bracts and with the whorls of flowers well separated. Fruiting sepals 4-5 mm, with stout marginal teeth, and all three with tubercles, though often one is larger than the other two. *Waste places and dry grassland; established and perhaps native locally near the South coast; a rare casual elsewhere.*

8. R. obtusifolius. *Copóg shráide.* **7-9.** Stem stout, 50-120 cm high, with suberect branches. Leaves large, broadly oblong, slightly crenate, truncate or cordate at the base. Panicle leafless, dense, with stiff, erect branches. Fruiting sepals 5-6 mm long, toothed at least at the base, one with a large tubercle, the other two with smaller ones. *Roadsides and fields; abundant.*

Hybrids with *R. crispus* are fairly frequent. They are intermediate in characters of leaf and fruit, and are nearly, but not completely sterile. Some other hybrids have been recorded in the genus, but are much rarer.

9. R. maritimus. Stem erect, 40-70 cm high. Leaves linear-lanceolate, 5-15 cm long. Panicle freely branches, leafy throughout; whorls of numerous flowers often widely spaced below but compacted above. Fruiting sepals 2-3 mm, with long, slender, flexible marginal teeth, giving the panicle a shaggy appearance. The whole plant turns yellow at fruiting time. *Ditches, and by recently drained lakes and ponds; very rare.*

The seeds can remain viable for long periods in the soil, germinating when exposed to the light; the plant is therefore very intermittent in its appearances.

XXX.   AMARANTHACEAE

* Amaranthus retroflexus. 8-9. Annual with erect, shortly pubescent stems up to 1 m high. Leaves, alternate, undivided, entire, petiolate, cordate; veins much paler than the lower leaf surface. Flowers monoecious, minute, actinomorphic, very densely clustered, forming thick, elongated spikes with a few largish leaves near the base. Bracteoles straw coloured, sharply and shortly pointed. Perianth of 5, narrow, oval, shortly pointed, straw-coloured segments with a green midrib. Stamens 5, concealed within the perianth. Ovary 1. Fruit a 1-seeded capsule. *Roadsides; occasional in the South half, especially near ports.* Native of tropical and North America.

XXXI.   CHENOPODIACEAE

Herbs or undershrubs with undivided, usually alternate leaves without stipules; leaves rarely absent. Flowers small, regular, greenish, sometimes unisexual. Sepals usually 5, sometimes fewer, persisting in fruit. Petals absent. Stamens 5 or fewer. Ovary superior, rarely partly inferior, 1-celled. Fruit a small, 1-seeded capsule or nut.

Various forms of *Beta* are cultivated as Beetroot, Sugar-beet, Swiss chard, etc.

1.	Stems leafless, jointed, fleshy			2
	Leaves present			3
2.	Annual; stems not at all woody; plant not rhizomatous, easily uprooted			
				5. Salicornia
	Perennial; stems woody; rhizomatous; difficult to uproot		**6. Anthrocnemum**	
3.	Leaves narrow, more or less cylindrical			4
	Leaves flat and fairly broad			5
4.	Leaves ending in a sharp point; plant hairy			**7. Salsola**
	Leaves blunt; plant hairless			**8. Suaeda**
5.	Flowers hermaphrodite; sepals 5			6
	Flowers unisexual (monoecious); female flowers without a true perianth, but with 2 bracteoles that enlarge round the fruit			7
6.	Leaves glossy and shining; base of fruit stringly swollen			**1. Beta**
	Leaves dull; base of fruit not swollen		**2. Chenopodium**	
7.	Annual herb; fruiting bracteoles not united above half-way, triangular or rhombic, or if 3-lobed, with the middle lobe much the largest		**3. Atriplex**	
	Perennial undershrub; fruiting bracteoles united nearly to the top and ending in 3 equal lobes			**4. Halimione**

1. Beta

Beta vulgaris (*B. maritima*). **Sea beet. 7-9.** A hairless often reddish, perennial with stout, spreading stems up to 100 cm long. Leaves rather large, stalked, oval or rhombic, nearly entire, shining and rather fleshy. Flowers hermaphrodite, green, in long, loose, slender, terminal spikes or panicles. Sepals 5, fleshy in fruit; stamens 5, ovary partly inferior. Fruit a small capsule, enclosed by the sepals, adhering together in small groups. *Rocky and gravelly seashores and cliffs; widespread, but occasional.*

2. Chenopodium

Hairless or mealy herbs, with hermaphrodite, stalkless flowers in spikes or panicles. Sepals usually 5, rarely 3 or 4; stamens as many as sepals. Seeds surrounded by the thin, translucent or silvery pericarp which is easily rubbed-off.

1. Leaves hastate; perennial; stigmas at least 0.8 mm long   **1. C. bonus-henricus**
   Leaves not hastate; annual; stigmas less than 0.8 mm long   ..   2
2. Sepals on many flowers only 2-4; plant not mealy, usually reddish
                                                       2. C. rubrum
   Sepals always 5; plant usually not reddish   ..   ..   3.
3. Leaves entire ..   ..   **3. C. polyspermum**
   Leaves toothed   ..   ..   ..   4.
4. Sepals with small, distinct teeth; seeds with a narrow wing   .. **5. C. murale**
   Sepals more or less entire; seeds without a narrow wing   .. **4. C. album**

1. * Chenopodium bonus-henricus. Good King Henry. 6-8. A stout perennial, with nearly unbranched stems 25-60 cm high, and dark green, triangular-hastate leaves, entire or with a few blunt teeth, mealy when young. Panicle terminal, leafless except at the base. Sepals and stamens 4 or 5. Seeds dark brown or black. *Roadsides and waste-places near houses or ruins; occasional.*

2. C. rubrum. 8-9. An erect or nearly prostrate annual, scarcely mealy, usually tinged with red. Leaves variable, usually rhombic, toothed. Inflorescence erect and compact. Sepals and stamens 5 in some flowers, but only 2-4 in many. Fruit protruding slightly from the sepals. Seeds reddish-brown. *Damp, often muddy waste-places, mainly by the sea; rare.*

3. * C. polyspermum. 7-9. An erect or somewhat decumbent annual, scarcely mealy, with usually 4-angled stems. Leaves oval, entire. Inflorescence open and spreading. Sepals and stamens 5. Seeds brown or black. *Established on the shores of Lough Neagh, elsewhere a rather rare casual.*

4. C. album. 7-9. An erect, somewhat mealy annual up to 1 m high. Leaves variable, lanceolate to rhombic, usually toothed. Sepals 5, closing completely over the fruit. Seeds black. *Field-margins and waste-places; frequent.*

5. * C. murale. 7-9. Very similar to *C. album*, differing only in the indistinctly winged seeds and toothed sepals. *Sparingly established on the shores of Lough Neagh, elsewhere a rare casual.*

3. Atriplex

More or less mealy annuals. Flowers monoecious; male with 5 sepals and stamens; female without sepals but with 2 triangular bracteoles, united only at base, enclosing the ovary and fruit. Styles 2. Fruit a small nut.

1. Lower leaves linear to linear-oblong   ..   ..   **2. A. littoralis**
   Lower leaves triangular or rhombic   2

2. Flowers in compact axillary spikes, shorter than leaves; plant silvery-white
   1. A. laciniata
   Flowers in long, loose panicles; plant green, red or somewhat mealy   3
3. Bracteoles united only at their base (for at most ¹/₄ of their length)
   4. A. prostrata
   Bracteoles united to about ¹/₂ way   4
4. Each bracteole usually with 2 teeth (1 large one on each side, near
   the base), sometimes with smaller subsidiary teeth   ..   **3. A. patula**
   Each bracteole usually with more than 2 teeth (2-3 small teeth on each
   side), all teeth more or less the same size   ..   **5. A. glabriuscula**

1. Atriplex laciniata (*A. maritima, A. sabulosa*). **7-8.** A branched and spreading annual, silvery-white and very mealy all over. Leaves small, stalkless or with very shorts stalks, rhombic or narrowly oval, usually tapered at the base, lobed or bluntly toothed. Flowers in very short compact spikes. Fruiting bracteoles triangular or rhombic, sometimes with 2 distinct lateral lobes, usually smooth, united to about ¹/₂ way. *Sandy shores; local.*

2. A. littoralis. 7-9. A mealy annual with erect branching stems up to 100 cm high. Leaves linear to linear-oblong, entire or slightly toothed. Flowers in a nearly leafless spike. Fruiting bracteoles united only at base, toothed. *Muddy and gravelly sea-shores; mainly in the East, local.*

3. † **A. patula. Orache. 7-9.** A slightly mealy annual, usually erect with spreading branches. Leaves shortly stalked, the lower ones opposite, mostly rhombic or lanceolate, often with a single large tooth on each side near the base, but tapered at the base and not truly hastate. Flowers in long, loose, nearly leafless panicles. Fruiting bracteoles triangular or rhombic, united to about ¹/₂ way, each with a single largish tooth on each side near the base. *Waste places; frequent.*

4. A. prostrata. (*A. hastata*). **7-9.** A spreading or prostrate, rarely erect annual, usually slightly mealy. Leaves triangular or hastate, with fairly long stalks, not tapered at the base. Inflorescence variable, often rather leafy. Fruiting bracteoles triangular, united only at or near the base, weakly toothed. *Seashores, and waste places; very frequent near the coast, rare inland.*

5. A. glabriuscula. 7-9. Very similar to *A. prostrata*, differing in the more broadly triangular, thicker bracteoles, united to about ¹/₂ way and which bear small more or less evenly sized teeth. *Sandy or shingly beaches; occasional on all coasts.*

4. Halimione

Halimione portulacoides (*Atriplex portulacoides, Obione portulacoides*). **Sea purslane. 7-9.** A straggling, much-branched undershrub, very white and mealy, with prostrate woody stems and erect flowering branches. Leaves small, oblong, linear-lanceolate, entire, tapered to a short stalk; lower ones, and sometimes all opposite. Flowers monoecious, in terminal, nearly leafless panicles. Fruiting bracteoles united almost to the top, with a narrow base and a broad tip divided into 3 nearly equal, blunt lobes. *Muddy seashores and salt-marshes; locally abundant on the East and South coasts, rare in the West and North.*

3. Salicornia

Hairless annual herbs with branched, fleshy, jointed, apparently leafless stems; really however, the fleshy, opposite leaves are pressed tight to the stem, and are partly fused together, concealing it. Flowers hermaphrodite, small, stalkless, deeply embedded in the stem, usually in 2 opposite groups of 3 at each node, but occasionally there are 2 opposite solitary flowers. Calyx fleshy, largely fused with the stem. Stamens 1-2. Ovary and fruit embedded in the calyx.

The delimitation of species in this genus is very difficult and controversial, and it is possible to recognise many local, apparently distinct local variants: even now, there is still much to be learnt about Irish plants.

1. Flowers mostly solitary; spike breaking into separate segments at maturity
    2. S. pusilla
    Flowers in long, loose panicles; spike not breaking-up   ..   2
2. Central flower of each group much longer than the visible part of the
    other two; spikes swollen alternately in two dimensions, so as to
    appear knobbly [Fig. XXXIa]   ..   ..   **1. S. europaea**
    Central flower of each group only a little longer than the visible part of
    the other two; spikes smoothly cylindrical or sometimes slightly knobbly
    [Fig. XXXIb]   3

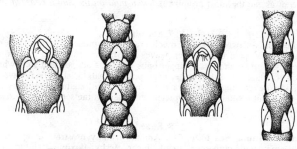

Fig. XXXIa   Fig. XXXIb

3. Plant brownish-mauve or orange; nodes sometimes distinctly narrower
    than the rest of the stem ..   ..   **3. S. nitens**
    Plant dark green, yellowish-green or reddish-pink; stem smoothly
    cylindrical   4
4. Plant usually yellowish-green or reddish-pink; spikes with usually less
    than 12 flowering segments   ..   ..   ..   **4. S. fragilis**
    Plant usually dark green, sometimes brownish; spikes with usually more
    than 12 flowering segments   ..   ..   **5. S. doliostachya**

1. Salicornia europaea (*S. ramosissima*). **8-10.** Stems erect, or more or less prostrate, up to 35 cm long, usually knobbly and freely branched [Fig. XXXIa]. Spikes up to 50 mm long. Flowers in groups of 3, with at least half of the central flower but only ¹/₄ to ¹/₃ of the lateral flowers visible during flowering [Fig. XXXIa]. *Salt-marshes; very frequent.*

2. S. pusilla. 8-10. Stems erect or prostrate, up to 25 cm long, freely branched, usually tinged with red or purple. Spikes 5-15 mm long, knobbly, breaking up into segments as the seeds ripen. Flowers solitary. *Upper parts of salt-marshes; frequent on the South coast, rare elsewhere.*

3. S. nitens. 8-10. Erect and sparingly branched up to 20 cm high, usually brownish or orange, nodes usually narrower than the rest of the stem, sometimes distinctly so. Flowers in groups of 3, with over half of the central flower and lateral flowers visible during flowering. *Middle and upper parts of salt-marshes; rare, possibly underrecorded, on the South and South-east coasts only.*

4. S. fragilis. 8-10. Erect, up to 35 cm high, variably branched, usually tinged with red or yellow. Spikes up to 55 mm long, smoothly cylindrical. Flowers in groups of 3, with over half of the central and lateral flowers visible during flowering [Fig. XXXIb]. *Frequent; lower parts of salt-marshes.*

5. S. doliostachya. 8-10. Like *S. fragilis* but usually dull, dark green or brown and with spikes often 100 mm long or more, with more than 12 flowering segments. *Soft mud, in the lower part of salt-marshes; frequent.*

6. Anthrocnemum

Anthrocnemum perenne. (*Sarcocornia perennis, Salicornia perennis*). **8-10.** Similar to *Salicornia,* but perennial and forming large tussocks with stems woody at the base, spreading and rooting, some stems without flowers; flowers in groups of 3 with the central one the most prominent. *Tidal mud on the South coast of Wexford; very rare.*

7. Salsola

Salsola kali. Saltwort. 7-8. A much-branched, spreading or prostrate annual, with small, fleshy, pale bluish-green leaves and bracts, ending in a sharp prickle; lower ones cylindrical and linear, upper ones shorter, flattened and somewhat triangular. Flowers stalkless, axillary, hermaphrodite; sepals 5, slightly fleshy, with an apical prickle, developing a membranous wing in fruit; stamens 5. Ovary superior with 2 styles. Fruit a small nut, completely enclosed, in the sepals. *Sandy seashores; occasional.*

8. Suaeda

Suaeda maritima. Sea blite. 7-9. Annual, usually prostrate or spreading, but sometimes erect, with numerous, small, linear, fleshy, flexible, cylindrical leaves, blunt at the tip, pale bluish-green, and pale green or reddish. Flowers as in *Salsola,* except that the calyx is rather more fleshy and does not develop a membranous wing. *Seashores; frequent.*

XXXII.   AIZOACEAE

Perennial shrubs or herbs with succulent, 3-angled, undivided, entire leaves. Flowers solitary, regular with a perianth of 4-5 segments; numerous petal-like stamens, normal stamens and carpels.

A number of species are cultivated as 'Ice Plants'; these include not only the two species below, which have become naturalised, but a number of others too. All were, up until recently, included in *Mesembryanthemum.*

1.   Flowers less than 6 cm across; leaves less than 5 cm long; fruit dry
                                                                    1. Lampranthus
     Flowers more than 6 cm across; leaves usually more than 5 cm long;
        fruit succulent   ..   ..   ..   **2. Carpobrotus**

1. Lampranthus

* **Lampranthus roseus. 5-7.** An erect bushy shrub to 30 cm. Leaves up to 4 cm long, with a sharp, acute tip; less than 3 mm thick; conspicuously dotted with translucent glands. Flowers up to 4.5 cm across; pale pink. Fruit a capsule. *Walls and cliffs by the sea; Cork.* Native of South Africa.

2. Carpobrotus

* Carpobrotus edulis. Hottentot fig. 5-7. Procumbent with trailing stems to 3 m. Leaves usually more than 5 cm long; about 5 mm thick. Flowers 7-8.5 cm across; pale yellow or pink. Fruit succulent, with the seeds embedded in mucilage. *Scattered on sea cliffs and walls in the South and East.* Native of South Africa.

XXXIII.   PORTULACEAE

Small, hairless herbs with somewhat fleshy, untoothed leaves. Sepals 2; petals 5, white; ovary superior. Fruit a capsule.

1. Capsule with 1 seed; leaves on stem 2 only, these fused to form a cup
   below the flowers   ..   ..   **1. Claytonia**
   Capsule usually with at least 3 seeds; leaves on stem usually more
   than 2, not fused   ..   ..   ..   **2. Montia**

1. Claytonia

* Claytonia perfoliata. 4-5. Annual with the two leaves on the stem fused to form a cup at the base of the flowers. Capsule with 1 seed. *Woodland margins and waste-places; rare.*

* *C. sibirica* with stalkless, but unfused leaves and pink flowers with the petals deeply notched is occasionally long-persistent in abandoned gardens and demesnes.

2. Montia

Montia fontana. Blinks. 5-8. Usually annual. Habit varying with situation; stems floating, prostrate, or erect and tufted. Leaves opposite, oval, with short wide, stalks. Flowers minute, solitary or in small cymes. Petals partly united, smaller than sepals; stamens 3-5. Fruit usually containing 3 seeds. *Streams, springs and damp ground; frequent, except in the Centre.*

Surface features of the seed have been used to delimit 4 sub-species of *M. fontana;* there appears to be no other difference between these groups in Ireland.

XXXIV.   CARYOPHYLLACEAE

Herbs with opposite, entire leaves, occasionally with stipules. Stems often thickened at the nodes. Flowers regular, solitary or in cymes. Sepals 5 (rarely 4), free or united. Petals equal in number to the sepals (rarely absent), free. Stamens 2-10. Ovary superior, 1-celled; styles 2-5. Fruit a capsule.

Cultivated plants belonging to this family include Pinks and Carnations (*Dianthus*) and also *Gypsophila.*

1. Petals absent   2
   Petals present   3
2. Leaves oval   ..   ..   **5. Stellaria**
   Leaves linear   ..   ..   **7. Sagina**
3. Sepals united, forming a tubular calyx with short lobes   ..   4
   Sepals free, or united only at the extreme base   7
4. Styles 2   5
   Styles 3-5   6
5. Calyx hairy; leaves not more than 5 mm broad; flowers 12-15 mm across
                                                    13. Dianthus
   Calyx hairless or very sparsely downy; leaves 15-25 mm broad; flowers
   25-30 mm across   ..   ..   ..   **12. Saponaria**

6. Petals deeply divided into 4 narrow lobes .. .. **10. Lychnis**
    Petals entire or 2-lobed .. .. **11. Silene**

7. Petals pink or lilac, at least in part .. .. **9. Spergularia**
    Petals pure white, or tinged with green 8

8. Leaves linear (at least 6 times as long as broad) 9
    Leaves not more than 4 times as long as broad 12

9. Petals deeply 2-lobed .. .. .. **5. Stellaria**
    Petals entire 10

10. Styles 3 .. .. **3. Minuartia**
    Styles 4-5 11

11. Leaves clustered at the nodes, so as to appear whorled; pedicels drooping
    in fruit .. .. **8. Spergula**
    Leaves clearly opposite, not clustered at the nodes; pedicels erect in fruit
    7. Sagina

12. Leaves fleshy; petals greenish-white .. .. **4. Honkenya**
    Leaves not fleshy; petals pure white 13

13. Petals 2-lobed, or notched at the tip 14
    Petals entire 15

14. Styles 3; leaf-blades hairless .. .. **5. Stellaria**
    Styles 4-5; leaf-blades hairy .. .. **6. Cerastium**

15. Leaves (including stalk) 12-20 mm long .. **2. Moehringia**
    Leaves not more than 8 mm long .. .. **1. Arenaria**

1. Arenaria

Small plants with oval to oblong leaves. Sepals and petals 5; petals white, entire. Stamens usually 10; styles 3.

1. Erect annual; petals shorter than sepals .. .. **1. A. serpyllifolia**
    Prostrate perennial; petals longer than sepals .. .. **2. A. ciliata**

1. Arenaria serpyllifolia. 5-8. A sparingly downy, usually bushy annual with erect or inclined stems. Leaves oval, stalkless, c. 5 mm long. Petals 2-3 mm, shorter than the acute sepals. Stamens often fewer than 10. *Walls and cultivated or bare ground, especially on sandy or limestone soils. Very frequent in South half; occasional in the North.*

The typical plant has a flask-shaped capsule, with a broad base and a narrow neck. Plants with a conical capsule, not markedly narrowed at the neck, and often with a more delicate, less bushy habit, may be distinguished as subsp. *leptoclados*.

2. A. ciliata. 5-8. A low-growing perennial forming small tufts; stems up to 8 cm long. Leaves 4-7 mm long, oblong, shortly stalked, the margins fringed with short hairs. Petals 5-6 mm, longer than the downy, subacute sepals. *Frequent on a small area of steep, grassy or rocky slopes on the North face of the Ben Bulben range, Co. Sligo.*

Not found in Britain, but very similar plants are known from the Arctic and the mountains of Central Europe.

A. norvegica, similar to *A. ciliata*, but with smaller flowers and sepals and leaves more or less hairless, was once reliably reported from limestone rocks in North-west Clare, but has never been re-found.

2. Moehringia

Moehringia trinervia. 5-7. A slightly downy annual with slender, diffuse stems up to 25 cm long. Leaves 12-20 mm, oval, acute, the upper ones stalked, all with 3 unbranched veins. Sepals lanceolate, acute, with membranous margins; petals 2-3 mm long, oblong, entire, shorter than the sepals, white. Styles 3. *Woods and other shady places; occasional in the East half, rare in the West.*

Similar to *Stellaria neglecta* or to luxuriant plants of *Stellaria media* in general appearance, but distinct in its entire petals and leaves with 3 unbranched veins.

3. Minuartia

Leaves linear, more or less needle-like. Petals and sepals 5; petals white, entire. Stamens 3-10. Styles 3.

1.	Cushion-forming perennial; petals longer than the sepals ..	2
	Slender, erect annual; petals shorter than the sepals ..	**3. M. hybrida**
2.	Leaves mostly straight; sepals with 3 veins	**1. M. verna**
	Leaves mostly curved downwards; sepals with 5-7 veins	**2. M. recurva**

1. Minuartia verna. 5-9. A hairless perennial, with short, prostrate to semi-erect stems, forming a compact cushion. Leaves mostly straight, in crowded tufts, the lowest c. 10 mm long, the upper shorter. Petals 3-5 mm, longer than the 3-veined sepals. *Limestone or basalt rocks or screes, rarely on sand-dunes. Locally frequent in Clare, Aran Islands, Antrim and Derry; unknown elsewhere.*

2. M. recurva. 6-8. Very like *M. verna*, but with leaves mostly curved downwards and with 5-7 veins on the sepals. *Siliceous mountain rocks on the borders of West Cork and Kerry; very rare.*

3. * M. hybrida (*Arenaria tenuifolia*). **7-9.** A slender, usually hairless annual with erect stems 15-30 cm high. Leaves rather few, 7-9 mm long. Flowers numerous; petals 3 mm, shorter than the very acute sepals. Stamens usually fewer than 10. *Dry, bare ground, mostly on or close to railway-lines; formerly very frequent, now rare.*

4. Honkenya

Honkenya peploides. 5-8. A partly dioecious perennial, with short, erect stems arising from long, creeping stolons. Leaves very thick and fleshy, oval, pointed, c. 12 mm long. Flowers 7-10 mm across, some hermaphrodite, but mostly unisexual; abortive stamens are, however, present in the female and abortive ovary in the male flowers. Petals greenish-white, entire, very small in the female flowers. Stamens 10. Capsule spherical; styles 3-5. Seeds few, large, brownish. *Maritime sands; more rarely on shingle. Very frequent round most of the coast.*

5. Stellaria

Annuals or perennials, hairless or sparsely hairy; stems weak and often brittle. Flowers in cymes, or rarely solitary. Sepals and petals 5. Sepals free; petals white, notched or 2-lobed (rarely absent). Stamens 10, rarely fewer; styles 3.

1.	Leaves oval, the lower ones stalked	2
	Leaves linear-lanceolate, stalkless	4
2.	Stamens 10; sepals usually more than 5 mm ..	**2. S. neglecta**
	Stamens 1-7; sepals usually less than 5 mm	3
3.	Stamens usually 3; petals usually present ..	**1. S. media**
	Stamens usually 2; petals absent	**3. S. pallida**
4.	Petals c. 2 mm, shorter than the sepals	**4. S. uliginosa**
	Petals at least 5 mm, longer than the sepals	5
5.	Petals cleft about half way to the base	**5. S. holostea**
	Petals cleft almost to the base	6
6.	Leaves very pale bluish-green; pedicels erect in fruit	**6. S. palustris**
	Leaves not pale bluish-green; pedicels drooping in fruit	**7. S. graminea**

1. Stellária media. Chickweed. *Fliodh.* **1-12.** A somewhat straggling annual up to 40 cm, mostly hairless, but with some hairs on the sepals and in vertical lines on the stems. Stems slender, up to 40 cm long. Leaves pale green, oval, at least the lower ones stalked. Sepals 3-5 mm; petals shorter than the sepals, lobed almost to the base; sometimes absent. Stamens usually 3, rarely 4-5. *Cultivated ground and waste places; abundant.*

2. S. neglecta. 5-8. Like *S. media*, but larger in all its parts. Stems up to 70 cm; leaves up to 40 x 20 mm; sepals usually 5-6 mm. Petals equalling the sepals or slightly longer. Stamens usually 10. *Damp or shady places, mainly in the West; apparently rare, but perhaps overlooked.*

3. S. pallida. 2-4. Like *S. media*, but smaller in all its parts. Stems less than 25 cm; leaves 3-7 mm long; sepals 2.5-3 mm. Leaves pale yellowish-green. Petals absent; stamens usually 2. *Walls, sand-dunes and bare ground; occasional.*

4. S. uliginosa (*S. alsine*). **5-7.** A hairless perennial, with weak, straggling stems up to 25 cm long. Leaves oval to lanceolate, acute, stalkless. Flowers 5-7 mm across. Petals 2-lobed almost to the base, shorter than the sepals. Stamens 10. *Ditches, streamsides and other wet places, mainly on acid soils; very frequent except in parts of the Centre.*

5. S. holostea. Stitchwort. 4-6. A nearly hairless perennial, with weak but more or less erect stems up to 60 cm. Leaves 2-5 cm long, stalkless, linear-lanceolate, acute. Flowers 17-20 cm across, in cymes of 7-11; bracts like the leaves but much smaller. Petals lobed half way to the base. Stamens 10. *Hedges and thickets; frequent in the East half; local and rather rare in the West.*

6. S. palustris. 5-7. Like *S. holostea*, but with stem and leaves very pale bluish-green, cymes with fewer flowers and petals lobed almost to the base. *Fens and calcareous marshes, mainly in the Centre; rather rare.*

7. S. graminea. 6-8. Hairless perennial, with slender, straggling stems. Leaves as in *S. holostea*, but only 15-25 mm long. Flowers numerous, 10-15 mm across. Petals about equalling the sepals, divided almost to the base into two narrow lobes. Stamens 10. Pedicels drooping in fruit. *Grassland, hedges, marshes and bog-margins; abundant in most districts.*

6. Cerastium. Mouse-ear chickweed

Low-growing, hairy plants with small, obtuse to subacute leaves, mostly stalkless but the lowest often shortly stalked. Flowers in usually small cymes; sepals and petals 5 (more rarely 4). Sepals free. Petals white, notched at the tip but not deeply lobed. Stamens 4-10. Capsule usually much longer than the calyx.

1. Petals about twice as long as the sepals ..   ..   **1. C. arvense**
   Petals shorter than the sepals, or only slightly longer   ..   2

2. None of the hairs gland-tipped; plant not sticky; perennial, with short,
   non-flowering branches ..   ..   ..   **2. C. fontanum**
   Gland-tipped hairs present, at least on the upper part of the plant,
   making it sticky; annual, without non-flowering branches   ..   3

3. Inflorescence crowded, with all the pedicels shorter than the calyx;
   stamens 10 ..   ..   **3. C. glomeratum**
   Inflorescence relatively lax, with most pedicels longer than the calyx;
   stamens 4 or 5   4

4.   Bracts with membranous margins and tips; ripe capsule nearly twice as
        long as calyx; petals 5   ..   ..   ..   **4. C. semidecandrum**
     Bracts entirely herbaceous, without membranous tip or margins;
        ripe capsule only slightly longer than the calyx; petals usually 4
        (occasionally 5)   ..   ..   ..   **5. C. diffusum**

1. Cerastium arvense. 5-7. Perennial, with more or less prostrate stems forming
a loose mat. Leaves up to 20 mm long, oblong-lanceolate, downy with numerous
hairs, some of them gland-tipped. Flowers solitary or in small cymes. Sepals and
petals 5; stamens 10. Petals 10-12 mm, about twice as long as the sepals. *Dry
grassland, rocky ground and shingle beaches. Locally frequent in the Burren, near
Galway, and by the coast North of Dublin; very rare elsewhere.*

   * *C. tomentosum*, widely grown for ornament, and occasionally more or less
naturalised near gardens, is generally similar, but the whole plant is white with
densely matted, non-glandular hairs.

2. C. fontanum (*C. vulgatum, C. holosteoides*). **4-10.** Perennial, hairy but not
sticky, with erect, usually unbranched flowering stems, and short, prostrate non-
flowering branches. Leaves oblong, 8-20 mm long. Cymes fairly lax; bracts mainly
herbaceous, but usually a few with membranous margins. Sepals, petals and styles 5;
stamens 10. Petals about the same length as the sepals. Capsule nearly twice as long
as the sepals. *Grassland of all types, waste places and cultivated ground; abundant.*

3. C. glomeratum (*C. viscosum*). **5-8.** A bushy annual 6-15 cm high, sticky with
numerous gland-tipped hairs. Leaves broadly oval. Flowers numerous, in congested
cymes; pedicels very short. Bracts entirely herbaceous. Sepals, petals and styles 5;
stamens 10. Petals 4 mm, scarcely longer than the sepals. Capsule nearly twice as
long as the sepals. *Cultivated ground, waste places and walls; very frequent.*

4. C. semidecandrum. 4-5. Annual, with erect, branched stems 5-15 cm high,
downy and somewhat sticky throughout. Leaves oblong to oval. Flowers in fairly
open cymes, with most of the pedicels distinctly longer than the calyx. Bracts with
wide membranous margins and tips. Sepals, petals and stamens 5; petals with a very
short notch, usually shorter than the sepals. Capsule drooping at first, but later erect,
nearly twice as long as the sepals. *Maritime sands; occasional. Also very rarely on
dry soils inland.*

5. C. diffusum (*C. tetrandrum, C. atrovirens*). **4-7.** A downy and somewhat
sticky annual with spreading or semi-erect stems. Leaves oblong to broadly oval.
Flowers in small, fairly lax cymes; pedicels mostly much longer than the calyx.
Sepals, petals, stamens and styles 4 (occasionally 5). Petals 4 mm, about equalling
the sepals. Capsule erect, only slightly longer than the sepals. *Maritime sands, or
occasionally in other dry, open habitats. Very frequent by the sea; rare inland.*

7. Sagina. Pearlwort

Small, freely branched plants, hairless or rather sparsely glandular-hairy. Leaves
small, linear. Flowers solitary, or in cymes of 2-3. Sepals and styles 4 or 5; petals
white, entire, equal in number to the sepals, or absent; stamens 4-10. Capsule
equalling or slightly exceeding the calyx.

1.   Petals conspicuous, at least as long as the sepals   2
     Petals minute or absent   3
2.   Petals 6 x 4 mm, much longer than the sepals; flowering stems leafy
        almost up to the flower ..   ..   **1. S. nodosa**
     Petals 2 x 1.5 mm, about equalling the sepals; flowers on relatively long,
        leafless pedicels   ..   ..   ..   **2. S. subulata**

3. Mat-forming perennial with creeping stems　　　　..　　**3. S. procumbens**
   Annual, with more or less erect stems　..　　　　..　　　..　　　　4
4. Leaves ending in a slender, bristle-like awn　　　..　　..　**4. S. apetala**
   Leaves obtuse to subacute, without an awn　　　..　　　　**5. S. maritima**

1. Sagina nodosa. 7-8. A sparingly glandular-hairy perennial, with a tuft of basal leaves, from which arise slender, erect flowering stems. Leaves ending in a short point, but not awned, those of the basal tuft up to 20 mm long, the upper much shorter. Flowers solitary, 10-15 mm across; petals twice as long as the sepals. Sepals, petals and styles 5; stamens 10. *Marshes, lake-shores and other damp places, especially on peaty or sandy ground. Locally frequent in the Centre and West; occasional elsewhere.*

2. S. subulata. 6-8. Perennial, with numerous prostrate, rooting stems bearing solitary flowers on more or less erect, leafless, usually hairless pedicels. Leaves 4-8 mm long, with a slender but sometimes short awn at the tip. Flowers 4-5 mm across; sepals, petals and style 5; petals about equal in length to the sepals. Stamens 10. *Rocks, shallow peaty soils and sandy roadsides; occasional near the North and West coasts; unknown elsewhere.*

3. S. procumbens. 5-11. Perennial, with a rosette of basal leaves and spreading, prostrate flowering stems. Leaves 5-10 mm long, those of the basal rosette longer than those of the branches, all ending in an acute point, but scarcely awned. Flowers solitary; sepals 4 rarely 5; stamens as many or twice as many, petals minute or sometimes absent. *Paths, lawns, roadsides, streamsides and other open, usually damp habitats; abundant.*

4. S. apetala (incl. *S. ciliata*). **5-7.** Annual, with a basal leaf-rosette and numerous erect flowering stems. Basal leaves 10-15 mm, ending in a short awn. Sepals, stamens and styles 4; petals minute, often absent. *Walls and dry, bare ground; frequent.*

5. S. maritima. 5-8. Like *S. apetala*, but of more spreading habit, and with thicker, fleshy leaves, which are obtuse or subacute, but not awned. *Rocks, walls and waste ground near the sea; occasional. Especially characteristic of the chinks in the masonry of piers.*

8. Spergula

Spergula arvensis. 5-8. A diffusely branched, usually somewhat glandular-hairy annual 15-35 cm high. Leaves 25-50 mm long, arranged in two clusters at each node, which merge to form an apparent whorl of about 8. Flowers 10 mm across, in regularly forked cymes; sepals, petals and styles 5; stamens 5-10. Petals white, entire, about as long as the sepals. Fruiting pedicels drooping at first, later erect. *Arable fields, mainly on acid soils; rather rare in the Centre, very frequent elsewhere.*

9. Spergularia

Annuals or perennials of low, tufted habit. Leaves linear, often rather fleshy, with silvery, membranous stipules. Flowers in terminal cymes. Sepals and petals 5; stamens 5-10; styles 3.

1. Petals uniformly coloured (lilac or pink)　　　　..　　　..　　　2
   Petals white at the base　..　　　　..　　　　..　　　..　　　3
2. Annual; flowers 3-6 mm across; plant hairless in lower part　..　**4. S. rubra**
   Perennial; flowers 8-12 mm across; stems glandular-hairy throughout
   　　　　　　　　　　　　　　　　　　　　　　　1. S. rupicola

3. Annual; petals 2.5-3 mm, slightly shorter than the sepals; some or all
        of the seeds without a membranous wing   ..   .. **3. S. marina**
    Perennial; petals 4-6 mm, at least as long as the sepals; all seeds
        usually with a membranous wing   ..   ..   .. **2. S. media**

1. Spergularia rupicola. 6-8. Perennial, with a stout, woody stock. Stems glandular-hairy throughout. Leaves 5-15 mm long, fleshy, mucronate. Petals 4-6 mm long, about equalling the sepals, bright lilac-pink. Seeds finely tuberculate, not winged. *Maritime rocks and walls; frequent round most of the coast.*

2. S. media (*S. marginata*). **6-9.** Perennial, with densely tufted stems, and a stout tap-root. Stems hairless except near the tip. Leaves up to 25 mm long, fleshy, acute or obtuse, usually hairless. Flowers 8-12 mm across; petals usually slightly longer than the sepals, lilac pink in upper part, white at the base. Stamens 8-10. Most of the seeds with a membranous wing. *Salt-marshes and muddy or gravelly sea-shores; frequent.*

3. S. marina (*S. salina*). **6-8.** Generally similar to *S. media*, but annual, with a slender tap-root, rather more glandular-hairy, and with flowers only 6-8 mm across, with petals slightly shorter than the sepals, stamens 7 or fewer, and many of the seeds without a membranous wing. *Similar situations to those of* S. media; *very frequent.*

4. S. rubra. 5-9. Annual, with a basal rosette of leaves and prostrate branches, usually more or less hairless except on the sepals and pedicels. Leaves mostly 5-10 mm long, acute, mucronate or shortly awned, not fleshy. Flowers 3-6 mm across; petals about as long as the sepals, uniformly lilac-pink. Seeds tuberculate, not winged. *Dry, sandy or gravelly ground; rare.*

10. Lychnis
Lychnis flos-cuculi. Ragged robin. 6-8. An erect perennial, sparingly hairy, with flowering stems 30-75 cm high, and a few prostrate non-flowering shoots at the base. Leaves linear-oblong, acute. Flowers in terminal cymes; sepals united to form a tube; petals 20-25 mm long, the upper half deeply cleft into 4 narrow lobes, bright pink; stamens 10; styles 5. *Marshes and wet meadows; abundant.*

11. Silene. Campion
Mostly perennial. Flowers sometimes unisexual. Calyx tubular; petals 5; stamens 10; styles 3 or 5.

1. Dwarf, moss-like plant, forming compact cushions ..   .. **2. S. acaulis**
    Stems, erect, distinct; habit not cushion-like   2
2. Calyx inflated and bladder-like, hairless   ..   **1. S. vulgaris**
    Calyx hairy   3
3. Flowers 5-6 mm across; styles 3   ..   ..   .. **5. S. gallica**
    Flowers 18-30 mm across; styles 5   4
4. Petals white; teeth of ripe capsule erect or spreading   .. **3. S. latifolia**
    Petals reddish-pink; teeth of ripe capsule sharply rolled back   .. **4. S. dioica**

1. Silene vulgaris. Bladder campion. 6-8. Hairless or sparsely downy perennial. Leaves narrowly oval, usually pale bluish-green. Calyx inflated, bladder-like, conspicuously net-veined. Flowers 18-30 mm across, sometimes unisexual. Petals white, deeply 2-lobed. Styles 3. Capsule enclosed in the calyx.

A variable plant, represented in Ireland by two fairly distinct subspecies, though intermediates can be found.

Subsp. *vulgaris*. Stems mostly erect, up to 80 cm tall. Cymes with numerous flowers, each about 18 mm across. Calyx in fruit narrowed at the mouth. *Roadsides and disturbed ground. Frequent in the Centre and South-east, occasional elsewhere.*

Subsp. *maritima* (*S. uniflora, S. maritima*). Stems spreading, not more than 30 cm tall. Flowers solitary or in cymes of 3-4, about 25 mm across. Calyx in fruit parallel-sided, scarcely narrowed at the mouth. *Maritime rocks and shingle beaches, rarely inland on mountains or rocky lake-shores. Very frequent round most of the coast.*

2. Silene acaulis. 6-7. A dwarf perennial of moss-like habit, with short, crowded, leafy stems, forming a small cushion. Leaves 6-10 mm, linear-oblong, fringed with hairs. Flowers bright pink, notched at the tip but scarcely lobed. Styles 3. Capsule longer than the calyx. *Mountain ledges and cliffs in the North-west (Mayo to Derry); rare.*

3. S. latifolia (*S. pratensis, S. alba*). **White campion. 6-8.** Perennial (sometimes annual) with erect, hairy stems up to 100 cm high. Leaves oval-lanceolate, entire. Flowers in terminal cymes, usually dioecious, faintly scented at evening. Petals white, deeply 2-lobed. Calyx hairy, swollen in fruit. Styles 5. *Cultivated ground and waste places; locally frequent in the Centre and South-east, rare elsewhere.*

4. S. dioica (*Melandrium rubrum*). **Red campion.** *Coireán coilleach.* **5-7.** Like *S. latifolia*, but with rather broader leaves and somewhat smaller, scentless flowers with red petals. *Woods and hedges; locally frequent in parts of the North and East; rare elsewhere.*

Hybrids between the last two species are occasionally found. They have flowers of various shades of pink.

5. * S. gallica (*S. anglica*). **6-9.** An annual up to 40 cm high; stems erect, freely branched; whole plant sticky with glandular hairs. Leaves narrowly oblong. Flowers 5-7 mm across, in raceme-like cymes. Petals white or pale pink, slightly notched. Styles 3. *Arable fields, mainly on sandy soils; rare.*

12. Saponaria

* Saponaria officinalis. Soapwort. 8-9. An erect, usually hairless perennial 60-90 cm high. Leaves narrowly oval, with 3 conspicuous veins. Flowers numerous, 20-30 mm across. Calyx narrow, tubular. Petals pale pink, entire or slightly notched. Stamens 10. Styles 2. *Roadsides and river-banks, as an escape from gardens; occasional in the South and East; rare elsewhere.*

Most of the Irish plants have 'double' flowers, with some of the stamens replaced by extra petals.

13. Dianthus

Dianthus armeria. 6-8. Annual or biennial, with erect, branched stem about 40 cm high. Leaves linear-lanceolate, keeled, downy, 30-50 x 1-3 mm. Flowers 12-15 mm across, stalkless, in small, terminal clustres, surrounded by numerous bracts. Calyx tubular, with 5 pointed teeth, closely surrounded at its base by 2 pointed bracts. Petals 5, pink with white spots. Stamens 10 or fewer. Capsule slightly longer than the calyx; styles 2. *Recently discovered on a grassy cliff-top on an island in West Cork.*

XXXV. ILLECEBRACEAE

Scleranthus annus. 6-8. A small, spreading, slightly pale bluish-green annual (rarely biennial), with linear leaves up to 15 mm long. Flowers minute, green, mostly in crowded, terminal cymes. Calyx with an ovoid tube and 5 triangular teeth, which are spreading in flower but nearly erect in fruit. Petals absent. Stamens variable in number, inserted at the top of the calyx-tube. Styles 2. Fruit a small nut, enclosed in the calyx-tube. *Waste places and roadsides on dry, sandy soils. Rare in the North-east, very rare elsewhere.*

XXXVI. NYMPHACEAE. Water-lily

Aquatic perennial herbs, with stout rhizomes and large, more or less round, undivided, floating leaves on long stalks. Flowers solitary, large, regular, hermaphrodite, floating or raised slightly above the water-surface. Perianth of numerous free segments; which gradually grade into the numerous stamens. Carpels numerous, united or embedded separately in the receptacle. Fruit a fleshy capsule with numerous seeds.

1. Flowers yellow; leaves clearly oval, some floating, some permanently
   submerged ..   .. **1. Nuphar**
   Flowers white; leaves almost circular, all floating when mature   **2. Nymphaea**

1. Nuphar
Nuphar lutea. Yellow water-lily. 5-7. Leaves large; floating leaves broadly oval, deeply cordate; blade *c.* 15-22 x 15 cm, green on both sides, submerged leaves thin in texture and with wavy margins; veins clearly visible close to the margin of the leaf. Flowers *c.* 5 cm across, floating or raised slightly above the water surface. Perianth segments numerous, rounded, yellow; the outer larger and sometimes greenish on the outer surface, the inner much smaller. Outer stamens with broad, yellow filaments. Ovary superior, of many fused carpels. Fruit a bottle-shaped, somewhat fleshy capsule, ripening above water. *Pools, lakes, canals and slow-moving streams; frequent from Lough Neagh to Clare, rarer elsewhere.*

2. Nymphaea
Nyphaea alba. White water-lily. *Duilleóg bháite.* **6-7.** Leaves large, all floating, blade almost circular, 15-20 cm across, deeply cordate, often reddish beneath; veins not clearly visible close to the margin of the leaf. Flowers *c.* 8-13 cm across, floating. Perianth segments very numerous, acute, mostly white, though the outer are greenish-brown on the outside. Outer stamens with broad petal-like filaments, showing a gradual transition to the petals. Ovary partly inferior; of many fused carpels which are embedded separately in the receptacle; stigmas uniting to form a star-shaped pattern in the centre of the flower. Fruit a spongy mass, consisting of the receptacle and embedded carpels, ripening underwater and dehiscing irregularly. *Pools, lakes and slow-moving streams; frequent in the West half (especially Cork, Kerry, Galway and Mayo); rather rare in the East half.*

Plants from West Galway with leaves only 9-13 cm across, flowers 5-12 cm across, never opening fully and with stamens absent from the upper part of the ovary have been distinguished as subsp. *occidentalis* but intermediates are frequent.

Various exotic species and cultivars are planted in gardens and may persist.

XXXVII. CERATOPHYLLACEAE

Ceratophyllum
Submerged aquatic, rootless perennial herbs with branched stems. Leaves numerous dividing by forking two or three times into linear segments. Flowers minute, axillary, stalkless and monoecious, seldom produced. Ovary superior, of a single carpel.

1. Leaves forked 1-2 times; fruits with basal spines or tubercles   **1. C. demersum**
    Leaves forked 3-4 times; fruits lacking basal spines and tubercles
                                                                 2. C. submersum

1. Ceratophyllum demersum. Hornwort. 6-7. Stems up to 1 m long. Leaves very numerous, 1-2 cm long, in whorls of 6-8, rather rigid, with finely toothed segments. Perianth of numerous, narrow, free segments, green or dull purple, larger in male than female flowers. Stamens 5-20, purple, anthers with minute teeth. Fruit a black, ovoid nut, usually with 2 long spines at the base (though these may be missing or reduced to tubercles), 4-5 mm long, rarely produced. *Lakes, pools and canals; rare and apparently decreasing.*

2. † C. submersum. 6-7. Similar to *C. demersum* differing only in its more highly divided leaves (forked 3-4 times as opposed to 1-2 times) which are also usually paler, less rigid and only weakly denticulate and fruits without basal spines. *Recently recorded from four lakes in Down; perhaps overlooked elsewhere.*

XXXVIII. RANUNCULACEAE

Annual or perennial herbs; occasionally woody climbers. Leaves usually alternate or basal. Flowers usually regular, hermaphrodite. Sepals and petals free, variable in number; sepals often petal-like and true petals sometimes absent. Stamens hypogynous, indefinite and usually numerous, free. Carpels numerous, superior, free. Fruit a cluster of achenes or follicles.

A number of common garden plants belong to this family. These include Delphiniums (*Delphinium*), Winter aconite (*Eranthis hyemalis*), Monkshood (*Aconitum*) and Love-in-a-mist (*Nigella*), as well as many species and hybrids of *Anemone*, *Aquilegia*, *Helleborus* and *Clematis*.

1. Woody climber; leaves opposite; perianth-segments 4; achenes crowned
      with long, feathery styles   ..   ..   .. **4. Clematis**
    Herb; leaves alternate or basal; perianth-segments and achenes not as above   2
2. Perianth small, less conspicuous than the stamens   ..   **8. Thalictrum**
    Perianth conspicuous   3
3. Fruit a cluster of follicles   4
    Fruit a cluster of small achenes   7
4. Flowers yellow   5
    Flowers not yellow   6
5. Leaves round, triangular or kidney-shaped, not lobed   ..   **2. Caltha**
    Leaves deeply divided into jagged lobes   ..   .. **1. Trollius**
6. Flowers blue (rarely pink or white)   ..   ..   .. **6. Aquilegia**
    Flowers green   ..   ..   ..   **7. Helleborus**
7. Perianth consisting only of petal-like sepals   ..   .. **3. Anemone**
    Perianth clearly differentiated into sepals and petals   **5. Ranunculus**

1. Trollius
Trollius europaeus. Globe flower. 6-7. An erect, hairless perennial, 30-60 cm tall. Basal leaves stalked, palmately divided into jagged lobes; upper leaves similar but stalkless. Flowers 2-4 cm across, terminal, regular, usually solitary, pale yellow, globular. Sepals *c.* 10, strongly incurved and overlapping; petals about equal in number but smaller. Stamens numerous. Fruit a head of numerous follicles. *Lake-and river-banks in Donegal, Fermanagh and Cavan; very rare.*

2. Caltha

Caltha palustris. Marsh marigold, King cup. 3-6. A hairless perennial with thick, fleshy stems and leaves. Leaves undivided, mostly basal, in large tufts, round, triangular or kidney shaped, rather fleshy, with crenate margins and long stalks. Flowers 2-5 cm across, in small, leafy cymes, on stout peduncles, regular; sepals large, bright yellow, petal-like; petals absent. Fruit of 5-10 follicles. *Marshy places and wet grassland; abundant in most districts.*

Plants from upland areas with procumbent stems rooting at the nodes, which eventually produce one small flower have been distinguished as var. *radicans.*

3. Anemone

Rhizomatous perennial herbs, with palmately lobed leaves. Flowers large, regular, solitary, with a whorl of leaf-like bracts on the flowering stem; sepals large and petal-like; true petals absent. Fruit a cluster of achenes.

1. Flowers white, rarely violet-blue or pink; rhizome long-creeping. Sepals 6-7
   1. A nemorosa
   Flowers blue, rhizome short. Sepals 9-15 .. **2. A. apennina**

1. Anemone nemorosa. Wood anemone. *Nead coille.* **3-5.** Delicate, hairless or somewhat hairy herb with a long-creeping rhizome. Basal leaves appearing only after flowering, deeply 3-lobed, the lobes further lobed or toothed. Flowers 2-4 cm across; bracts large, about two thirds of the way up the flower stem. Sepals usually 6 or 7, narrowly oblong, white (sometimes tinged with purple or pink), hairless. *Woods and shady places. Very frequent in the North; local elsewhere.*

2. * A. apennina. 3-5. Like *A. nemorosa* but with a short rhizome. Basal leaves appearing after flowering. Flowers 2-5 cm across; bracts large, about half-way up the flowering stem. Sepals usually 9-15, clear blue, hairy. *Extensively cultivated in gardens; frequently persists in old demesnes, especially around Dublin and Cork.* Native of southern Europe.

4. Clematis

* Clematis vitalba. Traveller's joy. 7-9. A scrambling climber with long, woody stems, clinging by its twisted petioles. Leaves opposite, with usually 5 oval pointed leaflets. Flowers regular, in loose cymes. Sepals 4, petal-like, creamy greenish-white to white, hairy; petals absent; stamens numerous. Fruit a cluster of achenes, each crowned by a long feathery style. *Hedges and thickets; frequent in the South half, rather rare in the North.*

5. Ranunculus. Buttercup

Flowers usually solitary. Sepals and petals 5 (unless otherwise indicated), clearly distinct from each other; petals with a minute nectar-secreting pit near the base. Fruit a head of achenes.

The aquatic, white-flowered plants of this genus (Nos 10-19), are often placed in a separate sub-genus (*Batrachium*). They are often hard to identify, chiefly because the general appearance of the plant, and the size and form of its leaves, varies greatly in appearance in accordance with the depth of water in which it grows and the rate of its movement. In many species of this subgenus the leaves are of two sharply contrasted types: *laminar*, which are on or above the water-surface with a flat, lobed blade, and *capillary*, which are submerged and have a blade divided into numerous hair-like segments.

1. Flowers yellow 2
   Flowers white 10

2. Leaves entire or slightly toothed   3
    Leaves compound or deeply lobed   5
3. Sepals 3 (rarely 4); petals more than 6 ..   ..   .. **7. R. ficaria**
    Sepals and petals 5   4
4. Plant not more than 60 cm tall; flowers less than 20 mm across **8. R. flammula**
    Plant 60-120 cm tall; flowers *c.* 35 mm across   ..   .. **9. R. lingua**
5. Plant hairless, or very sparsely hairy   6
    Stem and leaves plentifully hairy throughout   7
6. Achenes hairless, small, numerous and tightly packed, forming an
        elongated, cylindrical head; sepals bent backwards down the pedicel
                                                                6. R. sceleratus
    Achenes downy, at least 3 mm across, forming a globular head; sepals
        spreading horizontally or curved upwards   ..   **5. R. auricomis**
7. Flowers *c.* 5 mm across   ..   ..   ..   **4. R. parviflorus**
    Flowers 15-30 mm across   8
8. Base of stem swollen into an underground corm; sepals bent sharply
        backwards down the pedicel   ..   .. **3. R. bulbosus**
    Base of stem not swollen into an underground corm; sepals not bent
        sharply backwards along the pedicel   9
8. Pedicels smooth; creeping stems or runners absent ..   .. **2. R. acris**
    Pedicels ridged; creeping stems or runners present   ..   .. **1. R. repens**
10. Leaves all undivided, with rounded lobes   11
    At least the lower leaves dissected into hair-like segments   ..   12
11. Leaf-lobes broadest at their base [Fig. XXXVIIIa]; flowers 4-7 mm across
                                                                10. R. hederaceus
    Leaf-lobes broadest above their base [Fig. XXXVIIIb]; flowers 10-13 mm
        across   ..   .. **11. R. omiophyllus**
12. Flowers not more than 12 mm across   13
    At least some of the flowers larger than 12 mm across   ..   14
13. Young achenes hairy; sepals without blue tips   .. **17. R. trichophyllus**
    Young achenes hairless; sepals with blue tips   .. **12. R. tripartitus**
14. Flowers at least 18 mm across   15
    Flowers not more than 17 mm across   16
15. All leaves capillary, longer than adjacent internode ..   **19. R. fluitans**
    Usually some laminar leaves present; dissected leaves shorter than
        adjacent stem internode ..   ..   .. **14. R. peltatus**

Fig. XXXVIIIa   Fig. XXXVIIIb   Fig. XXXVIIIc   Fig. XXXVIIId

16. Young achenes hairless and numerous (40 or more) ..   **13. R. baudotii**
    Young achenes hairy and usually fewer than 40   17

17. All leaves capillary, rigid, circular in outline, the segments all lying in
    one plane   ..   ..   **18. R. circinatus**
    Some laminar leaves often present; capillary leaves not rigid nor lying
    all in one plane   18

18. Petals usually more than 1 cm; nectar-pit pear-shaped [Fig. XXXVIIIc]
    15. R. penicillatus
    Petals usually less than 1 cm; nectar-pit circular [Fig. XXXVIIId]
    16. R. aquatilis

1. Ranunculus repens. Creeping buttercup. 5-8. Erect, hairy perennial up to 40 cm tall, hairy; spreading extensively by stout, creeping and rooting runners. Lower leaves with long stalks, the blade 3-lobed, coarsely toothed and triangular in outline. Flowers 20-30 mm across. Sepals yellowish, hairy, spreading horizontally; petals yellow. Pedicels furrowed. Achenes hairless. *Damp fields, roadsides and ditches; abundant.*

2. R. acris. Meadow buttercup. 5-8. Erect, hairy perennial up to 70 cm tall, without runners. Lower leaves long-stalked; blade more or less circular in outline, deeply divided into 5-7 narrow, jagged lobes; uppermost leaves stalkless with a few narrow, more or less entire lobes. Flowers 15-25 mm across. Sepals yellowish, hairy, spreading horizontally; petals yellow. Pedicels smooth. Achenes hairless. *Meadows, pastures and hedgerows; abundant.*

3. R. bulbosus. Bulbous buttercup. 5-7. Erect, hairy perennial; 20-40 cm tall, without runners, stem expanded at the base into an underground corm. Leaves like those of *R. repens* but usually more finely divided. Flowers 20-30 mm across. Sepals bent sharply backwards down the pedicel; petals bright shining yellow. Pedicels furrowed. Achenes hairless. *Sandhills, gravel banks and dry grassland. Frequent except in parts of the South-west, where it is rare and usually found near the coast.*

4. * R. parviflorus. 4-6. A hairy annual, with weakly ascending stems; 10-30 cm tall. Blade of the basal leaves semi-circular to circular in outline and not deeply dissected; upper linear and deeply divided. Flowers 3-6 mm across. Sepals bent backwards down the pedicel. Petals 5 or fewer, pale yellow, as long as the sepals. *Arable fields and field-margins in Clare, East Cork and Wexford; very rare and decreasing.*

5. R. auricomus. Goldilocks. 4-5. Perennial herb; 15-25 cm tall. Lower leaves with long stalks, the blade lobed or toothed, the lobes usually rounded and obovate; upper leaves divided into a few narrow, entire segments. Flowers 15-25 mm across. Petals yellow, 5 or fewer. Achenes downy. *Woods and shaded hedge banks; fairly frequent in the East half, rare in the West half.*

6. R. sceleratus. *Torachas biadhain.* **6-8.** An erect, hairless or very sparsely hairy annual up to 60 cm tall. Lower leaves semicircular in outline with a long petiole, deeply 3-lobed, the lobes further divided; uppermost leaves stalkless. Flowers 5-10 mm across. Sepals bent sharply backwards down the pedicel; petals yellow, about the same length as the sepals. Receptacle elongating as the flower matures, giving an ovoid or cylindrical fruit, consisting of numerous very small and hairy achenes. *Ditches and marshy ground; frequent near the sea and Lough Neagh, rare elsewhere.*

7. R. ficaria. Lesser celandine. 3-5. An erect, hairless perennial, up to 25 cm tall. Rootstock a mass of small, white tubers. Leaves mostly basal, heart-shaped or nearly round, almost entire. Flowers 15-30 mm across. Sepals 3 (rarely 4), yellowish, often falling early; petals about 8-10, narrow, bright, shining yellow. Achenes usually minutely hairy. *Damp, shady places; very frequent and locally abundant.*

Two subspecies are normally distinguished;

Subsp. *bulbilifer* has small white tubers formed in the axils of the leaves after flowering, few, narrow petals and rather few ripe achenes

Subsp. *ficaria* has no aerial tubers and many ripe achenes.

8. R. flammula. Lesser spearwort. 6-8. A more or less hairless perennial, usually erect but with the stem slightly flexuous and sometimes creeping and rooting in the lower part; 15-50 cm tall. Leaves lanceolate, entire or slightly toothed, the lower ones stalked; the uppermost stalkless. Flowers 10-20 mm across; solitary or in few-flowered heads. Sepals greenish-yellow; petals yellow. Achenes hairless. *Ditches, marshes and lake-shores; frequent.*

Plants from North Kerry and Clare with cordate basal leaves have been distinguished as subsp. *minimus*, but scarcely warrant this status.

9. R. lingua. Greater spearwort. 6-7. Similar to *R. flammula* but much more robust and spreading by underground stolons. Stems 50-120 cm tall. Leaves lanceolate, stalkless, usually slightly toothed. Flowers 25-40 mm across. *Marshes, fens, canals and reed-beds; frequent in the Centre, rather rare elsewhere.*

All of the following species belong to the sub-genus *Batrachium* and are white flowered.

10. R. hederaceus. Ivy-leaved crowfoot. 4-8. Annual or perennial. Leaves all laminar, with usually 5 short, rounded lobes broadest at the base and a long petiole [Fig. XXXVIIIa]. Flowers 4-8 mm across. Sepals not bent backwards down the pedicel. Petals scarcely longer than sepals. Young achenes hairless. *Shallow pools, ditches and wet mud, frequent except in parts of the Centre.*

11. R. omiophyllus. 5-8. Like *R. hederaceus* but with more clearly and deeply lobed leaves, in which the lobes are widest above the base [Fig. XXXVIIIb]. Flowers 7-18 mm across. Sepals bent backwards down the pedicel. Petals about twice as long as sepals. Young achenes hairless. *Shallow pools, ditches and wet mud; frequent in the South and South-east (Kerry to Dublin and inland to Laois), unknown elsewhere.*

12. R. tripartitus. 3-5. Like *R. hederaceus* but sometimes with capillary as well as laminar leaves; the laminar leaves with a deeply 3- to 5-lobed blade with the lobes wedge-shaped and crenate. Flowers 5-10 mm across. Sepals blue-tipped and bent backwards down the pedicel. Young achenes hairless. *Pools and small lakes; known only from South Kerry and West Cork, very rare.*

13. R. baudotii. 5-8. Annual or perennial with rigid capillary leaves always present; floating leaves sometimes present, with a deeply 3-lobed blade. Flowers 12-18 mm across. Sepals bent back down the pedicel. Petals with a crescent-shaped nectar-pit. Achenes very small and numerous, with a narrow wing, hairless. Pedicels in fruit longer than adjacent leaf. *Pools and ditches near the sea, often in brackish water; mainly in the South and West, occasional.*

14. R. peltatus. 5-6. Annual or perennial; usually with both floating and capillary leaves. Floating leaves with a very long leaf-stalk to 7 cm; the blade semi-circular to circular with 3-7 obscurely crenate lobes. Capillary leaves rigid or collapsing when taken out of the water, shorter than or about the same length as the stem-internodes. Flowers 15-30 mm across. Sepals spreading. Petals sometimes more than 5; with a pear-shaped nectar-pit [Fig. XXXVIIIc]. Young achenes downy. Pedicels in fruit at least as long as petiole of adjacent leaf. *Rivers; frequent.*

Some doubt attaches to the frequency of occurrence of *R. peltatus* which is easily confused with the next species.

15. R. penicillatus. 5-6. (*R. peltatus* subsp. *pseudofluitans*). Very like *R. peltatus*, differing chiefly in the capillary leaves, which are usually longer than the adjacent internode and have more numerous, very limp segments, which collapse to form a tassel when the leaf is withdrawn from the water. *Rivers and streams; frequent.*

16. R. aquatilis. 5-7. Generally similar to *R. peltatus*, but with rather smaller flowers (12-17 mm across); petals with a circular nectar-pit [Fig. XXXVIIId]; fruiting pedicels shorter than the adjacent internode. *Streams, ditches and lake-margins; generally frequent, but rare in parts of the West.*

17. R. trichophyllus. 4-7. Smaller than most of the related species. Annual or perennial with only capillary leaves present; the segments short, firm and spreading, arranged in a bush-like form. Flowers 8-10 mm across. Sepals spreading. Petals usually clearly separate from each other and with a crescent-shaped nectar-pit. Young achenes downy. Fruiting pedicels about the same length as the adjacent leaf. *Shallow, still or slow-moving water in ditches, small pools or lake-margins; often semi-terrestrial, on wet mud; occasional in the Centre and South-east, rare elsewhere.*

18. R. circinatus. 5-7. A perennial with capillary leaves only present, these 1-2.5 cm across; with rather stout, short and rigid segments, which lie in a flat circle like the spokes of a wheel. Flowers 10-20 mm across. Sepals spreading. Petals contiguous. Young achenes hairy. Fruiting pedicel longer than adjacent leaf. *Lakes, rivers and canals; occasional in the Centre, rare elsewhere.*

19. R. fluitans. 6-8. Perennial with only capillary leaves present, at least as long as the internodes, with long, limp segments. Flowers 15-25 mm across. Sepals spreading. Petals 5-10. Young achenes hairy; older hairless. Fruiting pedicel not longer than adjacent leaf. Receptacle (seen by removing all the achenes) hairless (it is hairy in all other related species). *Known only from one river in Antrim.*

6. Aquilegia

Aquilegia vulgaris. Columbine. 4-6. An erect, almost hairless perennial, 30-90 cm tall. Leaves finely pinnately divided, the segments with rounded lobes; pale bluish-green beneath. Flowers complex in appearance, 3-4.5 cm across, regular, drooping, dull purple (rarely pink or white). Sepals 5, flat, spreading, petal-like; petals 5, tubular, ending in a conspicuous hooked spur. Fruit of 5 follicles. *Thickets and rocky limestone pastures; mainly in the Centre, rare.*

Hybrid Columbines are sometimes found in waste ground as garden escapes. They are generally larger and have flowers of various colours.

7. Helleborus. Hellebore

* Helleborus viridis. 3-4. Robust perennial with a stout, ascending stem which is hairless below and sometimes hairy above. Basal leaves two, dying before winter, palmate with 5-11 toothed segments; upper similar but stalkless. Flowers 3-5 cm across, 2-4 per inflorescence, slightly nodding. Sepals green, with more or less flat margins, spreading. Petals absent; represented by vase-shaped nectaries. Fruit a group of usually three many-seeded follicles. *A garden escape which occurs in hedges, sometimes far from cultivation; rare.*

A number of species, hybrids and colour-forms of Hellebore are grown in gardens and may persist *e.g. H. niger*, the Christmas rose.

8. Thalictrum. Meadow rue

Erect, hairless perennials. Leaves finely pinnately divided. Flowers regular, in racemes of various degrees of complexity. Sepals 4 or 5, small and inconspicuous; petals absent. Stamens numerous, usually the most conspicuous part of the flower. Fruit a cluster of small achenes. This genus includes some of the few wind pollinated members of the family.

1. Flowers in an unbranched raceme; plant very small (usually less than 15 cm)
   1. T. alpinum
   Flowers in more complex infloresences; plant usually larger than 15 cm.　　2.
2. Flowers greenish, drooping, with long pedicels, in a loose inflorescence
   2. T. minus
   Flowers yellowish, erect, with short pedicels, in a compact inflorescence
   3. T. flavum

1. Thalictrum alpinum. 6-8. Very small and delicate, 5-15 cm tall. Leaves mostly basal, bipinnate, with very small rounded, shallowly toothed leaflets (terminal, *c.* 5 mm). Inflorescence erect, with the few flowers drooping and clearly separated from each other. Stamens *c.* 10, much longer than the sepals; anthers with a minute, sharp and extended point at the tip. *Mountains in the West (Galway, Mayo & Sligo) (not found recently in the North-east); very rare.*

2. T. minus. 6-9. Very variable, but always with relatively fine, flexuose branches, 30-100 cm tall. Leaves bipinnate with the leaflets shallowly toothed or lobed (terminal, 5-20 mm). Inflorescence erect, with the flowers spreading or drooping and usually clearly separated from each other. Sepals greenish. Stamens usually more than 12; anthers with a minute, sharp and extended point at the tip. *Mountains, stony lake-shores, rocky ground and sand-hills; local and mainly near the coast, becoming increasingly rare.*

A number of ill-defined sub-species, based on differences in glandulosity and hairiness have been recognised in Britain. Irish material appears less variable, but needs further study.

3. T. flavum. Meadow rue. 6-8. Moderately robust, with relatively stout, flexuose branches, 60-120 cm tall. Leaves bipinnate, with the segments shallowly toothed or lobed (terminal, 15-30 mm). Inflorescence erect, with the flowers erect and borne in dense clusters. Stamens usually more than 12; anthers without a minute, sharp and extended point at the tip. *Fens and marshy fields; locally frequent in the Centre and around Lough Neagh, rare elsewhere.*

XXXIX.　BERBERIDACEAE

† **Berberis vulgaris. Barberry. 5-6.** A deciduous shrub, up to 2.5 m high; branches armed with slender, very sharp spines in groups of three. Leaves undivided, alternate, oblong to oval, finely toothed, 2-3 cm long. Flowers 3-7 mm across, yellow, regular and hermaphrodite, in drooping racemes. Perianth segments about 15, petal-like. Ovary superior, of a single carpel. Fruit a scarlet, oblong berry. *Hedges and rocky ground; very rare. Formerly more frequent, but exterminated in most districts as the carrier of the rust-fungus of wheat.*

Various species and hybrids of this genus are cultivated for ornament, and bird-sown seedlings have been recorded. The only one, however, which can be regarded as naturalised is *B. darwinii* which is a shrub to 3 m with dark-green glossy, oblong leaves, spines less than 1 cm, clusters of bright orange flowers and a bluey-black fruit. It is established among native vegetation in a few places in the West and North.

XL. PAPAVARACEAE. Poppy

Erect herbs with white or yellow latex. Leaves alternate, pinnately divided. Flowers regular, hermaphrodite. Sepals 2, falling as the flower opens. Petals 4, crumpled in bud, free, large and brightly coloured, soon falling. Stamens numerous, free. Ovary superior, of 2-12 fused carpels. Fruit a capsule with numerous seeds.

Many poppies are cultivated in gardens. Some can persist for short periods as garden throw-outs. These include a number of species and hybrids of *Papaver* (especially common is *Papaver orientale*, with large flowers (4 cm+) of various colours (pink-red); the perennial Blue poppy (a large blue-flowered and coarsely hairy *Meconopsis* from the Himalayas); and the sometimes perennial, yellow-flowered Californian poppy (*Eschscholzia californica*)).

1. Flowers red, purple or white . . . . . . **1. Papaver**
    Flowers yellow 2
2. Stigma with 4 or more lobes; fruit less than six times as long as wide
    2. Meconopsis
    Stigma with 2-lobes; fruit at least ten times as long as wide . . 3
3. Flowers more than 3 cm across; fruit more than 10 cm long **3. Glaucium**
    Flowers less than 3 cm across; fruit less than 6 cm long **4. Chelidonium**

1. Papaver. Poppy. *Poipín*

Annuals, with large solitary flowers and, unless otherwise stated, white latex. Leaves pinnate or pinnatifid, the segments often with a single hair or sharp point at the tip. Fruit a globular or club-shaped capsule, with a persistent stigmatic disc at the top, opening by pores below the disc.

1. Stem leaves distinctly pale bluish-green, toothed but not divided. Petals
    white or lilac. Sepals hairless. . . . . **1. P. somniferum**
    Stem leaves not pale bluish-green, pinnately divided. Petals bright red.
    Sepals hairy . . . . . . 2.
2. Ovary and capsule hairy; inner pair of petals smaller than outer . . 3.
    Ovary and capsule not hairy; all petals more or less the same size 4.
3. Capsule more or less globular. Peduncle with spreading hairs (at least
    at the base) . . . . **2. P. rhoeas**
    Capsule at least twice as long as broad. Peduncle with non-spreading
    hairs . . . . **3. P. dubium**
4. Capsule less than 1.5 cm, nearly as long as broad . . **4. P. argemone**
    Capsule more than 1.5 cm long, at least 3 times as broad **5. P. hybridum**

1. * Papaver somniferum. Opium poppy. *Codlaidín.* **7-8.** The most robust of the Irish poppies. An erect, often very tall (50+ cm) annual; more or less hairless (hairs sometimes present on the petiole). Leaves oblong, pale bluish-green, toothed but not divided, the upper ones stalkless and clasping the stem. Flowers 5-10 cm across; petals mauve or white with a purple centre. Capsule hairless, globular *c.* 2-5(-9) cm long. *Sandy soils by roadsides and in waste places; occasional, commonest on the central part of the East coast.* Native of Turkey.

2. † P. rhoeas. Corn poppy. *Caithleach dearg.* **6-8.** Distinctive because of the coarse, spreading hairs on the pedicels; usually about 60 cm tall. Latex occasionally yellow. Leaves stalkless and pinnatafid with the lobes coarsely toothed. Flowers 5-10 cm across, petals bright red; outer pair larger than inner. Capsule hairless, more or less globular *c.* 2 cm long, often with a whitish bloom. *Arable land, roadsides, gravel pits and waste places; frequent in the East, occasional in the Centre, rare in the West and very rare in the North.*

3. † **P. dubium. 6-8.** Similar to *P. rhoeas* but the hairs on the pedicels not spreading, the flowers only 3-6 cm across, the petals pale red to pink, and the capsule narrowly club-shaped (two to three times as long as broad). *Similar habitats to* P. rhoeas; *frequent in the East and Centre, local and rather rare elsewhere.*

Plants with white latex and yellow anthers or with yellow latex and brownish to bluish anthers appear to be about equally frequent. The latter are usually distinguished as subsp. *lecoquii*, but other supposedly distinguishing characteristics appear to be unreliable.

4. * **P. argemone. 5-7.** A slender plant, seldom more than 40 cm tall. Lower leaves stalked and pinnate with pinnatifid segments. Flowers 3-5 cm across. Petals relatively pale, orange-red with an indigo centre, more or less equal in size. Capsule narrowly ovoid to club-shaped (about three to four times as long as broad) with a scattered covering of bristly hairs, *c.* 2.5 cm long. *Sandy and gravelly ground; mainly in the South and East; rare and decreasing.*

5. * **P. hybridum. 6-7.** Erect, up to 45 cm tall. Leaves pinnate with deeply toothed or pinnatifid segments. Flowers 3-5 cm across. Petals crimson, more or less equal in size. Capsule ovoid with a dense covering of bristly hairs, c. 1-1.5 cm long. *Sandy fields; formerly occasional, now very rare in the East (Dublin).*

2. Meconopsis

Meconopsis cambrica. Welsh poppy. 6-7. A slightly hairy perennial, 20-40 cm tall, with yellow latex and a strong tap-root. Leaves pinnate with the segments coarsely toothed; distinctly stalked. Flowers 4-7 cm across, petals bright yellow. Stigma 4- 6-lobed, raised on a very short but distinct style. Capsule narrowly club-shaped (about 3-4 times as long as broad), hairless, *c.* 2-3 cm long. *Damp, shady, rocky places, mainly in the mountains; rare. Also occasionally near houses as an escape from gardens.*

3. Glaucium

Glaucium flavum. Horned poppy. 6-8. A robust, pale bluish-green, somewhat hairy perennial with yellow latex. Leaves irregularly pinnatifid, thick; the basal ones stalked and hairy; the upper ones stalkless, sometimes hairless; the uppermost clasping the stem. Flowers 5-8 cm across. Petals orange-yellow. Capsule thin, up to 30 cm long, usually much more than fifteen times as long as broad, splitting along its length from the top. *Sand- or shingle-beaches; absent from the North-west, (Antrim to Mayo), locally frequent elsewhere.*

4. Chelidonium

* **Chelidonium majus. 5-7.** A slender, branching and slightly hairy perennial with bright, orange-yellow latex. Leaves pinnate, with large, irregularly lobed segments. Flowers 1.5-2 cm across, in loose clusters of 3-5. Petals yellow. Capsule long and thin, usually more than ten times as long as broad, splitting from the bottom towards the top, 2-5 cm long. *Walls and hedges, usually near houses; locally frequent in the East half, rarer in the West and South.*

XLI. FUMARIACEAE

Delicate, hairless annual herbs with alternate leaves which are pinnately divided into small segments. Flowers irregular, hermaphrodite, in racemes whose base is opposite to that of a leaf. Sepals 2, small, often falling early. Petals 4, of which two are larger, partly united, and prolonged into a backward pointing spur at the base

[Fig. XLIa]. Stamens 6, but united into 2 bundles each with three lobes, the central part bearing a 2-celled anther and the lateral lobes a single-celled anther (some authorities offer another interpretation; that there are two stamens which have split into three lobes). Ovary superior, fused, of 2 carpels. Fruit a nut.

Some authors prefer to treat the Fumariaceae as a subfamily of the Papavaraceae. *Dicentra* (Bleeding-heart) is commonly grown in gardens.

1. Flowers bright yellow; fruit a pod-like capsule .. **2. Pseudofumaria**
   Flowers purple, pinkish white or yellowish-white .. .. 2.
2. Fruit an ovoid, one-seeded, nut-like achene .. .. **3. Fumaria**
   Fruit a dehiscent capsule with more than one seed .. **1. Ceratocapnos**

1. Ceratocapnos

Ceratocapnos claviculata (*Corydalis claviculata*). **4-10.** A delicate, diffusely branched, scrambling herb up to 80 cm, with some of the terminal leaf segments converted into tendrils. Leaflets long-stalked, oval, obtuse with a minute apical point. Flowers 5-6 mm long, in dense racemes of approximately 6 flowers. Petals pale yellow or cream. Fruit a short, pod-like capsule with 2-3 seeds. *Shady places, among boulders; occasional, but local, in the South-east and South Centre, and once recorded for Donegal.*

2. Pseudofumaria

* **Pseudofumaria lutea** (*Corydalis lutea*). **5-8.** A small, bushy, hairless perennial. Some leaves arising from a central stock. Leaflets wedge-shaped, lobed, with a minute apical point. Flowers 12-18 mm long; in dense, short, often one-sided racemes of 6-10 flowers. Petals yellow. Fruit a capsule *c.* 1 cm long with the wall constricted around the 5 or more shiny seeds. *Grown in gardens; sometimes naturalised on old walls nearby.* Native of Europe.

3. Fumaria. Fumitory

Leaves all cauline. Flowers purplish pink to white. Upper and lateral petals dark coloured at the tip. The edges of the lower petal may be either more or less parallel along their entire length or spoon-shaped at the tip. Fruit a small, more or less spherical, one-seeded nut.

The differences between some species appear clearer and more consistent in Britain than Ireland.

1. Flowers more than or equal to 9 mm in length; lower petal not strongly
   spoon-shaped [Fig. XLIb] 2
   Flowers less than 9 mm in length; lower petal distinctly spoon-shaped
   [Fig. XLIc] 5

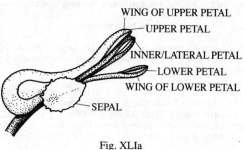

WING OF UPPER PETAL
UPPER PETAL
INNER/LATERAL PETAL
LOWER PETAL
WING OF LOWER PETAL
SEPAL

Fig. XLIa

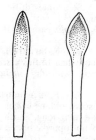

Fig. XLIb   Fig. XLIc

2. Fruiting pedicels curved stiffly downwards or horizontal; sepals often
   with a blunt tip   3
   Fruiting pedicels more or less erect; sepals often with an acute tip   4

3. Flowers creamy-white; racemes shorter than their peduncle; upper petal
   with spreading edges   ..   ..   ..   **1. F. capreolata**
   Flowers purple; racemes as long as their peduncle; upper petal with
   erect or curved-back edges   ..   ..   **2. F. purpurea**

4. Lower petal with parallel edges   ..   ..   .. **3. F. muralis**
   Lower petal slightly spoon-shaped   7

5. Bracts at least as long as pedicels   ..   ..   **6. F. densiflora**
   Bracts shorter than pedicels   ..   ..   ..   6.

6. Fruits wider than long   ..   ..   ..   **5. F. officinalis**
   Fruits longer than wide   7

7. Fruit not distinctly rough when dry; racemes about as long as peduncles,
   with 15 or fewer flowers   ..   ..   .. **3. F. muralis**
   Fruit distinctly rough when dry; racemes longer than peduncles, with
   more than 15 flowers   ..   ..   ..   **4. F. bastardii**

1. † **Fumaria capreolata. 5-9.** Scrambling by means of twisted petioles. Leaf-segments oblong or triangular, up to 15 mm long. Racemes dense, shorter than their peduncles. Sepals 4-6mm long, as broad as corolla [Fig. XLId]. Corolla 10-14 mm long, white or pale pink, tipped with darker purple; tip of upper petal with spreading margins. Fruit usually smooth when dry. *Roadsides, arable and waste ground; mainly coastal.*
  * *F. occidentalis* of robust, climbing habit, with a large flower 10-13 mm long; with the white petals turning bright pink later, with their edges and tips blackish-red and with the lower petal with broad spreading margins, is a rare casual. *(Dublin).*

2. * **F. purpurea. 6-8.** Similar to *F. capreolata* differing in sepals which are rather more acutely pointed [Fig. XLIe], and in the dark pinkish corolla the upper petal of which has a tip with erect margins. *Similar habitats; rare.*

3. † **F. muralis. 5-9.** Stem erect or diffuse, not climbing. Leaf segments variously shaped. Racemes lax, as long as their peduncles or rather longer. Sepals 3-5 mm long, narrower than corolla [Fig. XLIf]. Corolla white or pink, 9-12 mm long; lower petal usually with parallel margins. Fruit usually smooth when dry. *Waste ground, field margins and arable land; very frequent.*
  Sometimes difficult, if not impossible, to separate from the next species. Irish material is very variable and needs further investigation; sub-specific descriptions of *F. muralis* based on British material do not comfortably fit Irish specimens.

4. † **F. bastardii. 5-9.** Similar to *F. muralis* but with rather larger racemes of more than 15 flowers, sepals 2-3 mm long [Fig. XLIg] and the fruit usually distinctly rough when dry. *Similar habitats.*

5. † **F. officinalis. 6-9.** Stem more or less erect, not climbing. Leaf segments narrow-oblong or lanceolate, flat. Racemes much longer than their peduncles. Sepals 2-4 mm long, much narrower than corolla [Fig. XLIh]. Corolla 7-9 mm long, pinkish-purple tipped with dark red; lower petal spoon-shaped. Fruit distinctly rough when dry. *Field margins and waste places; frequent near the East coast, rarer elsewhere.*

Fig. XLId   Fig. XLIe   Fig. XLIf   Fig. XLIg   Fig. XLIh   Fig. XLIi

6. † F. densiflora (*F. micrantha*). **6-9.** Similar to *F. officinalis* but with narrower, channelled leaflets, even shorter peduncles, smaller, very densely packed flowers and sepals as broad as the corolla [Fig. XLIi]. *Field margins in the North half; rare.*

XLII.   CRUCIFERAE (BRASSICACEAE)

Herbs, mostly annual or biennial, with alternate leaves, undivided or pinnately divided. Flowers regular, in racemes. Sepals 4, free; petals 4, free; stamens 6, of which 2 are shorter or occasionally absent. Ovary superior, syncarpous, 2-celled. Fruit dry, usually dehiscent, with 2 valves and a central septum; either with persistent style, or with the fruit divided, horizontally, into 2 parts, an upper, often sterile, top section or beak and a fertile, usually larger, lower section.

To this family belong many familiar vegetables, such as Cabbage, Cauliflower and Turnip (*Brassica*), Raddish (*Raphanus*), Mustard (*Sinapis*), Cress (*Lepidium*) and Horse-radish (*Armoracia*); also such ornamental plants as Wallflower, (*Cheiranthus*), Stock (*Matthiola*), Honesty (*Lunaria*), Candytuft (*Iberis*), Aubretia and *Alyssum*.

1.	Flowers white or purple	2
	Flowers yellow or orange	26
2.	Leaves all pinnate or deeply pinnatifid	3
	Leaves, at least the upper ones, undivided or slightly lobed ..	6
3.	Usually prostrate annual with minute flowers and indehiscent, 2 seeded fruits .. .. **23. Coronopus**	
	Perennial or erect annual; fruit with more than 2 seeds ..	4
4.	Leaves coarsely hairy; petals usually with violet veins **32. Raphanus**	
	Leaves hairless or with a few soft hairs; petals uniformly mauve or white	5
5.	Flowers white or mauve; fruit somewhat flattened; stem more or less erect **12. Cardamine**	
	Flowers yellow; fruit usually round in cross section; stem weak, often rooting near the base .. .. .. **11. Nasturtium**	
6.	Petals purple or lilac	7
	Petals white (sometimes with purplish veins)	10
7.	Plant hairless	8
	Plant hairy	9
8.	Fruits ovoid or globose .. .. .. **17. Cochlearia**	
	Fruits much longer than wide, with 2 distinct segments .. **29. Cakile**	
9.	Plants white-tomentose with appressed, star-shaped hairs; lower leaves pinnate or pinnatifid, the upper entire .. **7. Matthiola**	
	Plants green, with unbranched, outstanding hairs; all leaves serrate **6. Hesperis**	

10. Submerged aquatic with narrow, pointed, cylindrical leaves   **24. Subularia**
    Terrestrial or marsh plant; leaves flat   11

11. Fruit an elongated pod with numerous seeds   12
    Fruit short (less than 3 times as long as wide) or only with 1-2 seeds   15

12. Leaves round or heart-shaped, smelling of garlic when crushed   **3. Alliaria**
    Leaves considerably longer than broad, not smelling of garlic   ..   13

13. Fruits stiffly erect   ..   ..   **14. Arabis**
    Fruits more or less spreading   14

14. Annual; petals less than 5 mm long; fruits more or less cylindrical;
        leaves toothed but not pinnatifid; frequent   ..   **4. Arabidopsis**
    Perennial; petals more than 5 mm long; fruits flattened; leaves pinnatifid;
        rare   ..   ..   **13. Cardaminopsis**

15. Plant with at least a few hairs   16
    Plant entirely hairless   19

16. Petals deeply 2-lobed   ..   .. **16. Erophila**
    Petals entire or slightly notched at tip   17

17. Fruit 2-seeded   ..   ..   ..   **21. Lepidium**
    Fruit with more than 2 seeds   18

18. Fruit heart-shaped, deeply notched at apex   ..   .. **18. Capsella**
    Fruit ovoid   ..   ..   **15. Draba**

19. Robust perennial with leaves up to 25 cm long   20
    Annual or biennial with leaves less than 15 cm long   23

20. Leaves pale greyish-green (appearing waxy), fleshy, irregularly
        pinnately-lobed   ..   .. **31. Crambe**
    Leaves green, not fleshy, not lobed   21

21. Rosette leaves 75-100 cm long; plant not setting fruit   **10. Armoracia**
    Rosette leaves either absent or much less than 75-100 cm long; plant
        setting fruit   22

22. Fruit dehiscent; usually with a distinct apical wing (if unwinged then less
        than 4 mm long)   ..   ..   ..   **21. Lepidium**
    Fruit indehiscent; without a distinct apical wing, more than 4 mm long
                                                                      22. Cardaria

23. Lower leaves pinnately-lobed   24
    Lower leaves undivided, though sometimes lobed   25

24. Fruit 1- or 2-seeded; leaves fleshy   ..   ..   .. **29 Cakile**
    Fruit 4-seeded; leaves not fleshy   ..   ..   **19. Teesdalia**

25. Fruit surrounded by a broad wing   ..   ..   .. **20. Thlaspi**
    Fruit not winged   ..   .. **17. Cochlearia**

26. All leaves entire or slightly toothed   ..   ..   **5. Erysimum**
    Lower leaves divided or distinctly lobed   27

27. Fruit deeply constricted around the seeds (sometimes only 1 seed present),
        not splitting into valves   28
    Fruit splitting into 2 lateral valves and a central septum; seldom deeply
        constricted   29

28. Fruits deeply constricted into 1-seeded, bead-like segments, not splitting
        into valves, 15-80 mm long   ..   ..   **32. Raphanus**
    Fruits with 1 or 2 segments, not bead-like, not more than 12 mm long
                                                                      30. Rapistrum

29. Seeds in 2 rows in each cell of the fruit 30
    Seeds in a single row in each cell of the fruit 31
30. Plant of wet places; flowering stem leafy; fruits 20 mm long or less **9. Rorippa**
    Plant of dry places; leaves mostly basal; fruits 25-50 mm long **25. Diplotaxis**
31. Leaves and lower parts of stems with minute, branched hairs **2. Descurania**
    Leaves and lower parts of stems with unbranched hairs or hairless 32
32. Plant hairless or almost so 33
    Plant hairy 34
33. Fruits widely spreading, horizontal or almost so, less than 20 mm long,
    without a distinct main vein .. .. .. **9. Rorippa**
    Fruits slightly spreading; more than 20 mm long, with a distinct main vein
    8. Barbarea
34. Fruit without a distinct upper portion; though often with a persistent style
    [Fig. XLIIa] .. .. .. **1. Sisymbrium**
    Fruit divided horizontally into 2 distinct, unequally sized parts .. 35
35. Upper part of fruit usually with 1, sometimes 2 seeds [Fig. XLIIb]
    28. Hirschfeldia
    Upper part of fruit sterile, without seeds 36

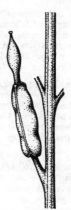

Fig. XLIIa   Fig. XLIIb

36. At least the lower flowers in a head with leaf-like bracts **33. Erucastrum**
    Lower flowers without leaf-like bracts 37
37. Sepals widely spreading, often held at right angles to the petals or bent
    backwards down the flower stalk .. .. .. **27. Sinapis**
    Sepals erect or slightly spreading .. .. .. **26. Brassica**

1. Sisymbrium

Erect annuals, often hairy near the base, with lyrate leaves, small, yellow flowers, and long, narrow, fruits with a bilobed, short, somewhat indistinct style [Fig. XLIIa].

1. Fruits less than 18 mm long, pressed close to the stem **4. S. officinale**
   Fruits more than 20 mm long, diverging from the stem .. 2

2. Pedicels about half the width of the ripe fruit; flowers 5 mm across
    or less   ..   ..   **1. S. irio**
    Pedicels about as wide as the ripe fruits; flower more than 5 mm across   3
3. Uppermost leaves divided into almost linear segments; young fruits more
    or less hairless   ..   ..   ..   **2. S. altissimum**
    Uppermost leaves more or less entire, at most with 2 lateral lobes; young
    fruits hairy ..   ..   **3. S. orientale**

1. * Sisymbrium irio. London rocket. 5-10. Much branched, sparsely hairy, up
to 50 cm high. Basal leaves deeply divided with a smallish terminal lobe and 2-6
lateral paired lobes; stem leaves with a hastate terminal lobe and up to 3 lateral lobes.
Flowers about 5 mm across. Fruits hairless when young, up to 50 mm long, usually
diverging slightly from the stem, the upper overtopping the flowers. *Waste places
near Dublin; formerly frequent, now very rare.*

2. * S. altissimum. 5-9. Branched, sparsely hairy, up to 100 cm high. Basal
leaves deeply and finely divided with 5-10 pairs of narrowly oblong segments; stem
leaves similar but more finely divided into linear segments. Flowers 7-10 mm across.
Fruits hairless when young, up to 90 mm long, usually diverging considerably from
the stem. *Waste places, mainly in the South and East; occasional.* Native of Europe.

3. * S. orientale. 5-9. Often unbranched, hairy, up to 100 cm high. Basal leaves
with a large hastate terminal lobe and 1-4 pairs of lateral lobes; stem leaves similar
but often with no lateral segments, or only 1 pair of lateral, finely divided, linear
segments. Flowers about 8 mm across. Fruits hairy when young, up to 90 mm long,
usually diverging, sometimes considerably, from the stem. *Waste places in the North
(rare outside the Belfast area) and East; occasional.* Native of the Mediterranean.

4. * S. officinale. Hedge mustard. 5-9. Stems tough, up to 80 cm high. Basal
leaves with a broadish terminal lobe and 2-4 similar lateral lobes, all conspicuously
and irregularly toothed; stem leaves similar but smaller and with fewer segments.
Flowers about 4 mm across. Fruits hairless when young, distinctly hairy on maturity,
up to 18 mm long, pressed against the stem, in a long, slender raceme. *Waste places
and roadsides; very frequent except in the North-west.*

2. Descurania
* Descurania sophia (*Sisymbrium sophia*). **Flixweed. 6-8.** A rather delicate
annual, 30-80 cm high, covered with soft, whitish down. Leaves finely divided,
usually pinnate with deeply pinnately-lobed leaflets, the segments short and linear.
Flowers very small, yellow, about 2 mm across, in long racemes; petals barely as
long as sepals. Fruits hairless, somewhat beaded, up to 25 mm long, the pedicel
spreading, the fruit-body slightly curved and fairly erect. *Sandy fields and waste
places near the East coast, (mainly near Dublin and Carrickfergus); rare.*

3. Alliaria
Alliaria petiolata (*Sisymbrium alliaria*). **Garlic mustard. 5-6.** A nearly hairless,
little branched biennial up to 120 cm high. Leaves mostly stalked, large, round or
heart-shaped, with blunt teeth, smelling of garlic when crushed. Flowers white, 5 mm
across. Fruits 30-60 mm long, somewhat spreading and beaded. *Hedges and woods;
frequent in the East and Centre, rare in the West.*

4. Arabidopsis
Arabidopsis thaliana (*Sisymbrium thaliana*). **Thale cress. 3-7.** A slender,
branching annual, 8-25 cm high. Leaves mostly basal, stalkless, oblong, coarsely
toothed. Flowers white, very small, 2-3 mm across. Fruits slender, 10-20 mm long,
spreading. *Dry banks, waste ground, rocks and field margins; occasional.*

5. Erysimum

Plants with short branched hairs (which may appear unbranched on superficial examination), with entire or somewhat toothed leaves and orange or yellow flowers.

1. Flowers 4-5 mm across .. .. .. **1. E. cheiranthoides**
   Flowers about 25 mm across .. .. .. **2. E. cheiri**

1. * Erysimum cheiranthoides. Treacle mustard. 6-9. A stiff erect annual, 20-50 cm high covered with minute whitish hairs. Leaves green, lanceolate, entire or weakly toothed. Flowers small, yellow, 4-5 mm across. Fruits spreading, usually upcurved, 4-angled, slender, about 25 mm long; style short, evident. *Waste places, mainly in the Centre; rare.*

2. * E. cheiri (*Cheiranthus cheiri*). **Wallflower. 5-6.** Hairless or slightly hoary perennial, with bushy, rather woody stems 20-50 cm high. Leaves lanceolate, pointed, entire. Flowers large, yellow or orange, about 25 mm across, fragrant. Fruits somewhat flattened, upright, about 40 mm long; style bilobed, relatively long. *Old walls, rocks and waste ground; occasional.* Native of southern Europe.

6. Hesperis

Hesperis matronalis. Dame's violet. 5-8. A coarse, hairy, erect biennial 60-100 cm high. Leaves large, broadly lanceolate, toothed, shortly stalked. Flowers 15-20 mm across, usually violet, sometimes pale pink, rarely whitish, fragrant at night. Fruits elongated, cylindrical, beaded, 50-100 mm long; style relatively long. *Frequent in hedges near gardens; rarely by riversides far from houses.* Native of Eurasia.

7. Matthiola

Matthiola sinuata. Sea stock. 6-9. An erect biennial, hoary with short white down, 50-100 cm high. Stems tough at the base. Leaves narrow, fleshy, the lower ones pinnately-lobed or with sinuate teeth. Flowers, large, lilac, about 18-20 mm across. Fruits long, cylindrical, somewhat spreading, 100-120 cm long; style indistinct, with 2 small lobes. *Sand-hills and sea-cliffs in Clare and Wexford; very rare, possibly extinct.*

8. Barbarea

Virtually hairless biennials with small, yellow flowers; clasping, pinnate leaves with a large terminal lobe and usually 4-angled fruits with a moderately long, style.

1. Uppermost stem leaves toothed but usually not divided; style slender
   [Fig. XLIIc] .. .. .. **1. B. vulgaris**
   Uppermost stem leaves divided; style stout .. 2
2. Flowers about 5 mm across; fruits usually 30-60 mm long .. **2. B. verna**
   Flowers about 3 mm across; fruits less than 30 mm long **3. B. intermedia**

1. Barbarea vulgaris. Winter cress. 5-7. Erect, 30-60 cm high. Lower leaves pinnate, the terminal segment much longer and broader than the rest; upper ones toothed but usually not divided. Flowers bright yellow, in dense racemes, about 3 mm across. Fruits 4-angled, 15-30 mm long, ascending, with a relatively long, slender style [Fig. XLIIc]. *Roadsides, waste places and field margins; very frequent.*

2. * B. verna. 4-8. Very variable in habit, 30-90 cm high. All leaves pinnate with a large terminal lobe. Flowers in open racemes, about 5-7 mm across. Fruits 4-angled, sometimes rounded, 30-60 mm long, with a stout style [Fig. XLIId]. *Wasteground and roadsides; rare in the South and East.* Native of Europe.

3. * B. intermedia. 3-7. Similar to *B. verna* but with flowers only about 3 mm across and fruits less than 30 mm long. *Frequent in disturbed ground in Down and Antrim; rare elsewhere.* Native of Europe.

9. Rorippa

Hairless perennials of wet places with yellow flowers. Fruits with a shortish style.

1. Petals about the same length as the sepals   2
    Petals at least 1.5 times as long as the sepals   3

2. Plant usually leaning-over to prostrate, stems not bronze coloured;
    petals no more than 1.5 mm long; fruit more than twice as long as
    its pedicel ..   ..   **4. R. islandica**
    Plant usually more or less erect, stems often bronze coloured; petals
    1.5-2.5 mm long; fruit less than twice as long as its pedicel   **3. R. palustris**

3. Fruits ovoid or globular. Stem 60-120 cm high; at least the upper
    leaves entire, sometimes shallowly lobed   ..   **1. R. amphibia**
    Fruit narrow, cylindrical. Stem 30-60 cm high; leaves compound or
    strongly pinnate [Fig. XLIIe]   ..   ..   **2. R. sylvestris**

Fig. XLIIc

Fig. XLIId   Fig. XLIIe   Fig. XLIIf   Fig. XLIIg

1. Rorippa amphibia (*Nasturtium amphibium*). **6-8.** Stem 60-120 cm high. Leaves variable, pinnately-lobed, toothed or almost entire, the upper usually so. Flowers about 4 mm across, petals longer than sepals. Fruits very small, ovoid or nearly globular, about 6 mm long, widely spreading. *River-banks and ditches; locally frequent in parts of the Centre and East, seemingly absent from the extreme West, rare elsewhere.*

2. R. sylvestris (*Nasturtium sylvestre*). **6-8.** Stem creeping at the base; flowering branches erect, 30-60 cm high. Leaves pinnate, with lanceolate, toothed leaflets [Fig. XLIIe]. Flowers about 4-5 mm across; petals longer than sepals. Fruits narrow, cylindrical, about 10-18 mm long, upright [Fig. XLIIe]. *River-banks and lake-shores; rare in the Mid- and South-west, occasional elsewhere.*

R. x *anceps*, the hybrid between *R. sylvestris* and *R. amphibia*, is intermediate in most characters. It differs from *R. sylvestris* in its widely spreading fruiting pedicels and stem leaves which are more shallowly lobed at their apex than their base and from *R. amphibia* in its deeply divided stem leaves [Fig. XLIIf]. *Occasional; in similar habitats to its parents, though often in their absence; apparently absent from the North-east, Middle and South-west, but probably overlooked.*

3. R. palustris (*Nasturtium palustre*). **6-8.** Stem 15-40 cm, more or less erect, often bronze-coloured. Leaves pinnately-lobed with toothed segments [Fig. XLIIg]. Flowers about 3-5 mm across. Fruit oblong-ovoid, not more than twice as long as its pedicel, widely spreading 5-10 mm long [Fig. XLIIg]. *Marshes and wet mud; widespread but rather rare.*

4. R. islandica. 6-8. Similar to *R. palustris* but more prostrate, stems not bronze-coloured, with sepals and petals only 1-1.5 mm long and fruits more than twice as long as their pedicels. *Turloughs; formerly only recorded from a few sites in Clare and Galway, now known to be more widespread in the West with sites scattered from East Mayo to Kilkenny, but still very rare.*

10. Armoracia

* Armoracia rusticana. Horse-radish. 5-7. A hairless perennial up to 150 cm high, with large, stalked, oval-oblong, crenate or serrate leaves, and a large panicle of white flowers 8-10 mm across. Fruits not ripening in this country. *Waste places; rather rare.* Probably native of western Asia.

11. Nasturtium. Water cress. *Biolar*

Hairless perennials of wet places with white flowers. Fruits with a longish, often stout style.

The 'Nasturtiums' of gardens are quite unrelated; their botanical name is *Tropaeolum* and they belong in their own family, the Tropaeolaceae.

1. Fruit with many well formed seeds   2
   Fruit with at most 2-3 well formed seeds in each side, the rest deformed
      or abortive   ..   ..   **3. N. x sterilis**
2. Seeds in two rows in the fruit; each seed coarsely reticulate with fewer
      than 12 depressions across their width [Fig. XLIIh]   **1. N. officinale**
   Seeds more or less in a single row in the fruit; each seed finely
      reticulate with more than 12 depressions across their width
      [Fig. XLIIi]   ..   ..   ..   **2. N. microphyllum**

1. Nasturtium officinale (*Rorippa nasturtium-aquaticum*). **6-8.** Usually green in winter. Stem branched, stout but weak, partly floating or creeping. Leaves pinnate

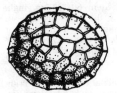

Fig. XLIIh

Fig. XLIIi

Fig. XLIIj

with oval leaflets. Flowers about 6 mm across. Fruits cylindrical oblong, 12-18 mm x 3-4 mm; seeds numerous, in 2 rows in each cell, coarsely reticulate with no more than 12 depressions across their width [Fig. XLIIh]. *Ditches and streams; very frequent in most districts.*

2. N. microphyllum (*Rorippa microphylla*). **6-8.** Very like *N. officinale*, but with a fruit 18-25 x 2 mm, and with the seeds arranged more or less in a single row in the fruit, each finely reticulate with more than 12 depressions across their width [Fig. XLIIi]. *Similar situations; about as frequent.*

3. N. x sterilis (*Rorippa* x *sterilis*). **6-8.** The hybrid between *N. officinale* and *N. microphyllum* is often purplish-brown in Winter and has fruits which are short, but narrow, with, at most, 3 well-formed seeds in each side (other malformed seeds may be present). The normal seeds have 10-14 depressions across their width [Fig. XLIIj]. *Similar situations to the parents and sometimes in the absence of either; occasional.*

12. Cardamine

Erect plants with pinnate leaves and white or mauve flowers. Fruit a narrow pod, with the seeds in a single row.

1. Flowers at least 12-20 mm across 2
   Flowers 3-6 mm across 3
2. Leaflets of upper leaves much narrower then those of lower. Anthers
        yellow. Petals usually mauve .. .. **2. C. pratensis**
   All leaflets more or less similar in shape. Anthers violet. Petals white
        1. C. amara
3. Stem-leaves clearly clasping the stem by 2 acute, basal lobes **5. C. impatiens**
   Stem leaves not clearly clasping the stem, without 2 acute basal lobes 4
4. Stems hairless at base. Stamens 4 .. .. .. **4. C. hirsuta**
   Stems hairy at base. Stamens 6 .. .. **3. C. flexuosa**

1. Cardamine amara. 5-6. A hairless perennial with weak stems, creeping at the base, 30-60 cm high. Leaflets all oval, slightly toothed. Flowers 12-14 mm across, pure or creamy white. Fruits with a fairly long style. Anthers violet. *Meadows, riversides and wet Alder woods; rare, and confined to Ulster.*

2. C. pratensis. Cuckoo-flower, Lady's smock. *Biolar griagáin, Léine Mhuire.* **6-8.** A hairless perennial up to 60 cm high. Leaflets entire or bluntly toothed, those of the basal leaves round or oval, those of the stem leaves narrowly lanceolate. Flowers 15-20 mm across, mauve or almost white; anthers yellow. Fruit with a short or longish style. *Marshes, wet meadows and grassland; very frequent.*

3. C. flexuosa. 4-8. Annual, biennial or perennial, 12-30 cm high. Stem wavy, hairy at base. Leaves mostly basal; leaflets round, entire or toothed. Flowers very small, white, about 3-4 mm across; stamens 6. Fruits often not overtopping the younger flowers; style short. *Woods, streamsides and shady wet places; very frequent.*

4. C. hirsuta. 4-8. Similar to *C. flexuosa*, but annual, shorter, with a straighter, hairless stem, 4 stamens and fruits which overtop the younger flowers. Waste places, walls and disturbed ground, though often in similar situations to *C. flexuosa*.

5. C. impatiens. 4-8. Biennial to 80 cm. Stem erect, slightly wavy near the top. Leaves finely pinnate, with narrowly oval or lanceolate segments; the base strongly clasping with 2 sharply pointed auricles. Flowers sometimes 2 mm or less across. Fruits with a fairly long style. *Known, possibly as a native, only from esker woodland in Westmeath; very rare and apparently introduced elsewhere.*

13. Cardaminopsis

Cardaminopsis petraea (*Arabis petraea*). **6-8.** A small, slightly hairy perennial, with mainly basal more or less pinnately-lobed leaves. Stem-leaves few, nearly entire, shortly stalked. Flowering stems 8-25 cm high; flowers white, about 7 mm across, sometimes more. Fruit slender, 15-30 mm long. *Confined to 2 mountain cliffs in Tipperary and Leitrim (Galtee Mountains and Glenade).*

14. Arabis

Arabis hirsuta. 6-7. A hairy, stiffly erect biennial, 20-35 cm high. Basal leaves undivided, slightly toothed, in a loose rosette. Stem-leaves few, stalkless, usually clasping the stem with short basal lobes. Flowers small, white. Fruits long and slender, very erect and crowded. *Rocks, walls and dry banks; local but frequent in parts of the Centre and West.*

A. brownii (*A. ciliata*) differs in being nearly hairless, except for a few stiff hairs on the leaf-margins; also the stem-leaves are often not clasping. It is probably best regarded as a variety of *A. hirsuta*. *Sandhills on the West coast; rare.*

15. Draba

Densely hairy plants with a strong basal rosette of stalkless, ovate leaves, small, white flowers and short, oblong, flattened fruits.

1.   Stem-leaves more or less lanceolate; fruits erect   ..   .. **1. D. incana**
    Stem-leaves ovate; fruits spreading   ..   ..   **2. D. muralis**

1. Draba incana. 6-8. An erect perennial, 15-30 cm high, covered with whitish hairs. Leaves small, stalkless, oblong, toothed; many of them basal, forming a rosette, but also several on the stem, not clasping it. Flowers small, white, 3-4 mm across; petals very slightly notched at the apex. Fruits erect, often twisted when mature. *Rocks and sand-hills in the North-west; rare.*

2. * D. muralis. 6-8. Annual, up to 40 cm high, hairy but not whitish. Leaves oval, toothed, clasping the stem. Flowers and fruits similar to *D. incana* but the petals are not notched and the fruits are spreading. *Walls, waste places, railway ballast; rare.*

16. Erophila. Whitlow-grass

Small annuals, usually with hairy leaves, arranged in a basal rosette, and undivided stems. Petals bifid. Fruits flattened, erect, oval.

Very variable; often individual populations are highly distinctive even after cultivation.

1. Leaves very hairy, appearing greyish; seeds less than 0.5 mm long
                                                    2. E. majuscula
    Leaves hairless or moderately hairy, appearing greenish; seeds more
        than 0.5 mm long   ..   ..   2.
2. Petals bifid to more than half-way [Fig. XLIIk]; stem with at least some
        hairs   ..   ..   **1. E. verna**
    Petals bifid to a maximum of half-way [Fig. XLIIm]; stems either
        hairless or with a few scattered hairs near the base only   **3. E. glabrescens**

1. Erophila verna. 2-6. Up to 15 cm high. Leaves with obvious petioles; leaves and flowering stems with a light covering of star-shaped hairs, green. Petals usually bifid for $^{1}/_{2}$-$^{3}/_{4}$ of their length [Fig. XLIIk]. Seeds at least 0.5 mm long. *Walls, dry banks, sand-hills and gravelly places; frequent.*

2. E. majuscula (*E. simplex*) **2-6.** Similar to *E. verna*, differing in the short petioles, greyish leaves, densly covered with star-shaped hairs, petals bifid for $^{1}/_{2}$ of their length [Fig. XLIII] at most and seeds less than 0.5 mm long. *Similar habitats; scattered throughout, occasional.*

Fig. XLIIk   Fig. XLIII   Fig. XLIIm

3. E. glabrescens (*E. quadriplex*). **2-6.** Also similar to *E. verna*, differing in the very sparsely hairy leaves and petals bifid for $^{1}/_{2}$ of their length at most [Fig. XLIIm]. *Similar habitats; scattered throughout, rarish; probably less frequent than* E. majuscula.

17. Cochlearia. Scurvy-grass. *Biolar trá*

Annuals or biennials, with undivided, or shallowly lobed, hairless, usually succulent leaves, and basal ones on long stalks. Flowers white or mauve. fruit short and rounded with a short but prominent style.

Intermediates between the species are not uncommon; such plants are likely to be hybrids which, by experiment, have been easily artificially synthesised.

1. Mature fruit distinctly flattened. Basal leaves tapering gradually to the base
                                                    3. C. anglica
    Mature fruit ovoid or globose. Basal leaves kidney-shaped or cut-off
        square at the base   2
2. Petals less than 4 mm long. Plant usually less than 13 cm high   **1. C. danica**
    Petals more than 4 mm long. Plant usually more than 13 cm tall   **2. C. officinalis**

1. Cochlearia danica. 3-7. A small, erect annual. Leaves all stalked, slightly fleshy, the basal rounded to triangular, the uppermost ivy-shaped. Flowers small, in short racemes, about 4-5 mm across; petals usually mauve, sometimes white, no more than 4 mm long. Fruit ovoid, often narrowed at both ends. *Rocks, walls and banks near the sea; occasional. Rarely on walls or railway tracks, inland.*

2. C. officinalis. 5-7. A robust biennial with spreading stems and fleshy leaves; the basal ones large, entire, broadly triangular or kidney-shaped, on long stalks, the upper ones toothed, stalkless, and clasping the stem. Flowers about 8 mm across, in crowded racemes; petals 4-5 mm long, white. Fruit nearly globular. *Rocky and muddy sea-shores; frequent.*

The above description applies to subsp. *officinalis*. In addition two further subspecies may be recognised:

Subsp. *alpina* (*C. alpina, C. officinalis* subsp. *pyrenaica, C. pyrenaica* subsp. *alpina*) differs in the basal leaves which are not fleshy, and capsule which is usually narrowed at both ends and occurs on rocks and by streams in the higher mountains.

Subsp. *scotica* (*C. scotica*) with flowers 5-6 mm across; petals less than 4 mm long; upper leaves almost stalkless, not clasping the stem and with the fruit variable in shape, often ovoid, often narrowed at both ends, sometimes globose, occurs on rocks, cliffs, salt-marshes and occasionally sandy areas near the coast.

3. C. anglica. 4-6. Annual, rarely biennial, with more or less erect stems up to 30 cm high. Basal leaves elliptic-lanceolate, tapering gradually to a long stalk. Flowers about 8 mm across; petals 5-6 mm long, white. Fruit, flattened, ovoid to elliptical. *Muddy shores and estuaries; rather rare.*

Hybrids with the previous species are intermediate in morphology and fairly frequently recorded. However the frequency with which they really do occur is difficult to determine because the parent species are themselves so variable. It appears essential, unfortunately, to count the chromosomes to be certain of hybridity.

18. Capsella
Capsella bursa-pastoris. Shepherd's purse. 6-7. A rather slender, branched, hairy annual, 10-40 cm high. Basal leaves in a loose rosette, pinnately-lobed or almost entire; upper leaves entire or slightly toothed, clasping the stem. Flowers very small, less than 2 mm across, white. Fruits flat, triangular to heart-shaped, 6-8 mm long. *Waste places and field margins; abundant.*

19. Teesdalia
Teesdalia nudicaulis. 5-7. A delicate, hairless annual with numerous unbranched flowering stems 5-15 cm high, arising from a rosette of small pinnately-lobed leaves. Flowers very small, 2.5 mm across, white, in racemes slightly less than half the height of the plant. Fruits flattened, nearly as broad as long, with an apical notch, spreading on longish pedicels. *Sandy lake-shores of Lough Neagh and in sand-dunes near Dundrum, County Down and Coleraine, County Derry; very rare.*

20. Thlaspi
* Thlaspi arvense. Penny-cress. 5-9. An erect, hairless, annual, 25-60 cm high. Leaves oblong, slightly toothed or lobed, the upper ones stalkless and clasping the stem with acute, rather divergent auricles. Flowers white, 6 mm across, or less. Fruits round and flat, 12-18 mm across, including the broad wing, deeply notched at the top. *Disturbed and waste ground and roadsides; rare.*

21. Lepidium
Erect herbs with undivided leaves. Flowers numerous, small, white. Fruit short, dehiscent, 2-seeded.

1. Upper leaves clasping the stem   2
    Upper leaves not clasping the stem   ..   ..   **3. L. latifolium**
2. Stem branched from the base. Anthers violet   ..   **1. L. heterophyllum**
    Stem unbranched in lower part. Anthers yellow   ..   **2. L. campestre**

1. Lepidium heterophyllum (*L. smithii*). **6-8.** Perennial, usually covered with white down; stems 15-40 cm high, branched from the base. Leaves lanceolate, entire or slightly toothed, stalkless and clasping the stem. Flowers 3 mm across, in very crowded racemes. Anthers violet. Fruit oblong, longer than broad, its upper part consisting of a flattened wing; style projecting from the shallow apical notch. *Walls, dry heathland, acid sandy ground; locally frequent in the South and East, rare elsewhere.*

2. * L. campestre. Pepperwort. 6-8. Similar to *L. heterophyllum* but annual or biennial, usually with an unbranched stem; flowers smaller, in longer, looser racemes; anthers yellow and fruits rough and scaly. *Field margins and roadsides, mainly in the Eastern half; very rare.*

3. * L. latifolium. 7-8. Stems 50-100 cm high, arising from a creeping rhizome. Leaves large, lanceolate, stalked, slightly toothed. Flowers very numerous and crowded, about 3 mm across. Fruit nearly globular, not winged; style stout, short. *Waste places near the sea, mainly in the South and East; rare.*

22. Cardaria
* Cardaria draba (*Lepidium draba*). **5-9.** An erect, perennial, 20-60 cm high. Leaves broadly elliptic; stem-leaves stalkless and clasping the stem with 2 large auricles. Flowers white, small, about 2 mm across. Fruits heart-shaped and flat, 4 mm across, unwinged, without an apical notch; style long and prominent. *Established around Belfast and Dublin; occasional in coastal towns elsewhere.*

23. Coronopus. Swine's cress
Prostrate annuals, with pinnately divided leaves, minute white flowers, with 6 stamens, and an indehiscent, 2-seeded fruit.

1. Plant usually hairless; fruit rounded or pointed at the top; its surface
    very rough ..   ..   **1. C. squamatus**
    Plant usually hairy; fruit with a deep apical notch, its surface slightly
    rough   ..   ..   **2. C. didymus**

1. * Coronopus squamatus (*C. procumbens*). **6-9.** Hairless, with numerous branched stems. Leaves fairly finely divided, with narrow segments. Flowers 2-3 mm across, in stalkless axillary clusters which lengthen into racemes in fruit; petals 1-1.5 mm; all stamens with anthers. Fruit 4 mm across, with an apical notch, deeply ridged and wrinkled. *Roadsides and waste places; occasional near the coast, very rare inland.*

2. * C. didymus. 7-9. Similar to *C. squamatus* in habit, but usually hairy and with finer leaf segments. Flowers about 1 mm across, in regular, fairly compact racemes; petals minute or absent; only 2 stamens with anthers. Fruit 2-3 mm across, rounded or pointed at the top, its surface slightly rough. *Similar situations; frequent in the South half, especially near the coast; rare elsewhere.* Native of South America.

24. Subularia
Subularia aquatica. 7-8. A dwarf annual, 3-8 cm high, usually submerged. Leaves all basal, solid, slender, cylindrical, gradually tapering to a fine point, 12-25

mm long. Flowers white, minute, in a short, open raceme. Fruit ovoid, 3-4 mm long. *Lake margins, mainly in the West, but also in the North-east; very rare and possibly decreasing.*

25. Diplotaxis
* **Diplotaxis muralis. Wall mustard. 5-8.** A small annual, with several stems 15-40 cm high. Leaves mostly basal, somewhat pinnately-lobed but not deeply divided, with an unpleasant smell. Flowers yellow, 8-10 mm across, rather few, in loose racemes. Fruits spreading, hairless, slender, cylindrical, with a very short, evident style. *Waste ground, and dry banks, mainly along railways in the South half; rare.*

26. Brassica
Erect, coarse, largish annuals. Lower leaves pinnately-lobed-lyrate. Flowers yellow. Fruit cylindrical, beaked [Fig. XLIIn]; seeds in a single row in each cell.
Cabbage is *Brassica oleracea* subsp. *oleracea.*

1. Fruits more or less erect, fairly closely applied to the stem; upper
    stem-leaves not clasping . . . . **3. B. nigra**
    Fruits spreading; upper stem-leaves clasping the stem . . 2
2. Rosette-leaves distinctly pale bluish-green; flowers about 17 mm across;
    petals more than 13 mm long . . . . . . **1. B. napus**
    Rosette-leaves green; flowers 9-13 mm across; petals less than 13 mm
    long . . . . **2. B. rapa**

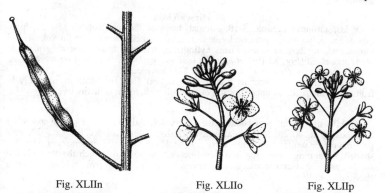

Fig. XLIIn   Fig. XLIIo   Fig. XLIIp

1. * **Brassica napus. Swede, Oil-seed rape. 3-6.** 30-100 cm high. Lower leaves lyrate, hairless or with a few stiff hairs; upper leaves clasping the stem with broad, rounded auricles. Flowers about 17 mm across, usually shorter than the buds [Fig. XLIIo]. Fruits spreading, with a long, thin beak. *Waste places, roadsides and field margins; occasional.*

2. * **B. rapa. Wild turnip. 7-9.** Similar to *B. napus,* but the rosette leaves are usually green, the flowers smaller, usually overtopping the buds [Fig. XLIIp] and 9-13 mm across. *Similar situations; frequent in the South half, especially near the coast; rare elsewhere.*

3. * **B. nigra. 6-8.** Similar to *B. napus* but taller and with the upper leaves stalked and not clasping the stem. Flowers about 9-13 mm across. Fruits erect, pressed close to the stem, 10-18 mm long, with a short, slender beak. *Banks and waste places, usually near the sea in the South half; rare.*

27. Sinapis

Annuals, differing from *Brassica* only in the larger number of veins on the fruit and, in Irish species, in the widely spreading sepals.

1. Uppermost stem-leaves undivided or with 2 lobes; fruits with a conical
    beak   ..   ..   **1. S. arvensis**
    Uppermost stem-leaves pinnately-lobed or deeply toothed; fruits with a
    flattened beak   ..   ..   **2. S. alba**

1. † **Sinapis arvensis** (*Brassica arvensis*). **Charlock.** *Praiseach bhuidhe.* **5-8.** 30-70 cm high, with sparse, stiff hairs. Upper leaves stalkless, usually pinnately-lobed or deeply toothed. Flowers 12-18 mm across, bright yellow. Fruits spreading, hairless or with stiff hairs pointing downwards, 25-50 mm long, including the conical beak which makes up about $^1/_3$-$^1/_2$ of the total length, slightly beaded. *Waste places, roadsides and field margins; frequent.*

2. * **S. alba** (*Brassica alba*). **6-8.** Similar to *S. arvensis,* but slightly taller, the upper leaves usually stalked and more deeply divided, and the fruits covered with stiff, spreading, white hairs and ending in a flattened beak at least as long as the rest of the fruit. *Similar situations; rather rare.* Native of the Mediterranean and South-west Asia.

28. Hirschfeldia

* **Hirschfeldia incana. 5-10.** Annual, hairy at the base, up to 150 cm high. Lower leaves pinnate; upper undivided, usually toothed. Flowers bright yellow, 7-9 mm across, in long racemes. Fruits cylindrical, with the beak containing a single seed, appressed [Fig. XLIIb]. *Roadsides and waste places; now very frequent in the Dublin area, rare elsewhere.* Native of the Mediterranean.

Often identified in error as *Brassica nigra*, and distinguishable from it only in fruit, when the seedless upper portion of the fruit of *B. nigra* is distinctive.

29. Cakile

Cakile maritima. Sea-rocket. 6-8. A bushy, hairless annual with spreading branches up to 40 cm long. Leaves few, fleshy, oblong, pinnately-lobed. Flowers pale mauve or white, 12-15 mm across. Fruit 15-25 mm long, indehiscent, spindle-shaped, separating when ripe into two 1-seeded portions, of which the lower is the smaller and sometimes sterile. *Sandy shores; frequent in the North and East, rarer in the South and West.*

30. Rapistrum

* **Rapistrum rugosum. 6-8.** A bushy annual; the upper parts hairless; lower parts with a scattering of coarse, spreading hairs. Leaves mainly basal in a rosette; rosette-leaves lyrate; stem-leaves more or less stalkless and weakly toothed or lobed. Flowers about 7 mm across, in crowded, corymbose heads which elongate in fruit. Fruit beaked; the upper segment single seeded, strongly ribbed, with a prominent style; lower much smaller, sterile. *Roadsides and waste places; frequent in the Dublin area; rare in Meath, very rare elsewhere.* Native of the Mediterranean.

31. Crambe

Crambe maritima. Sea-kale. 6-8. A stout, hairless perennial with large, pale bluish-green leaves (appearing somewhat waxy), irregular pinnately-lobed and waved at the margin. Flowers white, 10-15 mm across, in a large corymbose panicle. Fruit, globose, 1-seeded. *Seashores; very rare; sometimes cultivated as a vegetable.*

32. Raphanus. Radish

* **Raphanus raphanistrum. 6-9.** A coarse, somewhat hairy annual or biennial with large, lyrate leaves. Flowers 18-25 mm across; petals white or yellow, often with violet veins. Fruit indehiscent, deeply constricted between the seeds and eventually breaking at the constrictions, with a long, pointed beak at the apex.

Two subspecies of this variable plant occur in Ireland:

* Subsp. *raphanistrum* is an occasional weed of sandy or peaty fields; it is annual, usually with whitish flowers and fruits no more than 5 mm wide.

Subsp. *maritimus* (*R. maritimus*) is an occasional plant of sandy shores, but very abundant in places; it is biennial with yellow (sometimes white) flowers and fruits more than 5 mm wide.

The cultivated radish is *R. sativus.*

33. Erucastrum

* **Erucastrum gallicum. 6-8.** An erect, usually unbranched, hairy annual up to 50 cm high. Leaves pinnate or pinnately lobed, the upper more divided. Flowers pale yellow, about 7 mm across, the lower in the axils of leaf-like bracts. Fruits shortly cylindrical, spreading with an evident style [Fig. XLIIq]. *Roadsides and waste places in the South; spreading.* Native of Europe.

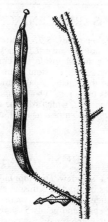

Fig. XLIIq

XLIII.   RESEDACEAE

Reseda

Usually biennial herbs, with alternate leaves with wavy edges and flowers in long spikes or racemes. Sepals 4-6; petals 4-6, some of them deeply divided; stamens numerous. Ovary superior, of fused carpels, 1-celled. Fruit a capsule opening at the top long before the seeds are ripe.

R. odorata, the garden Mignonette belongs to this genus.

1. Upper leaves deeply lobed   2
    Upper leaves entire or minutely toothed   . .   . . **1. R. luteola**

2. Petals yellowish; carpels 3 . .   . .   **2. R. lutea**
    Petals white; carpels 4   . .   . .   **3. R. alba**

1. † Reseda luteola. *Buidhe mór*. **6-8.** Stem usually unbranched, erect and stiff, 50-100 cm high. Leaves narrowly lanceolate, entire. Pedicels about the same length as the yellowish-green flower. Sepals usually 4; petals 4 or 5, the upper ones larger and deeply divided; stamens usually 20-25. Capsule nearly globular. *Roadsides, sandy waste ground and dry gravelly places; frequent throughout.*

2. R. lutea. Mignonette. 6-8. Stem usually branched, almost bushy, 30-50 cm high. Leaves ternately or pinnately divided, with linear segments. Pedicels longer than the yellowish-green flower. Sepals and petals 6, sometimes 5; the upper petals variously divided. Stamens usually 15-20. Capsule oblong. *Sandy and gravelly ground usually near the coast mainly in the Eastern half; rare.*

3. * R. alba. 6-8. Similar to *R. lutea* but with more regularly pinnately-divided leaves, white flowers, 5-6 petals and sepals and 4 carpels. *Now known only from sand-dunes at Portmarnock, County Dublin, where it has been long established.* Native of the Mediterranean and South-west Asia.

XLIV. SARRACENIACEAE

* Sarracenia purpurea. Pitcher-plant. 5-7. A rather fleshy, hairless perennial. Leaves all basal, in the form of hollow, inverted cones with lid-like flaps at their mouth; often purplish-red. In the liquid inside the cone insects are trapped and digested. Flowers solitary, 5-7 cm across, on stout stems 25-45 cm high. Sepals and petals 5, free; petals smaller than the sepals; sepals dark purplish-red on the inside, and petals on both sides. Stamens numerous. Ovary superior; style single, expanded at the tip into a large yellow-green disc, which fills the centre of the flower. Fruit a capsule. *Planted in a few bogs in the Centre and West, and well naturalised.* Native of Canada and the U.S.A.

XLV. DROSERACEAE

Drosera. Sundew. *Drúchtín móna*
Small perennial herbs. Leaves covered in crimson, sticky, gland-tipped hairs, by which insects are trapped and digested. Flowers small, regular, white, in racemes, usually open only in sunshine. Sepals and petals 5; sepals united at the base; petals free, white, oval, slightly longer than the sepals. Stamens 5. Ovary superior, 1-celled; styles 3, forked almost to the base. Fruit a capsule.

1. Leaf-stalk hairy; blade circular   . .   . .   **1. D. rotundifolia**
    Leaf-stalk hairless, at least in lower part; blade distinctly longer than broad   2
2. Leaves 3-5 cm long, almost as long as the peduncle. Flowering stem
        produced laterally from the rosette   . .   . .   **3. D. intermedia**
    Leaves 5-10 cm long, considerably shorter than the peduncle. Flowering
        stem produced terminally from the rosette   . .   . .   **2. D. anglica**

1. Drosera rotundifolia. 6-8. Plants solitary. Leaves spreading horizontally; leaf-stalk hairy, 15-30 mm; blade circular, 7-10 mm across. Flowering stem arising from the axil of one of the uppermost leaves, and thus appearing terminal, 7-10 cm high, with 8-15 flowers 6-7 mm across. Seeds c. 2 mm long, with very loose-fitting coat. *Bogs; frequent and locally abundant.*

Fig. XLVa   Fig. XLVb

2. D. anglica (*D. longifolia*). **6-8.** Like *D. rotundifolia*, but with leaves inclined or erect; leaf-stalk hairless; blade oblong, 4-5 times as long as broad; flowering stem up to 15 cm high, with 5-8 flowers, arising from the centre of the rosette [Fig. XLVa]; seeds 1 mm long, with slightly loose-fitting coats. *Bogs; locally frequent in the North-west, West and parts of the Centre, rare elsewhere.*

3. D. intermedia. 7-8. Plants forming dense mats of interconnected rosettes. Leaves inclined, or nearly erect; leaf-stalk hairless at least in the lower part, longer than the blade, which is narrowly oval-oblong, 2-3 times as long as broad. Peduncle arising from the axil of one of the lower leaves of the rosette [Fig. XLVb], curved at the base, about the same length as the leaves; raceme of 5-8 flowers. Seeds less than 1 mm long, with tight-fitting coats. *Bog-pools and very wet peat. Locally frequent in the West half, unknown in the East.*

Hybrids (*D.* x *ovata*) between *D. rotundifolia* and *D. anglica* are occasionally found. They resemble *D. intermedia* in leaf-shape, but differ in being sterile, with a very small capsule, and in having a straight, apparently terminal peduncle.

XLVI.   CRASSULACEAE

Perennial or biennial herbs with thick, fleshy leaves, usually alternate. Flowers regular, variable in structure, but always with a superior pistil of 4-8 free carpels. Fruit a collection of small follicles.

1. Petals united to form a bell-shaped corolla . . . . **1. Umbilicus**
    Petals free 2
2. Sepals and petals 5 or more . . . . . . **2. Sedum**
    Sepals and petals 4 3
3. Terrestrial; rhizome stout; flowers in a dense panicle . . **3. Rhodiola**
    Aquatic; stem slender; flowers solitary, axillary . . **4. Crassula**

1. Umbilicus

Umbilicus rupestris (*Cotyledon umbillicus-veneris*). **Pennywort.** *Carnán caisil.* **6-8.** Biennial, 15-40 cm high. Leaves 3-6 cm across, circular, mostly peltate, slightly crenate, long-stalked. Flowers numerous, pendulous, in an erect raceme; pedicels short. Sepals 5, small; attached to the corolla; filaments very short. Carpels 5, closely pressed together, but free. *Walls and non-calcareous rocks; frequent and locally abundant in the South, South-east, North-east and West, rather rare elsewhere.*

2. Sedum. Stonecrop

Usually hairless perennials. Sepals 5 (rarely up to 8), united at the base; petals as many, free; stamens twice as many; carpels as many as the petals.

1. Flowers yellow   2
    Flowers purple, red, pink or white   4
2. Leaves 4-7 mm long, obtuse   ..   ..   **4. S. acre**
    Leaves 10-20 mm long, pointed   3
3. Living leaves of non-flowering shoots crowded into a dense tassel at
     the tip; below these are persistent dead leaves; leaves on flowering
     stems erect ..   ..   **3. S. forsterianum**
    Living leaves well spaced out on non-flowering shoots; dead leaves not
     persistent; leaves on flowering stems spreading or bent-back   **2. S. reflexum**
4. Leaves flat   ..   ..   **1. S. telephium**
    Leaves almost as thick as wide   5
5. Leaves mostly opposite; glandular hairs present on pedicels   **7. S. dasyphyllum**
    Leaves all alternate; plant without glandular hairs   6
6. Leaves 2-4 mm long, with a short, obtuse spur at the base   **5. S. anglicum**
    Leaves 5-8 mm long, not spurred   ..   ..   **6. S. album**

1. † **Sedum telephium** (*S. fabaria*). **7-8.** Stems undivided, stiff, erect, 20-40 cm high. Leaves fleshy but flat, alternate, oval or bolong, tapered at the base, coarsely toothed, 5-7 cm long. Flowers 8-10 mm across, in dense corymbs. Petals pinkish-purple. *Damp woods, ditches, walls and waste places. Possibly native in woods in the North-Centre, occasional elsewhere as a garden escape or outcast.*
 A variable species. All Irish plants seem to belong to subsp. *fabaria*.
 * *S. spurium*, with prostrate, woody stems, opposite, more or less circular leaves and erect, white, red or pink petals, is occasionally seen on roadsides as an escape from cultivation.

2. * **S. reflexum. 6-8.** Leafy shoots prostrate, rooting, rather woody, bearing erect flowering stems 30-35 cm high. Leaves alternate, cylindrical, acute, slightly spurred at the base, not crowded; those on the flowering stems spreading or reflexed. Dead leaves not persistent. Flowers 15 mm across, in compact, rounded cymes. Petals 5-8 (usually 6), bright yellow. *Walls, usually near houses; rather rare.*
 The name *S. rupestre* has been used by some authors for *S. reflexum*, by others for *S. forsterianum*. It is best avoided.

3. * **S. forsterianum. 6-7.** Like *S. reflexum*, but with the living leaves of the prostrate shoots crowded into a dense, terminal tassel, below which are some persistent dead leaves; leaves on the flowering stem erect; all leaves slightly flattened on upper side. *Granitic rocks and walls; rare.*

4. S. acre. 6-8. Leafy stems prostrate and rooting; flowering stems erect, 5-10 cm high. Leaves 5 mm long, ovoid, bluntly pointed, scarcely spurred at the base, with a peppery taste. Flowers 15 mm across, in small cymes. Petals 5, bright yellow. Ripe follicles spreading horizontally. *Walls, rocks and sand-dunes, mainly on limestone; frequent.*

5. S. anglicum. 6-8. Similar to *S. acre* in general habit, but smaller and more delicate. Leaves 3-4 mm long, ovoid, often tinged with red, with a short but distinct spur at the base. Flowers 12 mm across, in small cymes with 2-3 principal branches. Petals white above, pink beneath; sepals and carpels pink. Ripe follicles erect. *Granitic rocks and dry, shallow, peaty soil. Very frequent near the coast, rather rare inland.*

6. * S. album. 6-8. Like *S. anglicum* but larger and coarser. Leaves 5-8 mm long, not spurred at the base. Flowering stems up to 10 cm high. Cymes with several principal branches. Petals and carpels white; leaves reddish. *Walls, less often on rocks. Frequent in the South half, occasional in the North.*

7. † S. dasyphyllum. 6-8. Intermediate in general appearance between *S. anglicum* and *S. album*. Leaves 3-6 mm, mostly opposite, pale bluish-green, often purplish-pink, not spurred. Petals 5-6, pale pink. Glandular hairs usually present on pedicels and sometimes on leaves. *Limestones rocks and walls; perhaps native near Cork, a rare escape elsewhere.*

3. Rhodiola
Rhodiola rosea (*Sedum rosea*). **Roseroot. 5-8.** Dioecious perennial with a stout, woody rhizome, scented when bruised, from which arise erect stems 10-25 cm high, bearing leaves and compact, terminal cymes. Leaves pale bluish-green, fleshy but flat, oblong, bluntly toothed, stalkless, c. 25 mm long. Flowers 5 mm across; sepals, petals and carpels 4; stamens 8. Petals free, greenish-yellow, often tinged with purple. Follicles erect. *Mountain rocks and sea-cliffs, mainly in the North and West; occasional.*

4. Crassula
* Crassula helmsii. 6-8. Perennial, with slender stems, submerged or creeping on wet mud. Leaves 5-15 mm long, distant, opposite, linear. Flowers axillary, solitary, shortly stalked, minute. Sepals, petals, stamens and carpels 4. Petals free, pale pink. *Ponds, usually naturalised from aquaria; very rare but likely to increase.* Native of Australia and New Zealand.

XLVII. SAXIFRAGACEAE

Small herbs, mostly perennial, with alternate or basal (very rarely opposite) leaves. Flowers hermaphrodite, regular. Sepals 4 or 5, free. Petals 5, free (rarely absent). Stamens twice as many as the sepals. Ovary 2-celled, superior, or semi-inferior with the lower part sunk in the hypanthium and united to it. Styles 2. Fruit a capsule.

1. Sepals 4; petals absent   ..   ..   ..   **2. Chrysosplenium**
    Sepals and petals 5   2
2. Petals entire, not green   ..   ..   **1. Saxifraga**
    Petals mostly green, fringed with long, narrow lobes   ..   **3. Tellima**

1. Saxifraga. Saxifrage
Sepals and petals 5. Petals entire. Ovary superior to semi-inferior.

1. Leaves opposite, not more than 5 mm long   ..   **11. S. oppositifolia**
    Leaves alternate or basal, some of them more than 5 mm long   ..   2
2. Petals yellow   3
    Petals white, sometimes tinged or spotted with pink   4
3. Leaves stalkless, fleshy; ovary semi-inferior; sepals spreading   **7. S. aizoides**
    Leaves soft, not fleshy, the lower ones stalked; ovary superior; sepals
       turned downwards   ..   ..   ..   **5. S. hirculus**
4. Ovary superior; sepals turned downwards   5
    Ovary semi-inferior; sepals erect or spreading   7
5. Leaf-stalks long, slender, not flattened ..   ..   **4. S. hirsuta**
    Leaf-stalks short, broad, flat, sometimes not distinct from blade ..   6

6. Petals spotted with pink and yellow; leaves with a narrow, colourless,
    cartilaginous margin .. .. .. **3. S. spathularis**
    Petals with yellow, but no pink spots; leaves without a colourless
    margin .. .. **2. S. stellaris**
7. Flowers 3-8 mm across 8
    Flowers 12-20 mm across 9
8. Annual; inflorescence diffuse, leafy .. .. **6. S. tridactylites**
    Perennial; flowers in a compact terminal cyme; leaves confined to a
    basal rosette .. .. **1. S. nivalis**
9. Leaves with cordate base, boldly crenate or somewhat lobed, but with
    the lobes at least as broad as long .. .. **10. S. granulata**
    Leaves with truncate base, or tapered to the stalk, many of them lobed,
    with lobes longer than broad 10
10. Leaf-lobes obtuse to mucronate, but without an awn-like tip
    [Fig. XLVIIa]; flower-buds erect .. .. .. **8. S. rosacea**
    Leaf-lobes with a fine, awn-like bristle at the tip [Fig. XLVIIb];
    flower-buds nodding .. .. .. **9. S. hypnoides**

   1. Saxifraga nivalis. 7-8. A small perennial with a short rhizome. Leaves in basal
rosettes, diamond-shaped to broadly oval, crenate or bluntly toothed, dark green
above, often crimson-purple beneath, with a short, flat stalk. Flowering stem 5-15
cm, glandular-hairy, leafless. Flowers 4-6 mm across, in a compact cyme. Sepals
erect; petals white, tipped with pink; ovary semi-inferior. *Known only from a small
ledge of shaley rock on the North face of the Ben Bulben range, Co. Sligo.*

   2. S. stellaris. 6-8. Leaves in basal rosettes arising from a short rhizome, broadly
oval to oblong, with 3-5 rather blunt teeth on each side, narrowed at the base to a
short, sometimes scarcely distinct stalk, sparsely hairy. Flowering stems 8-20 cm,
leafless except for small bracts, bearing a cyme of 3-9 starry flowers. Sepals turned
downwards; petals narrow, white, with two yellow spots; anthers pink; ovary white,
superior. *Wet rocks and streamsides in the mountains; occasional.*

   3. S. spathularis (*S. umbrosa* of earlier writers). **St. Patrick's Cabbage.**
Cabáiste Phádhraic, Cabáiste an mhadra rua. **5-7.** Rhizome slender, with rosettes of
basal leaves; blade oval or nearly circular, coarsely toothed, hairless, rather thick and
leathery, with a very narrow but distinct translucent margin; leaf-stalk broad, flat,
sparsely hairy on the margins, usually longer than the blade [Fig. XLVIIc].
Flowering stems up to 50 cm, leafless, bearing a branched, terminal cyme with
numerous flowers. Sepals red, turned downwards. Petals white, with two yellow
spots near the base and several pink spots near the middle. Anthers pink; ovary pink,
superior. *Woods, shady rocks and mountains; locally abundant in the West and
South-west, rare and local in the higher mountains elsewhere.*
   S. x *urbium* (*S. spathularis* x *umbrosa*), the London pride of gardens, was for
long confused with *S. spathularis.* It differs in its leaf-stalk, which, though also flat
and broad, has more numerous hairs on its margins, and is almost as long as the
blade, which is crenate or very bluntly toothed, with a more conspicuous translucent
margin [Fig. XLVIId]. It seldom sets seed. It is found in a few places as a garden
escape.

   4. S. hirsuta (*S. geum* of earlier writers). **5-7.** Like *S. spathularis* in general habit,
but the leaves have a hairy, circular or kidney-shaped blade and a narrow, hairy stalk
[Fig. XLVIIe]. The petals and ovary are white or very pale pink. *Woods and other
shady places in Kerry and West Cork; occasional.*

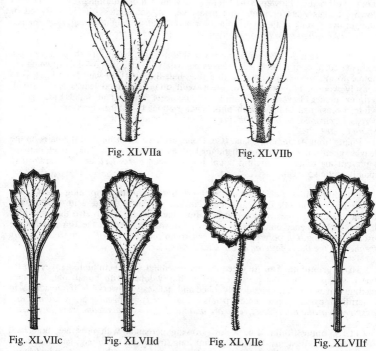

Fig. XLVIIa   Fig. XLVIIb

Fig. XLVIIc   Fig. XLVIId   Fig. XLVIIe   Fig. XLVIIf

Hybrids (*S. x polita*) between *S. hirsuta* and *S. spathularis* are frequent throughout the range of the former, and are found in a few places in Galway and Mayo where *S. hirsuta* is not now to be found. They have leaves of intermediate structure [Fig. XLVIIf].

5. S. hirculus. 8-9. Perennial, with soft, reddish-brown hairs on the stems and leaf-stalks, with trailing, leafy runners and an erect flowering stem 15-35 cm high. Leaves oblong, the lowest with long stalks. Flowers few, 25 mm across; sepals turned downwards; petals bright yellow; ovary superior. *Wet bogs in Mayo and Antrim; very rare.*

6. S. tridactylites. 4-7. A small, usually branched annual up to 15 cm high with glandular hairs. Leaves entire or with 3-5 oblong lobes, stalked or stalkless. Stems and leaves often tinged with red. Flowers numerous, in terminal or axillary cymes. Sepals erect; petals 3 mm, white; ovary deeply sunk in the hypanthium, almost inferior. *Walls, rocks, sandhills and gravel-pits, mainly on limestone; very frequent in the South and West parts of the Centre, rather rare elsewhere.*

7. S. aizoides. 7-8. Perennial, with short, horizontal leafy shoots, forming a loose cushion, and erect flowering stems up to 20 cm. Leaves up to 20 x 4 mm, but often less, linear-oblong, fleshy, mostly hairless, but sometimes with a few marginal, tooth-like bristles. Flowers 10-12 mm across, in a loose, terminal cyme; pedicels downy. Sepals erect or spreading; petals yellow, sometimes spotted with red or orange; ovary sunk in the hypanthium for about half its height. *Damp, rocky places in the North (Sligo to Antrim), mostly in the mountains; rather rare.*

8. S. rosacea. 5-7. Perennial, very variable in habit, with leafy shoots forming a compact cushion or a loose mat. Leaves palmately divided into 3-7 lobes, which are obtuse to mucronate, but never with a fine, hair-like tip; they vary from hairless to densely woolly. Flowering stems erect, with often undivided leaves and a small, terminal cyme. Flowers 12-20 mm across; pedicels erect in bud; sepals erect; petals white, occasionally tinged with pink. Ovary about two-thirds inferior. *Rocks and screes; occasional in the mountains of Kerry, very local elsewhere in the West and South Centre.*

Plants from Arranmore Island (Co. Donegal) have all or most of the hairs on the leaves gland-tipped, and are distinguished as subsp. *hartii.* They may perhaps represent the relics of a hybrid population between *S. rosacea* and *S. cespitosa* (a mainly arctic species).

9. S. hypnoides. 5-7. Perennial, with prostrate leafy shoots forming a loose mat. Some leaves undivided, linear-oblong; others palmately lobed, with 3-7 usually forward-pointing lobes, which end in a fine, hair-like tip, as do also the undivided leaves. Inflorescence and flowers as in *S. rosccea*, except that the flower-buds are usually nodding. *On bare rock, or in grassland on shallow soil over rock. Locally frequent in the Burren region of Co. Clare, rare elsewhere.*

10. S. granulata. 5-6. An erect, downy perennial, 20-50 cm high. Leaves mostly basal, stalked, kidney-shaped, crenate or shortly lobed with broad, obtuse lobes; cauline leaves smaller, more deeply lobed and stalkless. Flowers 15-20 mm across, in a terminal cyme. Sepals erect; petals white; ovary semi-inferior. *Sandhills and pastures near the East coast; very rare and local, often as an escape from gardens.*

11. S. oppositifolia. 4-6. A low-growing perennial with prostrate, branched, somewhat woody stems. Leaves 2-4 mm long, triangular to oblong, hard and rigid, opposite, crowded and overlapping, dark green, usually with some marginal hairs. Flowers more or less stalkless, solitary, 8-15 mm across. Sepals erect; petals purple or pink; ovary semi-inferior. *Mountain rocks in the North and West (Derry to Galway); rare.*

2. Chrysosplenium

Chrysosplenium oppositifolium. Golden saxifrage. *Glóiris.* **3-5.** A small, loosely tufted perennial with spreading, leafy stems. Leaves circular, shortly stalked, opposite, somewhat hairy, crenate, 15 mm across. Flowers yellowish, 4 mm across, in small, flattened cymes surrounded by a rosette of yellowish bracts. Sepals 4, triangular, spreading; petals absent; stamens 8; ovary almost inferior, surmounted by a yellow disc; styles 2, very short. *Wet woods, damp rocks and streamsides; rare in the Centre, frequent elsewhere.*

3. Tellima

* Tellima grandiflora. 4-6. An erect, glandular-hairy perennial 40-60 cm high. Leaves mostly basal, kidney-shaped, stalked, shortly lobed and bluntly toothed, 7-10 cm across. Flowers in a long, terminal raceme; pedicels drooping. Calyx bell-shaped; petals 5, fringed with long, narrow lobes, green, sometimes tinged with red. Stamens 10. Ovary about $1/3$ inferior, 1-celled; styles 2. Fruit a 2-beaked capsule. *Woods and shady walls and banks; rather rare.* Native of western U.S.A.

XLVIII. PARNASSIACEAE

Parnassia palustris. Grass of Parnassus. 7-9. An erect, hairless perennial, 15-40 cm high, with long-stalked, entire, heart-shaped basal leaves. Stem with a single stalkless leaf. Flowers 20-25 mm across, solitary, regular. Sepals slightly united at the base. Petals free, white, with translucent veins, slightly notched at the tip. Stamens 5, alternating with 5 staminodes; these have a broad, white base, divided above into about 12 slender branches, each ending in a greenish-yellow gland. Ovary superior, 1-celled; stigma 4-lobed, stalkless. Fruit a capsule. *Fens, damp grassland, lake-shores and mountain cliffs. Very frequent in the West and West-Centre; local and rather rare elsewhere.*

XLIX. ESCALLONIACEAE

* Escallonia rubra (*E. macrantha*). **6-9.** An evergreen shrub up to 3 m high. Young shoots sticky with glandular down. Leaves alternate, stalkless, oval, finely toothed, shining, rather leathery, hairless, 3-6 cm long. Flowers in terminal racemes or panicles. Sepals 5, united at the base with the hypanthium. Petals 5, deep reddish-pink, free but with their lower parts forming an apparent tube. Stamens 5. Ovary 2-celled, semi-inferior; style single. Fruit a capsule (rarely formed in Ireland). *Cultivated for ornament and as a wind-break near the sea; very locally naturalised in the South and West.* Native of temperate South America.

L. GROSSULARIACEAE

Ribes

Deciduous shrubs. Leaves alternate, palmately lobed. Flowers in axillary racemes or clusters. Sepals 5; petals 5, free; stamens 5; ovary 1-celled, inferior; styles 2, united in lower part. Fruit a berry.

1. Stems armed with sharp spines; flowers in small, axillary clusters
   3. R. uva-crispa
   Stems without spines; flowers in drooping racemes   2
2. Lower side of leaves covered with stalkless glands with characteristic
   odour; fruit black   ..   ..   ..   **2. R. nigrum**
   Lower side of leaves not glandular; fruit red or whitish   **1. R. rubrum**

1. * Ribes rubrum. Red or White currant. 4-5. Up to 150 cm high; very sparsely hairy. Leaves 4-5 cm across, with usually 5 toothed lobes. Racemes axillary, drooping, with up to 15 flowers. Petals much smaller than the sepals, green. Fruit bright red or yellowish-white. *Hedges and waste ground near houses, rather rare.*

2. * R. nigrum. Black currant. 4-5. Like *R. rubrum*, but sometimes taller; leaves rather larger, and covered on the lower surface with stalkless, aromatic glands; petals 3 mm oval; fruit black. *Damp woods and riversides; rather rare.*

3. * R. uva-crispa. Gooseberry. 3-5. Up to 150 cm high, freely branched. Stems armed at the nodes with groups of slender, very sharp spines. Leaves 2-4 cm long and wide, with usually 5 deeply toothed lobes. Flowers in axillary clusters of 2-3. Petals white, much shorter than the sepals. Fruit 1-2 cm across, green, yellow or dark red, usually hairy. *Hedges; rather rare.*

LI.　ROSACEAE

Herbs, trees or shrubs with alternate, often compound leaves, with leafy stipules. Flowers regular. Calyx of 4-5, rarely 8 sepals; sometimes apparently doubled by the presence of an epicalyx. Petals free, as many as sepals; rarely absent. Stamens usually numerous, attached to the top of the ovary or the rim of the calyx-tube; rarely absent. Pistil usually of one or many, unfused carpels.

To this family belong a large number of cultivated fruits and ornamental plants. *Prunus* includes Plums, Peaches, Almonds and Cherries, as well as many flowering trees and shrubs. The majority of the other genera mentioned are represented in orchards (*Rubus, Fragaria, Malus*) or gardens (*Kerria, Cotoneaster, Spiraea, Geum, Potentilla, Rosa, Cotoneaster*), as are also *Pyrus* (Pear) and *Cydonia* (Quince).

1.	Petals absent	2
	Petals present	5
2.	Flowers in reddish heads; leaves pinnate	3
	Flowers in yellowish or greenish clusters; leaves undivided, palmately lobed or palmate	4
3.	Fruit without spines; stems more or less erect ..	**6. Sanguisorba**
	Fruit with long spines; some stems trailing ..	**7. Acaena**
4.	Medium to large perennial with undivided, palmately lobed or palmate leaves; flowers with 4 stamens, borne in terminal cymes	**12. Alchemilla**
	Small annual with deeply palmately lobed leaves and axillary clusters of flowers, each with 1-2 stamens ..	**13. Aphanes**
5.	Petals about 8	**8. Dryas**
	Petals 4 or 5	6
6.	Leaves undivided	7
	Leaves divided or deeply lobed	12
7.	Leaves evergreen, stiff	**17. Cotoneaster**
	Leaves deciduous, soft	8
8.	Stipules absent; receptacle flat	**1. Spiraea**
	Stipules present (though often small); receptacle concave ..	9
9.	Style single; ovary sunk in calyx-tube but free from it ..	**19. Prunus**
	Styles 2-5; ovary fused with calyx-tube ..	10
10.	Inflorescence unbranched; pedicels all arising from the same point	11
	Inflorescence branched; pedicels scattered along the inflorescence	**16. Sorbus**
11.	Styles fused at base; anthers yellow; fruit apple-shaped ..	**15. Malus**
	Styles free at base; anthers purplish; fruit pear-shaped ..	**14. Pyrus**
12.	Calyx in 1 whorl, with as many teeth as there are petals ..	13
	Apparantly 2 calyx whorls present, giving twice as many teeth as petals (actually a calyx and epicalyx are present)	19
13.	Perennial herbs	14
	Shrubs or trees	15
14.	Flowers yellow	**5. Agrimonia**
	Flowers white or tinged with red	**2. Filipendula**
15.	Leaves lobed but not pinnate	16
	Leaves pinnate.	17
16.	Branches spineless	**16. Sorbus**
	Branches spiny	**18. Crataegus**

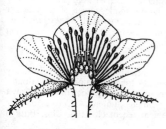

Fig. LIa

Fig. LIb

17. Branches spineless	..	..	..	**16. Sorbus**
Branches spiny	..	..	..	18

18. Ovaries borne on a mound and so directly visible (cut flower in half
lengthwise) (Fig. LIa); leaflets 3 or 5..   ..   ..   **3. Rubus**
Ovaries borne inside a basin or cup and so hidden from view (cut flower
in half lengthwise) (Fig. LIb); leaflets 5, 7 or 9   ..   ..   **4. Rosa**

19. Styles long, hooked in fruit   ..   ..   ..   **9. Geum**
Styles short, not hooked in fruit   20

20. Fruit dry   ..   ..   **10. Potentilla**
Fruit fleshy   21

21. Apical tooth of leaflet usually about the same length as its neighbours;
petals without a large gap between them   ..   **11. Fragaria**
Apical tooth of leaflet small, distinctly shorter than its neighbours;
petals with a large gap between them (through which the sepals
can be seen)   ..   ..   ..   **10. Potentilla**

1. Spiraea

* **Spiraea salicifolia. 6-8.** A suckering shrub with erect stems up to 2 m high.
Leaves oblong, toothed, undivided, hairless. Flowers small, bright pink, in crowded
panicles. Sepals and petals 5; carpels 5, on a flat receptacle, developing into small
follicles. *Planted in hedges, and spreading and perhaps naturalised in some districts.*

The frequency and distribution of this species is uncertain as it has been confused
with * *S. pseudosalicifolia* (which differs in its hairy leaves and sepals bent-
backwards in fruit) and with * *S. douglasii* (which also has hairy leaves but these are
toothed only in the top half).

2. Filipendula

Erect perennials. Leaves pinnate, with numerous toothed leaflets. Stipules leafy,
toothed. Flowers white. Calyx 5-toothed; petals 5; stamens 7-20. Carpels many, with
short styles, quite free from the calyx-tube, developing into achenes.

1. Petals usually 5; leaves with 5 or fewer pairs of leaflets   **1. F. ulmaria**
Petals usually 6; leaves with numerous small leaflets   **2. F. vulgaris**

1. Filipendula ulmaria (*Spiraea ulmaria*). **Meadow-sweet.** *Airgead luachra.* **6-
8.** Usually 30-70 cm high. Stem with both long and short non-glandular hairs, as well
as short glandular hairs. Flowers creamy-white. Leaves white on the lower surface;
with 3-5 pairs of leaflets; the terminal one 3-lobed. Achenes twisted together.
Roadsides and bushy places; frequent.

2. F. vulgaris (*Spiraea filipendula*). **6-8.** Smaller than *F. ulmaria*, with very numerous, finely pinnate leaflets, not white on the underside, fewer, slightly larger flowers tinged with red, with 6 petals and fruits erect, not twisted. *Rocky pastures; frequent in one district in North Clare and South Galway (around Gort), unknown elsewhere.*

3. Rubus

Perennials, usually with scrambling, woody, prickly, stems. Leaves usually compound, with 3 or 5 toothed leaflets, occasionally lobed but undivided; stipules small and narrow, fused with the petiole. Flowers in short cymes or corymbs. Calyx simple, 5-toothed; tube very shallow. Petals 5. Stamens numerous. Carpels usually numerous, with short styles, arranged on a conical receptacle (Fig. LIa). Fruit a collection of rather small red or black drupes.

1.	Leaves undivided but lobed	..	..	**1. R. chamaemorus**
	Leaves divided	.. ..	..	..	2
2.	Flowering stems clearly herbaceous, 50 cm long or less; fruit of 2 or 3 drupes	..	..	..	**2. R. saxatilis**
	Flowering stems long and woody; fruit of many drupes		..	3
3.	Stems erect; fruit bright-red or orange-yellow	..	..	4
	Stems arching or trailing; fruit black or dark red	..	..	5
4.	Petals white; flowers in small cymes	..	..	**3. R. idaeus**
	Petals purple; flowers solitary	..	..	**4. R. spectabilis**
5.	Fruits with a white bloom, partly enclosed by the persistent sepals; lateral leaflets stalkless	..	..	**5. R. caesius**
	Fruits without a white bloom and not partly enclosed within the persistent sepals; lateral leaflets stalked	..	**6. R. fruticosus agg.**

1. Rubus chamaemorus. Cloudberry. Stems short, hairy, not prickly, herbaceous. Leaves simple, palmately lobed. Flowers white. Fruits amber. *A stunted, apparently non-flowering colony is known from one place in the Sperrin Mountains (County Tyrone); very rare.*

2. R. saxatilis. Stone bramble. 6-7. Stems slender, prickly, unbranched, herbaceous, downy, 15-50 cm long. Stipules nearly free from petiole; leaves ternate. Flowers 8 mm across, dirty white, 2 or 3 together. Petals small and narrow, usually upright. Fruit of 2-5 bright red drupes. *Lake-shores and stony places and dunes; locally frequent.*

3. R. idaeus. Wild raspberry. *Sú craobh.* **6-7.** Stems erect, 80-150 cm high, covered with bristles and weak prickles, flowering their second year. Leaves pinnate, with 3 or 5 leaflets, covered with white down beneath. Flowers 8-10 mm across, drooping, in small cymes; petals small, erect, white. Fruit a hollow hemisphere of small, bright red or yellowish drupes, separating easily fromn the large conical receptacle. *Woods, thickets and riversides; frequent in the North, occasional in the South.* Frequently cultivated and persistent after abandonment.

4. * R. spectabilis. 6-7. Differs from *R. idaeus* in its leaves which always have 3 leaflets, are green beneath, and solitary flowers, 25 mm across with purple petals. *Naturalised from gardens and shrubberies in a few places.* Native of North America.

5. R. caesius. Stems more or less creeping, whitish; prickles slender. Leaflets 3, usually deeply toothed, sometimes lobed. Flowers white. Fruit of a few (about 10) very whitish drupes, which are partly enclosed by the large, persistently erect sepals. *Sandy and stony places; frequent in parts of the South and West; rare elsewhere.*

6. R. fruticosus agg. Bramble. *Dris.* **6-8.** The remaining forms of *Rubus*, aggregately known as Brambles or Blackberry-bushes are extremely difficult to classify satisfactorily. Over 80 'species' have been recorded for Ireland, but most of them can be named only by specialists. These difficulties arise from a mainly asexual method of seed production, complicated, however by occasional hybridisation.

All the brambles have woody stems, armed with prickles and flowering in their second year, trailing or arching and sometimes rooting at the tip; leaves with 3 or 5 toothed leaflets, panicles of white or pinkish-mauve flowers and a black (rarely dark red) fruit of numerous small drupes which adhere to the small, conical receptacle. *R. fruticosus* agg. can be divided up into three sections:

1. Leaflets overlapping; inflorescence usually an unbranched corymb
                                    a. R. fruticosus agg. Section Corylifolia
    Leaflets not usually overlapping; inflorescence branched   ..   2
2. Stems erect, often suckering   ..   **b. R. fruticosus agg. Section Rubus**
    Stems arching to spreading; not suckering
                                    c. R. fruticosus agg. Section Glandulosus

One species, in Section Glandulosus, is frequent and easily recognised:

R. ulmifolius (*R. rusticans*). Stems arching, dull purplish-red with a slight whitish bloom; prickles stout. Leaflets 3-5, white beneath with felted hairs. Inflorescence without stalked glands. Flowers often deep pink. Fruit with numerous, tightly-packed drupes. *Abundant in hedges on base-rich soils, rarer on acid soils.*

4. Rosa. Rose. *Rós*

Shrubs with erect or scrambling, prickly stems and pinnate leaves, usually 1-2 m tall; leaflets 5-9, toothed. Stipules fused with petiole. Flowers large; calyx 5-toothed (the teeth are referred to as sepals in the key for the sake of simplicity), with a deep tube constricted at the mouth so as to form an *orifice*; petals 5; stamens numerous; carpels numerous, sunk in the calyx-tube, which becomes fleshy in fruit. In fruit the orifice is surrounded by an evident *disc* differentiated from the rest of the fruit by its lack of red coloration (Fig. LIc).

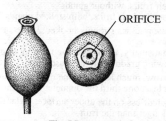
ORIFICE

Fig. LIc

Roses may be difficult to name; hybridisation is common and gives rise to many intermediate, often widespread forms. The calyx-tube is a complex structure, at least in part hypanthial.

1. All sepals undivided   2
    Outer sepals lobed or toothed   3
2. Flowers in groups of 2-5; styles united into a persistent column which
        protrudes through the orifice   ..   ..   **1. R. arvensis**
    Flowers usually solitary or in pairs; styles not united into a column
        and hidden within the fruit, only the stigmas protruding   ..   4

3. Leaves hairless; leaflets more or less smooth   ..   **2. R. pimpinellifolia**
   Leaves densly hairy beneath; leaflets rough, with an irregular upper
     surface   ..   .. **3. R. rugosa**

4. Styles united into a column which protrudes through the orifice ..   5
   Styles not united into a column protruding through the orifice   ..   6

5. Stems slender, weak and trailing; stylar column *ca.* 2.5 mm long
     (excluding stigmas); disc more or less flat   **1. R. arvensis**
   Stems stout, suberect; stylar column not more than 1 mm (excluding
     stigmas); disc conical   ..   .. **4. R. stylosa**

6. Styles not or scarcely obscuring the disc; leaflets not scented   ..   7
   Disc largely obscured by the styles; leaves usually scented   ..   8

7. Stems and leaves not reddish; sepals on young fruits bent backwards
     down the fruit; disc scarcely obscured by the styles and stigmas **5. R. canina**
   Stems and leaves reddish tinged; sepals on young fruits somewhat
     erect; disc largely obscured by the styles and stigmas
                                                         6. R. canina x R. caesia

8. Sepals strongly bent-back along the ripening fruit   9
   Sepals not strongly bent-back along the ripening fruit, or fallen ..   12

9. Pedicels glandular   10
   Pedicels without glands   11

10. Leaflets usually hairless on upper surface; stylar disc rounded;
      pedicels not longer than fruit   ..   ..   **14. R. micrantha**
    Leaflets usually rather hairy on upper surface; stylar disc pentagonal;
      pedicels clearly longer than fruit   ..   ..   **10. R. x scabriuscula**

11. Leaves odourless; prickles strongly hooked, paired; leaflets broad near
      the base   ..   ..   **7. R. obtusifolia**
    Leaves somewhat smelly; prickles curved but not strongly hooked,
      not paired; leaflets narrowing gradually to the base   **12. R. agrestis**

12. Pedicels and their fruits, without glands   13
    Pedicels, and usually their fruits, with stalked glands   ..   14

13. Leaves odourless; prickles strongly hooked; leaflets broad near the
      base   ..   ..   **7. R. obtusifolia**
    Leaves somewhat smelly; prickles curved but not strongly hooked;
      leaflets narrowing gradually to the base   ..   **12. R. agrestis**

14. Orifice very narrow, much less than one third the diameter of the disc   15
    Orifice wide, at least one third the diameter of the disc   ..   16

15. Leaflets usually hairless on the upper surface; stylar disc rounded;
      pedicels not longer than the fruit   ..   ..   **13. R. micrantha**
    Leaflets usually rather hairy on the upper surface; stylar disc
      pentagonal; pedicels clearly longer than the fruit ..   **9. R. x scabriuscula**

16. Orifice very wide, at least half the diameter of the disc; prickles
      quite straight; sepals persistent until the fruit decays and often
      completely untoothed   ..   .. **10. R. mollis**
    Orifice usually about one third the diameter of the disc; at least
      some prickles hooked; sepals not persistent until the fruit decays
      and often toothed   17

16. Glands on the lower side of leaves very small (about 0.1 mm across)
      and sometimes appearing almost stalkless; leaves with a resinous,
      turpentine-like scent when crushed   ..   ..   **8. R. sherardii**

Glands on the lower side of leaves small (about 0.2 mm across)
  clearly stalked; leaves with a sweet, apple-like scent, which may
  become less noticable after crushing . .   . .   **11. R. rubiginosa**

1. Rosa arvensis. 7. Stems very long, slender and trailing, with sparse, rather slender, mostly hooked prickles. Leaflets mostly about 18 x 12 mm, usually hairless. Flowers in terminal groups of 2-5, white. Styles united into a column which projects from the narrow orifice and persists at the top of the scarlet, hairless, globular fruit. Disc flat. *Hedges and thickets; occasional in the West half, frequent in the South-east; occasional to rather rare elsewhere.*

2. R. pimpinellifolia (*R. spinossisima*). **Scotch rose, Burnet rose. 5-6.** An erect, very busy shrub, 25-80 cm high, with numerous slender, straight prickles not expanded at the base, passing into bristly hairs. Leaves small, hairless. Flowers solitary, rather small, pink or white; styles free, not projecting; fruit black (rarely red), globular, hairless, crowned by persistent sepals (spreading, then erect as hips become ripe). Disc flat to concave. *Sand-hills, rocky heaths and limestone pavement; frequent near the sea, rather rare elsewhere.*

3. * R. rugosa. 6-7. An erect hairy shrub, 0.5-1.5 m high. Stems stout with straight prickles of various sizes, not expanded at the base and underlying fine hairs. Leaves usually large, with a rough, irregular upper surface, hairy. Flowers solitary, large, usually bright purplish-pink; fruit large, flattened-globose, with a few gland tipped hairs on the surface, often nodding when ripe with the persistent sepals erect. Disc concave. *Occasional but widespread, perhaps more frequent in the Mid-west; hedgerows. Often planted in gardens and parks.*

4. R. stylosa. 6-7. Stems sub-erect, 2-3 m; prickles hooked, with stout bases. Leaflets about 4 x 2 cm, slightly downy. Flowers white, rarely pale pink. Stylar column only just protruding from the orifice. Fruit ovoid, hairless, on long stalks (up to 4 cm) without persistent sepals and a strongly convex (conical) disc. *Hedges in the South half; rare.*

Hybrids with the next species (*R.* x *andegavensis*), occasional in the Centre, are very similar to *R. stylosa* but the prickles are less stout, the pedicels much shorter and the disc less conical.

5. R. canina. Dog rose. 6-7. Stems sub-erect, but arched and straggling. Prickles strong, hooked, broad-based. Leaflets acute, hairless but not shining, often evenly toothed. Flowers large, pale pink or white, scented, solitary or in small groups. Styles free, not projecting. Sepals on young fruits bent backwards down the fruit; disc scarcely obscured by the styles; orifice very small (about one fifth the diameter of the disc). Fruit scarlet, ovoid, hairless, without persistent sepals; pedicels 1.5-2.5 cm. *Hedges, thickets and waste-places; very frequent.*

Otherwise similar material but with leaflets hairy, though not glandular underneath, formerly labelled *R. dumetorum* is now placed in the 'Pubescentes' group of *R. canina.*

6. R. canina x R. caesia (**R.** x **dumalis**). **6-7.** Differs from *R. canina* most evidently in its red stems and leaves; semi-erect sepals on young fruits and rather larger bracts. *Similar situations but on higher ground and frequent in Clare.*

R. caesia (incl. *R. afzeliana*) with red stems and leaves, fruits with semi-erect sepals and large bracts concealing short pedicels and an orifice about one third the diameter of the disc, is very rare.

7. R. obtusifolia. 6-7. Also similar to *R. canina* but the leaflets hairy, and with both large and small teeth, the teeth with dark-tipped glands; the prickles paired; the sepals strongly pressed backwards against the fruit and the pedicels no more than 1.5 cm long. *Hedgerows; reliably and recently recorded only from Laois and Kildare.*

8. R. sherardii. 6-7. Stems rather zig-zag. Leaves with minute, almost stalkless glands; resinous with a turpentine-like scent when crushed. Sepals somewhat persistent, usually until the fruit is soft, spreading but erect. Pedicels about the same length as the fruit or shorter. Stylar disc circular; orifice less than 2.5 mm wide and less than 3.5 times the width of the disc. *Hedgerows throughout; occasional, most frequent at moderate elevation.*

Hybrids with *R. canina* are similar to *R.* x *scabriuscula*; those with *R. caesia* have reddish stems.

9. R. x scabriuscula (*R. canina* x *R. tomentosa*). **6-7.** Somewhat similar to *R. sherardii* but sweeter smelling; the sepals are bent backwards down the fruit and soon fall; the stylar disc is pentagonal; the orifice *ca.* 1.4 mm and no more than one quarter the diameter of the disc and the peduncle is about 15 mm long and is longer than fruit (11.5 mm long). *Hedges, especially in the Centre and lowlands; occasional.*

Many early records for *R. tomentosa*, whose occurrence in Ireland is doubtful, belong here. Specimens with rather longer pedicels (over 17 mm long) may be *R. canina* x *R. sherardii* (*R.* x *rothschildii*) or a more complex triple hybrid.

10. R. mollis (*R. villosa*). **6-7.** Erect, low-growing, about 1.5 m tall. Stems straight, sometimes tinged reddish in bright sunlight; prickles straight. Leaves hairy, greyish beneath, glandular and resinous. Sepals erect and persistent on the almost globular fruit until it decays. Orifice large, about 2.5 mm across, *ca.* half the diameter of the disc. *Open scrubby areas and low-growing or sparse hedges; mainly in the North; rather rare.*

11. R. rubiginosa. Sweet-briar. 7-8. Stems with large, hooked prickles and often with smaller straight ones. Leaves weakly hairy or hairless above, covered with very small, fruity-scented glands beneath (crushing the leaf may hide the smell). Flowers 3-4 cm across, pink; pedicels glandular-hairy. Fruit usually sparsely glandular, on short glandular pedicels of about 10 mm. Orifice less than 2.5 mm, about one third the diameter of the disc. *Hedges and thickets often on calcareous soil; rare but widespread.*

12. R. agrestis. 6-7. Differs from *R. rubiginosa* in its hairless fruits and pedicels; leaflets which are gradually narrowed to their base, prickles all more or less the same size and white flowers. *Damp scrub and hedges, especially lake-shore scrub in the Centre; rare.*

13. R. micrantha. 6-7. Somewhat similar to *R. rubiginosa* but with the prickles all more or less the same size and without any needle-shaped hairs; rather smaller flowers usually about 3 cm across and fruits with the sepals bent-backwards. *Hedges in Cork, Kerry, Kildare, Kilkenny and Wexford; rare.*

5. Agrimonia. Agrimony

Erect perennials. Leaves hairy, pinnate, with numerous toothed leaflets of varying sizes. Stipules leafy, toothed. Flowers bright yellow, in very long spikes. Calyx 5-toothed, with a deep tube. Petals 5; stamens 7-20; carpels 1-2. Fruit of 1-2 achenes, enclosed in persistent calyx-tube, which bears hooked bristles at the mouth.

1. Stem with long and short non-glandular and short, glandular hairs;
   fruiting calyx deeply furrowed for at least $3/4$ of its length and all
   the bristles pointing upwards (Fig. LId) .. **1. A. eupatoria**
   Stem lacking short, non-glandular hairs, only with short glandular
   hairs and long non-glandular hairs; fruiting calyx shallowly
   furrowed for at most $3/4$ of its length and some bristles
   curved downwards (Fig. LIe) .. .. **2. A. procera**

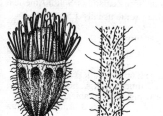
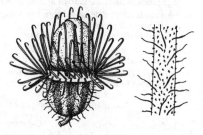

Fig. LId   Fig. LIe

1. Agrimonia eupatoria. 6-8. Usually 30-70 cm high. stem with both long and short non-glandular hairs, as well as short glandular hairs. Leaves greyish-tomentose on the lower surface. Flowers 5-7 mm across. Fruiting calyx usually parallel-sided, deeply furrowed for almost all of its length; bristles all pointing upwards (Fig. LId). *Roadsides and bushy places; frequent.*

2. A. procera (*A. odorata*). **6-8.** Very like *A. eupatoria,* but usually larger and coarser; stem only with short glandular hairs and long non-glandular hairs. Fruiting calyx bell-shaped, with shorter and less pronounced furrows; some of the bristles usually curved downwards (Fig. LIe). *Similar situations, mainly on acid soils; occasional.*

6. Sanguisorba

Hairless, erect perennials. Leaves pinnate, with toothed leaflets; stipules leafy, toothed. Flowers small, massed in terminal heads. Calyx with a nearly globular tube, constricted at the mouth, and 4 spreading lobes. Petals absent. Stamens inserted on rim of calyx-tube. Carpels 1-2, sunk in calyx-tube but not fused with it. Fruit a ridged or winged achene.

1. Flower-heads oblong, dark red throughout; stamens 4; stigma not feathery
   1. S. officinalis
   Flower-heads globular, pale reddish at the top, greenish lower down;
   stamens numerous; stigmas feathery at tip .. .. **2. S. minor**

1. Sanguisorba officinalis (*Poterium officinale*). **Burnet. 6-8.** Stems robust, 60-100 cm high. Leaflets 30-40 mm long. Flower heads oblong, dark red; all flowers hermaphrodite. Stamens 4; stigma not feathery. *Lake-shores in Mayo (Conn & Cullin) and dry banks in Down (Donaghadee) and Antrim (Carnlough).*

2. S. minor (*Poterium sanguisorba*). **Salad burnet. 5-6.** Stems slender, 15-35 cm high. Leaflets 10 mm long. Flower-heads globular, pale reddish at the top, greenish lower down; flowers mostly unisexual (male and female in the same head) but a few hermaphrodite. Stamens numerous; stigmas reddish-purple, feathery. *Dry grassland and gravelly banks; locally frequent on limestone in the South; very rare in the North.*

Plants with the area between the ridges of the fruit evidently very rough belong to
* subsp. *muricata*.

7. Acaena

Creeping, somewhat hairy perennials with a woody base. Leaves pinnate,
toothed, silvery-hairy on the veins underneath. Flowers borne in spherical heads, on
usually long stalks. Sepals 4; petals absent; stamens 2. Fruit an achene armed with 2-
4 long spines, which are barbed at the tip. Natives of New Zealand or South America.

1. Apical leaflets at least 1.3 times as long as broad; some usually 1.5 - 2.5
    times as long as broad   2
    Apical leaflets no more than 1.3 times as long as broad   .. **4. A. pusilla**
2. Apical leaflets with (12-) 17-23 teeth   ..   **1. A. ovalifolia**
    Apical leaflets with 8-12 (-13) teeth   3
3. Leaves bright, glossy green; stems sometimes red; apical leaflets usually
        at least twice as long as broad, rarely only 1.5 times   **2. A. novae-zeylanica**
    Leaflets light, dull green; whole plant often brownish tinged; apical
        leaflets less than twice as long as broad   ..   **3. A. anserinifolia**

1. * Acaena ovalifolia. 6-8. Moderate sized; apical leaflets 15-40 mm, at least
1.3 times as long as broad. Each achene with 2 spines, both about 1 cm long.
Grassland, roadsides, wood-margins and riversides; occasional.

2. * A. novae-zeylanica. 6-7. Mat-forming with ascending annual stems. Apical
leaflets 1.5-2 times as long as broad. Each achene with 2-4 spines, 1 or 2 of which
are often rather shorter or absent. *Scattered throughout; rare.*

3. * A. anserinifolia. (*A. sanguisorbae*). **6-7.** Similar to *A. novae-zeylanica*
differing in its coppery-red tinted foliage and apical leaflets no more than twice as
long as broad. *Open grassy areas, roadsides; rare.*
    The frequency and distribution of this species is uncertain; some early records
refer to *A. ovalifolia*.

4. * A. pusilla. 6-7. Similar to *A. anserinifolia* differing in its smaller size,
relatively broader apical leaflets and stipules at most thrice (as opposed to usually 5-
6 times) divided. *Western Galway and Mayo; rare.*
    Investigation of the status of this species in its native range (New Zealand)
suggests that it forms part of an unresolved complex of species associated with *A.
anserinifolia*.

8. Dryas

Dryas octopetala. *Leathín.* **5-8.** A prostrate undershrub with tortuous, creeping,
woody stems. Leaves 15-20 mm long, dark green above, white beneath, shaped like
those of an Oak. Flowers solitary, white, 25-35 mm across, on erect flower stalks.
sepals and petals usually 8; stamens numerous; carpels numerous, superior, not sunk
in calyx-tube. Fruit a collection of achenes crowned with long, white, feathery styles.
*Rocky places; abundant in Clare; occasional on limestone thence northwards to
Fermanagh; very rare (on basalt) in mountains in the North; unknown elsewhere.*

9. Geum

Erect perennial herbs, with irregularly pinnate leaves. flowers solitary or in
cymes. Calyx 5-toothed, with an epicalyx of 5 bracts superimposed on it, looking like
5 smaller sepals alternating with the real ones. Petals 5; stamens numerous; carpels
numerous, not sunk in calyx-tube, developing into achenes with long, stiff, hooked
styles.

1. Flowers drooping, cup-shaped; petals dull red, long-drawn-out at base
   1. G. rivale
   Flowers more or less erect, open; petals yellow, without a long-drawn-out base .. .. .. **2. G. urbanum**

1. Geum rivale. Water avens. *Machall uisce.* **6-8.** Leaves with the terminal leaflet very large, sometimes almost circular; stipules small and narrow; flowers drooping, cup-shaped; petals dull red, with a long-drawn-out base. *Damp places by streams, woods and mountain cliffs; locally frequent in the North; rather rare elsewhere.*

2. G. urbanum. Wood avens. *Machall coille.* **6-7.** Less hairy than *G. rivale*; leaves similar, but with the terminal leaflet smaller and oval; stipules broad and leafy, lobed or toothed; flowers more or less erect, open; petals yellow, without a long-drawn-out base. *Hedges and shady places; frequent.*

The hybrid between these two species (*G.* x *intermedium*) is fairly frequent, widespread, rarely occurs in the absence of both parents and is very variable; the full spectrum of intermediates between the parents may be found.

10. Potentilla

Perennial herbs or undershrubs with compound leaves. Sepals and petals 5, rarely 4; epicalyx present as in *Geum*; calyx-tube short. Stamens usually numerous. Carpels numerous, superior; forming a collection of seed-like achenes, on a receptacle which is not swollen and fleshy as in *Fragaria*.

1. Flowers dark purple .. .. .. **2. P. palustris**
   Flowers yellow or white 2
2. Flowers white .. .. **7. P. sterilis**
   Flowers yellow 3
3. Small shrub; leaflets undivided .. .. **1. P. fruticosa**
   Herb; leaflets toothed 4
4. Leaves pinnate .. .. .. **3. P. anserina**
   Leaves palmate or ternate 5
5. Petals 5 in all flowers; leaves mostly with 5 leaflets .. **6. P. reptans**
   Petals 4 in at least some flowers; upper leaves with 3 leaflets .. 6
6. Petals 4; carpels usually less than 12; stipules deeply divided .. **4. P. erecta**
   Petals 4 or 5; carpels usually at least 20; stipules entire or shortly 3-lobed .. .. **5. P. anglica**

1. Potentilla fruticosa. 5-8. A small shrub 30-80 cm high, with peeling bark. Leaves pinnate, usually with 5 entire, lanceolate leaflets. Flowers yellow, 20-30 mm across. *Rocky places subject to flooding; locally frequent from North Clare to Southeast Mayo, unknown elsewhere.*

In Ireland this species is always dioecious, but the sterile stamens in female and sterile carpels in male plants are fairly conspicuous. Now frequently planted for hedging, in various colour forms.

2. P. palustris (*Conarum palustre*). **Marsh cinquefoil. 6-7.** Stems rooting at base, erect in upper part, about 30 cm high. Leaves pinnate, with usually 5 oblong, toothed leaflets 30-50 mm long, whitish beneath. Flowers 20-30 mm across; petals dull brownish-purple, much smaller than the sepals. whole plant often tinged with reddish purple. *Marshes, bogs and drains; frequent in most districts.*

3. P. anserina. Silverweed. *Briosclán.* **5-7.** Stems red, long, slender, creeping and rooting. Leaves silvery with silky hairs, especially on the lower side, pinnate, with numerous toothed, oval leaflets, alternately large and small. Flowers solitary, on long flower-stalks, 20-25 mm across, bright yellow, with 5 petals. *Roadsides, waste-places, grassland; abundant.*

4. P. erecta. Tormentil. *Néalfhartach.* **6-9.** Stems suberect, or trailing, not rooting. Upper leaves stalkless. Leaves mostly ternate but sometimes palmate with 5 leaflets; leaflets oval, deeply toothed near the apex; stipules deeply lobed, rather like the leaflets. Flowers bright yellow, numerous, 6-10 mm across, in a loose, leafy cyme. Petals and sepals 4; stamens 15-20; carpels usually 4-12. *Heaths, pastures and banks; abundant, especially in mountain districts.*

More robust material with the stem-leaves toothed for most of their length, teeth more than 1.5 mm long and flowers 10-13 mm across has been distinguished as subsp. *strictissima* and appears widespread, even at low altitude; however investigation of the stability of this combination of features in Ireland is needed.

5. P. anglica (*P. procumbens*). **6-9.** Similar to *P. erecta* but stems trailing, rooting at the tips; upper leaves usually only shortly stalked; lower with long stalks; the stipules undivided or shortly 3-lobed, and flowers slightly larger (12-18 mm across) with sepals and petals sometimes 5 and carpels at least 20. *Banks and roadsides; fairly frequent.*

P. x suberecta, the partially fertile, and fairly frequent hybrid between *P. erecta* and *P. anglica*, resembles *P. erecta* in habit but is intermediate in all other morphological characters (the leaf-stalks are fairly obvious, and usually a plant has mixture of leaves with 3,4 or 5 leaflets and flowers with 4 or 5 petals).

6. P. reptans. Creeping cinquefoil. *Cuig-mhéarach.* **6-9.** Stems long and slender, creeping and rooting at the nodes. Leaves long-stalked, nearly all palmate with 5 toothed leaflets; stipules undivided or slightly lobed. Flowers bright yellow, 20-25 mm across, axillary. Petals and sepals 5; carpels very numerous. *Roadsides and waste-places; frequent in most of the South and Centre; rarer in the North.*

Hybrids with *P. erecta* and *P. anglica* (*P. x mixta*) occur; they are distinguishable only on the basis of their low fertility.

7. P. sterilis. Barren strawberry. **3-6.** A small herb with creeping, but not rooting stems; leaves ternate; leaflets oval, toothed with soft hairs. Flowers white, 10-12 mm across; petals 5. *Hedges, walls and woods; frequent.*

Closely resembles *Fragaria vesca*, but, apart from the dry fruit, differs in the absence of true runners, in flowering 1-2 months earlier, in the widely separated petals and in the very small apical tooth, much shorter than its neighbours, of the leaf.

11. Fragaria

Fragaria vesca. Wild strawberry. *Sú talún.* **5-7.** A small perennial, with slender runners forming new plants at each node. Leaves mostly basal, ternate; leaflets oval, strongly toothed, clothed with flattened silky hairs on the underside. Flowers white, 15-20 mm across, in loose, irregular cymes of about 6. Calyx with epicalyx as in *Geum*; sepals and petals 5; stamens and carpels numerous; styles short. Petals adjoining or overlapping. Fruit consisting of numerous small, seed-like achenes on the surface of the swollen, scarlet, fleshy receptacle. *Hedges and shady banks; very frequent.*

For differences from *P. sterilis* see above.

* *F. x ananassa*, the Garden strawberry, similar but with much larger leaflets, flowers and fruits, is naturalised on roadsides in a few places. It is a hybrid between two American species.

12. Alchemilla. Lady's mantle. *Bratóg Mhuire*

Perennials, with leaves mainly basal, palmately divided. Flowers small, greenish, numerous, in terminal cymes. Calyx with epicalyx; sepals and bracts 4; petals absent; stamens 4; carpel 1, deeply sunk into the calyx-tube, developing into a small achene.

1. Leaves palmate, with 5-7 distinct leaflets .. .. **1. A. alpina**
   Leaves lobed but not palmately divided 2
2. Plant hairless .. .. **5. A. glabra**
   Plant hairy, sometimes sparsely so 3
3. Leaves hairless on the upper side (or with a few scattered hairs in the folds) 4
   Leaves hairy on upperside 5
4. Pedicels hairless .. .. .. **3. A. xanthochlora**
   Pedicels hairy .. .. .. **4. A. filicaulis**
5. Base of petiole not reddish; lobes at the base of the leaf on either
      side of the petiole close together, sometimes almost obscuring
      the petiole .. .. **2. A. glaucescens**
   Base of petiole reddish; lobes at the base of the leaf on either side of
      the petiole widely separated from each other, usually forming an
      angle of more than 45° .. .. .. **4. A. filicaulis**

1. Alchemilla alpina. 6-8. Leaves palmate, consisting of 5-7, narrow-oblong leaflets, white and silky beneath, toothed at the tip. Stems slender, erect, 15-20 cm high, bearing clusters of yellow-green flowers 3-4 mm across. *Mountain cliffs in Kerry (Brandon & Boughil) and Wicklow (Lough Ouler); very rare.*

2. A. glaucescens (*A. minor*). **5-7.** Silvery-hairy all over, including pedicels. Leaves very small (20-25 mm across); lobes rounded, each with 9-13 teeth; lobes at the base of the leaf on either side of the petiole close together, sometimes almost obscuring the petiole. *Known only from two limestone hills in Leitrim, north of Dromahair.*

3. A. xanthochlora. 5-7. Plant hairless (or nearly so) on the upper surface of the leaves and on the inflorescence, all other parts hairy. Leaves up to 12 cm across; lobes rounded, each with 13-19 teeth; lobes at the base of the leaf on either side of the petiole widely separated from each other, usually forming an angle of more than 40°. *Grassland; frequent except in parts of the South.*

4. A. filicaulis. 6-7. Hairy, though sometimes sparsely so, all over. Leaves medium to rather small, up to 7 cm across; lobes rounded, each with 13-19 teeth; lobes at the base of the leaf on either side of the petiole widely separated from each other, usually forming an angle of more than 45°. *Dry or rocky grassland, especially on limestone; frequent in most districts.*

Two subspecies are distinguished: the common subspecies (subsp. *vestita*) is densely hairy all over; whilst in subsp. *filicaulis*, known only from County Sligo, the inflorescence branches and upper parts of the stem are hairless and the leaves bear rather few hairs.

5. A. glabra. 5-7. Hairless or with a few inconspicuous flattened hairs. Leaves medium, about 6 cm across; lobes rounded, each with 13-19 teeth; lobes at the base of the leaf on either side of the petiole widely separated from each other, usually forming an angle of more than 40°. *Upland pastures and mountain streams; frequent in the North and West, rather rare elsewhere.*

13. Aphanes. Parsley-piert

Small, hairy annuals. Leaves small, shortly stalked, irregularly and very deeply palmate with narrow lobes. Stipules large, lobed. Flowers green, very minute, in stalkless axillary heads, partly concealed by the stipules. Calyx with a very small epicalyx. Sepals 4; petals absent; stamen 1; carpel 1, deeply sunk in calyx-tube. Fruit a small achene, enclosed in calyx-tube and crowned by persistent calyx-teeth.

1. Sepals on fruiting specimens reaching or exceeding the apex of the
     stipules; fruit more than 2 mm long (including calyx-teeth)   **1. A. arvensis**
     Sepals on fruiting specimens fully enclosed within the stipules;
     fruit less than 2 mm long (including calyx-teeth) . .   **2. A. inexpectata**

1. Aphanes arvensis (*Alchemilla arvensis*). **5-8.** Stems 7-20 cm. Leaves greyish-green. Stipules divided less than halfway into broadish, triangular lobes. Calyx-teeth relatively large, reaching the apex of the stipules in fruit, slightly spreading. *Field margins, roadsides, railway balast and walls; frequent on limestone, rare elsewhere.*

2. A. inexpectata (*A. microcarpa*). **5-8.** Rather smaller and slenderer than *A. arvensis*. Stipules divided half-way into oblong lobes. Calyx-teeth in fruit small, convergent, fully enclosed within the stipules. *Similar habitats, but often on acid soils; fairly frequent.*

14. Pyrus

* Pyrus pyraster (*P. communis*). **Pear. 4-5.** Small tree with oval, shallowly toothed leaves. Flowers in short, branched clusters. Sepals and petals 5; stamens numerous; carpels 2-5 embedded in the calyx-tube and more or less fused to it; styles free. Fruit a pear. *Hedges, very rare.*

15. Malus

Small trees with oval, shallowly toothed leaves. Flowers in clusters on long pedicels. Sepals, petals and styles 5; carpels imbedded in the calyx-tube and more or less fused to it. Fruit an apple, consisting of the 5 membranous carpels embedded in the succulent calyx-tube and receptacle.

1. Leaves hairless, even on the underside, when mature; pedicels and
     outside of calyx-tube hairless   . .   . .   **1. M. sylvestris**
     Leaves hairy when mature; pedicels and outside of calyx-tube hairy
                                                                        2. M. domestica

1. Malus sylvestris (*M. pumila*). **Crab-apple.** *Cran fia-úill* **5.** Leaves 25-40 mm long, hairless when mature. Flowers 30 mm across, pink and white. Fruit a sour, yellowish apple, 25 mm across. *Hedges and woods; locally frequent.*

2. M. domestica. Apple. 5. Similar to *M. sylvestris* but with the mature leaves, pedicel and outside of the calyx-tube hairy and the fruit usually much larger. *Similar situations.*

M. domestica is a variable species; for example plants with leaves hairy only on the veins beneath are fairly frequent.

16. Sorbus

Trees with flowers in corymbs. Sepals and petals 5; stamens numerous, carpels 2-5, inferior, embedded in the calyx-tube and more or less fused to it. Fruit red and berry-like. Stipules small and soon dropping.

1. Leaves pinnate   . .   . .   . .   **1. S. aucuparia**
     Leaves undivided, but toothed, rarely deeply so   2

The species keyed out below set seed asexually and therefore difficult to distinguish from each other.

2. Leaves clearly toothed only in the top two-thirds .. **4. S. rupicola**
    Leaves clearly toothed along the whole of their margins .. 3

3. Leaves deeply lobed at least at the base **7. S. intermedia**
    Leaves more or less unlobed throughout, or with 1 or 2 shallow lobes
    near the base 5

5. Leaves weakly lobed, lobes more obvious near the base .. 6
    Leaves unlobed 9

6. Leaves white with very dense hairs beneath 7
    Leaves grey or greyish-white without very dense hairs beneath .. 8

7. Leaves with more than 10 secondary veins (mainly Galway) .. **3. S. aria**
    Leaves with 10 or fewer lateral veins (Killarney only) .. **5. S. anglica**

8. Fruit red, without large lenticels (Killarney only) .. **5. S. anglica**
    Fruit orange-brown, with many large lenticels (South-east only)
    6. S. devoniensis

9. Leaf-teeth straight and symmetrical (Fig. LIf) .. **2. S. hibernica**
    Leaf-teeth swept up towards the tip (Fig. LIg) .. .. **3. S. aria**

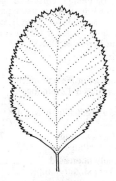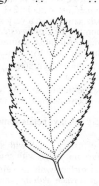

Fig. LIf   Fig. LIg

1. Sorbus aucuparia. Rowan, Quicken tree, Mountain ash. *Caorthann.* **5-6.** A smallish tree with smooth, grey bark. Leaves pinnate, with about 15 lanceolate, toothed leaflets. Flowers 6-9 mm across, very numerous. Fruits scarlet, globular, without persistent sepals, containing 2-4 woody achenes, embedded in orange pulp. *Glens, rocky places, hedgerows and by mountain streams; frequent.*

Species 2-7 are very similar; their descriptions are written so as to highlight their differences from the commonest species, *S. hibernica,* and must be used in conjunction with the key. Further investigation of Irish material is needed.

2. S. hibernica (*S. porrigens*). **Irish whitebeam. 5-6.** A shrub or small tree. Leaves oval, toothed (except at the extreme base) and the teeth symmetrical (Fig. LIf), hairless above, pale grey with silky hairs beneath. Flowers 12-15 mm across. Fruit red, globular, with persistent sepals. *Woods, cliffs and rocky places, usually on calcareous soils, mainly in the Centre; occasional.*

3. S. aria. Whitebeam. 5-6. Leaf teeth swept-up towards the tip of the leaf (Fig. LIg); leaf sometimes shallowly lobed; often densely white-hairy beneath; fruit ovoid. *Rare as a native but locally frequent in Galway, scattered as an obvious introduction elsewhere.*

4. S. rupicola. 5-6. Leaves toothed only in the top two-thirds; often widest in the top third, narrowing evenly towards the base. *Mainly in the West and North; occasional.*
Specimens from Down require detailed study.

5. S. anglica. 4-5. Leaves shallowly or moderately lobed, *Killarney only*.

6. S. devoniensis. 5-6. Leaves usually shallowly lobed near the base; fruits orange-brown. *Known only from the South-east corner; rare.*

7. S. intermedia. 5-6. Leaves with large, deep lobes at least at the base. *Known only from Cos. Galway, Dublin and Wicklow.*

17. Cotoneaster

Shrubs with small, stiff, evergreen, untoothed leaves. Flowers white or pinkish, about 10 mm across, solitary or in complex cymes of 12-50. Calyx 5-toothed; petals 5; stamens numerous; carpels 2-3. Fruit red or orange, berry-like, globular, with persistent sepals, containing a very stony carpel hardly fused to the hypantial tube.

A large number of *Cotoneaster* species, in addition to those listed below, are grown in gardens. All those naturalised are originally derived from cultivated stock but because they are bird-dispersed, often occur in remote places.

1. Leaves less than 1.5 cm long 2
    Leaves more than 1.5 cm long 3
2. At least some flowers in pairs (often 1 member of the pair much
    later to open); petals rather erect, pink; leaves 6-12 mm long
    1. C. horizontalis
    All flowers solitary; petals somewhat spreading, white; leaves 4-8 mm
    long .. .. **3. C. integrifolius**
3. Upper leaf surface rough with small, distinct swellings **7. C. bullatus**
    Leaf surface not rough with small, distinct swellings .. 4
4. Upper leaf surface with the veins very deeply impressed .. 5
    Upper leaf-surface with the veins not (or very slightly) impressed 7
5. Leaves more than 5 cm long; petals somewhat spreading, white
    6. C. x watereri
    Leaves less than 5 cm long; petals rather erect, pink .. 6
6   Flowers in clusters of no more than 4; only the main vein clearly
    impressed on the upper surface of the leaf (but all impressed when
    leaf dry) .. .. **2. C. simonsii**
    Flowers in clusters of 5-15; all veins deeply impressed on the upper
    surface of the leaf .. .. .. **4. C. franchetii**
7. Leaves less than 3 cm long; flowers in groups of no more than 5 **2. C. simonsii**
    Leaves more than 6 cm long; flowers in groups of 20 or more **7. C. frigidis**

1. * Cotoneaster horizontalis. 5-6. Undershrub, usually less than 1.5 m tall with widely spreading branches. Leaves very small, usually less than 1 cm long, rather dull and with the main vein impressed on the upper surface; sometimes turning orange or purple in Autumn. At least some flowers in pairs, others solitary; petals rather erect, pink. *Rock outcrops and walls; mainly in the South-west and North-east, but spreading.*

2. * C. simonsii. 5-6. Shrub 2-3 m tall with smallish, usually less than 1.5 m tall with widely spreading branches. Leaves about 1.5-2.5 cm long, the main vein sometimes impressed on the upper surface (all veins may be impressed when the specimen is dry). Flowers solitary or in groups of up to 4; petals rather erect, pink. *Scrub and woodland edges, road and railway sides; throughout, increasing.*

3. * C. integrifolius (*C. microphyllus*). **5-6.** Undershrub with creeping and arching stems. Leaves about 6-8 mm long, rather glossy and with the main vein impressed on the upper surface. Flowers solitary; petals somewhat spreading, white. *Rocky and gravelly places; throughout.*

4. * C. franchetii. 5-6. Undershrub with creeping and arching stems. Leaves 2-4 cm long, dull and with the veins deeply impressed on the upper surface. Flowers solitary; petals rather erect, pink. *Rocky and gravelly places; throughout.*

5. * C. frigidis. 5-6. Large erect shrub, sometimes over 4 m tall. Leaves 6-13 cm long, with the veins not impressed on the upper surface. Flowers in clusters of 20 or more; petals somewhat spreading, white. *Forest edges and roadside banks; throughout.*

6. * C. x watereri. 5-6. Similar to *C. frigidis* differing in its rather larger fruits (7-8 mm rather than 5-6 mm) and upper leaf surface with the veins strongly impressed. *Similar situations, but less frequent.*

7. * C. bullatus. 5-6. Large erect shrub about 3m tall with arching branches. Leaves 3.5-7 cm long with the upperside rough with small, distinct swellings. Flowers in clusters of 12-30. *Riversides and scrub; rather rare but increasing, frequent in cultivation.*

18. Crataegus

Small, trees or bushes with spiny branches. Leaves dull green, somewhat triangular, deeply pinnately-lobed, with a long leaf-stalk. Flowers 12 mm across, white or rarely pink, in corymbose cymes of 12-50. Calyx 5-toothed; petals 5; stamens numerous, epigynous. Calyx and pedicels hairy. Fruit red and berry-like, with persistent sepals, containing a very stony carpel.

1. Carpel 1; base of leaves with the lobes acute   ..   **1. C. monogyna**
    Carpels 2-3; base of leaves with the lobes blunt   ..   **1. C. laevigata**

1. Crataegus monogyna. Hawthorn. *Sceach geal.* **5-6.** Leaves deeply lobed, the basal lobes reaching about three-quarters of the way to the mid-rib, acutely pointed. Flowers white or, in hedgerows, frequently pink. Carpels and styles solitary. *Hedges and copses; locally frequent.*

2. * C. laevigata (*C. oxycanthoides*). **5-6.** Differs from *C. monogyna* in its leaves shallowly lobed to about half-way with broad, round-tipped basal lobes and 2-3 carpels. *Heavy, clay soils in woods in the Centre; locally frequent; rare elsewhere.*

Hybrids between the two *Crategus* species are fairly frequent in the North-east and Centre; the hybrids have almost thornless branches which tend to be drooping and shining leaves of intermediate shape.

19. Prunus

Shrubs or trees with undivided leaves and small stipules. Flowers white, in small clusters arising directly from the woody stems, or more rarely in racemes. Calyx 5-toothed, basin-shaped, not persisting round the fruit; petals 5; stamens numerous; pistil consisting of a single carpel, quite free from the calyx-tube. Fruit a drupe.

1. Flowers in longish axillary racemes, usually of more than 10 flowers   2
    Flowers borne singly or in clusters of 10 or fewer on the woody stem   ·   3
2. Racemes usually drooping, leaves evergreen   ..   .. **5. P. padus**
    Racemes stiffly erect, leaves deciduous   ..   **6. P. laurocerasus**
3. Flowers solitary or in pairs, nearly stalkless   4
    Flowers in groups of 3 or more, on long pedicels   5
4. Spines numerous; leaves usually less than 35 mm long; flowers
        appearing before the leaves   ..   ..   .. **1. P. spinosa**
    Spines few or absent; leaves usually more than 35 mm long; flowers
        appearing at the same time as the leaves   ..   **2. P. domestica**
5. Tree with few suckers. Leaves dull on upper surface, soft and
        drooping when young; calyx-tube narrowed at top   ..   **3. P. avium**
    Shrub with many suckers. Leaves shiny on upper surface, firm and
        erect when young; calyx-tube not narrowed at top   .. **4. P. cerasus**

1. Prunus spinosa. Blackthorn, Sloe. *Draighean.* **3-5.** A dense, busy shrub, with dark greyish-brown or blackish branches ending in a stout spine. Leaves oval, nearly hairless, finely toothed, 20-35 mm long. Flowers 10-15 mm across, nearly stalkless, solitary or in pairs, appearing before the leaves. Fruit erect, 12 mm across, bluish-black with a pale, waxy bloom, very sour and astringent. *Hedges, thickets and rocky places; very frequent.*

2. * P. domestica. Bullace, Wild plum. 4-5. Similar to *P. spinosa* but branches brown and much less spiny; leaves larger and hairier; flowers larger and appearing with the leaves; and fruit much larger and drooping. *Hedges and woods, usually near houses; occasional.*
    Two sub-species are sometimes distinguished: subsp. *domestica* has almost hairless and spineless twigs, whereas subsp. *institia* has somewhat spiny, densely hairy twigs; however intermediates abound.

3. P. avium. Wild cherry. *Crann silín.* **4-5.** A handsome tree with shining bark and few suckers. Leaves oval-lanceolate, pointed, toothed, soft and drooping when young, and hairy on the underside. Flowers 20-25 mm across, on long, slender pedicels, arranged in small clusters; sepals bent strongly back on flowering. Calyx-tube constricted (sometimes only slightly so) at the top. Fruit dark red, bitter. *Woods and hedges; occasional.*

4. * P. cerasus. Dwarf cherry. 4-5. Similar to *P. avium*, but forms a bushy shrub, with numerous suckers; leaves erect and hairless when young and the calyx-tube not constricted at the top. *Hedges; locally frequent.*

5. * P. padus. Bird cherry. 5-6. A shrub or small tree with oval-lanceolate leaves, finely toothed, usually hairless (sometimes with tufts of hairs along the midrib underneath). Flowers 15 mm across, numerous, in drooping, axillary racemes; sepals usually erect or slightly spreading in flower and not bent strongly back. Calyx-tube shallow and not constricted at the top. Fruit, small, black, bitter. *Woods and damp, rocky places; frequent in the North-west, rare elsewhere.*

6. * P. laurocerasus. Cherry-laurel. 4-6. A large, evergreen shrub with oblong, dark green, glossy, almost untoothed leaves up to 15 cm long, and erect racemes of numerous white flowers 8 mm across. Fruit small, black. *Planted in woods and demesnes, and extensively spreading in many districts.*
    * *P. lusitanica*, the Portuguese laurel, is often planted but only rarely naturalised. Similar to *P. laurocerasus* but smaller, and with pointed, sharply toothed leaves and red petioles.

LII. LEGUMINOSAE (FABACEAE)

Herbs, trees or shrubs with alternate, usually compound leaves, with stipules. Flowers irregular. Calyx tubular, usually 5-toothed. Petals 5, free or rarely partly united, unequal, consisting of a broad, usually flat *standard* at the back of the flower, 2 *wings* at the sides and a *keel*, made up of the two lower petals [Fig. LIIa]. Stamens 10, hypogynous; filaments all united in a tube round the style and ovary, or 9 of them so united and the upper one free. Ovary superior, 1-celled, consisting of a single carpel. Fruit a pod, usually splitting down both margins.

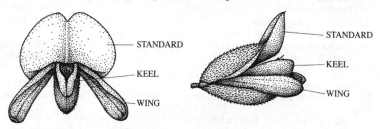

STANDARD

KEEL

WING

STANDARD

KEEL

WING

Fig. LIIa

Among the numerous cultivated plants belonging to this family are vegetables such as Peas (*Pisum*), Beans (*Vicia*), Lentils (*Lens*), French beans (*Phaseolus*) and Ground-nuts or Peanuts (*Arachis*); fodder crops such as Sainfoin (*Onobrychis*) as well as species of Clover and Vetch; and many ornamental garden plants including Brooms (*Genista, Cytisus*), *Laburnum, Robinia* (usually known as "Acacia"), *Wisteria*, Lupins (*Lupinus*) and Sweet pea (*Lathyrus*).

The Irish plants described below, and all those mentioned above, belong to the subfamily *Papilionoideae*, with the characteristic 'pea-flower'; the other subfamilies are mainly tropical and subtropical and include such plants as *Acacia* ('Mimosa' of florists) and *Cercis* (Judas-tree).

1.	Leaves palmate, with more than 5 leaflets	.. ..	**4. Lupinus**
	Leaves pinnate, or with 2-3 leaflets, or undivided	.. ..	2
2.	Tree or shrub	.. ..	3
	Herb, sometimes slightly woody at the base	.. ..	5
3.	Spiny. Calyx yellow in flower	.. ..	**3. Ulex**
	Not spiny. Calyx green in flower	.. ..	4
4.	Shrub, with erect, green branches. Flowers solitary in leaf-axils ..		**2. Cytisus**
	Tree. Flowers in hanging racemes	.. ..	**1. Laburnum**
5.	Leaf ending in a terminal leaflet	.. .. ..	6
	Leaf ending in a tendril or a small point; no terminal leaflet	..	13
6.	Leaflets 3 or 5	.. ..	7
	Leaflets 7 or more	.. .. ..	11
7.	Leaflets 5	.. .. ..	**12. Lotus**
	Leaflets 3	.. .. ..	8
8.	Flowers in long, slender racemes	.. ..	**9. Melilotus**
	Flowers solitary, or in heads or clusters	.. ..	9
9.	Plant sticky with glandular hairs; flowers solitary in leaf-axils ..		**8. Ononis**
	Plant without glandular hairs; flowers usually in heads or clusters		10

10. Pod strongly curved or spirally twisted, not enclosed in the calyx;
    midrib of leaf ending in a point .. .. **10. Medicago**
    Pod straight, usually enclosed in the calyx; midrib of leaf not ending
    in a point .. .. **11. Trifolium**
11. Flowers in small, axillary clusters; mature fruit constricted between
    the seeds .. .. **14. Ornithopus**
    Flowers numerous, in stalked heads; mature fruit not constricted
    between the seeds 12
12. Leaflets usually 7-11. Flowers yellow or red .. **13. Anthyllis**
    Leaflets usually 15-25. Flowers violet .. .. **5. Astragalus**
13. Leaflets at least 5 pairs .. .. **6. Vicia**
    Leaflets not more than 4 pairs 14
14. Leaflets not more than 15 mm long .. .. .. **6. Vicia**
    Leaflets mostly more than 20 mm long .. .. .. **7. Lathyrus**

1. Laburnum

Small trees. Leaves long-stalked, with 3 more or less stalkless, elliptical leaflets. Flowers bright yellow, in hanging, leafless racemes 10-40 cm in length. Pod 4-5 cm long.

1. Inflorescence, young fruit and lower side of leaflets densely silky-
   hairy; upper margin of pod thickened but not winged **1. L. anagyroides**
   Inflorescence, young fruit and lower side of leaflets hairless or
   sparsely hairy; upper margin of pod winged .. .. **2. L. alpinus**

1. * Laburnum anagyroides. 4-5. Twigs greyish-green, silky-hairy. Leaflets usually rather densely hairy beneath. Inflorescence downy. Pod hairy when young, with the upper margin thickened at maturity, but not winged. *Planted in hedges, mainly in the South and East, and perhaps rarely self-sown; occasional.* Native of Central Europe.

2. * L. alpinum. 5-6. Similar to *L. anagyroides*, but much less hairy in all its parts; inflorescence longer and appearing three weeks later; pod with upper margin narrowly winged. *Planted in hedges in parts of the North; local.* Native of Central Europe.

2. Cytisus

Cytisus scoparius (*Sarothamnus scoparius*) **Broom.** *Giolcach sléibhe.* **5-6.** A shrub 1-2 m high, with upright, green, wiry branches. Leaves few and small, mostly with 3 oval leaflets, hairless or sparsely silky. Flowers bright yellow, 25 mm long. Calyx small and green. Pod flat, hairy on the margins, 3-5 cm long. *Heaths and dry, bushy places. Rare in the Centre; locally frequent elsewhere.*

Prostrate plants (subsp. *maritimus)* occur on exposed sea-cliffs in Cos. Dublin, Cork and Kerry.

3. Ulex. *Aiteann*

Bushy shrubs, with green, very spiny branches; leaves mostly reduced to scales or spines. Flowers intermixed with spines in irregular racemes. Calyx yellow, split into two lips, almost as long as the corolla. Pod with few seeds, not much longer than the calyx.

1. Hairs on calyx spreading; bracteoles at least 2 mm long **1. U. europaeus**
   Hairs on calyx lying flat; bracteoles less then 1 mm long .. **2. U. gallii**

1. Ulex europaeus. Gorse, Furze, Whin. 4-6. 70-200 cm high. Stems and thorns of a somewhat bluish green, sparsely covered with black hairs. Spines up to 25 mm, strongly furrowed. Flowers 15-20 mm long. Hairs on calyx spreading. Corolla bright yellow. Bracteoles (at base of calyx) at least 2 mm long. *Heaths, rough grassland and rocky ground; abundant in the East, more local in the West, and in some districts only where planted for hedges.*

Although the main flowering is in late spring, some bushes may usually be seen in flower throughout the winter.

2. U. minor. Autumn gorse. 7-10. Like *U. europaeus,* but seldom over 80 cm high, and of a deeper, not bluish green; spines shorter, less deeply furrowed; flowers 12-14 mm long; hairs on calyx lying flat; corolla deep, golden yellow; bracteoles not more than 1 mm long. *Heaths and mountainsides; very frequent in much of the South and East, local in the West and rare in the Centre.*

4. Lupinus

* Lupinus arboreus. Tree lupin. 6-9. A small shrub; leaves palmate with 5-12 (usually 9) oblong leaflets, silky beneath. Flowers in terminal racemes. Corolla pale yellow, more rarely white, sometimes tinged with blue. Pod flattened, downy, with about 10 seeds. *Roadsides and sandy ground near the sea in the South-east; rare.* Native of California.

5. Astragalus

Astragalus danicus. 6-8. Perennial, with prostrate or straggling stems up to 35 cm. Leaves pinnate, with numerous small leaflets. Flowers violet-purple, in stalked, terminal, short racemes. Fruits ovoid, hairy, flattened. *Rocky or sandy ground; occasional, but local in the Aran Islands; unknown elsewhere.*

6. Vicia. Vetch. *Pis*

Herbs with diffuse, often climbing stems and pinnate leaves, usually with numerous leaflets and ending, not in a leaflet but in a tendril or a short point. Flowers solitary or in clusters or stalked racemes in the leaf-axils.

1. Flowers in clusters of 3 or more 2
   Flowers solitary or in pairs 6
2. Tendril present 3
   Tendril absent: leaf ending in a short point .. .. **1. V. orobus**
3. Flowers 4-5 mm long; pod pubescent .. .. .. **4. V. hirsuta**
   Flowers 10-18 mm long; pod hairlessless 4
4. Flowers white veined with blue .. .. **3. V. sylvatica**
   Flowers blue or purple 5
5. Leaflets more or less parallel-sided; flowers bright blue .. **2. V. cracca**
   Leaflets widest near the base; flowers dull reddish purple .. **5. V. sepium**
6. Leaflets widest near the base .. .. **5. V. sepium**
   Leaflets widest near the tip.. 7
7. Flowers at least 10 mm long; mature seeds with a smooth surface
   [Fig. LIIb] .. .. **6. V. sativa**
   Flowers 5-8 mm long; mature seeds with a rough surface [Fig. LIIc]
   7. V. lathyroides

Fig. LIIb   Fig. LIIc

1. Vicia orobus. 6-8. A slightly hairy perennial, with erect, rather stout stems. Leaves without tendrils, ending in a short point; leaflets 8-10 pairs, oblong. Flowers 15 mm long, in short, dense, long-stalked racemes. Corolla white, tinged with purple. Pod with 3-5 seeds. *Thickets and rocky ground in the West, Centre and North-east; rather rare.*

2. V. cracca. Common vetch. 6-8. A usually downy or silky perennial, with climbing stems up to 150 cm long. Leaf ending in a branched tendril; leaflets 8-12 pairs, more or less parallel-sided, pointed, 12-18 mm long. Stipules entire. Racemes long-stalked, with numerous flowers 10-12 mm long, all facing one way. Corolla bright blue. Pod with 6-8 seeds. *Hedges and waste places; abundant.*

3. V. sylvatica. 6-8. A hairless perennial with trailing or climbing stems. Leaves ending in a branched tendril; leaflets 6-10 pairs, oval. Stipules strongly toothed at the base. Flowers 15-18 mm long, in rather lax racemes. Corolla white, veined with blue. *Woods, thickets and rocky ground, mostly in the East; rare.*

4. V. hirsuta. Hairy tare. 6-8. A hairy annual with weak stems 30-60 cm long. Leaves with 6-10 pairs of small, usually blunt leaflets, and ending in a branched tendril. Flowers 4-6 mm long, 2-6 together on a slender peduncle. Corolla pale blue. Pod hairy, with 2 seeds. *Field-margins and dry banks. Locally frequent in the East half, rare in the West.*

5. V. sepium. Bush vetch. 5-7. A slightly hairy perennial with straggling stems up to 80 cm high. Leaves ending in a branched tendril; leaflets 5-7 pairs, broadest near the base. Flowers 15 mm long, 2-6 together in more or less stalkless clusters or short racemes. Calyx-teeth unequal. Corolla dull purple. *Hedges and thickets; abundant.*

6. V. sativa (*V. angustifolia*). **5-7.** Annual, with weak straggling stems. Leaves ending in a unbranched or branched tendril; leaflets 4-6 pairs, widest near the tip. Flowers dark reddish purple, solitary or in pairs in the leaf-axils, almost stalkless. Seeds small and smooth [Fig. LIIb].

* Subsp. *sativa.* Flowers 20-30 mm long; pod 40-60 mm long. *Cultivated for fodder, and occasionally persistent in field-margins and waste ground.*

Subsp. *nigra* (*V. angustifolia*). Flowers 12-16 mm long; pod 25-50 mm long. *Sandy and gravelly ground; fairly frequent in the East and South; rather rare elsewhere.*

7. V. lathyroides. 4-5. A downy annual, with spreading stems up to 12 cm long. Leaves ending in a undivided tendril or a short point; leaflets 2-4 pairs, 8 mm long, widest near the tip. Flowers solitary, 6 mm long, stalkless in the leaf-axils. Corolla purple; pod 20 mm long; seeds rough [Fig. LIIc]. *Sandy ground near the North and East coasts; rare.*

7. Lathyrus

Hairless or slightly downy perennials, similar to *Vicia*, but usually with fewer and larger leaflets. Style hairless on the lower side, hairy on the upper (unlike *Vicia* where the style is hairy on the lower side only).

1.	Flowers yellow; leaflets one pair	..	..	**4. L. pratensis**
	Flowers red, blue or purple; leaflets 2-6 pairs	..	..	2
2.	Tendrils absent	..	..	..	**2. L. montanus**
	Tendrils present	..	..	..	3
3.	Leaflets at least four times as long as broad; stipules much smaller than leaflets	..	..	..	**3. L. palustris**
	Leaflets less than three times as long as broad; stipules nearly as large as leaflets	..	..	..	..	**1. L. japonicus**

1. Lathyrus japonicus (*L. maritimus*). **6-8.** Stems more or less prostrate, angled but not winged, up to 80 cm long. Leaves ending in an unbranched or branched tendril; leaflets 2-5 pairs, broadly oval, 1.5-2 times as long as broad, obtuse, up to 2 cm long. Flowers in shortly stalked racemes. Corolla purple, fading to dull lilac-blue, 19 mm long. Pod hairless, with 4-8 seeds. *Sandhills in Kerry (Rossbeigh and Inch), Cork (Rosscarberry) and Donegal; very rare.*

Viable seeds of this species are often washed up on western beaches, and it is possible that the Irish populations are ultimately of American origin.

2. L. montanus. 5-7. Stems erect, usually unbranched, winged, up to 40 cm high. Leaves without tendrils; leaflets 2-4 pairs, narrowly oblong, 3-7 times as long as broad. Flowers 15 mm long, in short racemes. Corolla purple, fading to greenish-blue. Pod with 4-6 seeds. *Woods, river-banks and heathy or rocky grassland. Frequent except in the Centre, where it is rare.*

3. L. palustris. 6-7. Similar to *L. montanus*, but stems straggling; leaves ending in a branched tendril and corolla lilac. *Marshes and wet meadows, mainly in the Centre; rare.*

4. L. pratensis. Meadow vetchling. *Pis bhuidhe.* **6-8.** Slightly downy. Stem straggling, angled. Leaves ending in an unbranched or branched tendril, and with a single pair of lanceolate, acute, somewhat pale bluish-green leaflets. Stipules nearly as large as the leaflets, with pointed lobes at the base. Flowers 12-15 mm long, bright yellow. Pod flattened, with up to 10 seeds. *Meadows, hedges and ditches; abundant.*

8. Ononis

Ononis repens. Rest-harrow. *Sreang-bogha.* **6-8.** Perennial, somewhat woody at the base. Stems prostrate, branched, sometimes ending in a spine. Young shoots somewhat hairy and sticky. Leaves mostly with 3 oval, toothed leaflets 12-15 mm long; upper leaves sometimes undivided. Flowers pink, solitary in the leaf-axils, 15 mm long. Pod about as long as the calyx, with 1-3 seeds. *Sand-hills, dry pastures and waste places; fairly frequent in the East and South; rare elsewhere.*

9. Melilotus. Melilot

Erect herbs; leaves with 3 leaflets. Flowers numerous, in slender, elongated racemes. Pod short, with 1-2 seeds.

1.	Flowers white	..	..	.. .. **3. M. albus**
	Flowers yellow	..	..	.. 2
2.	Flowers and fruit 2-3 mm long	..		**4. M. indicus**
	Flowers and fruit both more than 3 mm long	..		3
3.	Fruit 5-6 mm long, hairy at least when young, black [Fig. LIId]			
				1. M. altissimus
	Fruit 3-4 mm long, hairless, brown [Fig. LIIe]	..		**2. M. officinalis**

Fig. LIId   Fig. LIIe

1. * Melilotus altissimus. 7-8. A hairless biennial, 60-120 cm high. Leaflets rather indistinctly toothed, 15-25 mm long. Flowers yellow, 5-6 mm long. Pod 5-6 mm long, hairy at least when young, with rather indistinct transverse ridges, black [Fig. LIId]. *Sandhills, railway-banks and waste places; frequent in County Dublin, rare elsewhere.*

2. * M. officinalis. 7-9. Very similar to *M. altissimus*; best distinguished by the pod, which is 3-4 mm long, hairless, with a conspicuous network of ridges and brown [Fig. LIIe]. *Similar habitats, mostly in the South and East; rare.* Native of Eurasia.

3. * M. albus. 7-8. Annual or biennial, somewhat similar to *M. altissimus*, but with white corolla, and a slightly smaller, hairless, brown pod. *An occasional casual, mainly near the principal ports.* Native of Eurasia.

4. * M. indicus. 6-9. Annual, similar to *M. altissimus*, but smaller in all its parts. Flowers 2-3 mm long; corolla pale yellow. Pod 2-3 mm long, hairless, with a conspicuous network of ridges, greenish-brown. *Distribution as in* M. albus. Native of Eurasia.

10. Medicago

Herbs; leaves with three leaflets, the middle one stalked. Leaflets often mucronate, with a short, spine-like tip. Flowers in heads or short racemes. Pod curved or spirally coiled, longer than the calyx.

1.	Pod spiny		2
	Pod without spines		3
2.	Leaflets with a black spot		**3. M. arabica**
	Leaflets without a black spot		**4. M. polymorpha**
3.	Flowers 2-3 mm long, clear yellow		**1. M. lupulina**
	Flowers 5-10 mm long, violet or greenish		**2. M. sativa**

1. Medicago lupulina. Black medick. 5-8. A softly hairy annual or short-lived perennial, with more or less prostrate stems up to 50 cm long. Leaflets round or oval to triangular, toothed, shortly mucronate, 8-15 mm long. Flowers 2-3 mm long, in heads or very short racemes of 10 or more. Corolla bright yellow. Pod flattened, hairless and without spines, black at maturity, coiled in a nearly complete circle 2 mm across, containing a single seed. *Roadsides, dry grassland and sand-dunes, mainly on base-rich soils; abundant in most districts, but rare in the North-west.*

Easily confused with *Trifolium dubium*, which differs in its straight pod and leaflet which is not mucronate.

2. * M. sativa. Lucerne. 6-8. Perennial, hairless or slightly downy. Leaflets oblong, toothed at the tip, 8-30 mm long. Flowers 5-10 mm long, in erect racemes. Pod hairless, without spines.

Very variable. Two subspecies occur in Ireland:

Subsp. *sativa*. Erect, up to 80 cm high. Leaflets 20-30 mm long. Corolla purple. Pod coiled in a spiral of 1-3 turns. *Cultivated for fodder, and occasionally naturalised in field-margins, banks and sandhills.*

Subsp. *varia (M. sylvestris)*. Stems shorter and more spreading. Leaflets 8-15 mm long. Corolla blackish green. Pod curved, but not coiled in a spiral. *Naturalised on sandhills North of Dublin.*

This latter is usually interpreted as a hybrid between subsp. *sativa* and subsp. *falcata*, a yellow-flowered plant not found in Ireland except as a rare casual.

3. * M. arabica. 5-9. A more or less hairless annual, with spreading stems up to 60 cm long. Leaflets 10-25 mm long, triangular, obtuse, not mucronate, each bearing a large black spot. Flowers yellow, 5-7 mm long, in stalked clusters of 2-4. Pod spirally coiled, with hooked prickles. *Waste places and sandy ground near the South and East coasts; rare.*

4. * M. polymorpha. 6-9. Similar to *M. arabica*, but leaflets smaller, shortly mucronate and without a black spot; flowers slightly smaller. *Waste places near Cork and Dublin; very rare.*

11. Trifolium. Clover, Shamrock.[1] *Seamair, Seamróg*

Herbs. Leaves with 3 usually stalkless leaflets. Flowers small, in compact heads, more rarely solitary or in small clusters in the leaf-axils. Petals partly united with each other and with the united stamens. Pod straight, usually shorter than the calyx.

1. Flowers white, pink or red ..   2
   Flowers yellow   14
2. Flowers solitary or in heads of 2-5   3
   Flowers numerous, in crowded heads ..   4
3. Leaves hairless; pod oblong, with several seeds ..   **1. T. ornithopodioides**
   Leaves hairy; pod nearly globular, with a single seed   **15. T. subterraneum**
4. Flower-heads stalked   5
   Flower-heads stalkless in the axils or between uppermost pair of leaves   11
5. Stems creeping, rooting at the nodes ..   6
   Stems more or less erect, not rooting at the nodes ..   7
6. Veins of leaflets translucent; calyx-teeth divergent; leaf-stalk hairless
               2. T. repens
   Veins of leaflets opaque; calyx-teeth convergent; leaf-stalk slightly
   downy   **3. T. occidentale**
7. Calyx inflated and membranous in fruit   **6. T. fragiferum**
   Calyx not inflated in fruit ..   8
8. All calyx-teeth much longer than the tube; whole flower-head with
   a soft and downy appearance   **12. T. arvense**
   Most of the calyx-teeth shorter than the tube; flower-head without
   a soft and downy appearance   9
9. Corolla white, tinged with pink; calyx-teeth equal ..   **4. T. hybridum**
   Corolla purplish-red; calyx-teeth unequal (one or two being longer
   than the others)   10
10. Free portion of stipules narrowed suddenly at the tip to a hair-like
    point [Fig. LIIf]; leaflets usually about twice as long as broad **13. T. pratense**
    Free portion of stipules evenly tapered to the tip [Fig. LIIg];
    leaflets usually about 3 times as long as broad ..   **14. T. medium**

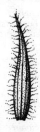

Fig. LIIf   Fig. LIIg

---

[1] The species most commonly worn as shamrock are *T. dubium* and small-leaved plants of *T. repens*, but also *Medicago lupulina*.

11. Calyx-tube hairless   ..   ..   ..   **5. T. glomeratum**
    Calyx-tube hairy   12
12. Flowers 15-18 mm long   ..   ..   ..   **13. T. pratense**
    Flowers 5-6 mm long   13
13. Calyx with golden hairs in flower; lateral veins of leaflets straight
        near the margin [Fig. LIIh]   ..   ..   **10. T. striatum**
    Calyx with whitish hairs in flower; lateral veins of leaflets curved
        downwards near the margin [Fig. LIIi]   ..   **11. T. scabrum**
14. Heads 9-12 mm across, with more than 20 flowers ..   **7. T. campestre**
    Heads 3-8 mm across, with less than 20 flowers   15
15. Heads 5-8 mm across, with 8-20 flowers; middle leaflet stalkless
                                                                      8. T. dubium
    Heads 3-5 mm across, with 2-4 flowers; middle leaflet shortly stalked
                                                                      9. T. micranthum

   1. Trifolium ornithopodioides (*Trigonella ornithopodioides*). **6-7.** A small
annual, with spreading, tufted stems. Leaflets heart-shaped, toothed. Flowers 10 mm
long, white or pale pink, solitary or in shortly stalked umbels of 2-4 in the leaf-axils.
Pod much longer than the calyx. *Grassy or gravelly places near the South and East
coasts (Cork to Down); rare.*

   2. T. repens. White clover. 5-9. A nearly hairless perennial with prostrate stems
rooting at the nodes. Leaflets oval or heart-shaped, toothed, often with a pale V-
shaped mark. Flowers white, rarely pale pink, drooping when faded, in long-stalked,
globular axillary heads about 25 mm across, slightly scented. *Meadows, pastures and
roadsides; abundant.*
   Widely sown for fodder.

   3. T. occidentale. 4-6. Very like *T. repens*, but slightly smaller in all its parts;
leaflets thicker, with opaque veins and without a V-shaped mark; leaf-stalk slightly
downy; flowers not scented. *Grassland on shallow soils near the sea by the East and
South-east coasts; rare.*

   4. * T. hybridum. Alsike clover. 6-9. Like *T. repens*, but with stems more or
less erect, not rooting at the nodes, and flowers usually pink. *Formerly cultivated for
forage, and occasionally naturalised on roadsides and in rough grassland.* Native of
Eurasia.

   5. T. glomeratum. 6-8. A hairless annual with prostrate or semi-erect stems up to
25 cm. Leaflets triangular or heart-shaped, 5-6 mm long. Flowers lilac-pink, axillary
clusters; calyx-teeth equal, acute, spreading. *Sandy or gravelly ground by the South
and East coasts; very rare.*

   6. T. fragiferum. Strawberry clover. 7-9. Perennial, with prostrate stems
rooting at the nodes, as in *T. repens*. Leaflets oval, 15-20 mm long. Flowers 8 mm
long, in long-stalked heads 12-15 mm across. Corolla lilac-pink. Calyx hairy,
strongly inflated and membranous in fruit. *Damp grassland, usually near the sea.
Occasional in the East; rather rare elsewhere.*

   7. T. campestre (*T. procumbens*). A semi-erect, somewhat hairy annual, with
stems up to 40 cm. Leaflets 10 mm long, oval, the middle one clearly stalked.
Flowers 5 mm long, in globular heads of about 30. Corolla bright yellow. Standard
notched at the tip and folded downwards. *Dry pastures and waste places. Locally
frequent in the South half, rare in the North.*

8. T. dubium. Yellow clover. 5-8. A slender, nearly hairless, prostrate or nearly erect annual with stems up to 40 cm long. Leaflets 8 mm long, triangular to oval, stalkless. Flowers 4 mm long, in shortly stalked heads of 10-15. Corolla rather pale yellow, acute; standard longitudinally folded, not notched at the tip. *Pastures, sand-dunes and waste places; abundant.*

Easily confused with *Medicago lupulina*, which is best distinguished by its black, coiled fruits without persistent corolla, and mucronate leaf.

9. T. micranthum (*T. filiforme*). **6-8.** Like *T. dubium* but smaller in all its parts; middle leaflet stalkless; flowers 3 mm long, in heads of 2-6; standard shortly notched. *Lawns, roadside verges and pastures; rare, and in many places introduced.*

10. T. striatum. 5-6. A softly hairy annual with spreading stems. Leaflets 12 mm long, heart-shaped; lateral veins straight near the margin [Fig. LIIh]. Flowers 6 mm long, in ovoid heads 10-15 mm long. Corolla pink. Calyx-teeth erect in fruit. *Dry grassland and rocky ground near the South and East coasts; rare.*

Fig. LIIh   Fig. LIIi

11. T. scabrum. 5-7. Like *T. striatum* but with leaflets only 8 mm long and with lateral veins strongly curved downwards near the margin [Fig. LIIi], corolla white, and calyx-teeth spreading and recurving in fruit. *Sandy ground near the South and East coasts; very rare.*

12. T. arvense. Hare's-foot clover. 7-8. A delicate, erect, downy annual up to 30 cm high. Leaves shortly stalked with narrowly oblong leaflets 8-10 mm long. Flowers 5-6 mm long, in cylindrical heads 25-30 mm long. Calyx-teeth with long hairs, giving the whole flower-head a softly downy appearance. Corolla very pale pink, shorter than calyx. *Sandy or rocky ground by the sea; occasional in the East half, rare in the West.*

13. T. pratense. Red clover. 5-9. A more or less erect, somewhat hairy perennial, with stems up to 60 cm. Leaflets up to 35 mm long, oval, often with a whitish v-shaped mark near the base. Stipules narrowed suddenly near the tip to a hair-like point [Fig. LIIf]. Flowers 10-15 mm long, in large, globular heads which are usually stalkless between the uppermost pair of leaves, but sometimes shortly stalked, Calyx-teeth unequal, one tooth much larger than the rest. Corolla purplish-red. *Meadows, pastures and roadsides, often cultivated; abundant.*

14. T. medium. 6-8. Like *T. pratense*, but with narrower, oblong leaflets; stipules evenly tapered to the tip [Fig. LIIg]; flower-heads stalked; and flowers of a rather brighter red. *Grassy and rocky ground; rather rare.*

15. T. subterraneum. 5-6. A hairy annual with prostrate stems rooting at the nodes. Leaflets oval or heart-shaped, entire. Flowers 10 mm long, in small heads of about 4. Corolla white. These flowers are usually accompanied by or replaced by sterile flowers consisting only of calyx with long tube and spreading teeth. Peduncles strongly recurved in fruit, so as to bury the fruits in the soil. *Known only from one gravelly bank in Wicklow.*

12. Lotus

Herbs; leaves with 5 leaflets. Flowers yellow or orange, more or less stalkless, in umbels. Pod much longer than the calyx.

1. Flowers 7-8 mm long; corolla orange ..   ..   **3. L. subbiflorus**
    Flowers 10-15 mm long; corolla yellow, sometimes tipped with red   2
2. Stem solid; calyx-teeth pressed to the corolla in bud   **1. L. corniculatus**
    Stem hollow; calyx teeth spreading in bud   ..   **2. L. uliginosus**

1. Lotus corniculatus. Bird's-foot trefoil. 6-9. Perennial, usually almost hairless but occasionally hairy, with solid, spreading stems up to 40 cm long. Leaflets oval. Flowers 15 mm long, in umbels of 3-6. Calyx-teeth closely appressed to the corolla in bud. Corolla bright yellow, often tipped or streaked with red. Pod 25-30 mm long. *Pastures, roadsides and sandhills; abundant.*

2. L. uliginosus (*L. pedunculatus*). **6-8.** An erect, usually rather hairy perennial with hollow stems up to 80 cm high. Leaflets oval. Flowers 10-12 mm long, in umbels of 5-10. Calyx-teeth spreading in bud. Corolla bright yellow. Pod 25-30 mm long. *Ditches and damp meadows; abundant in many districts, but rare in the Centre and parts of the West.*

3. L. subbiflorus (*L. hispidus, L. suaveolens*). **7-8.** Annual, with plentiful brownish hairs; stems more or less prostrate, up to 40 cm long. Leaflets oblong-lanceolate. Flowers 7-8 mm long, in umbels of 3-4. Corolla orange. Pod 15 mm long. *Grassland near the sea in West Cork and Wexford; very rare.*

13. Anthyllis

Anthyllis vulneraria. Kidney vetch. 6-8. A tufted, spreading perennial, covered with silky hairs. Leaves pinnate, with 7-13 entire, lanceolate leaflets, often unequal in size, the terminal one being the largest. Flowers 12-15 mm long, stalkless, in spherical heads up to 4 cm across. Calyx contracted at the mouth. Corolla yellow or red. Pod short, 1-seeded, concealed within the calyx. *Dry grassland; frequent near the coast and in parts of the Centre; rather rare elsewhere.*

14. Ornithopus

Ornithopus perpusillus. 5-7. A small, downy, more or less prostrate annual. Leaves pinnate, with up to 10 pairs of oblong-oval leaflets. Flowers 3-4 mm long, in stalked, axillary umbels of 2-4. Corolla white or pale yellow, veined with red. Pod 10-15 mm, curved, constricted between the seeds. *Dry, sandy ground near the South and East coasts; very rare.*

LIII. OXALIDACEAE

Oxalis

Perennial herbs with basal, somewhat clover-like, petiolate leaves; leaflets heart-shaped. Flowers hermaphrodite, with petals and sepals 5, free; 10 stamens (5 long and 5 short) and a superior 5-celled ovary, often with long styles. Fruit a capsule.

1. Flowers white, veined with purple   ..   ..   **1. O. acetosella**
    Flowers yellow, or pink not white   2
2. Flowers pink ..   ..   **4. O. articulata**
    Flowers yellow; carpels 3   3
3. Plant creeping and freely rooting   ..   ..   **2. O. corniculata**
    Plant more or less erect, not creeping and rooting   ..   **.. 3. O. stricta**

1. Oxalis acetosella. Wood sorrel. 4-5. Leaflets green. Flowers solitary, on long stalks, 15-20 mm across, white veined with purple. *Woods and shady places, very frequent.*

2. * O. corniculata. 6-9. Plant creeping and rooting at the nodes. Leaflets often purple. Flowers 4-7 mm across, yellow, in umbels of about 6 flowers, umbels on longish stalks.*Walls and waste-ground; rare.*

3. * O. stricta (*O. europaea*). **6-9.** Plant more or less upright. Leaflets green. Flowers 5-9 mm across, yellow, in rather few flowered umbels of no more than 5. *Waste places; rare.*

4. * O. articulata. 5-10. Plant more or less upright. Flowers 10-15 mm across, pink, in few to many flowered umbels, umbels on long stalks. *Roadsides, waste ground, banks and hills, especially near the coast; occasional.* Native of eastern South America.
* *O. debilis,* similar to *O. articulata* but rather larger and less hairy in all its parts, with flowers 15-20 mm across, is an occasionally naturalised casual.

LIV. GERANIACEAE

Herbs; leaves divided or lobed, with stipules, mostly opposite. Flowers regular, usually purplish. Sepals and petals 5, free; stamens 5 or 10; ovary superior. Fruit dry, consisting of 5 1-seeded protions, united at first, but later peeling away separately from the central axis; each bears a long, persistent style.
The 'Geraniums' of gardens are hybrids of *Pelargonium,* a mainly South African genus belonging to this family. Some foreign species of *Geranium* are also cultivated.

1. Stamens 10; style of fruit usually straight; leaves palmately or
    ternately lobed   ..   ..   ..   **1. Geranium**
    Stamens 5; style of fruit spirally twisted; leaves pinnately lobed   **2. Erodium**

1. Geranium. Cranesbill
Leaves palmately or ternately lobed. Style of fruit usually straight. Stamens 10.

1. Leaves triangular in outline, with 3 principal lobes   2
    Leaves circular or kidney-shaped in outline, with 5-7 principal lobes   3
2. Petals 9-10 x 6-8 mm; anthers orange   ..   ..   **13. G. robertianum**
    Petals 5-8 x 2-3 mm; anthers yellow   ..   ..   **14. G. purpureum**
3. Flowers all solitary   ..   ..   ..   **1. G. sanguineum**
    Flowers paired, two on each peduncle   4
4. Leaves shining; sepals sharply keeled, hairless   ..   **12. G. lucidum**
    Leaves not shining; sepals hairy, not keeled   5
5. Petals 10-20 mm long   6
    Petals 4-9 mm long   10

6. Petals distinctly notched at the tip   7
  Petals rounded, flattened or shortly pointed at the tip   ..   8
7. Plant with rhizome; petals white or pale lilac-pink   ..   **4. G. versicolor**
  Plant without rhizome; petals reddish-purple   ..   **6. G. pyrenaicum**
8. Petals blackish-purple, about as broad as long, usually shortly pointed
                   5. G. phaeum
  Petals violet-blue or reddish-purple, longer than broad, rounded at the tip   9
9. Petals violet-blue; immature fruits drooping   ..   **2. G. pratense**
  Petals reddish-purple; fruits erect, even when immature   **3. G. sylvaticum**
10. Leaves lobed almost to the base; ultimate segments more or less linear   11
  Leaves lobed not more than 2/3 of the way to the base; ultimate
   segments oval to oblong   12
11. Peduncles mostly less than 2.5 cm, shorter than adjacent leaf-
   stalks   ..   ..   **11. G. dissectum**
  Peduncles mostly more than 2.5 cm, longer than adjacent leaf-
   stalks   ..   ..   ..   **10. G. columbinum**
12. Fruits hairless, wrinkled   ..   ..   **8. G. molle**
  Fruits hairy or downy, not wrinkled   13
13. Leaves lobed less than half-way to the base; all 10 stamens with
   anthers   ..   ..   **7. G. rotundifolium**
  Leaves lobed at least half-way to the base; 5 stamens without
   anthers   ..   ..   **9. G. pusillum**

1. Geranium sanguineum. 6-8. Perennial, with stout, woody rhizome. Stems hairy, up to 60 cm long. Leaves circular in outline, deeply lobed; lobes jaggedly toothed or lobed. Flowers solitary, axillary, 25-30 mm across. Petals bright reddish-purple. Fruits smooth, sparsely hairy. *Rocky ground and dry banks; locally frequent in the West (Clare and Galway); very rare elsewhere.*

2. G. pratense. 6-8. A downy perennial with short, stout rhizome. Stems up to 70 cm. Leaves round or kidney-shaped in outline, lobed almost to the base, with jaggedly toothed lobes. Flowers 30-35 mm across; petals bright violet-blue. Pedicels drooping during the ripening of the fruit. Fruits downy, smooth. *Sand-dunes and coastal grassland; locally abundant on the North coast of Co. Antrim; occasional elsewhere on roadsides as a garden escape.*

3. G. sylvaticum. 6-7. A hairy perennial with short, stout rhizome. Stems up to 60 cm. Leaves kidney-shaped in outline, up to 13 cm broad, divided about 4/5 of the way to the base into toothed lobes. Flowers 25-30 mm across; petals purple. Fruits glandular-hairy, smooth, erect throughout. *Woods and rough grassland; frequent along the East coast of Antrim, from Larne to Glenarm; unknown elsewhere.*

4. * G. versicolor. 6-7. Perennial, with short, stout rhizome. Leaves kidney-shaped in outline, with bluntly toothed lobes. Stems 40-60 cm high. Flowers 25 cm across; petals white or pale lilac-pink, with purple veins. Fruits sparsely hairy, smooth. *Roadsides; occasional, mainly in the North-east, as a garden escape.*

 * *G. endressii,* similar but with bright pink petals, has also been recorded rarely as a garden escape, as has the hybrid between the two species.

5. * G. phaeum. 6-7. A downy perennial with a stout rhizome; stems up to 75 cm high. Leaves kidney-shaped in outline, divided rather more than half-way to the base. Flowers 20 mm across. Petals almost circular, flat, usually shortly pointed, purplish-black. Fruits hairy, with transverse ridges. *Hedges and shady roadsides, mainly in the North half; rare.* Native of South and Central Europe.

6. * **G. pyrenaicum. 5-8.** A softly hairy, much-branched perennial, without rhizome. Leaves semi-circular to circular in outline, divided about $2/3$ of the way to the base into bluntly lobed lobes. Flowers 20 mm across; petals reddish-purple, deeply notched at the tip. Fruits minutely downy, smooth. *Hedges and rough grassland, mainly in the East half; occasional.*

7. G. rotundifolium. 5-8. A small, hairy annual, with erect or spreading stems up to 35 cm long. Leaves round in outline, divided less than half-way to the base into broad, bluntly toothed lobes. Flowers 6-8 mm across; petals lilac-pink, rounded or flattened at the tip. Fruit downy, smooth. *Walls and roadsides in the South half; rather rare.*

8. G. molle. 5-8. A downy annual with mainly prostrate stems up to 30 cm long. Leaves 1-3 cm wide, kidney-shaped in outline, divided rather more than half-way to the base. Flowers 10-12 mm across; petals lilac-purple, notched at the tip. Fruits hairless, wrinkled. *Dry pastures, sandhills, banks and roadsides; very frequent in most districts, but rather rare in the North-west.*

9. * **G. pusillum. 6-9.** Like *G. molle*, but with the leaves rather more deeply divided, the flowers not more than 8 mm across, the fruits hairy, but not wrinkled, and the 5 outer stamens with normal filaments but without anthers. *Arable fields, waste ground and roadsides in the South and East; rare.*

10. G. columbinum. 6-7. A sparsely hairy annual with scrambling or suberect stems up to 50 cm long. Leaves divided almost to the base, the lobes divided into linear segments. Peduncles long (mostly 3-10 cm). Flowers 8-10 mm across; petals purplish. Fruits smooth, very sparsely hairy. *Rocky ground and roadsides; rare in the Centre and North-west, occasional elsewhere.*

11. G. dissectum. 5-9. Like *G. columbinum*, but with much shorter peduncles (1-2 cm) and more densely hairy fruits. Petals notched at the tip, bright purple. *Roadsides, field-borders and waste places; very frequent.*

12. G. lucidum. 5-7. A shining, nearly hairless annual with stems up to 35 cm. Leaves often red, round in outline, divided about half-way to the base into bluntly toothed lobes. Flowers 10 mm across; petals bright pink, rounded at the tip. Sepals hairless, strongly keeled. Fruits slightly downy, ridged. *Walls and rocks, usually on limestone; frequent in parts of the West and Centre, very local elsewhere.*

13. G. robertianum. Herb-robert. *Earball rí.* **5-9.** A somewhat hairy annual, with stems up to 50 cm. Leaves triangular in outline, divided to the base into 3 lobes, which are further lobed or bluntly toothed, usually strongly tinted with red. Peduncles long. Flowers 15-20 mm across; petals 9-10 x 6-8 mm, pink. Pollen orange. Fruits downy, ridged. *Hedges, walls and roadsides; abundant.*

Some plants from coastal rocks in the West have pale green, nearly hairless stem and leaves and paler flowers; they have been distinguished as subsp. *celticum.*

14. G. purpureum. 5-9. Like *G. robertianum*, but with petals 5-8 x 2-3 mm, deeper purplish-pink, hairless fruit and yellow pollen. *Rocks and walls near the South coast; very rare, perhaps extinct.*

2. Erodium. Storksbill

Leaves pinnately lobed or divided. Stamens 5, alternating with scale-like staminodes. Fruits hairy, with spirally twisted style.

1. Leaves undivided, pinnately lobed or bluntly toothed. Flowers solitary or in pairs .. .. **1. E. maritimum**
   Leaves pinnate; leaflets lobed or toothed. Flowers in umbels of 3-7 2

2. Leaflets lobed almost to the midrib. Pits at the base of the style of the fruits
    smooth, without glands [Fig. LIVa] .. .. **2. E. cicutarium**
    Leaflets not lobed beyond half-way to the midrib. Pits at the base of the style of
    the fruits bearing conspicuous raised glands [Fig. LIVb] **3. E. moschatum**

Fig. LIVa   Fig. LIVb

1. Erodium maritimum. 5-8. A more or less prostrate annual with stems 10-15
cm long. Leaves oval, bluntly toothed or pinnately lobed, but not deeply, shortly
stalked. Flowers 4-5 mm across, solitary or in pairs on short, axillary peduncles.
Petals usually absent; if present pale lilac-pink, shorter than the sepals. *Sandy or
stony ground, or in short grassland, near the South and East coasts; rather rare.*

2. E. cicutarium. 5-9. A rather hairy and sometimes sticky annual, with
spreading stems up to 50 cm long. Leaves pinnate; leaflets 1-2 cm long, deeply
lobed, almost to the midrib, the lobes further lobed or toothed. Flowers 8-12 mm
across, in umbels of 3-6, on long peduncles. Petals lilac-pink, some of them often
with a dark patch at the base. Pit at base of style of fruit smooth, without glands [Fig.
LIVa]. *Sandy ground by the sea, rarely inland; very frequent.*
   Very variable. Plants sticky with numerous glandular hairs, and with fewer,
smaller, paler flowers, recorded from the South and East coasts, are sometimes
treated as a separate species (*E. lebelii, E. glutinosum*), but are best regarded as a
subspecies — subsp. *bipinnatum.*

3. † E. moschatum. 5-7. Like *E. cicutarium*, but coarser and more robust.
Leaflets not lobed more than half-way to the midrib. Flowers 10-15 mm across, in
umbels of 4-7. Petals lilac-pink, without dark spots. Pit at the base of the style of the
fruit with prominent raised glands [Fig. LIVb]. *Waste ground and rough grassland
near the coast; rather rare.*

LV. LINACEAE

Annual or biennial herbs. Leaves undivided, entire, without stipules. Flowers in
cymes. Sepals 4 or 5; petals as many, free; stamens as many, united at the base;
ovary superior. Fruit a more or less spherical capsule.

1. Sepals and petals 5; petals 4-10 mm .. .. .. **1. Linum**
    Sepals and petals 4 .. .. **2. Radiola**

1. Linum

Sepals and petals 4.

1. Leaves opposite; petals white   ..   ..   **1. L. catharticum**
    Leaves alternate; petals blue   ..   ..   .. **2. L. bienne**

1. Linum catharticum. Fairy flax. 6-9. A delicate annual, with very slender, erect stems up to 15 cm high, usually forked above. Leaves 5-10 mm, narrowly oval, opposite. Flowers 6-8 mm across, in terminal cymes. Sepals narrow, acute; petals 4 x 2 mm, white. *Usually in dry, short, base-rich grassland, but occasionally in bogs, fens or heaths; abundant.*

2. L. bienne. 6-8. Biennial, with erect, sparingly branched stems up to 60 cm high. Leaves alternate, linear-obling, acute. Flowers 15-20 mm across, in small, terminal cymes. Sepals broad, mucronate. Petals pale blue. *Dry banks and pastures in the South-east (Dublin and East Cork) (formerly also in the South-west); occasional.*

* L. usitatissimum (Cultivated flax) was formerly cultivated for linen, especially in the North-east, and occurs rarely as a casual. It is like *L. bienne* but has broader leaves and larger, bright blue flowers.

2. Radiola

Sepals and petals 4.

Radiola linoides. Allseed. 7-9. A minute annual of bushy habit with thread-like, repeatedly forked stems 2-6 cm high. Leaves 2-3 mm long, opposite, oval. Flowers 2 mm across, numerous, in terminal cymes. Sepals 3-lobed, with acute lobes. Petals white. *Damp, sandy or peaty ground; locally frequent near the West coast; very rare elsewhere.*

LVI. EUPHORBIACEAE

Erect herbs with undivided leaves and small, greenish, unisexual flowers. Corolla and sometimes calyx absent. Ovary superior, 2- or 3-celled; fruit a capsule, splitting into 2 or 3 nearly globular, 1-seeded portions.

Many foreign species of *Euphorbia* are grown in greenhouses because of their cactus-like appearance. *E. pulcherrima* with spectacular large red bracts is the familiar pot plant "Poinsettia".

1. Latex present. Lowest leaves mostly alternate   ..   **1. Euphorbia**
    Latex absent. Leaves all opposite   ..   ..   **2. Mercurialis**

1. Euphorbia

Latex present. Lowest leaves alternate; those of the inflorescence opposite or whorled; stipules absent. Flowers mostly in terminal umbels, whose main branches fork once or several times. At the tips of the branches and at the points of forking are borne what look like single hermaphrodite flowers with stalked ovaries. These actually comprise a ring of male flowers (each consisting of a single stamen) surrounding a stalked female flower (consisting of a 3-celled ovary with 3 styles; stigmas usually forked). Surrounding this entire cluster, and resembling the perianth of the apparent flower, is a ring of minute, scale-like bracts and, alternating with these, a ring of thickened, yellowish glands, often the most conspicuous part of the inflorescence.

1. Leaves finely toothed   ..   ..   ..   **1. E. helioscopia**
    Leaves entire   2

2. Glands surrounding flower-clusters oval or kidney-shaped, entire.
    Fruit very warty   ..   ..   ..   **2. E. hyberna**
    Glands surrounding flower-clusters crescent-shaped or with two
    outwardly pointing horns. Fruit smooth or wrinkled, but not warty   3
3. Stems downy ..   ..   **3. E. amygdaloides**
    Stems hairless   4
4. Leaves thin and soft   5
    Leaves fleshy and leathery   6
5. Leaves linear to lanceolate, stalkless   ..   ..   .. **7. E. exigua**
    Leaves oval, very shortly stalked   ..   ..   .. **6. E. peplus**
6. Leaves broadest at or below the middle, blunt at the tip, very
    crowded and erect; midrib obscure on underside [Fig. LVIa]   **4. E. paralias**
    Leaves broadest above the middle, ending in a short point,
    moderately erect; midrib evident on underside [Fig. LVIb]   **5. E. portlandica**

Fig. LVIa   Fig. LVIb

1. † Euphorbia helioscopia. Sun spurge. 4-9. A hairless annual, with a stout
unbranched stem, sometimes branched from the base, 20-45 cm high. Leaves, oval or
broadest near the tip, tapered strongly to base, finely toothed in upper part, spreading;
bracts similar but broader. Infloresence very leafy and crowded; umbel with 5 main
branches. Glands small and round. Fruit smooth and shining; seeds brown and pitted.
Tilled ground and waste places; very frequent.

2. E. hyberna. Irish spurge. *Bainne caoin.* **4-6.** A slightly downy perennial with
unbranched stems, 30-60 cm. Leaves oblong or oblong-lanceolate, entire, 4-8 cm
long, slightly hairy beneath. Inflorescence compact, bright yellow; umbel usually
with 5 main branches. Bracts broadly oval, entire. Glands oval or kidney-shaped.
Fruit very warty; seeds yellowish, smooth. *Rocky and bushy places, woods and river-
banks in the South and West; abundant in West Cork and South Kerry, very rare and
local elsewhere.*

3. † E. amygdaloides. 3-4. A downy perennial with erect stems 30-60 cm high
which retain their terminal leaves through the winter and flower in their second year.
Leaves oblong, entire, dark green, 4-7 cm long. Inflorescence rather diffuse; umbel
with 5-10 main branches. Bracts broad, partly united at base. Glands crescentic; fruit
slightly granular, not warty; seeds grey, smooth. *Woods and river banks near
Bandon, County Cork; very rare.*

4. E. paralias. 6-8. A stout hairless perennial 25-50 cm high, with several stems
arising from a stout, woody rootstock. Leaves pale bluish-green, thick and fleshy,
very crowded, overlapping and erect, 12-25 mm long, oblong, blunt, with the midrib

scarcely visible below [Fig. LVIa]. Inflorescence compact; umbel with 3-7 main branches; bracts round or kidney-shaped. Glands crescentic, with short horns. Fruit wrinkled; seeds pale grey, smooth. *Sand-hills and sandy shores; frequent on the East coast, rather rare elsewhere.*

5. E. portlandica. 5-7. Similar to *E. paralias*, differing in its more slender root stock; shorter stems; leaves which are less erect and crowded, broadest above the middle, ending in a short point, with the midrib prominent below [Fig. LVIb]; more diffuse inflorescence, often with axillary branches below the umbel; larger horns to the glands and darker pitted seeds. *Rocky and sandy shores. Occasional on the East and North coasts, rare elsewhere.*

6. † E. peplus. Petty spurge. 5-8. A hairless bushy annual 15-30 cm high. Leaves spreading, pale green, oval, entire, blunt; bracts broader with a short fine point. Inflorescence large and diffuse; umbel usually with 3 main branches. Glands crescentic with long, slender points. Capsule slightly keeled or winged on the back of each carpel; seeds pale grey, pitted. *Tilled ground and waste places; very frequent in the South half, decreasing northwards.*

7. † E. exigua. Dwarf spurge. 6-8. Habit, inflorescence and seeds as in *E. peplus*, but smaller (8-20 cm) with spreading or erect, linear to linear-lanceolate leaves and lanceolate bracts. Capsule not keeled. *Tilled ground, sand-pits and waste places especially in the Centre; rare and declining.*

2. Mercurialis

Latex absent. Leaves opposite, stalked, with small stipules. Dioecious. Flowers small, green, unisexual, distinct in axillary spikes or clusters; each with 3 sepals united at the base and either 9-12 stamens or a 2-celled ovary with a forked stigma.

1. Plant hairy, flowering stems unbranched   ..   **1. M. perennis**
    Plant hairless, flowering stems much branched   ..   .. **2. M. annua**

1. † Mercurialis perennis. Dog's mercury. 4-5. A downy perennial, with creeping underground stems and erect, unbranched flowering stems 20-45 cm high. Leaves dark green, oval or oval-lanceolate, bluntly toothed, pointed. Male flowers in clusters in long, lax spikes; female flowers solitary or in groups of 2 to 3, stalked. *Woods and shady places, usually in estates, where it may be introduced, but possibly native in one or two places; very rare.*

2. * M. annua. 3-10. An erect, hairless, much branched annual. Leaves bright green, hairless. Male flowers in clusters on suberect or erect spikes. Female flowers in almost stalkless clusters. Capsule coarsely hairy. *Tilled ground and waste places, mostly near towns. Frequent around Dublin; local elsewhere in the South half.* Native of Eurasia and North Africa.

LVII. POLYGALACEAE

Polygala. Milkwort. *Glúineach*

Low-growing, hairless perennials, with small, entire leaves and irregular flowers in racemes. Sepals 5, of which 3 are small and green, 2 are large and petal-like, but persist round the fruit and turn greenish. Petals 3, united to form a tube with 3 lobes, of which the middle one is fringed at the tip. Stamens 8, filaments united and only the anthers distinct. Ovary superior; fruit a small, flat capsule, enclosed by the persistent sepals; seeds 2.

1. Leaves all alternate; longer racemes with 10-30 flowers   **1. P. vulgaris**
    Lower leaves opposite; racemes mostly with 7-12 flowers   **2. P. serpyllifolia**

1. Polygala vulgaris. 5-8. Stems up to 25 cm, semi-erect or straggling, woody at the base. Leaves up to 35 mm long (the uppermost the largest), elliptical, stalkless, all alternate. Flowers 4-7 mm long. Longest racemes with 10-30 flowers. Corolla blue, lilac, pink or white. *Pastures, banks, sandhills and rocky ground; very frequent in most districts.*

2. P. serpyllifolia. 5-8. Similar to *P. vulgaris*, but with usually shorter stems, less woody at the base; lower leaves (and sometimes some of the upper) opposite; racemes shorter, with usually not more than 12 flowers; corolla nearly always blue. *Heaths, bog-margins, and pastures on non-calcareous soils; very frequent and locally abundant.*

LVIII.　ACERACEAE

Acer

Deciduous trees with opposite, palmately lobed leaves without stipules. Flowers small, greenish, regular, mostly unisexual, in panicles. Sepals and petals 5, free; stamens 8; ovary superior; styles 2. Fruit of 2 indehiscent, seed-like portions joined together, each with an oblong, membranous wing.

* **Acer pseudoplatanus. Sycamore.** *Crann bán.* **4-6.** A large tree with spreading branches; bark smooth and grey at first, but scaling on old trunks. Winter buds greenish. Leaves 8-15 cm, about as broad as long, cordate at the base, with 5 acute, coarsely toothed lobes. Flowers in long, drooping, catkin-like panicles, appearing with or after the leaves. Wings of fruit diverging at rather more than a right angle. *Woods, hedges and waste ground; abundant.*

* *A. campestre*, the Field maple, a fair sized tree, but usually seen as a shrub, is occasionally planted in hedges and rarely naturalised. It has smaller leaves, with obtuse, entire lobes, the flowers are in erect panicles, and both wings of the fruit lie in the same straight line.

* *A. platanoides*, the Norway maple, is often planted and is naturalised in woods and hedges in a few places. It has leaves like those of *A. pseudoplatanus*, but with finely pointed lobes and milky sap in the leaf-stalk. The yellowish flowers in erect panicles appear before the leaves.

LIX.　HIPPOCASTANACEAE

* **Aesculus hippocastanum. Horse-chestnut. 4-6.** A large, broad-headed, deciduous tree with scaling bark. Buds large, very sticky in spring. Leaves opposite, palmate, with 5-7 leaflets up to 20 cm long. Leaf-scars with a characteristic pattern suggestive of a horse-shoe. Flowers in erect panicles. Calyx tubular, 5-lobed; petals 5, white with pink or yellow spots; stamens usually 7; ovary superior, 3-celled. Fruit a large, spiny, leathery capsule with 1-2 large brown seeds. *Planted for ornament and occasionally self-sown in hedges.* Native of Europe.

LX.　BALSAMINACEAE

* **Impatiens glandulifera. Indian balsam. 7-9.** A stout, erect, hairless annual, with a reddish, sappy stem up to 150 cm. Leaves opposite or in whorls of 3, oval-lanceolate, acute, stalked, toothed. Flowers 25-30 mm across, irregular, pink, in axillary racemes. Sepals 3, petal-like, the lowest in the form of a broad pouch ending in a small spur. Petals 3, free. Stamens 5, very short, cohering round the pistil. Ovary 5-celled, superior. Fruit a club-shaped, soft-walled capsule, exploding at a touch when ripe. *Waste ground, river-banks and damp, shady places; occasional.* Native of Himalaya.

LXI. AQUIFOLIACEAE

Ilex aquifolium. Holly. *Cuileann.* **5-8.** A dioecious, evergreen shrub or small tree, with smooth, grey bark and green twigs. Leaves alternate, thick and leathery, shining, oval, shortly stalked, those on young trees and the lower branches of old trees with a wavy margin armed with spiny teeth; those on the upper branches of older trees flat, entire, without spines. Flowers 8-10 mm across, regular, in small, axillary cymes. Sepals and petals 4, free; stamens 4, present but sterile in female flowers; ovary superior, 4-celled, abortive but visible in male flowers. Petals white. Fruit a scarlet, berry-like drupe with several seeds, each enclosed in a stony endocarp. *Woods, hedges and rocky ground; very frequent.*

LXII. CELASTRACEAE

Euonymus europaeus. Spindle-tree. *Feoras.* **5-6.** A deciduous shrub with green, 4-angled twigs. Leaves opposite, oval, acute, shortly stalked, entire or minutely toothed. Flowers 8-10 mm across, regular, in small, axillary cymes. Sepals, petals and stamens 4. Petals free, pale green. Ovary 4-celled, superior; stigma stalkless. Fruit a somewhat fleshy capsule, bright pink, splitting to expose the orange arils in which the seeds are enclosed. *Hedges, thickets, rocky ground and lake-shores, mainly on limestone; occasional and locally frequent.*

LXIII. RHAMNACEAE

Shrubs with alternate, undivided leaves and small, greenish flowers in axillary clusters. Sepals 4 or 5; petals as many, very small or absent; stamens as many, alternating with the sepals, sometimes vestigal. Ovary superior; fruit a berry-like drupe.

1. Usually spiny, leaves with fine teeth   ..   ..   .. **1. Rhamnus**
    Always spineless; leaves not toothed   ..   ..   .. **2. Frangula**

1. Rhamnus
1. Rhamnus cathartica. Buckthorn. 5-6. Usually rather spiny to 6 m. Leaves broadly oval, toothed, about 4-5 cm long, sometimes nearly opposite, with five, or fewer, pairs of lateral veins. Flowers dioecious; sepals, petals and stamens 4. Fruit black. *Rocky places and lake-shores; occasional in the West and Centre, very rare elsewhere.*

2. Frangula
2. Frangula alnus (*Rhamnus alnus*). **5-6.** Spineless. Leaves broadly oval, margin entire but undulate, always alternate, mostly with 6, or more, pairs of lateral veins. Flowers hermaphrodite; sepals, petals and stamens 5. Fruit first green then red, later dark purple. *Rocky or boggy places; very rare.*

LXIV. MALVACEAE

Herbs, sometimes woody at the base, with alternate, broad, stalked leaves and small stipules. Flowers regular, each with 3 or more bracts immediately below the calyx or attached to it, forming an epicalyx. Sepals 5, united at the base; petals 5, free. Stamens numerous; filaments united in a tube which surrounds the styles; anthers free. Ovary superior; carpels numerous, united at first, but separating in fruit into its separate carpels. Styles numerous, projecting from the staminal tube.

The garden plants belonging to this family include various species of *Alcea* (Hollyhock), *Abutilon* and *Lavatera*.

1. Epicalyx of 6-9 bracts   ..   .. **3. Althaea**
   Epicalyx of 3 bracts   2
2. Bracts of epicalyx divided to the base, inserted on the calyx   .. **1. Malva**
   Bracts of the epicalyx united below into a cup-like structure,
       inserted on the pedicle, below the calyx   ..   .. **2. Lavatera**

1. Malva. Mallow. *Hocas*

Small to medium-sized herbs. Epicalyx of 3 free bracts, inserted on the calyx.

1. Leaves lobed almost to the base; flowers pink or white   **1. M. moschata**
   Leaves lobed less than half-way to the base; flowers purple or lilac   2
2. Flowers 3-4 cm across, bright reddish-purple   ..   **2. M. sylvestris**
   Flowers 2 cm across, pale lilac   ..   ..   **3. M. neglecta**

1. * Malva moschata. Musk mallow. 7-8. An erect, hairy perennial; stems up to 75 cm high, often spotted with purple. Lower leaves round or kidney-shaped, not deeply lobed; middle and upper leavews palmately lobed almost to the base; lobes pinnately divided, with linear-oblong segments. Flowers 4-5 cm in diameter; petals notched, pink or white. Carpels hairy. *Roadsides and field-margins; frequent in the South-east, rare elsewhere.*

2. † M. sylvestris. 6-8. A straggling or nearly erect perennial, sparsely hairy. Leaves palmately lobed, about a third of the way to the base. Flowers numerous, in axillary clusters. Petals 15 mm, bright reddish-purple. Carpels usually hairless. *Waste places and roadsides, usually near houses or ruins; frequent in the South half, rather rare in the North.*

3. * M. neglecta. 6-9. A small herb, usually annual. Stems up to 50 cm, more or less prostrate, downy. Leaves round to kidney-shaped, with 5-7 shallow, crenate lobes. Flowers numerous, in axillary clusters; petals 10 mm, pale lilac. Carpels downy. *Roadsides and waste ground; occasional near the East coast, rare elsewhere.*

2. Lavatera

Lavatera arborea. Tree mallow. 7-9. A large, coarse, softly downy biennial; stems erect, up to 100 cm high, woody in the lower part, so that the plant is almost shrub-like. Leaves up to 10 cm across, nearly round, with usually 5 shallow, crenate lobes. Flowers in axillary or terminal panicles. Bracts of the epicalyx 3, united at the base, attached to the pedicel below the calyx, larger than the sepals and enlarging further in fruit. Sepals broadly triangular. Petals 10-15 mm, notched, overlapping, lilac-purple, with deep purple veins and base. Carpels downy. *Native on maritime rocks and bare ground near the sea; occasional but local. Also as an escape from cottage gardens, usually near the coast.*

3. Althaea.

* **Althaea officinalis. Marsh mallow. 8-9.** An erect, branched perennial, 50-100 cm high, covered with velvety down. Leaves broadly oval, often 3-lobed, toothed. Flowers in terminal racemes. Bracts of the epicalyx about 8, narrowly triangular, 5-7 mm long, free, inserted on the pedicel. Sepals ovate, pointed, slightly longer than the bracts. Petals 20 mm, scarcely notched, pale lilac-pink. Carpels downy. *Damp places by the South and West coasts, usually near houses; occasional.*

LXV. ELAEAGINACEAE

* **Hippophae rhamnoides. Sea buckthorn. 5.** A dense, bushy shrub, up to 5 m high; branches usually armed with stout spines. Leaves alternate, linear-lanceolate, entire, almost stalkless, covered on the lower side with a coating of silvery or brown, flattened, star-shaped scales and hairs which make the surface shiny but pustulate in appearance. Flowers small, green, dioecious; the female in small groups at the base of the lateral shoots, the male in short catkins. Calyx 2-lobed; corolla absent; stamens 4; ovary superior. Fruit orange-yellow; berry-like, 7 mm across, consisting of a small nut enclosed in the fleshy calyx-tube. *Sandhills and cliffs; local but spreading.*

Often planted as a sand-binder.

LXVI. GUTTIFERAE (CLUSIACEAE)

Hypericum. St. John's Wort. *Luibh Eoin Bhaiste*

Perennial herbs or low shrubs, mostly hairless, with opposite, entire, stalkless leaves without stipules. Flowers solitary or in terminal cymes, regular, hermaphrodite. Sepals 5, free. Petals 5, free, yellow. Stamens numerous, united at the base into 3 (less often 5) bundles. Ovary superior, 1- to 5-celled; styles 3 (rarely 5). Fruit a capsule, rarely somewhat succulent and berry-like; seeds numerous.

1.	Black glands present on leaves, sepals or petals	2
	Plant without black glands ..	7
2.	Stems prostrate	**7. H. humifusum**
	Stems erect ..	3
3.	Leaves downy	**4. H. hirsutum**
	Leaves hairless	4
4.	Petals tinged with red outside; sepals fringed with stalked black glands	**5. H. pulchrum**
	Petals not tinged with red outside; sepals with black or translucent glands only on the surface	5
5.	Sepals obtuse or subacute; leaves with few translucent glands or none	**9. H. maculatum**
	Sepals tapered to a long, fine point; leaves with numerous translucent glands	6
6.	Leaves 2.5 - 3 times as long as broad, without black glands; stem with 2 rather faint raised lines	**10. H. perforatum**
	Leaves twice as long as broad, usually with some black glands near the margin; stem with 4 acute ridges	**8. H. tetrapterum**
7.	Flowers 50-80 mm across; styles 5	**1. H. calycinum**
	Flowers not more than 35 mm across; styles 3	8

8. Stems creeping and rooting at the base; leaves more or less
        circular   ..   ..   **6. H. elodes**
    Stems not creeping or rooting at the base; leaves distinctly longer
        than broad   9
9. Stems not woody; flowers 5-7 mm across   ..   **11. H. canadense**
    Stems woody at the base; flowers 15-35 mm across   10
10. Styles longer than the ovary; stamens longer than the petals   **2. H. hircinum**
    Styles shorter than the ovary; stamens equalling the petals or
        shorter   ..   ..   **3. H. androsaemum**

1. * **Hypericum calycinum. Rose of Sharon. 6-9.** A low, usually evergreen
shrub, spreading by underground rhizomes, with prostrate woody stems and short
erect flowering shoots. Leaves 50-70 mm long, oval-oblong. Flowers 50-80 mm
across, solitary, terminal. Sepals obtuse. Stamens in 5 bundles; styles 5. *Cultivated
for ornament, and occasionally persistent or naturalised on shady banks; mainly in
the South-east.* Native of southern Europe and Turkey.

2. * **H. hircinum. 8-10.** A stiff, erect, more or less evergreen dwarf shrub; stems
branched, up to 80 cm high, woody at the base. Leaves oval 25-60 cm long. Flowers
35-40 mm across, in terminal and axillary cymes. Stamens in 5 bundles, longer than
the petals. Styles 3, much longer than the ovary. *Walls and banks, mostly in the South
and West, as an escape from gardens; occasional.* Native of Eurasia.

3. **H. androsaemum. Tutsan. 6-9.** A bushy plant up to 70 cm high; stems woody
at the base. Leaves 50-100 mm, oval obtuse. Flowers 20 mm across, in small,
terminal cymes. Stamens in 5 bundles, about equalling the petals. Styles 3, shorter
than the ovary. Capsule fleshy, berry-like, first red, then black. *Woods and hedges;
very frequent.*

4. **H. hirsutum. 7-8.** An erect, shortly downy perennial; stems cylindrical,
without raised lines, up to 100 cm high. Leaves oval-oblong, obtuse. Flowers 15-20
mm across, in terminal cymes. Sepals fringed with stalked black glands. Petals
sometimes streaked with red. *Woods and shady places; locally frequent in the Liffey
valley, very rare elsewhere.*

5. **H. pulchrum. 6-8.** A slender plant, with erect, smooth stems 25-35 cm high.
Leaves oval, obtuse, with numerous translucent glands. Petals and sepals fringed
with shortly stalked black glands; petals often tinged with red on lower side. *Heaths,
dry banks and rocky ground; abundant in most districts.*

6. **H. elodes. 7-8.** Usually woolly (but occasionally, when submerged in a stream
or pool, almost hairless). Stems creeping and rooting at the base, erect above. Leaves
10-15 mm, almost circular, clasping the stem. Flowers 15 mm across, in small,
terminal cymes. Sepals fringed with red glands; petals pale yellow. *Bogs, streams
and acid marshes; very frequent in the West and South-east, rare elsewhere.*

7. **H. humifusum. 7-9.** Stems numerous, trailing or prostrate, branched, 10-20
cm long. Leaves 10 x 3 mm, oblong, obtuse, with numerous translucent glands and a
few black glands near the margin. Flowers few, 8-10 mm across, in small, leafy
cymes. Sepals usually unequal, with marginal black glands. Petals pale yellow.
Sandy or peaty ground; occasional.

8. **H. tetrapterum. 7-9.** Stems stiffly erect, with 4 sharp ridges. Leaves oval,
with numerous translucent glands and a few black glands. Flowers 12-15 mm across,
numerous, in terminal and axillary cymes. Sepals very acute. Petals slightly longer

than the stamens, with a few black glands on the upper surface. *Ditches and other damp places; abundant.*

9. H. maculatum (*H. dubium*). **7-8.** Stems erect with 2 (or sometimes 4) raised lines. Leaves 12-30 mm long, oval, obtuse, with few translucent glands or none, but usually with some black glands near the margin. Flowers 15-25 mm across, in terminal cymes. Sepals obtuse. Petals bright yellow, slightly longer than the stamens, with black glands near the margin. *Thickets, banks and roadsides; frequent in the South half, rather rare in the North.*

10. H. perforatum. 7-8. Stems slender, erect, up to 90 cm high, with two slightly raised lines. Leaves 12-20 mm long, oblong, obtuse, with numerous translucent glands, but without black glands. Flowers 15-25 mm across, in terminal cymes. Sepals very acute. Petals bright yellow, usually with a few black glands near the margin, considerably longer than the stamens. *Dry banks and hedgerows, mainly on limestone soils; frequent in the Centre, occasional elsewhere.*

11. † H. canadense. 7-9. A delicate plant 10-25 cm high; stems slender, 4-angled, erect, smooth. Leaves narrowly oblong, obtuse, 7-15 mm long, with numerous translucent glands. Flowers rather few, 5-7 mm across. Sepals obtuse; petals narrow, pale yellow, with a crimson line on the lower side; stamens about 20. *Wet, peaty ground, and beside small streams; locally abundant by the West shore of Lough Mask, and in West Cork (near Glengarriff), unknown elsewhere.*

LXVII.   VIOLACEAE

Viola. Violet, Pansy. *Sail chuach*

Small, mostly perennial herbs. Leaves undivided, stalked, with stipules. Flowers solitary, on erect pedicels, bearing 2 (sometimes inconspicuous) bracts. Sepals 5, free, equal, prolonged below their insertion into a short rounded or truncate appendage. Petals 5, free, somewhat unequal, the lowest prolonged at the base into a short spur. Stamens 5; filaments very short. Ovary 1-celled, with 3 parietal placentae. Fruit a small capsule; seeds numerous.

The garden Pansies are complex hybrids, involving *V. lutea, V. tricolor* and an Asiatic species.

1. Petals violet, blue, lilac or white, never yellow; stipules narrow,
       often toothed but not lobed [Fig. LXVIIa]   2
    Petals often yellow, at least in part; stipules deeply lobed [Fig. LXVIIb]   9

Fig. LXVIIa   Fig. LXVIIb

2. Leaves and flowers all arising from the basal rosette; no overground
      stems apparent, except sometimes for prostrate stolons   ..   3
     Erect stems present (though sometimes short), bearing leaves and flowers   5

3. Stolons absent; leaves downy, distinctly longer than broad   ..   **2. V. hirta**
     Prostrate stolons present; leaves hairless or somewhat downy,
      circular or very slightly longer than broad   4

4. Flowers scented, deep violet or pure white; style hooked at tip   **1. V. odorata**
     Flowers scentless, usually pale lilac; style truncate at tip   **3. V. palustris**

5. Basal leaves fairly numerous   6
     Basal leaves very few or absent   7

6. Lowest petal c. 5 mm wide; spur paler in colour than the blade of
      the petal; basal appendages of sepals 1.5-2 mm in fruit   **4. V. riviniana**
     Lowest petal c. 3 mm wide; spur deeper in colour than the blade
      of the petal; basal appendages of sepals less than 1 mm in fruit
         5. V. reichenbachiana

7. Leaves 2.5 - 3 times as long as broad, tapered to the petiole   ..   **8. V. lactea**
     Leaves not more than twice as long as broad, truncate or cordate at the
      base   8

8. Petals bright blue; spur usually yellow; all stems arising from a
      single tuft   ..   ..   **6. V. canina**
     Petals rather pale blue; spur pale green; plant spreading below
      ground by buds from creeping roots   ..   ..   **7. V. persicifolia**

9. Petals usually shorter than the sepals, mostly creamy white   **9. V. arvensis**
     Petals longer than the sepals, at least the uppermost violet or yellow   10

10. Plant with long, creeping rhizome, from which arise erect, unbranched
      stems; petals up to 15 mm long   ..   ..   ..   **11. V. lutea**
     Rhizome short or absent; erect stems often brancheed; petals not more
      than 12 mm long   ..   ..   ..   **10. V. tricolor**

Several hybrids in this genus have been reported from Ireland. Most of them are rare, but as *V. persicifolia* is often accompanied throughout its limited range by *V. canina*, the hybrids between these two species are locally frequent.

1. Viola odorata. Sweet violet. 3-5. Perennial, with long, prostrate stolons. Leaves all basal, more or less circular, cordate, crenate, somewhat downy. Flowers deep violet or pure white, usually fragrant. Bracts at or above the middle of the pedicel. Capsule downy, more or less spherical; style hooked at the tip. *Hedges and other shady places; occasional.*

Probably native in some districts, but often an escape from gardens, especially in the North and West.

2. V. hirta. 4-5. Like *V. odorata*, but without stolons; leaves very downy, triangular-ovate; flowers pale lilac, not fragrant; bracts below the middle of the pedicel. *Dry grassland and limestone rocks in South half; rare.*

3. V. palustris. 4-6. Perennial, with slender, creeping rhizome. Leaves all basal, more or less circular, cordate; blade hairless but stalk often hairy. Bracts near the middle of the pedicel. Flowers dull lilac, often with darker veins. Capsule hairless, longer than broad; style truncate at the tip. *Bogs, acid marshes and wet woods; very frequent in the North, West and South-east, rather rare elsewhere.*

4. V. riviniana. Dog violet. 4-6. Hairless or sparsely downy perennial, without stolons. Basal leaves fairly numerous, forming a loose rosette in the centre of the plant; from the sides of this arise erect stems bearing flowers and leaves. Leaves broadly oval, cordate. Corolla violet, the spur pale lilac, curved, truncate and furrowed at the tip. Basal appendages of sepals conspicuous, enlarging in fruit to up to 2.5 mm long. *Hedgebanks, heaths, pastures, sandhills and woods; abundant.*

By far the commonest species of *Viola* in Ireland.

5. V. reichenbachiana. 3-5. Very like *V. riviniana* in leaves and general habit, but with narrower petals; spur of corolla deep violet, flattened and not furrowed at the tip; appendages to the sepals not more than 1 mm, not enlarging in fruit. *Woods and scrub, mainly on limestone soils; occasional.*

6. V. canina. 5-7. More or less branched perennial, with short, erect or inclined, leafy stems; rhizome short or absent; basal leaves few. Leaves broadly oval, truncate or cordate at the base. Corolla clear blue; spur usually yellow. *Sandhills and stony lake-shores; local.*

7. V. persicifolia (*V. stagnina*). **5-6.** Similar to *V. canina*, but spreading below ground by buds arising from creeping roots, so as to form clumps or patches; leaves slightly narrower and more pointed; flowers paler blue, with shorter petals (so that the flower appears circular in face-view) and greenish spur. *Grassland subject to flooding in the West (Clare and Fermanagh); very local.*

8. V. lactea. 6-7. Similar to *V. canina*, but with narrowly elliptical-oval leaves tapered gradually to the stalk, and pale, greyish-blue flowers. *Heathy grassland and siliceous rocks in the South half; rare.*

9. V. arvensis. Heartsease. 5-9. Hairless annual, with erect, branched, leafy stems. Leaves oval, crenate. Stipules conspicuous, deeply divided into narrow lobes. Flowers 12-15 mm across; petals usually slightly shorter than the sepals, mostly creamy white with a yellow eye, and often streaked with violet. *Cultivated ground; frequent in the South-east, occasional elsewhere.*

10. V. tricolor. 5-9. Leaves oval, crenate. Stipules deeply divided into narrow lobes. Flowers up to 25 mm across; petals longer than the sepals, violet-blue or yellow, or a combination of the two.

There are two distinct subspecies:

Subsp. *tricolor*. Annual; flowers usually violet. *Cultivated ground; mainly in the North, occasional.*

Subsp. *curtisii*. Perennial, with tufted, erect, often branched stems; flowers often partly or entirely yellow. *Frequent on sand-dunes; rarely on lake-shores.*

11. V. lutea. 6-8. Similar to *V. tricolor*, subsp. *curtisii*, but with somewhat larger flowers, and with a creeping rhizome from which arise distinct, unbranched stems. *Upland pastures in the South half; very local.*

Some populations in Clare and West Galway appear to be intermediate between *V. lutea* and *V. tricolor* subsp. *curtisii*. They may be hybrids, but require further investigation.

LXVIII. CUCURBITACEAE

Melons, Cucumbers and Vegetable marrows are among the cultivated plants belonging to this family.

* Bryonia dioica. White bryony. 6-9. A large, scrambling, coarsely hairy, dioecious herb, climbing by spirally coiled axillary tendrils. Leaves alternate, shortly stalked, palmately lobed. Flowers 10-12 mm in diameter, in axillary cymes. Calyx shortly 5-lobed; petals 5, free or slightly united at the base, green; stamens 5, partly united in pairs; ovary inferior; style single; stigma 3-lobed. Fruit a scarlet berry 5-8 mm in diameter. *Scrub and hedges; long naturalised by the cliff-path at Baily, Co. Dublin.*

LXIX. CISTACEAE

Small herbs or undershrubs with entire leaves. Flowers regular; sepals 5, free, unequal (3 large and 2 small); petals 5; stamens numerous, hypogynous, ovary superior, 1-celled; style single. Fruit a capsule.

Many species and hybrids of *Helianthemum* are grown in gardens. The shrubby Sun-roses belong to the related genus *Cistus*.

1. Erect annual; style very short   ..   ..   **1. Tuberaria**
   Dwarf, more or less prostrate shrub; style at least as long as the
      ovary   .·.   ..   ..   ·..   **2. Helianthemum**

1. Tuberaria
Tuberaria guttata (*Helianthemum guttatum*). **6-8.** A small, erect, hairy annual. Leaves oblong, hairy, mostly in a basal rosette; a few opposite or alternate on the stem. Flowers 15-20 mm across, in small, terminal cymes. Petals pale yellow, usually with a dark red patch at the base. Stigma 3-lobed, almost stalkless. *Dry, shallow, peaty soil overlying siliceous rock. Very local in the South-west and West (Cork to Mayo), mainly on the islands.*

2. Helianthemum. Rock-rose
More or less prostrate dwarf shrubs with wiry stems. Leaves green and sparsely hairy above, densely hairy and white beneath. Flowers in terminal cymes.

1. Flowers 20 mm across; stipules present   ..   **1. H. nummularium**
   Flowers 10-12 mm across; leaves without stipules   ..   ..   **2. H. canum**

1. † Helianthemum nummularium (*H. chamaecistus*). **6-9.** Leaves 10-15 mm long, oblong; stipules 2-3 mm. Petals bright yellow. Style longer than ovary. *Grassland overlying limestone; known only from one knoll in South-east Donegal, where it has persisted since 1893.*

2. H. canum. 5-7. Leaves 5-8 mm long, oblong; stipules absent. Petals pale yellow. Style strongly curved, about as long as the ovary; stigma 3-lobed. *Limestone rocks in Clare and Aran; locally frequent.*

LXX. ELATINACEAE

Elatine
Minute annuals, with short, creeping stems and opposite leaves. Flowers solitary, globular and axillary. Sepals 3-4, membranous, more or less free; petals similar but slightly larger and pink; stamens twice as many as petals. Ovary superior. Fruit a capsule with long and fairly slim, rough seeds.

1. Pedicels more or less absent, flowers stalkless; seeds strongly
       curved   ..   ..   ..   **2. E. hydropiper**
    Pedicels at least as long as flowers; seeds straight or slightly
       curved   ..   ..   ..   **1. E. hexandra**

1. Elatine hexandra. 7-9. Leaves spoon-shaped, almost stalkless. Flowers long-stalked. Sepals and petals usually 3. Seeds straight or slightly curved. *Shallow water in lakes and rivers; locally frequent in the South-west and North, very rare elsewhere.*

2. E. hydropiper. 7-9. Similar to *E. hexandra* but with the leaves more distinctly stalked, stalkless flowers with 4 sepals and petals and 8 stamens and seeds which are strongly curved. *Only known from the shores of a number of loughs in the North-east.*

LXXI.   LYTHRACEAE

Lythrum

Herbs with usually opposite, entire leaves without stipules. Flowers usually with a 12-toothed calyx; the teeth of two types; petals 6 or 0; stamens 12 or 6, attached to the inside of the calyx-tube, near the base; ovary superior; style single.

Yellow loosestrife, *Lysimachia vulgaris*, belongs to the Primulaceae.

1. Leaves lanceolate; petals large (more than 7 mm long)   **1. L. salicaria**
    Leaves oval; petals small (less than 4 mm long) or absent   **2. L. portula**

1. Lythrum salicaria. Purple loosestrife. *Earball caitín.* **7-8.** A stiff, erect, usually shortly hairy perennial up to 1 m high. Leaves opposite or in whorls of 3, stalkless, lanceolate, 5-10 cm long. Flowers in dense, reddish-purple whorls in terminal spikes. Calyx with twice as many teeth as petals, the narrowly triangular teeth alternating with the rounded. Petals usually 6. Stamens twice as many as petals of two distinct lengths in any one flower. Ovary deeply sunk in the calyx-tube but free from it. *Ditches, marshes and wet meadows; frequent in the East, abundant in the West.*

Plants bear flowers of one of three forms which differ in the relative lengths of the style and stamens.

2. L. portula (*Peplis portula*). **Water purslane. 7-8.** A creeping, hairless annual, forming small tufts. Leaves opposite, oval, 10-15 mm long, stalked at the base. Flowers very small, stalkless, axillary and numerous. Calyx 12 toothed; the broadly teeth triangular alternating with the linear. Petals 6, small, purple, sometimes absent. Stamens 6. Top of ovary overtopping the calyx. *Pools, ditches and wet ground; frequent in the South-west, occasional elsewhere.*

* *L. hyssopifolium*, an erect to decumbent annual with similar, small pink flowers, but linear leaves and a cylindrical capsule has been recently re-found in Wexford.

LXXII.   MYRTACEAE

Aromatic, evergreen, trees or shrubs with undivided leaves. Flowers hermaphrodite, actinomorphic, with 4-5 sepals and petals and numerous stamens.

1. Leaves on old shoots alternate. Fruit a capsule   ..   **1. Eucalyptus**
    Leaves leaves on old shoots opposite. Fruit a berry ..   **2. Amomyrtus**

1. Eucalyptus

Trees. Leaves often pale bluish-green, those on older branches alternate and of different shape to those on young shoots which are opposite. Petals forming a coherent cover which is lost as the flower opens and the attractive stamens expand. Fruit a capsule.

A number of species, in addition to those listed below, have been planted for ornament and small-scale forestry trials and may self-seed. Amongst these is * *E. globulus*, which differs from the species below in having solitary flowers rather than flowers in groups of at least 3.

1. Fruit urn-shaped; valves hidden inside the top. Flowers with distinct
   pedicels   ..   ..   **1. E. urnigera**
   Fruit bowl-shaped; valves clearly protruding from the top. Flowers
   more or less stalkless   2
2. Fruit ridged or wrinkled, 9-13 mm across   ..   **2. E. johnstonii**
   Fruit smooth, 5-9 mm across   ..   ..   **3. E. viminalis**

1. * Eucalyptus viminalis. 7-9. Very large tree with whitish or greyish bark, up to 40 m high. Young and adult leaves lanceolate. Flowers more or less stalkless. Fruit bowl-shaped with the valves clearly protruding from the top, up to 9 mm across, smooth. *Planted for forestry in a few areas and now self-seeding.* Native of Australia.

2. * E. johnstonii (*E. muelleri*). **7-9.** Very large tree to 40 m with orangish or yellowish or greyish bark. Young leaves becoming orbicular; adult lanceolate. Flowers more or less stalkless. Fruit bowl-shaped with the valves clearly protruding from the top, 9-13 mm across. *Planted for forestry in a few areas and now self-seeding.* Native of Australia.

3. * E. urnigera. 7-9. Moderately sized tree up to 12 m high with greyish or yellowish-brown bark. Young leaves orbicular; adult lanceolate. Flowers with distinct pedicels up to 4 mm long. Fruit urn-shaped with the valves hidden, 8-10 m across. *Planted for forestry in a few areas and now self-seeding.* Native of Australia.

* *E. gunnii* is similar but with smaller flowers and fruits.

2. Luma

* **Luma apiculata** (*Amomyrtus luma, Myrtus luma, Eugenia apiculata*). **7-9.** Shrub or small tree up to 10 m tall with all leaves oval, sharply pointed, opposite; flowers with white or pale-pinkish, curved petals and a dark purple, globose berry. *Planted in large gardens and demesnes and self-seeding in a number of localities.* Native of South America.

LXXIII.   ONAGRACEAE

Perennial herbs or shrubs, with undivided, usually opposite leaves, without stipules. Flowers axillary or in racemes. Calyx 2- or 4-lobed; petals as many; stamens 2 or 8, epigynous; ovary inferior, 2- or 4-celled.

Among garden shrubs belonging to this family are various kinds of *Fuchsia*, also *Clarkia*, *Godetia* and *Oenothera* (Evening primrose).

1. Shrub; calyx red and showy   ..   ..   ..   **1. Fuchsia**
   Herb; calyx inconspicuous   2
2. Petals yellow, large   ..   ..   **3. Oenothera**
   Petals pink, purplish or white   3
3. Petals 4, stamens 8   ..   ..   **4. Epilobium**
   Petals and stamens 2   ..   ..   **2. Circaea**

1. Fuchsia

* **Fuchsia magellanica. 7-9.** A bushy shrub with yellowish bark and hairless, opposite, stalked, oval, toothed leaves. Flowers axillary, drooping, 3-4 cm across. Calyx crimson, 4-lobed; petals 4, deep purple, shorter than calyx-lobes. Stamens 8,

very long. Fruit a blackish, fleshy berry. *Planted for hedges mainly in the West.* Native of South America.

The variety most commonly planted, with fat, nearly spherical buds (var. *riccartonii*), hardly ever sets fruit and is only occasionally naturalised. Other varieties, with narrower buds, are planted in a few districts.

2. Circaea

Erect perennials with opposite, stalked leaves and small white or pale pink flowers in terminal racemes. Calyx-lobes 2, turned downwards; petals 2, notched; stamens 2; ovary much shorter than in *Epilobium*. Fruit indehiscent, bristly, with 2 seeds.

1. Leaves scarcely toothed; pedicels densely hairy; fruit plentiful   **1. C. lutetiana**
    Leaves distinctly toothed; pedicels with few hairs; fruit nearly
       always abortive   ..   ..   ..   **2. C. x intermedia**

1. Circaea lutetiana. Enchanter's nightshade. *Fuinseagach.* **6-8.** 25-50 cm. high. Leaves usually slightly downy, not shining, somewhat triangular, very feebly toothed. Flowers 7-10 mm across; pedicels covered with glandular hairs. Fruit 2-seeded, drooping, covered with hooked bristles. *Woods, shaded roadsides and as a garden weed; frequent.*

2. C. x intermedia. 7-9. Similar to *C. lutetiana* but with leaves slightly cordate, thinner, somewhat shining, and more strongly toothed, with fruit nearly always abortive. *Rocky and shaded places in the North half; rare.*

A hybrid between *C. lutetiana* and *C. alpina*; the latter does not now occur in Ireland, but probably did in the past.

3. Oenothera. Evening primrose

Tall biennial herbs. Petals 4, yellow, broad and overlapping; stamens 8. Fruit many-seeded, cylindrical; seeds without a plume of hairs.

1. Hairs on green part of stem with green bulbous bases   .. **1. E. biennis**
    Hairs on green part of stem with red bulbous bases ..   **2. E. erythrosepala**

1. * Oenothera biennis. 7-9.Stems erect, 100-150 cm. Leaves hairy. Hairs on green parts of stem lacking red bulbous bases (though red-based on red parts of stem). Petals 1.5-3 cm. Sepals entirely green. *Waste ground, roadsides and sand dunes; rare.* Native of Eurasia.

2. * O. erythrosepala (*O. glazioviana*). **7-9.** Stem erect, 40-150 cm, with long stiff hairs with red bulbous bases even on green parts of stem. Leaves hairy. Petals 3-5 cm. Sepals red-striped or entirely red. *Similar situations; rare.* Native of North America.

4. Epilobium. Willow-herb

Perennial herbs. Petals 4, often notched; stamens 8; ovary very long and narrow. Fruit a 4-valved capsule; seeds small, each with a tuft of cottony hairs.

1. Stem prostrate; leaves nearly round, flowers solitary, axillary   ..   2
    Stem erect; leaves longer than broad; flowers in terminal and axillary
       racemes   3
2. Leaves entire, purplish on underside   ..   ..   **11. E brunnescens**
    Leaves dentate, green on underside   ..   ..   **12. E. pedunculare**
3. Flowers slightly irregular, in leafless racemes; all leaves alternate
                                                              1. E. angustifolium
    Flowers regular, in leaf-axils; leaves mostly opposite   ..   4

Fig. LXXIIIa   Fig. LXXIIIb

4. Stigma deeply 4-lobed [Fig. LXXIIIa]   5
    Stigma club-shaped, not 4-lobed [Fig. LXXIIIb]   7

5. Leaves with numerous soft outstanding hairs   6
    Leaves hairless or nearly so   ..   ..   **4. E. montanum**

6. Plant 80-150 cm high; flowers 20 mm across   ..   **2. E. hirsutum**
    Plant 30-90 cm high; flowers 8-10 mm across   ..   **3. E. parviflorum**

7. Leaves distinctly stalked ..   ..   ..   **7. E. roseum**
    Lesaves more or less stalkless   8

8. Stem smoothly cylindrical, without ridges though sometimes with
     two rows of curled hairs; stolons long, thread-like   **6. E. palustre**
    Stem with 2 or 4 longitudinal ridges running down from the leaf-
     bases; stolons leafy, shortly stalked or almost stalkless   ..   9

9. Stem prostrate at least at the base, less than 15 cm tall. Buds
     drooping ..   ..   ..   **8. E. alsinifolium**
    Stem erect, usually more than 20 cm tall. Buds erect   ..   10

10. Upper part of stem with spreading glandular hairs and appressed
     curled hairs   ..   ..   ..   **9. E. ciliatum**
    Spreading glandular hairs absent or confined to hypanthium   ..   11

11. Spreading glandular hairs present only on hypanthium. Mature
     capsule 4-6 cm. Stolons leafy, short, but with a distinct stem
     formed in autumn   ..   ..   **5. E. obscurum**
    Spreading glandular hairs absent. Mature capsule 7-10 cm. Stalkless
     leaf-rosettes formed in autumn   ..   ..   **10. E. tetragonum**

Many hybrids have been reported in this genus, involving especially *E. montanum*, *E. parviflorum*, *E. ciliatum* and *E. obscurum*. Among the most frequent are *E. ciliatum* x *E. montanum* and *E. obscurum* x *E. palustre*. Hybridisation between species with entire and 4-lobed stigmas is indicated by the presence of obscurely-lobed stigmas (sometimes with only one or two lobes distinct), petals with two contrasting shades of pink, and petal size - *e.g.* abnormally large or small-sized flowers on otherwise "normal" plants. The important glandular hair characters in *E. obscurum, E. ciliatum* and *E. tetragonum* are more apparent on younger, fresh material.

1. Epilobium angustifolium (*Chamaenerion angustifolium, Chamaerion angustifolium*). **Rose-bay. 7-8.** Nearly hairless; stem unbranched 80-150 cm high. Leaves alternate, narrowly lanceolate, shortly stalked. Flowers deep purple-red, 25 mm across, in long terminal leafless racemes. Petals entire; upper two larger than the lower pair. Stigma 4-lobed. *Very rare as a native in rocky places in mountains; locally frequent as an introduction on bog margins, railway sidings, roadsides and waste ground in cities.*

2. E. hirsutum. 7-8. Stems stout, 80-150 cm high, branched. Whole plant softly hairy. Leaves mostly opposite, stalkless, almost clasping the stem, oblong-lanceolate, toothed. Flowers deep rose-pink, *c.* 20 mm across; stigma 4-lobed. *Ditches, riversides and damp waste places; occasional in drier habitats; very frequent especially in East half.*

3. E. parviflorum. 7-8. Stem 30-90 cm high, more or less softly hairy. Leaves oblong-lanceolate, stalkless, slightly toothed or nearly entire, some alternate. Flowers pale pink, 8-10 mm across; stigma 4-lobed. *Ditches and damp waste places; very frequent.*

4. E. montanum. 6-8. Stem 15-60 cm high, slightly downy. Leaves hairless, oval-lanceolate, toothed, mostly opposite. Flowers pinkish mauve, 8 mm across; stigma 4-lobed. Buds slightly drooping. *Waste ground in cities, roadsides, hedgerow banks, woods and as a garden weed; abundant.*

5. E. obscurum. 7-8. Stem erect, branched, 30-60 cm high, with 2 or 4 longitudinal ridges running down from the bases of the leaves; short and leafy stolons formed above and below ground in summer. Leaves mostly opposite, stalkless, oblong-lanceolate, toothed, hairless. Buds erect. Flowers pale purplish-pink, 6-8 mm across, petals slightly lobed; stigma entire. Developing capsule with a few glandular hairs [Fig. LXXIIIc]. *Marshes and damp waste places; also on rocks and walls by rivers; frequent.*

6. E. palustre. 7-8. Similar to *E. obscurum*, but stem cylindrical, without ridges; stolons at base long and thread-like, often underground; leaves linear-lanceolate; flowers only 5 mm across and buds drooping. *Bogs, marshes and stream-sides; frequent.*

7. * E. roseum. 7-8. Stem slender, 30-60 cm high, slightly ridged, with some glandular hairs. Leaves stalked, oval, toothed, nearly hairless; many of them alternate. Flowers very pale pink, 5 mm across. Stigma entire. Buds drooping. *Damp shady places and waste ground; rare.*

8. E. alsinifolium. 6-8. Stem slender, decumbent, 5-15 cm, with slightly toothed, shortly stalked oval lanceolate leaves and drooping bluish-red flowers 8 mm across. Stigma club-shaped. *Confined to one mountain cliff in Leitrim (West side of Glenade).*

9. * E. ciliatum (*E. adenocaulon*). **6-8.** Stem 60-120 cm, stiff, with many sub-erect flowering branches and 4 longditudinal ridges (2 in lower part) running down from the leaves; hairless and reddish below, with both curled and spreading glandular hairs above. Leaves mostly opposite, oblong-lanceolate with an acute tip, a subcordate shortly-stalked base, and a hairless finely-toothed margin. Flowers 4-5 mm wide, numerous; petals pale pink with darker margins, deeply cleft. Stigma entire. Young capsule with both crisped and glandular hairs [Fig. LXXIIId], hairless later,

Fig. LXXIIIc

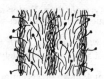

Fig. LXXIIId

Fig. LXXIIIe

4-6 cm. Seed with a pale translucent beak below the hair-tuft. *Waste ground in cities, gardens and on roadsides. Frequent, especially in urban situations and still increasing.* Native of North America.

10. * E. tetragonum. 6-9. Stem 20-50 cm stiff, with appressed, silky non-glandular hairs above, hairless below with 4 lines running down from the leaves, downy above with appressed hairs; forming almost stalkless leaf rosettes in Autumn. Leaves 4-6 cm x 6-9 mm, strap-shaped, blunt at tip, almost stalkless, decurrent, hairless . Flowers 6-8 mm, lilac-pink, slightly notched. Young capsule with short crisped hairs but lacking glandular hairs, 7-10 cm long when mature [Fig. LXXIIIe]. *Urban waste ground and gardens; rare.*

11. * E. brunnescens (*E. nerterioides*). **6-8.** Stems slender, creeping. Leaves opposite, round, slightly toothed, 4-6 mm across. Flowers small, white or pale pink, erect on short stalks. *Waste stony places, forest tracks, especially in mountains; local but spreading.* Native of New Zealand.

12. * E. pedunculare (*E. linnaeoides*). **6-8.** Similar to *E. brunnescens* but with larger (4-9 mm) more toothed leaves. *Naturalised at Leenane and Kylemore, Co Galway.* Native of New Zealand.

LXXIV.   GUNNERACEAE

Gunnera

* Gunnera tinctoria. Giant rhubarb. 5-8. A large, coarse perennial with a stout, prostrate rhizome-like stem, covered with scales. Leaves up to 200 cm across, circular, cordate, palmately 5- to 9-lobed; margin coarsely toothed; leaf-stalk erect, stout, spiny. Inflorescence a very large, erect, dense, cylindrical panicle. Flowers very small, mostly hermaphrodite, but some unisexual. Sepals, petals, styles and stigmas 2. Fruit a small drupe. *Streamsides, roadside banks and damp grassland near the West coast; occasional.* Native of South America.

Not at all related to ordinary Garden rhubarb which is a hybrid in the genus *Rheum* in the family Polygonaceae.

LXXV.   HALORAGACEAE

Perennials with flowers mostly small and unisexual (the male above, the female below), but a few hermaphrodite. Sepals inconspicuous or absent. Petals 4, oval, c. 2 mm, falling early, often absent from female flowers. Stamens 8. Ovary superior, 4-lobed; stigmas stalkless. Fruit of 4 1-seeded nutlets.

1. Leaves finely divided, whorled; plants usually aquatic   **1. Myriophyllum**
    Leaves undivided, opposite; plants growing on bare peat   **2. Haloragis**

1. Myriophyllum. Water-milfoil

Hairless, submerged, aquatic perennials. Leaves whorled, pinnately divided, with narrow-linear segments. Flowers small, in whorls or clusters, forming a loose, bracteate spike held above the water-surface,

1. Leaves mostly in whorls of 5; bracts all pinnately lobed or toothed,
    longer than the flowers ..   ..   ..   **1. M. verticillatum**
    Leaves mostly in whorls of 4; upper bracts entire or toothed but
    not lobed, shorter than the flowers   2

2. Leaves with 8-15 segments on each side; spike erect in bud; petals
   dull red .. .. **2. M. spicatum**
   Leaves with 5-8 segments on each side; spike nodding in bud; petals
   yellow streaked with red .. .. **3. M. alterniflorum**

1. Myriophyllum verticillatum. 6-8. Leaves mostly in whorls of 5, with about 15 segments on each side [Fig. LXXVa]. Spike erect in bud; lowest bracts resembling the leaves, the upper much shorter, but longer than the flowers, pinnately lobed or toothed. Petals usually yellow. Fruit 4 x 3 mm. *Pools, streams and canals, mostly in the Centre; occasional, apparently declining.*

2. M. spicatum. 6-8. Leaves mostly in whorls of 4, with 8-15 segments on each side [Fig. LXXVb]. Spike erect in bud; lowest bracts resembling the leaves, the middle and upper ones very small, shortly toothed, shorter than the flowers. Petals dull red. Fruit 2.5 x 1.8 mm. *Ponds, lakes and slow-moving rivers, usually in base-rich water; widespread and now locally abundant.*

Fig. LXXVa   Fig. LXXVb   Fig. LXXVc

3. M. alterniflorum. 6-8. Leaves mostly in whorls of 4, with 5-8 segments on each side [Fig. LXXVc]. Spikes nodding in bud, erect in fruit. Lowest bracts resembling the leaves but smaller, the middle and upper ones entire or toothed, shorter than the flowers. Flowers mostly arranged singly or in alternate clusters, not in regular whorls. Petals yellow, streaked with red. Fruit 2 x 1.5 mm. *Lakes, ponds and streams, usually in acid waters; fairly frequent in the North, West and Centre, rare in the South-east.*

Plants from calcareous lakes in the North and along the Shannon may be compact with very short leaves sometimes in borne in threes.

2. Haloragis

* **Haloragis micrantha. 7.** Minute spreading herb with opposite, oval, almost stalkless leaves, about 5 mm long, and tiny flowers with persistent sepals borne along a short spike. *Known only from one site on bare peat on moorland in West Galway.*

LXXVI. HIPPURIDACEAE

Hippuris vulgaris. Mare's tail. 6-7. An aquatic, rhizomatous perennial with erect, unbranched stems projecting above the surface of the water. Leaves linear, entire, stalkless, in whorls of about 10; those above the surface about 25 mm long, fairly stiff, those submerged often much longer, wider and limp. Flowers minute, axillary, without a perianth, consisting of an ovary with a single style and (in some flowers) a single stamen borne on top of the ovary. Fruit a one-seeded nut. *Canals, ditches, pools and lake-margins, very frequent in the Centre, occasional elsewhere.*

LXXVII. CORNACEAE

Two common garden plants used extensively for hedging are; Spotted laurel (*Acuba japonica*), with large, oval, yellow-spotted leaves and *Griselinia littoralis* with alternate, pale-yellowish-green, broadly-oval leaves. The latter may set fertile and abundant seed.

Cornus. Dogwood

Medium sized shrubs with reddish twigs. Leaves opposite, oval, entire, shortly stalked, pulling-apart to reveal long, elastic strands from the curved and paired veins, softly hairy when young. Flowers regular, hermaphrodite, in terminal umbel-like panicles. Calyx-tube united with ovary; surmounted by 4 minute teeth. Petals and stamens 4. Ovary inferior, 2-celled; style single. Fruit a berry-like drupe.

1. Larger leaves with at most 5 pairs of side veins; flowers 9-11 mm
    across; fruit purplish   ..   ..   ..   **1. C. sanguinea**
    Larger leaves usually with at least 6 pairs of side veins; flowers 6-7 mm
    across; fruit whitish   ..   .. **2. C. sericea**

1. Cornus sanguinea. 4-5. Shrub to 4 m. Flowers, fruits, leaves and young twigs with a covering of scattered, appressed hairs. Leaves with 4-5 (rarely 3) pairs of lateral veins; leaf-stalk about 5 mm. Flowers 9-11 mm across. Corolla broadly spreading. Fruit 4 mm across, purplish-black. *Rocky places and thickets in the Centre and West (Limerick, Clare and Galway); very rare elsewhere.*

2. * C. sericea. 4-5. Similar to *C. sanguinea*; but shorter and differing in its brighter, blood-red twigs; upturned, somewhat trailing branches which sucker and form large thickets; slightly larger leaves with a longer leaf-stalk and at least 5-7 pairs of veins; slightly smaller flowers (6-7 mm across) and white fruits. *Frequently planted by water, in large gardens and demesnes; spreading by suckering from these initial plantings; scattered but widespread.* Native of North America.

LXVIII. ARALIACEAE

Hedera

Hedera helix. Ivy. *Eidhneán*. **10-12.** A woody creeping or climbing perennial, clinging by small roots. Leaves dark green, glossy, up to 8 cm across, with a few star-shaped hairs; entire and diamond-shaped on the flowering shoots; broader and palmately 5-lobed on the barren ones. Flowers, regular, hermaphrodite, green, in umbels. Calyx-tube united with ovary, surmounted by 5 very small teeth. Petals 5, sepal-like. Stamens 5. Ovary largely inferior. Style single. Fruit a black berry. *Hedges, woods, walls and rocks; widespread and abundant.*

Two sub-species are sometimes distinguished. Subsp. *hibernica* differs from subsp. *helix* in its usually broader leaves and star-shaped hairs, the arms of which are all appressed to the leaf-surface rather than both appressed and outstanding. It is probably only a variety of *H. helix*.

LXXIX. UMBELLIFERAE (APIACEAE)

Herbs, mostly perennial, with alternate leaves, usually pinnately divided, and often with the base of the leaf-stalk forming a swollen sheath; stipules absent. Flowers small, usually regular, arranged in *umbels* which are usually compound, the stalks of the *partial umbels* meeting in a point to form the general umbel. *Bracts*, at the base of the umbel and *bracteoles* at the base of the partial umbels, are often present. Calyx usually reduced to a tube surrounding the ovary and fused with it, rarely with 5 projecting teeth. Petals 5, free, sometimes unequal, usually with notched or incurved tips. Stamens 5, epigynous. Ovary inferior, 2-celled, splitting when ripe into 2 indehiscent partial fruits. Styles 2.

Identification of many species is difficult without ripe fruit. Bracts and bracteoles may fall early.

Many familiar vegetables belong to the family, including Carrots (*Daucus*), Parsnips (*Pastinaca*), Celery (*Apium*) and Parsley (*Petroselenum*), as well as many pot herbs. Several species are poisonous, especially Hemlock (*Conium maculatum*), Water hemlock (*Cicuta virosa*) and *Oenanthe crocata*.

1. Flowers blue; leaves spiny .. .. .. **3. Eryngium**
   Flowers white, pink or yellow; leaves spineless 2
2. Leaves undivided or palmately lobed 3
   Some or all of the leaves pinnately or ternately divided .. 4
3. Stem erect; leaves palmately lobed .. .. .. **2. Sanicula**
   Stem creeping; leaves undivided .. .. **1. Hydrocotyle**
4. Fruit bearing prickles or bristles 5
   Fruit smooth or with a few soft hairs 7
5. Bracts pinnatifid .. .. **28. Daucus**
   Bracts entire or absent 6
6. Fruit with a short smooth beak .. .. **5. Anthriscus**
   Fruit prickly all over, not beaked .. .. **29. Torilis**
7. Flowers yellow, or yellowish-green 8
   Flowers white or pink 12
8. Leaves fleshy, with nearly cylindrical segments .. **14. Crithmum**
   Leaves flat or hairlike, not fleshy 9
9. Leaf-segments very narrow, hair-like .. .. **17. Foeniculum**
   Leaf-segments flat 10
10. Leaves pinnately divided 11
    Leaves ternately divided .. .. .. **8. Smyrnium**
11. Leaves once pinnate; leaflets coarsely toothed or lobed **26. Pastinaca**
    Leaves twice or thrice pinnate, dissected into small segments **20. Petroselinum**
12. Leaflets oval, mostly of uniform size, regularly and finely toothed,
    simply pinnate or biternate 13
    Leaflets, at least in some of the leaves, irregularly or jaggedly lobed
    or toothed, or else long and narrow 17
13. Most of the leaves once pinnate 14
    Most of the leaves biternate 16
14. Umbels stalkless or with very short stalks; bracts few or none .. **19. Apium**
    Umbels long-stalked; bracts numerous 15
15. Umbels terminal, with 20-25 rays. Fruit 3-4 mm long. Plant about
    1-2 m high§.. .. .. **12. Sium**
    Umbels opposite the leaves, with 10-15 rays. Fruit no more than
    2 mm long. Plant about 0.5 m high .. .. .. **13. Berula**
16. Infloresence hairless; plant green,with creeping rhizome, forming large
    patches; bracteoles absent .. .. **11. Aegopodium**
    Inflorescence slightly downy; plant purplish, with a white bloom;
    without rhizome; bracteoles present .. .. **24. Angelica**
17. Hairless, at least to the naked eye 18
    Hairy 28

18. Styles falling before the fruit ripens 19
    Styles persistent in fruit 21
19. Annual; bracteoles only on the outer part of each umbel .. **16. Aethusa**
    Biennial or perennial; bracteoles, if present, arranged symmetrically
    all around each partial umbel 20
20. Leaves mostly biternate; fruit broadly winged .. **25. Peucedanum**
    Leaves mostly once or twice pinnate; fruit ridged but not winged **19. Apium**
21. Calyx-teeth conspicuous and persistent in fruit [Fig. LXXIXa & b]
                                                            15. Oenanthe
    Calyx-teeth absent or very small 22
22. Styles straight and erect in fruit .. .. .. **9. Conopodium**
    Styles curved and diverging in fruit 23
23. Leaflets undivided .. .. **22. Carum**
    Leaflets toothed 24
24. Bracts present 25
    Bracts absent 27
25. Leaves once pinnate .. .. **13. Berula**
    Leaves twice pinnate or biternate 26
26. Plant at least 1 m tall when mature; leaves twice pinnate, with
       narrow leaflets; stem spotted with purple .. **18. Conium**
    Plant no more than 0.5 m tall when mature; leaves biternate, with
       broad leaflets; stem not spotted with purple .. **23. Ligusticum**
27. Marsh plant; bracteoles present. Fruit broader than long .. **21. Cicuta**
    Plant of dry ground; bracteoles absent. Fruit at least as long as
       broad .. .. **10. Pimpinella**
28. Umbels unbranched, or with 2-3 rays; fruit with beak 25-50 mm
       long .. .. **6. Scandix**
    Umbels with at least 5 rays; fruit with a short beak or none .. 29
29. Fruits strongly flattened, eventually splitting into 2 very flat partial
       fruits [Fig. LXXIXc] .. .. .. **27. Heracleum**
    Fruits rounded, eventually splitting into 2 rounded or semi-cylindrical
       partial fruits [Fig. LXXIXd] 30
30. Fruit with conspicuous sharp ridges [Fig. LXXIXd] .. .. **7. Myrrhis**
    Fruit with low rounded ridges or none 31

Fig. LXXIXa

Fig. LXXIXb

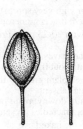

Fig. LXXIXc

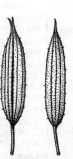

Fig. LXXIXd

31 Stems all solid, stained with purple; fruit slightly ridged   **4. Chaerophyllum**
    Older stems hollow, not tinged with purple; fruit quite smooth,
    shining   ..   ..   **5. Anthriscus**

1. Hydrocotyle
Hydrocotyle vulgaris. Marsh pennywort. 5-7. Stem slender and creeping, rooting at the nodes. Leaves round, long-stalked, slightly crenate, hairless, 15-25 mm across, peltate. Peduncles shorter than petioles. Flowers very small, greenish-white, in compact heads, or occasionally in 2 or 3 whorls on each peduncle. Fruit broad and flattened. *Marshes, fens, bog margins and damp grassland; frequent.*

* *H. moschata*, similar in general habit, but with the leaves hairy and more deeply lobed, not peltate and the flowers pinkish, a native of New Zealand is naturalised on grassy banks on Valentia Island, Co. Kerry.

2. Sanicula
Sanicula europaea. Wood sanicle. 5-7. A hairless, slender perennial, 30-60 cm high. Leaves mostly basal, long-stalked, 35-50 mm across, palmatifid, with usually five wedge-shaped, toothed lobes, often themselves divided. Flowers pink or white, in small globular heads, arranged in an irregular umbel. Bracts and bracteoles present. Calyx-teeth as long as the petals. Fruit round, covered with hooked bristles. *Woods and shady places; frequent.*

3. Eryngium
Eryngium maritimum. Sea holly. *Cuileann trá.* **7-8.** A rigid, bushy perennial, 30-50 cm high, hairless and bluish-green. Leaves broad, very prickly, with conspicuous veins. Flowers pale blue, in very dense heads interspersed with prickly bracts. Fruit with stiff, persistent calyx-teeth and covered with short spines. *Sandy shores; frequent though rather local.*

4. Chaerophyllum
* **Chaerophyllum temulum. Chervil. 6-7.** Biennial, with sparse, rough hairs; stem solid, grooved, swollen below the nodes, purple or purple-spotted, 50-100 cm high. Leaves twice or thrice pinnate; leaflets rather blunt. Umbels drooping in bud, with 5-10 unequal rays, the terminal umbels overtopped by the axillary ones. Bracts 0 or 1; bracteoles 5-8, drooping, shorter than the pedicels. Flowers white. Fruit 5-6 mm, 2-3 times as long as broad, slightly ridged. *Hedges and roadsides, mostly in the East and South-east; very rare and declining.*

5. Anthriscus
Leaves fern-like, twice or thrice pinnate. Bracts 0 or 1; bracteoles 4-5. Flowers white. Fruit ovoid or oblong, with a short beak.

1. Fruit 6-8 mm, smooth, shining   ..   ..   **1. A. sylvestris**
    Fruit 2 mm, covered in bristles   ..   ..   **2. A. caucalis**

1. Anthriscus sylvestris. Cow-parsley. 4-6. Erect perennial, 70-120 cm, hairy, especially in the lower part; stem stout, hollow, grooved. Leaves large, triangular, thrice pinnate; segments pointed. Umbels terminal, long-stalked, with 8-12 rays. Bracts absent; bracteoles broad, deflexed, often pinkish. Fruit 6-8 mm, very smooth and shining, 3 times as long as broad. *Hedges and shady places; abundant except in parts of the West.*

2. A. caucalis *(A. neglecta, A. vulgaris).* **5-6.** Annual. Stem weak, hollow, hairless, 25-50 cm high. Leaves hairy, rather small, twice or thrice pinnate. Umbels small, shortly stalked, opposite the leaves with 3-6 rays. Bracts 0 or rarely 1. Fruit 2 mm, ovoid, covered, except for the beak, with hooked bristles. *Sandy banks and roadsides near the sea, mainly in the South-east; rare.*

6. Scandix

* **Scandix pecten-veneris. Shepherd's needle, Venus' comb. 6-8.** A hairy annual, 15-50 cm high, with spreading branches. Leaves narrow, twice or thrice pinnate; segments linear. Umbels small, with 2 or 3 rays, or sometimes unbranched. Bracts absent; bracteoles about 5; fruit long, slender, consisting mainly of a long beak 3-4 times as long as the remainder. *Tilled fields; very rare.*

7. Myrrhis

* **Myrrhis odorata. Sweet cicely. 5-7.** A hairy, aromatic perennial, smelling of aniseed; stem stout, hollow, grooved, branched, 60-100 cm high. Leaves large, twice or thrice pinnate, fern-like, flecked with white; leaflets toothed and pinnatifid. Umbels terminal, small, with 8-12 rays. Bracts absent; bracteoles 5-8, membranous, drooping. Flowers white. Fruit 15-20 mm, black, 3-4 times as long as broad, sharply ridged [Fig. LXXIXd]. *Roadsides and waste places; occasional in the North, very rare in the South. A former pot-herb.*

8. Smyrnium

* **Smyrnium olusatrum. Alexanders. 4-6.** A coarse, hairless biennial or perennial, 50-120 cm high, with hollow, grooved stems. Leaves shining, ternate or biternate, the upper ones with a strongly inflated sheathing stalk; leaflets oval, toothed 4-5 cms long. Flowers yellowish green, in umbels with 8-12 rays; bracts absent, bracteoles very small. Fruit broadly ovoid, strongly ridged, with diverging styles. *Hedges, roadsides and waste places; locally abundant near the coast, rare inland. A former pot-herb.*

9. Conopodium

Conopodium majus. Pignut. 5-6. A hairless perennial, with a slender, smooth, often zig-zag stem 30-50 cm high, hollow after flowering, arising from a globular, deeply buried, underground tuber. Leaves few, mostly basal, triangular, mostly thrice pinnate, withering early; upper stem leaves twice pinnate with almost linear leaf-segments, with sheathing stalks. Umbels terminal, with 6-10 slender rays, drooping in bud; bracts very few or absent, bracteoles 2-5. Flowers small, white. Fruit 3-4 mm, ovoid-oblong, faintly ridged, with straight, almost erect styles. *Woods, heaths and pastures; very frequent.*

10. Pimpinella

Perennials with variously pinnate leaves. Bracts and bracteoles absent. Flowers white or pinkish. Fruits ovoid, slightly ridged.

1. Stem slightly downy, wiry; most leaflets less than 20 mm long   **1. P. saxifraga**
   Stem hairless, strongly ridged, brittle; most leaflets more than
   25 mm long   ..   .. **2. P. major**

1. Pimpinella saxifraga. Burnet saxifrage. 7-8. Hairless or very minutely downy. Stem slender, solid, wiry, nearly smooth, 25-50 cm high. Leaves mostly basal, pinnate, with 4-7 pairs of toothed or pinnatifid, stalkless leaflets 15-20 mm long; upper stem leaves usually finely dissected into numerous narrow segments. Flowers white in terminal umbels. Bracts and bracteoles absent. Fruit 2-2.5 mm, broadly ovoid. *Pastures and dry banks; frequent in the Centre and South-east, rare elsewhere.*

2. P. major. 7-8. Stem hollow, brittle, ridged, hairless, often 1 m high. Leaves large, coarse. Leaflets usually 3-4 pairs, stalked, 25-60 mm long, irregularly toothed and lobed. Flowers white or pink. *Roadsides and bushy places; locally frequent in parts of the South and West, absent elsewhere.*

11. Aegopodium

* **Aegopodium podagraria. Bishop's weed, Goutweed, Ground elder. 6-7.** A hairless perennial with creeping rhizomes; flowering stems erect, hollow, grooved, up to 70 cm high. Lower leaves biternate, the upper ternate and often opposite; leaflets broadly lanceolate, pointed, toothed. Umbels terminal, with 12-20 rays; bracts and bracteoles absent. Flowers white. Fruit small, ovoid with long, downwardly curved styles. *Woods, gardens and waste places, usually near houses; frequent in most districts. A former pot-herb.* Native of Eurasia.

12. Sium

Sium latifolium. 7-8. A hairless perennial with erect stems 1-2 m high. Leaves simply pinnate; leaflets large, 4-5 on each side, finely and regularly toothed. Umbels large, terminal, with about 25 equal rays; bracts and bracteoles conspicuous, often leafy. Flowers white. Fruit ridged, longer than broad. *Marshes and river-banks in the Centre; rare.*

13. Berula

Berula erecta *(Sium erectum).* **7-9.** A hairless stoloniferous perennial, about 60 cm high. Leaves simply pinnate; leaflets 7-9 pairs, finely, or coarsely and jaggedly toothed or even lobed. Umbels small, mostly opposite the leaves, with about 12 unequal rays. Bracts and bracteoles present. Flowers white. Fruit smooth, broader than long. *Ditches, streams and canals; frequent in the East and Centre, occasional elsewhere.*

14. Crithmum

Crithmum maritimum. Samphire. 7-8. A hairless, slightly bluish-greyish-green perennial 15-30 cm high. Stem solid. Leaves biternate or bipinnate; leaflets linear, very fleshy, almost cylindrical, entire. Umbels terminal, on stout peduncles, with 10-20 equal stout rays. Bracts and bracteoles numerous. Flowers greenish yellow; calyx teeth absent; petals small, incurved. Fruit ovoid, spongy, ribbed. *Seaside walls, rocks and cliffs. Frequent in most of the South, much rarer in the North.*

15. Oenanthe

Hairless perennials of wet places. Leaves variously pinnate. Flowers white; often with some of them male only, with enlarged petals. Calyx-teeth present, persisting in fruit. Fruit ovoid or oblong, rather spongy, with blunt ridges.

1. Umbels mainly lateral, opposite a leaf, with the peduncle often shorter
      than the rays   2
     Umbels all terminal with the peduncles longer than the rays   ..   3
2. Fruit not more than 4.5 mm long; lowest (submerged) leaves with
      hair-like segments less than 1 mm wide; upper part of plant
      usually above water-surface   ..   ..   **5. O. aquatica**
     Fruit at least 5 mm long; lowest leaves with linear-oblong segments
      2-3 mm wide; most of the plant usually submerged or floating **6. O. fluviatilis**
3. Stem very thin-walled, with large central cavity; rays of umbel not
      more than 5   ..   ..   ..   **1. O. fistulosa**
     Stem solid or, if hollow, with a small central cavity; rays of umbel
      6 or more   4
4. Segments of upper leaves more or less oval, lobed or toothed   **4. O. crocata**
     Segments of upper leaves linear-oblong, entire   5
5. Styles 1-1.5 mm; rays of umbel slender (less than 1 mm), even in
      fruit; roots uniformly thickened, without clearly defined tubers
                                                        2. O. lachenalii
     Styles 2.5-3 mm; rays of umbel thickened in fruit (up to 2-3 mm
      wide); roots with globular tubers near the end   ..   **3. O. pimpinelloides**

1. Oenanthe fistulosa. 7-8. Root spindle-shaped. Stem slender, thin-walled, 30-60 cm. Leaves long-stalked, the stalk much longer than the blade; upper leaves suberect, once pinnate with 3-6 pairs of entire linear-oblong leaflets; lower leaves sometimes twice pinnate. Umbels terminal, with 2-5 short stout rays; bracts 0, rarely 1, bracteoles several. Fertile flowers stalkless, the barren ones stalked. Fruit 3-4 mm, ovoid, somewhat flattened, with long (4-5 mm), rigid styles and calyx-teeth [Fig. LXXIXa]. *Canals and marshes; mainly in the East and Centre; rare.*

2. O. lachenalii. 8-9. Roots with cylindrical tubers developing from the base of the stem. Stem slender, solid or with a slight hollow when older, 30-80 cm high, ribbed. Lower leaves twice pinnate with lanceolate leaflets, withering early; upper leaves pinnate to twice pinnate, with linear leaf-segments. Umbels terminal, with 7-12 slender rays. Bracts and bracteoles usually present. Pedicels not thickening in fruit. Fruit 2 mm, ovoid, styles about 1 mm. *Salt-marshes; frequent but local.*

3. O. pimpinelloides. 6-7. Roots with several rounded tubers 3-5 mm diam developing some distance from the base of the stem. Stem solid, grooved. Lower leaves twice pinnate, the segments lanceolate to ovate; upper leaf segments linear. Pedicels thickening in fruit. Fruit 3 mm, cylindrical, ribbed, styles about 3 mm, stout, erect. *Damp ground near the sea near Mullagh, Co. Clare and formerly at Trabolgan Co. Cork.*

4. O. crocata. 6-7. Stem stout, hollow, grooved, 80-150 cm high. Sap especially of roots, turning yellow on exposure to air. Leaves large, triangular, thrice pinnate, leaflets oblong to ovate, with 2 or 3 angular lobes. Umbels large, terminal, with 15-25 long slender rays; bracts and bracteoles present. Flowers white or greenish-white; calyx teeth rather short. Styles 2 mm, erect in fruit. Very poisonous. *Riversides, drains and canals; frequent in the South, East and North, rare in the Centre and West.*

5. O. aquatica. 6-8. Stem erect, hollow, grooved, stout, 50-120 cm high. Leaves twice or thrice pinnate; submerged leaflets narrow-linear or hair-like; aerial leaves oblong, usually pinnately lobed, lanceolate to ovate. Umbels small, opposite the leaves, short-stalked, with 7-12 slender rays; bracts absent, bracteoles several. Flowers all stalked and hermaphrodite. Fruit 3-4 mm, ovoid [Fig. LXXIXb]. Calyx teeth short. *Riversides, canals, drains and lake margins; locally frequent in the Centre, rare elsewhere.*

6. O. fluviatilis. 6-8. Stem weak, submerged or floating, later erect, grooved, stout, 50-120 cm high. Segments of submerged leaves twice pinnate, wedge-shaped, deeply incised. Upper leaf-segments shallowly lobed. Umbels rather small, opposite the leaves, short-stalked, with 7-12 slender rays; bracts absent, bracteoles several. Fruit 5-6 mm long and narrow. Calyx teeth short. *Rivers and canals mainly in the Centre; rare.*

16. Aethusa

* Aethusa cynapium. Fool's parsley. 7-8. A dark green, hairless, annual. Stem hollow, slightly pale bluish-green (especially on larger plants), leafy, branched, 20-80 cm high. Leaves triangular, twice or thrice pinnate; leaflets oval-lanceolate, deeply pinnatifid. Umbels long-stalked, with 6-20 unequal rays. Bracts 0 or 1; bracteoles 3-5 on outer side of each partial umbel, long and directed downwards. Flowers white. Fruit ovoid, 3 mm, sharply ridged. *Tilled fields, gardens and waste places; frequent.*

17. Foeniculum

* Foeniculum vulgare. Fennel. 7-8. A hairless, aromatic perennial smelling of aniseed, up to 150 cm high. Stem stout, finely grooved, nearly solid. Leaves thrice pinnate, with hair-like, yellowish-green leaflets. Umbels large, terminal, with 10-25 rays; bracts and bracteoles absent. Flowers small, yellow; calyx-teeth absent. Fruit ovoid-oblong. *Dry banks and waste places; occasional near the coast in the South, very rare elsewhere. A garden herb.* Native of the Mediterranean.

18. Conium

* **Conium maculatum. Hemlock. 6-7.** A hairless, leafy, unpleasant-smelling, very poisonous biennial, 100-150 cm high, with a smooth, hollow stem spotted with purple in the lower part. Leaves large, triangular, thrice pinnate, with finely-toothed leaflets. Umbels terminal, relatively small, with 10-20 rays; bracts and bracteoles present. Flowers white. Fruit broadly ovoid 2.5-3 mm, with longditudinal, wavy ridges. *Farmyards and waste ground, especially near the coast; frequent.*

19. Apium

Hairless, with ternate or pinnate leaves. Umbels compound, mostly lateral, short-stalked. Bracts few or 0, bracteoles variable. Flowers white; petals not notched. Fruit short, somewhat ridged.

1. Bracteoles absent   ..   ..   ..   **1. A. graveolens**
   Bracteoles present   2
2. Leaves with undivided, oval leaflets   ..   ..   **2. A. nodiflorum**
   Leaflets 3-lobed, or divided into hair-like segments ..   **3. A. inundatum**

1. Apium graveolens. Wild celery. 6-8. Biennial, smelling strongly of Celery, 30-70 cm high; stem hollow and grooved. Leaves pinnate or ternate; leaflets coarsely lobed and toothed. Umbels nearly stalkless, with 6-10 unequal rays; bracts and bracteoles absent. Flowers greenish white. Fruit small (1.5 mm), round. *Salt-marshes and brackish ditches; local.*

2. A. nodiflorum. 7-8. Perennial, prostrate or semi-erect with hollow stems 25-80 cm long, rooting at the nodes. Leaves simply pinnate, with oval slightly lobed leaflets. Umbels shortly stalked, opposite the leaves, with usually 5-8 rays. Bracts usually absent; bracteoles numerous. Flowers white. Fruit ovoid, 2-2.5 mm. *Ditches, streams and bare mud; frequent.*

3. A. inundatum. 6-8. Stem creeping or floating, sometimes rooting at the nodes, up to 40 cm long. Submerged leaves often tripinnately divided into hair-like segments. Upper leaves pinnate; leaflets small, 3-lobed or pinnatifid. Umbels distinctly stalked, very small, with 2-4 rays. Bracts absent, bracteoles usually 3. Flowers white. Fruit narrowly ovoid, considerably longer than broad. *Lakes, pools and bog-holes; frequent.*

Apium x *moorei*, the reputed hybrid between this species and *A. nodiflorum* occurs rarely. It resembles *A. inundatum* in having few (2-3) rays. Its submerged leaves are pinnate or bipinnate. It rarely flowers and sets poor fruit.

20. Petroselinum

* **Petroselinum crispum** *(Carum petroselinum)*. **Parsley. 7-8.** A hairless aromatic biennial, 30-75 cm high; stem solid. Lower leaves triangular, twice or thrice pinnate, with oval, lobed leaflets; upper ones usually ternate, with entire, linear leaflets. Umbels flat-topped, on long stalks, with 10-20 rays; bracts 1-3, bracteoles several. Flowers greenish yellow. Fruit broadly ovoid, nearly globular, greenish brown, aromatic. *Old walls and ruins; rare but persistent.*

21. Cicuta

Cicuta virosa. Water hemlock. 6-8. A hairless, strong-smelling, very poisonous perennial; stem hollow, 50-120 cm high. Leaves twice or thrice pinnate (upper ones often biternate), with linear-lanceolate, toothed leaflets. Umbels large, terminal, with

10-20 long rays. Bracts absent; bracteoles several, narrow. Flowers white; calyx-teeth small but visible. Fruit broader than long. *Ditches, riversides and lake-margins in the North, Centre and North-east; locally frequent.*

Resembles *Sium latifolium* in its growth form and stature but that species has bracts and once pinnate leaves.

22. Carum

Hairless; leaves variously dissected. Umbels compound; flowers white. Fruit ovoid or oblong, with low ridges.

1. Leaflets hair-like, apparently in whorls ..   ..   **1. C. verticillatum**
   Leaflets twice or thrice pinnate   ..   ..   **2. C. carvi**

1. Carum verticillatum. 7-8. Leaves mostly basal, 10-25 cm long, with numerous very fine, linear leaflets, arranged in apparent whorls on the main axis. Flowering stems 30-60 cm high; umbels with 8-12 rays; bracts and bracteoles present. Flowers white or pinkish, small. Fruit 2 mm, ovoid, not aromatic. *Damp meadows and wet pastures in the North and West; very local.*

2. * C. carvi. Caraway. 6-7. Biennial; stem hollow, ridged and grooved, branched, 30-60 cm high. Leaves long and narrow, twice or thrice pinnate; leaflets linear-oblong. Umbels of 6-12 unequal rays; bracts and bracteoles few or absent. Flowers white. Fruit brown, 3-4 mm, twice as long as broad, with few low ridges, aromatic. *Waste places, mainly in the North; occasional.*

23. Ligusticum

Ligusticum scoticum. Lovage. 7-8. A dark green, shining perennial; stem hollow, grooved, 25-50 cm high (rarely up to 1.2 m). Leaves mostly biternate; leaflets 25-50 mm long, oval, toothed. Umbels terminal, long-stalked, with about 12 rays. Bracts few, narrow; bracteoles more numerous. Flowers white; calyx-teeth small but visible. Fruit ovoid-oblong, sharply ridged. *Cliffs and rocky shores in the North; rare.*

24. Angelica

Angelica sylvestris. 7-8. A stout, nearly hairless perennial; stem thick, hollow, often with a white bloom or reddish, up to 125 cm high. Leaves large, twice or thrice pinnate or ternate; stalk of upper leaves very inflated at the base; leaflets oval, 25-50 mm long, regularly toothed. Umbels large, hemispherical, with 20-30 rays; bracts few or absent, bracteoles few. Flowers white or pale pink. Fruit oblong, flattened, broadly winged. *By streams and ditches, and in damp meadows; abundant.*

25. Peucedanum

* Peucedanum ostruthium. Masterwort. 7-8. A downy perennial, 60-100 cm high. Leaves ternate or biternate; leaflets large, toothed and lobed. Flowers white; umbels large, with many rays. Bracts absent; bracteoles few and small. Fruit flattened and winged, nearly round. *Banks and roadsides in the North-east; rare. A former pot-herb.* Native of Central and southern Europe.

26. Pastinaca

* Pastinaca sativa *(Peucedanum sativum).* **Wild parsnip. 6-7.** A hairy biennial, 50-100 cm high. Stem hollow, grooved. Leaves pinnate, yellow-green; leaflets large, stalkless, coarsely toothed and lobed. Flowers yellow; umbels small with unequal rays. Bracts and bracteoles absent. Fruit 5-7 mm, flattened and winged. *Roadsides and waste ground; rare, but sometimes persistent.*

27. Heracleum
Large, coarse hairy plants with hollow, ridged stems. Leaves large or very large. Fruit flattened [Fig. LXXIXc].

1. Stems less than 2 m high. Umbels flat-topped. Bracts usually absent
1. H. sphondylium
  Stems more than 2 m high. Umbels hemispherical. Bracts present
2. H. mantegazzianum

1. Heracleum sphondylium. Hogweed, Cow-parsnip. *Feabhrán.* **6-8.** A perennial, 100-150 cm high; stem stout, grooved. Leaves large, simply pinnate; leaflets coarsely toothed and pinnatifid, downy beneath. Umbels terminal, large, flat-topped, with 15-30 stout rays. Bracts and bracteoles few or absent. Flowers creamy-white, large; outermost petals of umbel enlarged. Fruit oval, 7-8 mm, with dark streaks on upper part. *Hedges, meadows and waste places; abundant.*

2. * H. mantegazzianum. Giant hogweed. 6-8. A biennial or perennial with a strong resinous smell. Stem up to 4 m high and 10 cm diam, ridged. Leaves up to 1 m, pinnately divided. Umbels 30-40 cm across, hemispherical. Bracts and bracteoles linear. Flowers creamy-white. Fruit 10-12 mm, winged. *Naturalised in damp places; locally frequent and increasing. Substances secreted by this plant can cause a severe skin irritation, especially when handled in bright sunlight.* Native of S.W. Asia. Formerly planted in estates.

28. Daucus
Daucus carota. Wild carrot. 7-8. A hairy biennial; stem solid, grooved, 30-75 cm high. Leaves twice or thrice pinnate, with fine lobed leaflets. Umbels large, terminal, flat-topped or domed in flower, later concave; rays 20-40. Bracts numerous, large, pinnatifid; bracteoles slenderer, entire. Flowers white or pinkish white. Fruit ovoid, covered with prickles. *Banks, pastures and waste places; frequent near the coast, occasional on lime-rich ground inland.*

Separated by some authors into 3 subspecies distinguished on the basis of their root colour and umbel shape; however Irish material appears rather variable and requires further investigation. Subsp. *sativus* is the cultivated carrot.

29. Torilis.
Hairy annuals with finely divided, twice pinnate leaves. Bracteoles present. Flowers white or pink; calyx-teeth present. Fruit ovoid, bur-like, with numerous fine prickles.

1. Stem erect. Umbels terminal, long-stalked, with 5-12 rays   **1. T. japonica**
  Stem weak. Umbels opposite the leaves, almost stalkless, with
  2-3 rays   ..   .. **2. T. nodosa**

1. Torilis japonica *(Caucalis anthriscus).* **Hedge parsley. 7-9.** Stem erect, solid, slender, hispid. 40-90 cm high. Leaflets lanceolate, pinnatifid. Umbels terminal, long-stalked, with 5-12 rays. Bracts several, small. Flowers small, pinkish white. Fruit 3-4 mm. *Hedges, roadsides and waste places; very frequent.*

2. T. nodosa *(Caucalis nodosa).* **6-8.** Stem solid, weak often prostrate, 15-40 cm long. Leaflets lanceolate, deeply pinnatifid. Umbels small, opposite the leaves, almost stalkless, with 2 or 3 rays, or sometimes unbranched. Bracts absent; bracteoles long and narrow. Flowers small, pink. Outer fruits of each partial umbel prickly, inner nearly smooth. *Dry banks and waste places; occasional in the South and Southeast near the coast, very rare elsewhere.*

LXXX. ERICACEAE

Small shrubs, more rarely trees or perennial herbs, mostly evergreen. Leaves undivided, without stipules, alternate, opposite or whorled. Flowers regular or very slightly irregular, in racemes, panicles or umbel-like clusters. Sepals 4 or 5, free or united. Petals as many as the sepals, free, or more usually united into a bell- or urn-shaped corolla. Stamens twice as many as the petals, not attached to the corolla; anthers usually opening by pores. Ovary superior, more rarely inferior, of 4-5 united carpels; style and stigma single. Fruit a capsule or berry with numerous seeds, rarely a berry-like drupe.

Many species of *Erica* and *Rhododendron* are cultivated for ornament.

1. Plant without any green colour; leaves reduced to yellowish, fleshy
    scales   ..   ..   **3. Monotropa**
    Some of the leaves green   2

2. Petals free; stems soft and herbaceous   3
    Petals united into a usually bell-shaped or urn-shaped corolla; stems
        woody, at least at the base   4

3. Flowers in a one-sided raceme, all pointing one way   .. **1. Orthilia**
    Flowers in a symmetrical raceme, pointing in all directions   .. **2. Pyrola**

4. Ovary inferior   ..   ..   ..   **12. Vaccinium**
    Ovary superior   5

5. Sepals and corolla-lobes 4; stamens 8   6
    Sepals and corolla-lobes 5; stamens 10   8

6. Leaves alternate   ..   .. **7. Daboecia**
    Leaves opposite or whorled   7

7. Leaves opposite, crowded, scale like; calyx coloured like the corolla
        and more or less hiding it   ..   ..   .. **5. Calluna**
    Leaves in whorls of 3-5, not crowded or scale-like; sepals much
        smaller than the corolla and not hiding it   ..   .. **4. Erica**

8. Corolla 40-60 mm across, broadly bell-shaped   .. **6. Rhododendron**
    Corolla not more than 10 mm across, more or less urn-shaped,
        narrowed at the mouth   9

9. Leaves spine-tipped   ..   ..   ..   **10. Gaultheria**
    Leaves not spine-tipped   10

10. Large shrub or tree, flowering in Autumn   ..   .. **8. Arbutus**
    Low, more or less prostrate shrub, flowering in late Spring   ..   11

11. Leaves with a conspicuous network or veins on the lower side;
        fruit a red, berry-like drupe   ..   ..   **9. Arctostaphylos**
    Leaves pale bluish-green beneath, without conspicuous veins;
        fruit a capsule   ..   ..   ..   **11. Andromeda**

1. Orthilia

Orthilia secunda (*Ramischia secunda, Pyrola secunda*). **7-8.** A hairless, rhizomatous perennial, with erect stems 8-15 cm high. Leaves alternate, broadly ovate to elliptical, stalked, very finely toothed, 2-4 cm long, mostly situated near the base of the stem; much smaller, narrow leaves may be borne on the stem higher up. Flowers in a terminal, one-sided raceme 3-5 cm long. Petals 5, greenish-white; style 4-6 mm, straight. Ovary superior; fruit a capsule. *Rock-ledges in Antrim and Fermanagh; very rare.*

2. Pyrola. Wintergreen

Hairless, rhizomatous perennials. Leaves alternate, stalked; foliage-leaves confined to the lower part of the stem; above this small, narrow scale-leaves are often present. Flowers in terminal racemes. Sepals and petals 5. Ovary superior; fruit a capsule; seeds minute, with a very loose coat, which forms two membranous wings.

1. Style strongly curved; flowers cup-shaped .. **3. P. rotundifolia**
   Style straight; flowers more or less globose 2
2. Style 1-2 mm .. .. **1. P. minor**
   Style 4-7 mm .. .. **2. P. media**

1. Pyrola minor. 6-7. Stem 10-25 cm high. Leaves circular to broadly oval, entire or slightly crenate, obtuse, 2-4 cm long. Raceme 3-7 cm long. Petals pale lilac-pink, incurved so as to produce a more or less globular flower. Style 1-2 mm long, scarcely protruding from the petals. *Woods, shady glens and heaths; occasional in the North, rare elsewhere.*

2. P. media. 6-7. Like *P. minor* but slightly larger in all its parts; petals usually white, though sometimes tinged with pink, and style 4-7 mm, protruding some distance from the petals. *Similar in habitat and distribution to* P. minor.

3. P. rotundifolia. 7-9. Like *P. minor* and *P. media*, but with stems up to 35 cm high and racemes up to 10 cm long; petals pure white, not incurved, so that flower is cup-shaped; style strongly curved, up to 10 mm long. *Wet bogs and fens in the Centre; very local. Also in damp hollows in sand-dunes in Wexford.*

3. Monotropa

Monotropa hypopitys. Yellow bird's-nest. 7-8. A saprophytic perennial herb, with erect stems up to 30 cm. Whole plant pale yellow or cream-coloured; leaves in the form of numerous fleshy scales on the stem, 5-10 mm long. Flowers in a terminal raceme, drooping in flower but erect in fruit. Sepals 4 or 5, erect, united at the base. Petals free, dull yellow, 8-12 mm long. Ovary superior; fruit a capsule. Seeds as in *Pyrola. Woods, mainly in old demesnes; very local.*

Two subspecies are usually recognized, but the differential characters are rather inconstant. Most Irish plants appear to belong to subsp. *hypophegea* which usually has flowers hairless within.

4. Erica. Heather, Heath. *Fraoch*

Small, erect shrubs. Leaves whorled, needle-like or narrowly oblong, evergreen. Flowers purple or pink (rarely white), in racemes, panicles or umbels, which are usually terminal but sometimes intercalary (*i.e.* with the leafy stem continuing on beyond the tip of the raceme). Sepals 4, shorter than the corolla. Corolla urn-shaped or narrowly bell-shaped, with 4 short lobes. Anthers in some species with appendages at the base. Ovary superior; fruit a capsule, enclosed in the persistent corolla.

1 Anthers partly or wholly protruding from the mouth of the corolla 2
  Anthers concealed within the corolla 3
2 Flowering in spring; anthers only partly protruding from the corolla;
    pedicels shorter than the calyx .. .. .. **7. E. erigena**
  Flowering in late summer; anthers wholly protruding from the corolla;
    pedicels longer than the calyx .. .. .. **6. E. vagans**
3 Flowers in terminal umbels 4
  Flowers in racemes or panicles 5
4 Sepals with woolly hairs on the lower side; ovary downy .. **2. E. tetralix**
  Sepals hairless or very shortly downy on the lower side; ovary
    hairless .. .. **3. E. mackaiana**

5   Corolla 8-12 mm, usually slightly curved or asymmetrical; leaves
          with conspicuous marginal hairs; anthers without appendages   **1. E. ciliaris**
        Corolla 4-7 mm, symmetrical, not curved; leaves without marginal
          hairs; anthers with appendages   6
6   Flowers bright reddish-purple; leaf-margins rolled back so as to
          hide completely the lower surface of the leaf   ..   .. **5. E. cinerea**
        Flowers lilac-pink; leaf-margins rolled back, but leaving part of
          the lower surface visible   ..   ..   **4. E. terminalis**

1. Erica ciliaris. 8-10. Stems weak, 30-60 cm high, with numerous short branches. Leaves in whorls of 3 (rarely 4), oval-lanceolate, fringed with conspicuous, sometimes gland-tipped hairs; margins rolled back, but leaving visible part of the whitish lower surface. Flowers in terminal, spike-like racemes. Sepals like the leaves but smaller. Corolla 8-12 mm, bright pink, usually slightly curved and asymmetrical. Anthers included within the corolla, without appendages. *Known only from one bog-margin near Roundstone, Co. Galway.*

2. E. tetralix. 6-7. A downy, rather weak and straggling shrub 20-60 cm high, with thin, wiry branches. Leaves in whorls of 4, usually narrow and needle-like, but rarely oval-lanceolate; margins rolled back, but leaving visible a narrow strip of the lower surface [Fig. LXXXa]; those on the upper part of the flowering stems erect and widely spaced. Flowers in terminal umbels. Pedicels and sepals clothed with woolly hairs. Corolla pale, waxy pink, 6-9 mm long. Anthers with narrow appendages, included within the corolla. Ovary downy. *Bogs and wet moors; abundant in most districts.*

3. E. mackaiana. 7-8. Like *E. tetralix*, but of rather stronger and bushier habit; leaves oblong, fringed with stout, gland-tipped hairs; margins inrolled but leaving visible a considerable part of the lower surface [Fig. LXXXb]; those on the upper part of the flowering stems similar to the remainder (not erect and not widely spaced); sepals without woolly hairs; corolla brighter pink; ovary hairless. *Drier parts of bogs: locally abundant in three stations (two in West Galway, one in West Donegal); unknown elsewhere.*

For reasons not yet understood this species does not set seed in Ireland, though it reproduces freely by layering. Its pollen seems, however, to be able to produce hybrid seed when introduced to the flowers of *E. tetralix*, and sterile hybrids are frequent around all the colonies of *E. mackaiana.*

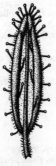   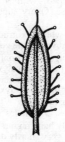

Fig. LXXXa   Fig. LXXXb

4. * **E. terminalis** (*E. stricta*). **7-8.** A bushy shrub up to 2 m high. Leaves in whorls of 3-5, narrow-oblong, minutely downy; margins rolled back but leaving a little of the lower surface visible, at least towards the base. Flowers in terminal umbels. Sepals triangular, minutely downy. Corolla 5-7 mm, urn-shaped to narrowly bell-shaped, pink. Anthers with triangular appendages, included within the corolla. *Naturalised in damp hollows in the sand-dunes behind Magilligan strand, Co. Derry; locally abundant.* Native of the Mediterranean.

5. E. cinerea. Bell-heather. 6-8. Erect but somewhat straggling, 45-60 cm high, hairless or slightly downy. Leaves in whorls of 3, mostly with conspicuous tufts of leaves in their axils. Flowers in long, narrow, leafy, irregular panicles. Sepals narrow, hairless, with translucent, papery margins. Corolla 4-7 mm long, urn-shaped, bright reddish-purple. Anthers with broad, toothed appendages, included within the corolla. *Heaths and drier parts of bogs; very local in the Centre, abundant elsewhere.*

6. † **E. vagans. Cornish heath. 7-9.** Stems up to 60 cm, rather weak. Leaves in whorls of 4-5, 6-11 mm long, needle-like; margins rolled back so as to conceal completely the lower surface. Flowers in intercalary (more rarely terminal) racemes up to 10 cm long. Sepals oval; corolla 2.5-4 mm long, bell-shaped, white or lilac-pink. Anthers without appendages, extending well clear of the mouth of the corolla. *Probably native in a damp hollow of moorland near Belcoo, Co. Fermanagh; very locally naturalised in Cos. Down & Antrim.*

7. E. erigena (*E. mediterranea*). **Mediterranean heath. 3-5.** A hairless, bushy shrub up to 150 cm high, with erect branches. Leaves in whorls of 3-4, needle-like; margins rolled back so as almost to conceal the lower surface, but usually leaving a narrow line visible. Flowers in terminal, somewhat one-sided racemes. Sepals lanceolate. Corolla cylindrical to bell-shaped, purplish pink. Anthers without appendages, protruding for about half their length from the mouth of the corolla. *Lake-shores, stream-sides and disturbed moorland; locally abundant in West Mayo, rare in West Galway, unknown elsewhere.*

5. Calluna

Calluna vulgaris. Ling, Heather. *Fraoch.* **7-8.** An erect, bushy shrub 30-120 cm high, with erect branches, usually hairless, but occasionally with numerous white hairs. Leaves opposite. Leaves 3 mm long, opposite, erect, very crowded and overlapping, oblong. Flowers numerous, in terminal, spike-like racemes; each flower with a few sepal-like bracts at its base. Calyx corolla-like, of 4 pinkish-purple sepals. Corolla similar in colour, smaller and concealed within the calyx, with 4 triangular lobes. Ovary superior; fruit a capsule, surrounded by the persistent calyx. *Drier parts of bogs, moors, and mountain slopes; abundant.*

6. Rhododendron

* **Rhododendron ponticum. 5-6.** A densely branched shrub up to 3 m high. Leaves alternate, hairless, shining, evergreen, oblong, 10-25 cm long. Flowers in short, terminal racemes. Calyx with 5 small, rounded lobes. Corolla 40-60 mm across, widely bell-shaped, with tube shorter than the 5 lobes, violet-purple. Ovary superior; fruit a capsule. *Extensively naturalised in woods and on bog-margins and mountain-sides.*

7. Daboecia

Daboecia cantabrica (*D. polifolia*). **St. Dabeoc's Heath.** *Fraoch gallda.* **6-8.** Stems up to 50 cm, glandular-hairy, woody below, rather weak, often straggling through other shrubs. Leaves alternate, oval, 8-10 mm long, entire, dark green above, white beneath. Flowers in loose, graceful, terminal racemes. Sepals 4, triangular, glandular-hairy. Corolla urn-shaped, 10-12 mm long, reddish-purple, falling before the fruit is ripe. Ovary superior; fruit a capsule. *Heaths and rocky ground; very frequent in West Galway, occasional in South-west Mayo, unknown elsewhere.*

8. Arbutus

Arbutus unedo. Strawberry-tree. *Caithne.* **9-10.** A bushy shrub or small tree up to 9 m high. Bark reddish; young twigs brown and downy. Leaves alternate, 5-8 cm long, narrowly oval, toothed, hairless, evergreen, shortly stalked. Flowers in small, terminal, drooping panicles. Calyx very small, with 5 rounded lobes. Corolla urn-shaped, with 5 short lobes, white, often tinged with green or pink. Ovary superior; fruit a tubercled berry, 15-20 mm across, orange-scarlet at first but dark crimson when quite ripe. *Wood-margins and rocky lake-shores and islands; frequent near Killarney; very locally in a few other places in the South-West, and by Lough Gill (Co. Sligo).*

The fruit takes a year to ripen, so that in Autumn flowers and fruit are borne together.

9. Arctostaphylos

Arctostaphylos uva-ursi. Bearberry. 5. Stems woody, prostrate, branched; young twigs shortly downy. Leaves alternate, oval, obtuse, entire, very shortly stalked, 15 mm long, dark green above, paler beneath, with a conspicuous network of fine veins. Flowers few, in small, terminal umbels. Calyx with 5 short, rounded lobes. Corolla pale pink, urn-shaped, with 5 short lobes. Ovary superior; fruit a scarlet, berry-like drupe 10 mm across. *Heaths, moors and rocky ground near the North and West coasts (Antrim to Clare); rather rare and apparently decreasing.*

10. Gaultheria

* Gaultheria mucronata (*Pernettya mucronata*). **5-6.** A low shrub up to 120 cm high, spreading by underground stolons. Leaves alternate, evergreen, hairless, spine-tipped, entire or weakly toothed, 9-12 mm long. Flowers axillary, drooping; corolla white, urn-shaped, 5-lobed, 5-6 mm long. Ovary superior; fruit a white, pink or purple berry 10 mm across. *Naturalised in a few places in woods or on moorland, mainly near the West and North coasts.* Native of southern Chile.

11. Andromeda

Andromeda polifolia. Bog rosemary. 4-5. Stems trailing or semi-erect, hairless, woody at the base. Leaves alternate, narrowly elliptical, entire, with the margins rolled back, dark, shining green above, pale bluish-green beneath. Flowers drooping, in short, terminal racemes. Sepals 5, triangular. Corolla urn-shaped, pale lilac-pink, 5-7 mm long. Ovary superior; fruit a capsule. *Bogs, mostly lowland; frequent in the Centre; rare elsewhere.*

12. Vaccinium

Small shrubs with alternate leaves. Ovary inferior; fruit a berry.

1. Leaves 4-8 mm long; corolla deeply divided into 4 lobes **1. V. oxycoccos**
    Leaves 15-20 mm long; corolla urn- or bell-shaped, with 4 or 5 short lobes   2

2. Leaves evergreen, more or less entire; young twigs downy; corolla 4-lobed; berry red   ..   ..   ..   **2. V. vitis-idaea**
    Leaves deciduous, finely toothed; young twigs hairless; corolla 5-lobed; berry black, with a blue bloom   ..   **3. V. myrtillus**

1. Vaccinium oxycoccos. (*Oxycoccus quadripetalus*). **Cranberry. 6-7.** Stems creeping, slender and wiry, hairless. Leaves 4-8 mm long, oval, entire, dark green above, whitish beneath. Flowers in groups of 1-3, on slender, erect pedicels. Calyx with 4 short, rounded lobes. Corolla pinkish-red, deeply divided into 4 lobes, which are bent back to reveal the narrow anthers clustered round the style. Berry red, acidic, 6 mm across. *Wet bogs; locally frequent in the Centre, rare elsewhere.*

2. V. vitis-idaea. Cowberry. 6-7. Stems erect, arching or prostrate, arising from a creeping rhizome; young twigs sparsely downy. Leaves oval to oblong, obtuse, more or less entire, leathery, evergreen. Flowers in short, terminal racemes. Sepals 4, triangular. Corolla narrowly bell-shaped, with 4 short lobes, pale pink. Berry red, acid. *Heathery mountains, mainly in the North and East; rather rare.*

3. V. myrtillus. Bilberry, Frochan. *Fraochán.* **6-7.** An erect, bushy shrub 25-60 cm high, with green, angular, hairless twigs. Leaves deciduous, pale green, oval, finely toothed, 15-20 mm long. Flowers solitary in leaf-axils, drooping. Calyx circular, scarcely lobed. Corolla shortly urn-shaped, with 5 short lobes, pinkish-white, tipped with green. Berry black, with blue bloom, sweet. *Mountains, moors and woods on acid soil; abundant.*

LXXXI. EMPETRACEAE

Empetrum nigrum. Crowberry. 5. A dioecious, prostrate shrub of heather-like aspect with slender, wiry stems. Leaves 5 mm long, mostly in whorls of 3 or 4, but some alternate, linear-oblong, with a white line beneath, representing the gap between the rolled-back margins. Flowers small, axillary, subtended by several small bracts. Sepals and petals usually 3, similar, green or purplish-pink. Stamens 3, with long, slender filaments. Ovary superior; stigma stalkless. Fruit a black, berry-like drupe, with usually 9 stones. *Bogs and moorland, mainly on the higher mountains, but locally on lowland bogs; frequent except in the South-west, where it is rare.*

LXXXII. PRIMULACEAE

Herbs, usually perennial. Flowers regular, hermaphrodite. Calyx 5- (rarely 4-) lobed (absent in *Glaux*). Corolla united, with the same number of lobes as the calyx. Stamens as many as the sepals, attached to the corolla, opposite the corolla-lobes. Ovary usually superior, 1-celled with free-central placentation and many ovules. Fruit a capsule.

A large number of species and hybrids of *Primula* (including the polyanthus and auriculas) as well as species of *Cyclamen* (notably *C. hederifolium (=C. neapolitanum)* and *C. repandum*) are cultivated in gardens and may occasionally be found as garden escapes or in abandoned gardens.

1.	Submerged aquatic; leaves pinnate	..	..	.. **2. Hottonia**
	Terrestrial; leaves undivided	..	..	.. 2
2.	Flowers yellow	..	..	.. 3
	Flowers not yellow	..	..	.. 4
3.	Leaves all basal; stem leaves absent	..	..	.. **1. Primula**
	Leaves not all basal; stem leaves present		..	**3. Lysimachia**
4.	Corolla absent; calyx pink or white, lobes clearly united to each			
	other at the base	..	..	.. **4. Glaux**
	Corolla present; calyx green, lobes not united to each other		..	5

5.	Leaves all basal; stem leaves absent	.. ..	**1. Primula**
	Leaves not all basal; stem leaves present	.. ..	6
6.	Capsule opening by 5 teeth at the top	.. ..	**6. Samolus**
	Capsule opening by a split round the middle	..	**5. Anagallis**

1. Primula

Perennial herbs, with oval-oblong, wrinkled basal leaves. Flowers solitary or in umbels. About half of the plants in any population have flowers with a long style and short stamens ("pin") whilst the others have a short style and long stamens ("thrum"). Calyx 5-toothed. Corolla yellow, 5-lobed, with a long tube. Ovary superior. Capsule opening by 5 teeth at the top.

* *P. japonica* with purple flowers, which have anthers and stigma attached at the same level, and which are borne in tiered whorls up the peduncle, is naturalised in wet woods in western Ireland (Galway & Roscommon).

1.	Flowers solitary, borne from the leaf rosette; leaves tapering gradually to the petiole ..	.. ..	**1. P. vulgaris**
	Flowers in umbels, borne on the top of a stout peduncle; leaves abruptly contracted to the petiole ..	..	**2. P. veris**

1. Primula vulgaris. Primrose. 4-5. Leaves gradually tapered at the base, downy and whitish below. Flowers solitary, 25-35 mm across, on sometimes very long pedicels, clothed with shaggy hairs, arising from the leaf-rosette. Calyx tubular, with the divisions between the teeth reaching almost half-way to the base. Petals with large lobes; usually yellow but occasionally orange-brown. *Shady banks, damp woods and hedges; frequent in most places.*

Pink forms, probably of hybrid origin with exotic garden Primulas, occur occasionally.

2. P. veris. Cowslip. 4-5. Leaves abruptly contracted at the base, with a distinct winged petiole. Flowers 10-15 mm across, in drooping clusters borne on the top of a stout, shortly hairy stalk. Calyx inflated, with short teeth. Corolla deeper yellow than in *P. vulgaris*, with an orange eye and the lobes of the petals small. *Pastures; frequent in the Centre, rather rare in the North-east and South-west.*

Hybrids (*P. x thommasinii*) between these two species are not uncommon. Usually the inflorescence is as in *P. veris*, but the flowers are larger and often paler.

2. Hottonia

* **Hottonia palustris. Water violet. 5-7.** An aquatic perennial with usually whorled, pinnate leaves with linear segments. Flowering stems erect, 25-60 cm high, bearing tiered whorls of 3-7 flowers, each 20 mm across. Calyx deeply 5-lobed; lobes linear. Corolla lilac with a yellow eye, deeply 5-lobed, with a short tube and spreading lobes. Ovary superior. Capsule splitting open by 5 valves. *Marshes and ditches in South Tipperary, Fermanagh and Down; very rare.*

3. Lysimachia

Perennials; leaves opposite (rarely whorled), entire. Flowers bright yellow. Calyx of 5 sepals, barely united at the base. Corolla deeply 5-lobed; tube short or absent. Capsule as in *Primula*.

1.	Plant erect		2
	Plant creeping	..	3
2.	Calyx-teeth with an orange margin; corolla-lobes glandular on the margin; leaf-margin densely covered with hairs		**2. L. punctata**
	Calyx-teeth without an orange margin; corolla-lobes without glandular hairs on the margin; leaf-margin with, at most, a few scattered hairs		**1. L. vulgaris**

3. Sepals broadly triangular; peduncles usually about as long
    as leaves; flowers usually more than 8 mm across **3. L. nummularia**
    Sepals linear-lanceolate; peduncles much longer than leaves;
    flowers usually less than 8 mm across .. **4. L. nemorum**

1. Lysimachia vulgaris. Yellow loosestrife. 7. Erect, downy perennial up to 1 m
tall. Leaves opposite, in whorls of 3-4 or occasionally alternate, stalkless or with a
short petiole, the blade oval-lanceolate, 5-8 cm long. Flowers 10-15 mm across, in a
leafy pyramidal panicle. Sepals narrowly triangular, hairy. Corolla without glandular
hairs on the margin. *River-banks, lake-shores and damp, shady places; occasional in
the Centre, rare elsewhere.*

2. * L. punctata. 7. Erect, clearly downy perennial up to 1 m tall. Leaves
opposite or in whorls of 3-4, with a short petiole, the blade oval-lanceolate, 5-10 cm
long. Flowers 15-20 mm across, in a leafy pyramidal panicle. Sepals narrowly triangular, hairy. Corolla with glandular hairs on the margin. *Rough often damp ground;
roadsides. Occasional in the West half.* Native of Eurasia.
    L. thyrsiflora, which differs from the above two species in its dense axillary
racemes of small flowers, 4-6 mm across, occurred in one, now destroyed, site in E.
Donegal.

3. † L. nummularia. Creeping-jenny. 7-8. Creeping, hairless perennial, rooting
at the lower nodes. Leaves opposite, with a short petiole, the blade almost round,
usually with a blunt tip about 2 cm across. Flowers 20-25 mm across, solitary in the
leaf-axils; pedicels usually about the same length as the leaves. Sepals broadly triangular. Corolla cup-shaped. *Damp, often shady and muddy places by lake, rivers and
in woods. Occasional in the North, mainly around Lough Neagh and Lough Erne;
very rare elsewhere.*
    In some places an escape from gardens, but native in others.

4. L. nemorum. Yellow pimpernel. 5-7. Creeping, hairless perennial, rooting at
the lower nodes. Leaves opposite, with a short petiole, the blade oval with a pointed
tip, usually about 2 cm across. Flowers 12 mm across, solitary in the leaf-axils;
pedicels very slender and usually longer than the leaves. Sepals linear-lanceolate.
Corolla flat, with widely spreading lobes. *Damp woods and mountain pastures;
frequent.*

4. Glaux
Glaux maritima. Sea milkwort. 6-7. A hairless, slightly succulent perennial,
with numerous leafy stems which are often prostrate for most of their length but turn
up at their tip. Leaves opposite, oval-oblong 6-10 mm long. Flowers axillary,
stalkless, 4-7 mm across. Calyx pale pink or whitish, corolla-like, 5-lobed. Corolla
absent. Capsule as in *Primula. Salt marshes, sandy, muddy or gravelly shores; very
frequent.*

5. Anagallis
Delicate, hairless herbs with entire leaves and axillary flowers. Leaves broadly
oval, with an acute tip. Flowers solitary in the leaf-axils. Calyx and corolla 4- or 5-
lobed. Calyx-lobes narrowly triangular to lanceolate, united only at the very base.
Capsule globular, opening by a split round the middle.

1. Flowers less than 3 mm across; upper leaves alternate **1. A. minima**
    Flowers larger than 3 mm; upper leaves opposite 2
2. Stems ascending; corolla-lobes broadly oval, more than twice as
        long as calyx-lobes, red or blue .. .. **2. A. arvensis**
    Stems creeping and rooting; corolla-lobes narrowly-oblong, less
        than twice as long as calyx-lobes, pale pink .. .. **3. A. tenella**

1. Anagalis minima (*Centunculus minimus*). **6-8.** A minute, erect, hairless annual, with stems much branched from the base, 2-7 cm high. Leaves mostly alternate, stalkless, oval; 3-5 mm long. Flowers very minute, stalkless. Calyx and corolla 4-lobed. Corolla white or pale pink. *Lake shores, and damp sandy places near the sea. Occasional in Kerry and the extreme North; very rare elsewhere.*

2. A. arvensis. Scarlet pimpernel. *Falcaire fiáin.* **5-8.** Annual, with ascending or trailing, 4-angled stems, 12-30 cm long. Leaves opposite, stalkless, oval or ovate-lanceolate; 0.5-1.5 cm. Flowers on long slender pedicels. Calyx 5-lobed. Corolla 5-lobed; lobes widely spreading, oval, red, 4-8 mm, more than twice as long as calyx-lobes. *Tilled fields, sand-hills and dry waste places; occasional to frequent though rare in the North-west.*

Plants with blue petals with sparse, 4-celled glandular hairs have been distinguished as sub-species *coerulea* but scarcely warrant such treatment.

3. A. tenella. Bog pimpernel. 7-8. Stem very slender, creeping and rooting, 7-18 cm long. Leaves opposite, shortly stalked, round or broadly oval; 4-8 mm long. Flowers on long, slender pedicels. Calyx 5-lobed. Corolla bell-shaped, 5-lobed; lobes oblong, pale pink; 5-10 mm, less than twice as long as calyx-lobes. *Bogs, damp pastures and moist peaty or sandy places; abundant in the West, local elsewhere.*

Superficially resembles *Epilobium brunnescens* from which it differs in its hairless stems, floral parts in fives (not fours) and seeds which lack a hairy plume.

6. Samolus

Samolus valerandi. Brookweed. 7-8. Erect, hairless, shining perennial; 12-35 cm high. Leaves spoon-shaped to oval-oblong, entire, shortly stalked; mostly in a basal rosette, but with a few alternately arranged on the stem. Flowers 2-4 mm across, in racemes. Calyx and corolla 5-lobed. Calyx-lobes broadly triangular, green. Corolla white. Ovary almost inferior. Capsule as in *Primula. Marshes, ditches, muddy shores and wet rocks in calcareous areas; frequent by the sea, especially in the West, and inland by limestone lakes.*

LXXXIII. PLUMBAGINACEAE

Perennial herbs with undivided, entire, basal leaves. Flowers regular, bisexual, small and numerous. Calyx 5-toothed, dry and membranous. Petals 5; free or barely joined at the base. Stamens 5. Ovary superior, 1-celled; styles 5. Fruit a minute, 1-seeded capsule. *Armeria* is heteromorphic with plants of one of two different forms. However unlike *Primula* the differences between the forms are less obvious and visible only with a good hand-lens or microscope: one form has rough pollen and a smooth stigma and the other smooth pollen and a rough stigma. In *L. recurvum* rough pollen is combined with a rough stigma.

1. Flowers pink; in dense globular heads ..   ..   ..   **1. Armeria**
    Flowers lilac; in elongated panicles   ..   ..   **2. Limonium**

1. Armeria

Armeria maritima. Thrift, Sea pink. 5-9. Leaves numerous, narrowly linear, in a dense basal tuft. Peduncles unbranched, 6-20 cm high, usually hairy, with a single, tightly packed head of bright pink, papery flowers. Each head surrounded by a series of bracts; the outer largely green, the inner membranous; bracts continued down the peduncle as a sheath. Calyx papery, with fine teeth. *Frequent on cliffs, rocks, banks and in marshes by the sea. Occasional on mountain tops in the West and North.*

2. Limonium. Sea lavender

Aerial stems branched; the final branches with small clusters of flowers with a bluish-purple corolla surrounded by a papery calyx and a series of bracts.

1.	Leaves with a single main vein; usually more than 5 cm long	**1. L. humile**
	Leaves with 2-3 main veins (rarely 1); usually less than 5 cm long	2
2.	Stem smooth or slightly rough to the touch at base, branched low-down; inner bracts mostly less than 5 mm long	**2. L. procerum**
	Whole of stem rough to the touch, unbranched low-down; inner bracts mostly greater than 5 mm long	**3. L. recurvum**

1. Limonium humile. 7-8. Leaves 5-25 cm long, distinctly stalked, with one obvious main vein. Flowering stems 10-30 cm high; usually bumpy to the touch; inflorescence open and the lower spiklets well separated. Calyx greenish purple, with 5 principle, acute, finely toothed lobes alternating with 5 very much smaller lobes. Corolla bluish-mauve. *Salt-marshes and muddy sea-shores; frequent but local; rare on the North coast.*

2. L. procerum. 7-8. Like *L. humile* but generally smaller; with smaller leaves which have more than one obvious main vein and stems usually smooth (though sometimes slightly rough to the touch at the base), with branches in the upper-part of the plant only and the calyx whitish with the ribs forming red stripes. *Rocks and other habitats by the coast from Wexford to Louth.*

3. L. recurvum. 7-8. Like *L. procerum* but with rough stems and branches in both the lower and upper parts of the plant and often with paler bluish-green leaves. *Limestone rocks and salt-marshes by the coast.*

This is an apomictic species in which a number of segregate groups can be recognised. *L. recurvum* subsp. *portlandicum* has been recorded from North Kerry; *L. recurvum* subsp. *pseudotranswallianum* (previously recorded as *L. transwallianum*) from Clare and *L. recurvum* subsp. *humile* (previously recorded as *L. paradoxum*) from Donegal. Material recorded as *L. binervosum* agg. in the past is probably *L. recurvum.*

LXXXIV. OLEACEAE

Trees or shrubs with opposite leaves without stipules. Flowers small, regular, in dense inflorescences. Stamens 0 or 2, attached to the corolla when present. Ovary 2-celled, superior; style single, stigmas 2.

Among familiar garden plants belonging to this family are the Jasmines (*Jasminium*) and *Forsythia*.

1.	Corolla absent	**1. Fraxinus**
	Corolla present	2
2.	Corolla white; fruit a berry	**2. Ligustrum**
	Corolla usually lilac or purple, occasionally white; fruit a capsule	**3. Syringa**

1. Fraxinus

Fraxinus excelsior. Ash. *Fuinnseóg.* **4-5.** A tall tree with black buds and grey bark, which is smooth at first but becomes furrowed on older trunks. Leaves opposite, pinnate, with 9-15 lanceolate, stalkless, toothed leaflets about 5 cm long. Flowers blackish green, small, monoecious or hermaphrodite, in dense panicles, appearing long before the leaves. Calyx and corolla absent; stamens with short filaments. Ovary superior, flask-shaped; stigma club-shaped. Fruit dry and indehiscent, with a membranous wing which causes it to spin as it falls. *Hedges, woods and rocky places; abundant, especially on limestone soils.*

2. Ligustrum

Ligustrum vulgare. Privet. 6-7. A medium-sized, very bushy shrub; young shoots and inflorescences downy. Leaves opposite, broadly lanceolate, 2-4 cm long entire, hairless, falling very late, and in mild Winters hardly at all. Flowers heavily scented, 5-6 mm across, in dense pyramidal panicles. Calyx small and falling early; corolla white, 4-lobed with a tube shorter than the corolla-lobes. Fruit a 1- to 2-seeded berry. *Very rare, on cliffs and rocky places as a native; occasional in hedges as an introduction.*

* *L. ovalifolium*, from Japan, is the common Privet planted for hedging. It occurs in various forms; with green, yellow, or variegated leaves. Occasional plants of this species may be found well away from houses. It can be distinguished from *L. vulgare* by its inflorescence and first-years growth which are both hairless, its broader leaves and by the corolla-tube which is distinctly longer than the corolla-lobes.

3. Syringa

* **Syringa vulgaris. Lilac. 5-7.** Deciduous, often suckering shrub or small tree to 6 m, with undivided, oval leaves 4-12 cm long. Flowers, sweet-scented, in dense, large, terminal, pyramidal panicles up to 20 cm long. Petals lilac, purple or white. Fruit a 2-celled capsule containing 4, winged seeds. *Occasional in hedges, sometimes well away from houses.* Native of southern Europe.

LXXXV.   GENTIANACEAE

Hairless, mostly annual herbs. Leaves undivided, entire and opposite. Flowers regular, bisexual; calyx 4- to 8- lobed. Corolla with a cylindrical tube and spreading lobes, as many as the calyx. Stamens attached to the corolla, alternate with the corolla-lobes and equal in number to them. Ovary superior, 1- or 2-celled; style single; stigma entire or two-lobed. Fruit a capsule with tiny seeds.

The most familiar garden plant in this family is *Gentiana acaulis,* a complex of closely related species from the Alps.

1.	Corolla yellow	..	..	2
	Corolla pink, purple, white or blue	..	..	3
2.	Corolla 4-lobed, 4-6 mm across; leaves narrow	..	**1. Cicendia**
	Corolla 6- to 8-lobed, at least 10 mm across; leaves broadly oval		**2. Blackstonia**
3.	Corolla pink (rarely white) ..	..	..	4
	Corolla blue or purple	..	..	5
4.	Corolla without forked scales in its mouth	..	**3. Centaurium**
	Corolla with forked scales in its mouth	..	**4. Gentiana**
5.	Corolla at least 20 mm across, with forked scales between the lobes (Fig. LXXXVa); calyx-tube with membranous lines		**4. Gentiana**
	Corolla less than 15 mm across, without forked scales between the lobes (but with a fringe of hairs in the mouth of the corolla, Fig. LXXXVb); calyx-tube entirely green		**5. Gentianella**

1. Cicendia

Cicendia filiformis. 7-8. A small, very slender, erect annual, 3-12 cm tall. Leaves minute, few; upper linear, lower broader. Flowers 4-6 mm across, solitary on long pedicels which are usually at least 5 times as long as the flower. Calyx and corolla 4-lobed; corolla yellow with spreading lobes; corolla-tube longer than lobes.

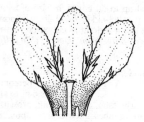 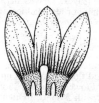

Fig. LXXXVa   Fig. LXXXVb

Calyx with short, triangular teeth. Capsule globular. *Damp peaty and sandy places; frequent in Kerry and West Cork, otherwise only known from one spot in West Mayo.*

2. Blackstonia

Blackstonia perfoliata. *Dréimire bui.* **6-9.** An erect, sparingly branched, pale blue-greyish-green annual, 15-50 cm tall. All leaves oval, united in pairs at their base, the stem apparently passing through the middle of the composite leaf. Flowers 15 mm across. Calyx and corolla 8- (rarely 6- or 7-) lobed; corolla yellow with spreading lobes; corolla-tube shorter than lobes. Calyx deeply divided almost to the base into linear lobes. Capsule globular. *Calcareous gravelly banks and sandhills; locally frequent in the Centre; rare in the South-west and absent from the North-east.*

3. Centaurium. Centaury

Flowers usually 5-merous (occasionally 4-merous). Corolla bright pink (rarely white) with a long, slender tube and spreading lobes. Calyx deeply divided, with linear teeth. Capsule cylindrical.

1.   Basal rosette-leaves absent at flowering; flowers with pedicels
    1-4 mm long   ..   ..   ..   **1. C. pulchellum**
    Basal rosette-leaves present at flowering; flowers stalkless or with
    pedicels less than 1 mm long   2
2.   Leaves linear or slightly spoon-shaped; basal usually less than 5 mm
    broad   ..   ..   **3. C. littorale**
    Leaves more or less ovate or elliptic; basal usually more than 5 mm
    broad   ..   ..   **2. C. erythraea**

1. Centaurium pulchellum. 6-8. Slender annual 5-10 (rarely up to 15) cm high. Basal rosette of leaves absent. Leaves ovate to broadly lanceolate. Small plants with one or two flowers; larger plants with many flowers in dense or spreading inflorescences. Flowers 4- or 5-merous, with a distinct pedicel. Corolla-tube usually longer than calyx; corolla-lobes 2-4 mm. *Sand-hills and dunes by the sea. Formerly known from the South coast, now confined to Waterford and North Dublin.*

Both this and the next species are very variable in morphology. Irish material requires further investigation.

2. C. erythraea. *Dréimire Mhuire.* **7-8.** Erect biennial up to 50 cm high, but often very dwarf. Generally similar to *C. pulchellum* but with a basal rosette of leaves present; all the leaves usually ovate, broadly lanceolate or broadly spoon-shaped; the flowers always 5-merous, numerous and forming tightly packed heads and the corolla-lobes 4-6 mm. *Dry pastures, banks and sandhills; very frequent near the sea, rare inland.*

3. C. littorale. (*C. minus*). **7-8.** Biennial up to 20 cm high with a distinct basal rosette of leaves. Leaves narrow, almost parallel-sided or slightly spoon-shaped. Flowers more or less stalkless. Corolla-tube about as long as calyx; corolla-lobes 5-7 mm. *Sandy places near the sea; known only from Derry (Magilligan and Portstewart).*

4. Gentiana. Gentian
Gentiana verna. Spring gentian. 4-5. A rosette-forming perennial, with unbranched flowering stems up to 10 cm high. All leaves stalkless and oval, usually crowded. Flowers solitary, 25 mm across. Calyx-tube, *c.* 1 cm long, brown, strongly 5-angled, with 5 short, triangular teeth. Corolla-lobes intense blue, spreading, with forked scales between the main lobes (Fig. LXXXVa); corolla-tube *c.* 2 cm. Capsule cylindrical, narrow. *Rocky pastures, bare rocks and sand-hills; locally abundant from mid-Clare to South-east Mayo, unknown elsewhere.*

4. Gentianella
Annuals or biennials with stalkless, oval-lanceolate leaves. Flowers in crowded heads. Calyx and corolla 4- or 5-lobed; corolla with short hairs at the throat (Fig. LXXXVb). Capsule cylindrical and narrow.

1. Calyx-lobes very unequal; two lobes very broad and overlapping
   the other two; corolla usually 4-lobed   ..   **1. G. campestris**
   Calyx-lobes all more or less the same size; corolla usually
   5-lobed   ..   ..   **2. G. amarella**

1. Gentianella campestris. 7-9. 2-15 cm high. Flowers dark bluish-purple; 10-15 mm across. Calyx and corolla 4-lobed. Calyx-lobes markedly unequal with two much larger and overlapping the other two. *Sea-side and mountain pastures and damp, sandy places. Frequent near the North and West coasts, rather rare elsewhere; possibly declining.*

2. G. amarella. 6-9. Like *G. campestris* but 3-30 cm high with flowers slightly smaller and usually bluish-purple, though sometimes pale blue or pink. Calyx and corolla 5-lobed, calyx-lobes narrowly lanceolate and all the same size. *Calcareous pastures, dry banks and sandy or gravelly places; occasional in the Centre, rare elsewhere.*

LXXXVI. MENYANTHACEAE

Hairless, creeping aquatic perennial herbs. Flowers conspicuous, regular, bisexual; calyx and corolla 5-lobed. Stamens 5, attached to the corolla. Ovary superior; style single. Fruit a capsule.

Members of this family are heterostylous so plants bear flowers of one of two types; ("pin") has long styles, anthers borne low-down on the corolla-tube and small pollen grains; whilst the other ("thrum") has the positions reversed and larger pollen grains.

1. Leaves with three oval, entire leaflets; petals pinkish white   **1. Menyanthes**
   Leaves undivided, Water-lily like; petals yellow   ..   **2. Nymphoides**

1. Menyanthes
Menyanthes trifoliata. Bogbean. *Bearnán lachan.* **4-7.** A usually aquatic perennial herb with long creeping, submerged stems. Leaves all basal, raised above the surface of the water on long stalks; with three oval entire leaflets, about 5 cm

long. Flowering stems 12-30 cm tall with a dense terminal head of 10-20 pinkish-white flowers. calyx deeply 5-lobed. Corolla 5-lobed; each lobe conspicuously fringed with many long white hairs on the inside. Stamens inserted either near the top of the corolla-tube or near its base. *Wet bogs and margins of pools and lakes; very frequent in most districts.*

2. Nymphoides

* Nymphoides peltata. Fringed water-lily. An aquatic perennial with floating leaves and flowers. Leaves 3-10 cm; orbicular and deeply cordate at the base on long petioles; leaves on flowering stems opposite; others alternate. Flowers in few-flowered clusters on long (3-10 cm) pedicels. Calyx deeply divided. Corolla yellow, 3 cm across. *Known only from two lakes near Belfast; formerly also in other sites in the North-east.*

LXXXVII. APOCYNACEAE

Vinca. Periwinkle

Hairless, perennial, creeping herbs. Leaves glossy, opposite, undivided and evergreen without stipules and with short petioles. Flowers solitary in the leaf axils, regular, bisexual. Calyx of 5 sepals; united at the base and with long, slender calyx-teeth. Corolla of 5 united petals, bright blue, with a short tube and 5 spreading lobes. Stamens 5, concealed within the corolla-tube to which they are attached by twisted filaments. Ovary superior, style solitary with a tuft of hairs at the top. Fruit a pair of follicles; rarely formed.

1. Corolla 25-30 mm across; leaf margin and calyx-teeth hairless .. **1. V. minor**
    Corolla 30-50 mm across; leaf margin and calyx-teeth with short
    hairs ..   .. **2. V. major**

1. * Vinca minor. 3-6. Stems rooting at intervals; flowering stems ascending to 20 cm. Leaf margin and calyx-teeth hairless; petioles *c.* 5 mm. Corolla 25-30 mm across. *Hedges and roadsides, usually near houses; occasional.*

2. * V. major. 3-6. Similar to *V. minor* but with longer petioles *c.* 10 mm, shortly hairy leaf margins and calyx-teeth and a much larger corolla, 30-50 mm across. *Hedges and roadsides, usually near houses; rare.*

LXXXVIII. RUBIACEAE

Herbs with leaves in whorls of 4-8 (rarely opposite) and 4-angled stems. Flowers small and regular, hermaphrodite, in cymes. Calyx-teeth usually absent, rarely 6. Corolla united, with 4 or 5 lobes. Stamens 4-5, attached to the top of the corolla-tube between the corolla-lobes; anthers usually clearly visible. Ovary, inferior, 2-celled; styles usually 1, often forked at the top. Fruit small, usually dry, separating into two 1-seeded nutlets.

The Rubiaceae are characterised by the presence of stipules. In all Irish species the stipules are so leaf-like that they are indistinguishable from the true leaves which are in opposite pairs. In our descriptions all stipules are therefore treated as leaves.

The greenhouse Gardenias as well as a number of important crops such as Coffee and Quinine belong to this family. Crosswort, *Cruciata laevipes*, a softly hairy, yellowish-green perennial has been found, as an introduction, in Meath and Down.

1. Corolla 5-lobed ..   .. **4. Rubia**
    Corolla 4-lobed. 2

2. Calyx-teeth clearly visible, especially in fruit (only 0.5-1 mm long
in flower) .. .. **1. Sherardia**
Calyx-teeth absent .. .. .. 3.
3. Leaves in the uppermost nodes of two distinct sizes; tube of corolla
longer than lobes .. .. **2. Asperula**
Leaves in the uppermost nodes all more or less the same size; tube
of corolla shorter than lobes .. .. .. **3. Galium**

1. Sherardia

Sherardia arvensis. 5-8. A hairy annual with slender, prostrate stems, 15-40 cm
long. Leaves 5-15 mm long, gradually narrowing to a sharp and fine point, in whorls
of 6; at least the upper leaves lanceolate, lower sometimes oval. Flowers in dense
clusters, surrounded by a whorl of leaves. Calyx-teeth 6, triangular, persistent and
somewhat enlarged in fruit. Corolla 2-4 mm across, lilac-pink with a long, slender
tube and 4, short, spreading lobes. Fruit a pair of minute nutlets, crowned by the
calyx-teeth. *Dry pastures, sand-dunes and tilled ground, rarely as a weed in lawns;
occasional.*

2. Asperula

Asperula cynanchica. 5-9. Prostrate perennial with slender, branched stems, 10-
25 cm long. Leaves mostly in whorls of 4, equal in size in the lower nodes; in the
upper nodes often 2 longer and 2 shorter, and sometimes only with 2 present.
Flowers in narrow cymes. Ovary minutely rough, calyx-teeth absent. Corolla white
or pink; 2-4 mm across; corolla-tube longer than corolla-lobes. Only the top of
anthers visible at mouth of corolla-tube. Fruit a pair of minute nutlets, slightly rough.
*Rocky pastures and sand-hills; locally frequent in the West from Kerry to Galway,
unknown elsewhere.*

Subsp. *occidentalis* (*A. occidentalis*) which differs in its usually orange runners,
corolla-lobes as long as the corolla-tube and smaller, spoon-shaped leaves has been
reported from calcareous sand-dunes in the West: however the characters are incon-
sistently associated.

3. Galium. Bedstraw

Perennials, apart from *G. aparine*. Flowers white, (except *G. verum*), in branched
heads. Calyx-teeth absent; corolla with 4, broadly spreading lobes; corolla-tube much
shorter than lobes (except *G. odoratum*). Fruit a pair of 2 spherical nutlets.

1. Corolla yellow .. .. **5. G. verum**
Corolla white 2
2. Fruit covered with hooked bristles 3
Fruit smooth or slightly rough 5
3. Stems rough, covered in short, hooked bristles .. **9. G. aparine**
Stems smooth 4
4. Leaves 3-veined, usually in whorls of 4 .. .. **1. G. boreale**
Leaves 1-veined, in whorls of 6-9 .. .. **2. G. odoratum**
5. Central part of the leaf-margin with hairs pointing backwards,
towards the leaf-base 6
Central part of the leaf-margin with hairs pointing forwards,
towards the leaf-apex or leaf margin smooth (without hairs) .. 7
6. Stems rough .. .. **4. G. uliginosum**
Stems smooth .. .. **8. G. sterneri**
7. Leaves blunt without a point or bristle protruding from the tip,
in whorls of 4-6 .. .. .. **3. G. palustre**
Leaves with a point or bristle protruding from the tip, in whorls of 6-9 8

8. Corolla-lobes with a long drawn-out point (>0.2 mm)
     [Fig. LXXXVIIIa]; stems usually more than 25 cm long;
     leaves more than 10 mm long   ..   ..   **6. G. mollugo**
     Corolla-lobes with a very short point (<0.2 mm) [Fig. LXXXVIIIb];
     stems usually less than 25 cm long; leaves less than 10 mm
     long   ..   ..   **7. G. saxatile**

1. Galium boreale. 6-8. Erect, with shortly hairy almost smooth stems 25-50 cm high. Leaves lanceolate to narrowly ovate, 15-30 mm long, 4-8 in a whorl, 3-veined, with short, rough hairs on the veins underneath and on the margins; leaf-tip rounded. Flowers numerous, in terminal and axillary cymes. Corolla 3 mm across. Fruit covered with hooked bristles. *Lake-shores and rocky places often by streams; locally abundant in parts of the West, rare and decreasing in the North and absent from most of the South and East.*

2. G. odoratum. (*Asperula odorata*) **Sweet woodruff. 5-6.** Erect with hairless stems up to 45 cm high. Leaves oblong-lanceolate, 20-40 mm long, in whorls of 6-9; 1-veined; leaf-tip with a short point; hairs on the margin of the leaf spreading to forward pointing. Flowers in small, terminal cymes. Corolla funnel-shaped, 4-5 mm across, with the tube about as long as the lobes. Fruit covered with hooked bristles. *Woods and other damp shady places; occasional, commoner in the North half.*

3. G. palustre. 6-8. Straggling, with stems rather weak, up to 100 cm long, usually rough with small, downwardly directed prickles. Leaves oblong-lanceolate, 5-20 mm long, in whorls of 4-6; 1-veined; the leaf-tip rounded and without a bristle-like point; the hairs mid-way along the margin of the leaf pointing forwards towards the apex [Fig. LXXXVIIIc]. Flowers in small clusters arranged in loose, terminal and axillary cymes. Corolla 2-3.5 mm across. Fruit *c.* 1.5 mm across, minutely rough. *Ditches and marshes; frequent and widespread.*

Two subsp. are sometimes recognised. Subsp. *elongatum* (*G. elongatum*) is generally larger than subsp. *palustre* with leaves greater than 20 mm long; corolla 3-4.5 mm across and fruits about 2 mm across and is known only from the North-east and Westmeath and Longford. The above sets of characters do not always appear to be well correlated in Irish material.

4. G. uliginosum. 6-8. Like *G. palustre* but stems finer, weaker and shorter; leaves, 8-12 mm long, in whorls of 6-8; with backwardly directed hairs mid-way along the margin of the leaf and leaf-tips with a bristle-like point [Fig. LXXXVIIId]; the corolla 2 mm across and fruit 1-2 mm across. *Marshes; mainly in the central belt, from North Galway and South Clare eastwards; absent from the North.*

Fig. LXXXVIIIa   Fig. LXXXVIIIb   Fig. LXXXVIIIc   Fig. LXXXVIIId

5. G. verum. Lady's bedstraw. 6-8. Hairless or slightly downy, with slender, trailing to erect stems to 100 cm. Leaves linear, 8-20 mm long, in whorls of 8 or more; 1-veined; leaf-tip acute; leaf-margin more or less hairless. Flowers in many-flowered, elongated panicles. Corolla bright yellow, 2-4 mm across. Fruit smooth. *Dry banks, hedges and sandy places; frequent in most places occasional in the North-west and South-west.*

6. * G. mollugo. 6-9. Stems scrambling to erect, up to 120 cm long. Leaves lance-olate to oblong-lanceolate, 8-12 mm long, in whorls of 5-8; 1-veined; leaf-tip with a fine point; hairs on leaf-margin minute, curved towards the tip of the leaf. Flowers in long, loose, branched axillary and terminal cymes. Corolla 3 mm across. Fruits smooth, *c.* 2 mm across. *Dry banks, pastures and lawns; widespread but very rare.*

Conventionally two sub-species, subsps. *mollugo* and *erectum* (*G. album*), are recognised. Intermediates between the two are not uncommon and the two probably not worthy of recognition.

7. G. saxatile. 6-8. Stems more or less prostrate, freely branched, up to 20 cm long. Leaves in whorls of 6-8, oblong-lanceolate, with a short, narrow point and not a bristle-like tip, with forwardly directed hairs on the middle of the margin [Fig. LXXXVIIIe]. Flowers in tightly clustered cymes. Corolla 2-3 mm across. Fruits slightly rough, less than 1 mm across. *Heaths and rocky places, on acid soils; frequent, except in parts of the Centre.*

8. G. sterneri (*G. pumilum*) **5-7.** Like *G. saxatile* but of more delicate habit with narrower, linear leaves which are shortly pointed and have a bristle-like tip and which have backwardly-directed hairs on the margin [Fig. LXXXVIIIf]. *Rocky ground, screes, cliff-edges and short grassland, on limestone or basalt; locally frequent in Clare & Galway and the North-east, unknown elsewhere.*

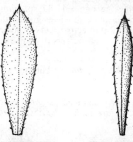

Fig. LXXXVIIIe   Fig. LXXXVIIIf ˙

9. G. aparine. Goose-grass, Cleavers, Robin-run-the-hedge. *Garbhlus.* **6-9.** Annual, with straggling stems up to 2 m long rough with small, hooked prickles. Leaves lanceolate to oblong-lanceolate, 15-40 mm long; 1-veined; in whorls of 6-8; with backwardly directed hairs on the margin of the leaf; leaf-tip with a fine point. Flowers in short cymes of 3-10. Corolla 2-2.5 mm across. Fruit 3-4 mm across. *Hedges, thickets, arable ground and waste-places; widespread and abundant.*

4. Rubia

Rubia peregrina. Wild madder. 6-8. A dark green, hairless perennial; rough to the touch with hooked prickles on the stems and leaves. Stems with 4 small wings, straggling, up to 1 m long. Leaves in whorls of 4 or 6, oval to lanceolate, evergreen, 3-

6 cm long. Flowers, terminal in loose cymes. Calyx-teeth absent. Corolla 5 mm across, pale yellowish-green; tube minute (forming a short ring at the base of the lobes); lobes pointed and widely spreading. Stamens 5, on short filaments. Fruit single-seeded, black, fleshy, berry-like. *Rocky and bushy places; locally frequent in Clare, occasional by the coast northwards to Mayo and Meath, very rare in the Centre.*

LXXXIX.   CONVOLVULACEAE

Herbs with slender, twining or prostrate stems; leaves undivided (though sometimes lobed), entire, alternate, stalked without stipules, sometimes absent. Flowers regular, hermaphrodite. Calyx of 5 free sepals. Corolla regular, with 5 fused petals, forming a funnel-shaped corolla with an entire margin. Stamens 5, attached to the corolla. Ovary superior, 1-celled; style solitary with two stigmas. Fruit a 4-seeded capsule. *Cuscuta* differs in having 4 or 5 fused, but deeply lobed, sepals; 4 or 5, lobed petals and 4 or 5 stamens.

Ipomoea (Morning glory), a climber with brilliant blue or purple flowers, is cultivated in gardens, as are a number of species of *Convolvulus*.

1. Plant green and leafy 2
   Plant red or yellow not green; leafless and rootless: parasitic .. **1. Cuscuta**
2. Corolla more than 30 mm across; calyx enclosed by two large
   bracteoles .. .. **2. Calystegia**
   Corolla less than 30 mm across; bracteoles small, some distance
   below the calyx and not enclosing it .. .. **3. Convolvulus**

1. Cuscuta

† **Cuscuta epithymum. Dodder. 7-9.** A thin-stemmed, rootless annual lacking hairs and chlorophyll and with leaves reduced to minute scales; parasitic on other plants to which it adhers by suckers. Stems red or yellowish, twining. Flowers 2-3 mm across, in small globular heads scattered along the stem. Calyx and corolla funnel-shaped, deeply 4 or 5 lobed; the lobes triangular. Stamens 4 or 5, attached to the corolla; anthers pink. Styles 2. *Rare in sand-dunes and sandy ground near the sea; absent from large regions of the coast.*

Variation in the numbers of floral parts often occurs on the same plant.

2. Calystegia

Perennial herbs with trailing or twining stems and far-creeping rhizomes. Flowers large, solitary, axillary, each with 2 large, leafy bracteoles immediately below the calyx and so enclosing it. Corolla much larger than calyx, broadly funnel-shaped, scarcely lobed. Sepals and stamens 5. Style solitary; stigmas two.

1. Seashore plant with fleshy, very obtuse leaves scarcely longer than
   wide .. .. **1. C. soldanella**
   Leaves triangular-oval and acute, distinctly longer than wide, not fleshy 2
2. Bracteoles flat (10-18 mm wide); corolla about 5 cm long .. **2. C. sepium**
   Bracteoles strongly inflated (18-45 mm wide when flattened);
   corolla 6-7 cm long .. .. 3.
3. Corolla white, sometimes pink striped; pedicels hairless **3. C. silvatica**
   Corolla pink; pedicels usually very shortly hairy .. **4. C. pulchra**

1. Calystegia soldanella. 6-8. Hairless, with prostrate or weakly climbing stems to 50 mm. Leaves with very long leaf-stalks, kidney-shaped, fleshy, 2-4 cm across. Flowers pink, 3 cm across; pedicels longer than leaves. Bracteoles about as long as calyx, not inflated; scarcely overlapping. Corolla pink. *Rare on sandy sea-shores on the South and East coasts; very rare in the North and West.*

2. C. sepium. Bindweed. 7-9. A hairless, climbing plant with long, twining stems. Leaves broadly triangular with a saggitate base, entire, 7-10 cm long. Flowers 3-6 cm across; pedicels as long or longer than leaf-stalk. Bracteoles about as long as calyx, not inflated and scarcely overlapping. Corolla white, rarely pink. *Hedges, woodland edges and waste ground; frequent throughout.*

* Subsp. *roseata*, which differs in its shortly hairy stems, leaf-stalks and pedicels and pink, white-striped, flowers, is known from coastal regions, mainly in the West (Cork to Galway).

3. * C. silvatica (*C. sylvestris*). **7-10.** Similar to *C. sepium* but larger in all its parts, with the corolla white though sometimes striped with pink on the outside, up to 8 cm across, and with the bracteoles overlapping, strongly inflated and pouch-like. *Waste places usually near habitation; occasional.*

4. * C. pulchra. 7-9. Similar to *C. sepium* but larger in all its parts with the corolla pink or pink with white stripes; with some short hairs on the stems, leaf-stalks and pedicels and with the bracteoles overlapping, strongly inflated and pouch-like. *Hedges near habitation; occasional.*

3. Convolvulus

Convolvulus arvensis. Bindweed. 6-9. Hairless perennial with prostrate or weakly climbing stems 15-60 cm long and a far-creeping rhizome. Leaves triangular, sagittate, 4-5 cm long. Flowers solitary or paired; 20-25 mm across; pedicel very long and slender with 2 linear bracteoles some way below the calyx. Sepals and stamens 5. Corolla white or pink, broadly funnel-shaped. *Waste and cultivated, often sandy ground, roadsides and railway tracks; scattered throughout.*

XC.   BORAGINACEAE

Herbs; usually conspicuously hairy, with undivided, entire, alternate leaves without stipules and often stalkless. Leaf surface often with obvious small, white spots at the base of each hair. Flowers more or less regular, hermaphrodite, in 1-sided, coiled cymes, which unroll as they mature. Calyx of 5 sepals; united at least at the base; often deeply divided with long teeth. Corolla fused, usually regular, with a long tube and 5 spreading lobes; commonly with small flaps of tissue (=scales) or hairs on the inside of the corolla-tube which may fill the tube's entrance. Stamens 5, attached to the corolla and alternating with its lobes. Ovary superior, divided deeply into 4-lobes by two furrows which form a cross; style solitary, arising from the centre of the cross. Fruit a group of 4, 1-seeded nutlets.

1. Plant hairless and pale greyish-green; growing on the sea-shore   **7. Mertensia**
    Stem and leaves hairy; usually conspicuously so   2
2. Most of the stamens projecting well beyond the corolla-tube   ..   3
    All stamens concealed within the corolla-tube   4
3. Petals divided nearly to base and widely spreading in flower; anthers
        longer than filaments   ..   ..   **8. Borago**
    Petals fused to form a distinct tube; anthers much shorter than
        filaments   ..   ..   **2. Echium**
4. Nutlets spiny; calyx spreading in fruit   ..   ..   **11. Cynoglossum**
    Nutlets not spiny; calyx not spreading in fruit   5
5. Open flowers nodding; usually at least 10 mm long   ..   **4. Symphytum**
    Open flowers erect; usually less than 10 mm long   6

6. Corolla of mature flowers white, yellow or orange, not blue .. 7
   Corolla of mature flowers blue (immature flowers sometimes yellow) 8
7. Nutlets conspicuously white, smooth and shining .. **1. Lithospermum**
   Nutlets brown or black .. .. **9. Amsinkia**
8. Basal leaves ovate at least 12 cm long 9
   Basal leaves lanceolate, spoon-shaped or ovate; if ovate then
      much less than 12 cm long 10
9. Basal leaves with large white spots; plants heterostylous;
      calyx cleft into teeth for about $^1/_3$ of its length .. **3. Pulmonaria**
   Basal leaves without large white spots; plants not heterostylous;
      calyx cleft into teeth for at least $^3/_4$ its length .. **6. Pentaglottis**
10. Leaves with a clearly wavy margin; nutlets rough with a
       number of ridges; corolla-tube longer than lobes .. .. **5. Anchusa**
    Leaves with the margin not wavy; nutlets smooth with a distinct
       keel; corolla-tube usually shorter than lobes .. .. **10. Myosotis**

1. Lithospermum

Lithospermum officinale. 6-8. Perennial, with several erect, branched, leafy stems, 30-65 cm high. Leaves 6-8 cm, lanceolate, with two distinct lateral veins; densely hairy on the upper surface, the hairs flattened. Lowermost bracts usually shorter than their corresponding internode. Flowers solitary in the leaf-axils; pedicels elongating on fruiting and at least 3 mm long. Calyx divided almost to the base into long, narrow teeth. Corolla yellowish-white, funnel-shaped, 6-7 mm across. Nutlets smooth, white and shining. *Hedges and sandy banks; widespread but rare and decreasing.*

2. Echium

Echium vulgare. Viper's bugloss. 6-8. An erect biennial, 30-90 cm high, with very stiff, almost prickly hairs. Leaves 12-15 cm, broadly lanceolate; the lower stalked; densely hairy and white-spotted. Calyx divided almost to the base into long, narrow teeth. Corolla reddish-purple at first, turning bright blue; funnel-shaped, with a broad, open tube. Stamens with long filaments, protruding from the corolla. Stigma 2-lobed. Nutlets brown, rough, with a clearly flat, triangular base. *Occasional on sand-dunes and sandy or gravelly fields on the East coast; very rare and casual elsewhere.*

3. Pulmonaria.

* Pulmonaria officinalis. Lungwort. 3-5. An erect, shortly creeping perennial to 30 cm with ovate basal leaves 10-15 cm long, with large white spots. Flowers in congested terminal heads; heterostylous [Fig. XCa]. Calyx divided almost to

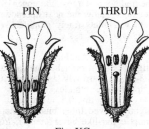

PIN   THRUM

Fig. XCa

halfway, forming broadly triangular teeth. Corolla pink in bud, turning bluish when open. Stamens concealed within the corolla-tube. Nutlets smooth and shortly hairy with a raised rim at the base. *Occasional by roadsides and in waste places.*

4. Symphytum. Comfrey. *Lus na gcnámh mbriste*

Perennial herbs covered in stiff hairs. Leaves oval to lanceolate; the lower stalked, the upper stalkless. Flowers in nodding, dense terminal heads. Calyx deeply divided forming long, narrow teeth. Corolla 12-20 mm long; corolla-tube much longer than lobes. Stamens concealed within the tube.

1. Upper stem-leaves shortly stalked neither decurrent or clasping the
    stem; calyx teeth rounded; corolla pinky-red in bud, sky-blue
    when open . .   . .   . .   **2. S. asperum**
    Upper stem leaves stalkless; calyx teeth acute; corolla not pinky-red in bud and
    sky-blue when open   2
2. Stems up to 50 cm, arising from a shortly creeping rhizome;
    calyx divided at least 3/4 of the way to the base   . .   **4. S. tuberosum**
    Stems up to 140 cm, arising from a short vertical rootstock;
    calyx usually divided less than 3/4 of the way to the base   . .   3
3. Stem leaves strongly decurrent with the wings extending below the
    next leaf; nutlets smooth   . .   . .   **1. S. officinale**
    Stem leaves at most weakly decurrent with the wings not extending
    below the next leaf; nutlets finely granulate   . .   **3. S. x uplandicum**

1. Symphytum officinale. 5-8. Stems usually branched, 50-150 cm high. Leaves 15-25 cm, stalkless; broadly oval, the lowest the largest; the upper leaves continued down the stems as wings which extend below the next internode. Calyx deeply divided; teeth acute. Corolla usually pale cream. Nutlets smooth and shining. *Riversides and other damp, shady places; throughout but commoner in the North.*

2. * S. asperum. 6-7. Like *S. officinale* but with the stem covered in short, hooked bristles; the stem leaves shortly petiolate and not decurrent; the calyx teeth slightly rounded and the corolla sky blue when open. Nutlets finely granulate. *Naturalised by a roadside in Sligo and a riverside in Dublin. Probably overlooked.* Native of South-west Asia.

3. * S. x uplandicum. 6-8. Like *S. officinale* but with the stem slightly bristly; the stem leaves very shortly decurrent; the corolla pink, blue or purple and the nutlets finely granulate. *Waste places; frequent throughout.*

4. * S. tuberosum. 5-7. Stems often unbranched, 30-50 cm high. Leaves 10-14 cm narrowly oval, with the middle the largest; the upper leaves unwinged or forming short wings which do not extend below the next internode. Calyx divided almost to the base. Corolla pale yellow. Nutlets finely granulate. *Occasionally planted and naturalised in woods; throughout.*

5. Anchusa

Anchusa arvensis. Bugloss. 5-8. A branched annual, 20-40 cm tall, covered with stiff, patent hairs. Leaves 5-15 cm; narrowly lanceolate with wavy, toothed margins; lower leaves petiolate, upper ones stalkless. Flowers 7 mm across, in tight, sometimes branched heads. Calyx divided to at least 3/4. Corolla with small, spreading lobes and a slightly curved tube; blue. Stamens with minute filaments. Nutlets rough with a distinct collar-like base. *Sandy fields and waste places on or near the North and East coasts; rare.*

6. Pentaglottis

* **Pentaglottis sempervirens. 5-8.** A branched annual, 20-40 cm tall, covered with stiff, patent hairs. Leaves up to 30 cm, oval to oval-lanceolate, the upper almost stalkless, the lower ones stalked. Flowers in short crowded cymes. Calyx lobes triangular, about as long as the tube. Corolla bright blue, 10 mm across; corolla-tube filled at the mouth by scales. Filaments very short. Nutlets rough with a distinct collar-like base. *Hedges and waste places in the North and East; very rare elsewhere.*

7. Mertensia

Mertensia maritima. 6-8. A prostrate, hairless, usually pale bluish-green perennial. Leaves up to 10 cm, oval, dotted with white; upper leaves stalkless, lower leaves stalked. Stems purplish. Flowers in dense terminal clusters. Calyx divided more or less to the base. Corolla 6 mm across, pink or blue. Nutlets flattened and fleshy with the outer coat becoming papery. *Shingle shores of the North and Northeast coasts (Donegal, Down and Antrim); formerly more widespread, now very rare and decreasing.*

8. Borago

* **Borago officinalis. Borage. 6-8.** A prostrate, hispid perennial. Leaves up to 10 cm, oval, dotted with white; upper leaves stalkless, lower leaves stalked. Stems purplish. Flowers in dense terminal clusters. Calyx divided nearly to the base. Corolla 6 mm across, blue. Nutlets flattened and fleshy with the outer coat becoming papery. *Rubbish tips and waste ground; occasional on the East coast.* Native of the Mediterranean.

9. Amsinckia

* **Amsinckia micrantha. 6-7.** A hairy, branched annual, to 50 cm high with stalkless, oval to lanceolate leaves with white dots. Flowers very small. Calyx 5-6 mm long; divided almost to the base. Corolla yellow; 3-5 mm long; with the corolla-tube without scales and longer than the lobes. Stamens included; filaments attached to the upper half of the corolla-tube. Nutlets rough. *A rare weed; but naturalised in a tilled field in Dublin.* Native of western North America.

* *A. lycopsoides* with slightly larger flowers of a deeper yellow, with evident scales inside the corolla and with filaments attached below halfway in the corolla-tube has been recorded from Wicklow.

10. Myosotis. Forget-me-not

Small, usually erect plants with oblong leaves. Flowers small, in slender, usually branched and often one-sided cymes. Calyx hairy. Corolla usually blue; with spreading lobes and a short tube, closed at the mouth by scales. Filaments very short, anthers not exserted. Nutlets very small, with a distinct ridge or wing, otherwise smooth, shining.

* *M. sylvatica*, a tufted, large perennial to 50 cm with hooked hairs on the calyx and flowers about 6-8 mm across is grown in gardens and has been reported as an escape.

1. Hairs on calyx lying flat, more or less straight; plant growing in wet
    places   2
    Hairs on calyx spreading, often curved or hooked; plant growing in
    dry places   4

2. Style at least as long as the calyx, clearly protruding from flowers
    where the corolla has dropped off; corolla usually 6-9 mm
    across   ..   ..   **6. M. scorpiodes**
    Style shorter than calyx, not protruding from flowers where the
    corolla has dropped off; corolla usually less than 6 mm across   3

3. Plant densely hairy at base, the hairs widely spreading [Fig. XCb];
    calyx-teeth narrowly lanceolate   ..   ..   **4. M. secunda**
    Plant weakly hairy or hairless at base, the hairs not or only slightly
    spreading [Fig. XCc]; calyx-teeth triangular   ..   ..   **5. M. laxa**
4. Flowers pale yellow in bud, turning pink then blue on opening   **3. M. discolor**
    Flowers blue, even in bud   5
5. Lowermost pedicels shorter than the calyx; nutlets light
    brown   ..   ..   **2. M. ramosissima**
    Lowermost pedicels longer than the calyx; nutlets greenish to
    black   ..   ..   **1. M. arvensis**

1. Myosotis arvensis. 5-8. Hairy annual or biennial, usually with branched stems and long, open inflorescences. Lower leaves spoon-shaped; upper oval-lanceolate and pointed. Lowermost pedicels much longer than calyx when in fruit. Calyx with hooked, spreading hairs [Fig. XCd]; calyx teeth triangular. Corolla 3-4 mm across; blue. Nutlets greenish to black. *Open well-drained ground; widespread and frequent.*

 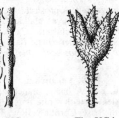 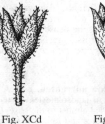

Fig. XCb   Fig. XCc   Fig. XCd   Fig. XCe

2. M. ramosissima. 4-5. Like *M. arvensis* but shorter, often more densely hairy; with smaller flowers 3 mm across; the calyx as long or longer than the pedicel and the nutlets pale brown. *Occasional in dry, open habitats on sandy or stony soils by the East coast; very rare elsewhere.*

3. M. discolor. 4-6. A hairy annual, usually less than 20 cm high, with erect, unbranched or sparingly branched stems. Calyx with hooked, sometimes spreading hairs; calyx-teeth narrowly triangular. Corolla 2-3 mm across; creamy-yellow in bud, turning first pink and then blue as the flower opens. Nutlets dark green. *Tilled fields, sandy banks, and stony soils; frequent; also rarely in marshy meadows; commoner in the North.*

4. M. secunda. 5-7. Perennial, 15-40 cm high, with creeping and rooting runners; the lower part of the plant with stiffly outstanding hairs [Fig. XCb]. Pedicels mostly longer than calyx. Calyx with non-spreading hairs [Fig. XCe]. Corolla 3-7 mm across. Style much shorter than the calyx. Nutlets finely granulate. *Wet acidic areas; mainly in the mountains; commoner in the North.*

5. M. laxa. 6-9. A usually much branched, weakly hairy or almost hairless biennial; the hairs sometimes slightly spreading [Fig. XCc]. Calyx with straight usually non-spreading hairs; divided about halfway to the base into triangular teeth. Corolla 4-5 mm across. Style much shorter than the calyx. *Marshes, ditches and streams; frequent and widespread.*

6. M. scorpiodes. 6-7. Perennial, usually hairy; sometimes with creeping and rooting runners. Pedicels at least as long as the calyx. Calyx with straight, usually non-spreading hairs; divided about $1/2$ way to the base into triangular teeth. Corolla usually 6-9 mm across, but sometimes much smaller. Style longer than the calyx and clearly protruding from flowers where the corolla has dropped off. *Muddy soils by ponds, streams and in wet fields; frequent and widespread; perhaps less frequent in the South-west.*

11. Cynoglossum

Cynoglossum officinale. Hound's tongue. *Teanga chon.* **6-7.** A biennial, 30-80 cm high, covered in dense soft hairs. Lower leaves large (up to 30 cm), oval to lanceolate, petiolate; upper leaves lanceolate, stalkless. Flowers in branched cymes which elongate after flowering. Calyx divided almost to the base, with the lobes spreading, widely in fruit. Corolla about 8 mm across; reddish-purple; funnel-shaped with a short, broad tube closed at the mouth by scales. Filaments very short. Nutlets large, flattened, with a clearly thickened margin. *Sand-hills and dry, sandy ground on the South and East coasts; occasional; very rare and declining inland.*

XCI.   VERBENACEAE

* Verbena officinalis. Vervain. 7-8. An erect, slightly hairy perennial, with angular stems branched near the top, 30-50 cm high. Leaves opposite, oblong, without stipules; uppermost lanceolate, stalkless and usually entire, lower stalked, and pinnatifid. Flowers slightly irregular, hermaphrodite, 4-5 mm across, in long, slender, branched spikes. Calyx with 5 short teeth. Corolla tubular, corolla-tube longer than calyx; corolla-lobes lilac, slightly unequal with an upper, 2-lobed and a lower, 3-lobed lip. Stamens 4, attached to the corolla; filaments absent. Ovary superior, 4-celled; style single. Fruit a group of 4, seed-like nutlets enclosed in the calyx-tube. Nutlets brown, slightly rough. *Roadsides and waste places; occasional in the South half, very rare in the North.*

XCII.   CALLITRICHACEAE

Callitriche

Aquatic or semi-aquatic perennials with opposite, undivided leaves. Flowers minute, axillary, monoecious, without perianth, consisting of a single stamen or a 4 lobed ovary with 2 styles. In some species the lobes of the fruit develop distinct keels or wings.

Species of this genus are very difficult to determine with certainty, and many Irish records require confirmation; for this reason the distribution and relative frequencies of the species are poorly known. Fruiting material is essential for accurate determination.

1. Plants entirely submerged   2
   Plants terrestrial or with floating leaves   5
2. Leaves transparent, 1-veined, leaf-surface hairless   3
   Leaves opaque, often with more than 1 vein, leaf-surface with
       minute, peltate hairs   4
3. Leaves less than 12 mm long; fruit wider than long and without
       a conspicuous wing   ..   ..   ..   **2. C. truncata**
   Leaves more than 12 mm long; fruit longer than wide and
       conspicuously winged   ..   ..   ..   **1. C. hermaphroditica**

4. Leaves expanded suddenly at the tip, with a deep notch; fruits
   with a minute keel, almost stalkless   ..   ..   **6. C. hamulata**
   Leaves not expanded suddenly at tip, with a shallow notch; fruits
   with a distinct wing, borne on a distinct stalk   ..   ..   **7. C. brutia**

5. Fruit borne on a distinct stalk   ..   ..   ..   **7. C. brutia**
   Fruits more or less stalkless   6

6. Fruits without a keel or wing   ..   ..   **5. C. obtusangula**
   Fruit with a distinct, though sometimes small, keel or wing   ..   7

7. Submerged leaves (if present) oval   ..   ..   **3. C. stagnalis**
   Submerged leaves absent or linear   8

8. Styles (if present) bent down against the margins of the fruit   **6. C. hamulata**
   Styles absent or erect or spreading, not bent down against the
   margins of the fruit   9

9. Fruit with a distinct wing more than 0.1 mm wide. Stamens less
   than 3 mm long   ..   ..   ..   **3. C. stagnalis**
   Fruit with a keel, scarcely winged. Stamens more than 3 mm
   long   ..   ..   **4. C. platycarpa**

   1. Callitriche hermaphroditica (*C. autumnalis*). **5-9.** Whole plant submerged, of
a deep, translucent green. Leaves 12-20 mm long, linear, notched at the tip. Fruit at
least as long as wide, with conspicuously winged lobes; styles spreading horizontally, falling early. *Lakes and streams; mainly in the North half, occasional.*

   2. C. truncata. Similar to *C. hermaphroditica* but with shorter leaves
(8-12 mm long) and fruits wider than long has been recorded from one site in County
Wexford.

   3. C. stagnalis. 5-9. Leaves oval, shortly stalked, 5-9 mm wide, all more or less
similar in shape; usually the uppermost forming a well-defined, floating rosette, with
the others submerged, but sometimes the whole plant is above water, creeping on wet
mud. Fruit about as long as wide; lobes conspicuously winged; styles erect or
spreading. *Ponds, muddy ditches and slow streams; frequent.* Seemingly the
commonest species of *Callitriche* in Ireland.

   4. C. platycarpa (*C. palustris, C. vernalis, C. polymorpha*). **5-9.** Like *C.
stagnalis* but with the lower leaves much narrower and the fruit wider than long, with
the lobes keeled rather than winged. *Similar situations; probably frequent.*

   5. C. obtusangula. 5-9. Plant with at least some leaves floating or terrestrial.
Upper leaves oval, forming a rosette; lower leaves linear, deeply notched at the tip.
fruit longer than wide, with blunt, rounded and unwinged lobes. *Similar situations to*
C. stagnalis; *occasional.*

   6. C. hamulata (*C. pedunculata*) **5-9.** Like *C. obtusangula* but with stalkless, less
strongly keeled fruits and submerged leaves suddenly expanded at the tip, which is
deeply notched. *Similar situations to* C. stagnalis; *apparently widespread but rare.*

   7. C. brutia (*C. intermedia*). **5-9.** Leaves mostly submerged, linear, with a deeply
notched tip; sometimes the uppermost are elliptical and form an ill-defined rosette.
Fruit distinctly stalked, about as long as wide; lobes distinctly keeled or winged;
styles curved downwards against the edges of the fruit, falling early. *Lakes and
streams; mainly in the North half, occasional.*

XCIII. LABIATAE (LAMIACEAE)

Herbs, mostly perennial, with square stems and opposite, undivided leaves. Flowers irregular, usually in axillary whorl-like clusters, which may form a terminal spike. Calyx tubular, usually 5-toothed. Corolla tubular, of 5 fused petals, 2-lipped or 4-lobed. Stamens 4 (rarely 2), attached to the corolla, usually in two pairs, one longer than the other. Ovary and fruits as in the Boraginaceae. Nutlets are rounded on top except in *Lamium*, *Lamiastrum* and *Lycopus*.

Many genera of this family are cultivated as aromatic herbs *e.g.* Thyme and Mint. Other garden plants include Lavender (*Lavendula*), Rosemary (*Rosmarinus*) and *Coleus*, grown, as a house-plant, for its coloured leaves.

1. Stamens 2 2
    Stamens 4 3
2. Corolla bluish-purple, strongly 2-lipped .. **18. Salvia**
    Corolla white, dotted with pink, with 4 nearly equal lobes .. **16. Lycopus**
3. Corolla 1-lipped [Fig. XCIIIa] 4
    Corolla 2-lipped [Fig. XCIIIb] 5

Fig. XCIIIa   Fig. XCIIIb

4. Corolla blue, with a small row of hairs on the inner surface near its base; lower lip of corolla with a large central lobe flanked by a small lobe on each side .. .. .. **1. Ajuga**
    Corolla greenish-yellow or pink, without a small row of hairs on the inner surface near its base; lower lip of corolla with a large central lobe flanked by 2 smaller lobes on each side .. **2. Teucrium**
5. Calyx consisting of 2 undivided lobes, the upper with a scale-like protuberance on its back .. .. **3. Scutellaria**
    Calyx with 5 teeth, sometimes markedly unequal in size or with the upper lip entire and the lower lip toothed 6
6. Corolla nearly regular, scarcely 2-lipped 7
    Corolla distinctly 2-lipped 8
7. Calyx with 5 almost equal teeth; leaves with the characteristic smell of Mint .. .. **17. Mentha**
    Calyx clearly 2-lipped; the upper lip with 3 short teeth, the lower with 2 longer teeth; leaves with the characteristic smell of Thyme .. .. .. **15. Thymus**
8. Calyx with the upper lip undivided and the lower lip toothed .. **11. Prunella**
    Calyx with 5 distinct teeth 9

9. Calyx strongly 2-lipped 10
   Calyx with 5 teeth; not or scarcely 2-lipped 11

10. Leaves deeply toothed, hairless underneath .. .. **12. Melissa**
    Leaves more or less undivided or at most shallowly toothed,
       hairy underneath .. .. .. **13. Clinopodium**

11. Leaves rounded at base or tapered to a petiole 12
    Leaves at least the lower ones, cordate or cut off square at the
       base or almost stalkless 13

12. Leaves more or less undivided .. .. .. **14. Origanum**
    Leaves clearly toothed .. .. **4. Galeopsis**

13. Upper lip of corolla flat, not hooded 14
    Upper lip of corolla hooded, not flat 15

14. Flowers whitish, in compact terminal inflorescences .. **9. Nepeta**
    Flowers violet, in distant axillary whorls .. **10. Glechoma**

15. Flowers yellow .. .. .. **6. Lamiastrum**
    Flowers purplish or white 16

16. Calyx-teeth as broad as long .. .. .. **7. Ballota**
    Calyx-teeth longer than broad 17

17. Lower lip of corolla 2-lobed .. .. .. **5. Lamium**
    Lower lip of corolla 3-lobed .. .. .. **8. Stachys**

1. Ajuga

Biennials or perennials with oval, stalked, entire or slightly crenate basal leaves. Flowers in axillary whorls, forming a loose or compact spike. Calyx with 5 equal teeth. Corolla with a minute upper lip and a long, 4-lobed lower lip. Corolla-tube with a small ring of hairs inside, near the base. Stamens 4, protruding from the corolla-tube. Anthers hairless.

1. Bracts green; stem hairy on two opposite sides only .. **1. A. reptans**
   Bracts tinged with violet or pink; stem hairy all round **2. A. pyramidalis**

1. Ajuga reptans. Bugle. 5-6. Delicate, hairless or somewhat hairy herb with a long-creeping rhizome. Basal leaves appearing only after flowering, deeply 3-lobed, the lobes further lobed or toothed. Flowers 2-4 cm long, about 6mm across; bracts large, about two thirds of the way up the flower stem. Sepals usually 6 or 7, narrowly oblong, white (sometimes tinged with purple or pink), hairless. *Woods and shady places. Very frequent in the North, local elsewhere.*

2. A. pyramidalis. 5. Softly hairy, without runners; stem erect, 8-15 cm high. Basal leaves with short stalks, the upper stalkless. Flowers pale violet-blue, in a rather diffuse spike; bracts usually tinged with violet or pink. *Rocky ground around Galway Bay and Rathlin Island; extremely rare.*

2. Teucrium

Perennials. Flowers about 12 mm long. Calyx 5-toothed. Corolla without an upper lip, and with a large, 5-lobed lower lip. Corolla-tube without a small ring of hairs inside, near the base. Stamens 4, protruding from the corolla. Anthers hairless.

1. Corolla greenish-white; upper tooth of corolla much larger than
      the others .. .. .. **1. T. scorodonia**
   Corolla pinkish-purple; upper tooth of corolla more or less the
      same size as the others .. .. .. **2. T. scordium**

1. Teucrium scorodonia. Wood sage. 7-8. Stems hard, erect, often nearly unbranched, 25-60 cm high. Leaves wrinkled, downy, oval-oblong, cordate, crenate. Flowers straw-coloured, often in long racemes, the axillary often 1-sided. Calyx 2-lipped, the upper lip composed of a single broad tooth, the lower of 4 narrow ones. Corolla-tube twice as long as calyx. Nutlets smooth. *Heaths, open areas in woods and rocky places; very frequent in mountain districts, rare in the lowlands.*

2. T. scordium. 7-8. Stems branched, softly hairy, prostrate or spreading, 10-20 cm long. Leaves stalkless, oblong, bluntly toothed, 2-3 cm long. Flowers pinkish-mauve, in 1-sided whorls of about 4. Calyx-teeth equal and narrow. Corolla-tube short. Nutlets rough. *Frequent on the shores of Lough Derg and Lough Ree; very rare elsewhere.*

3. Scutellaria. Skull-cap

Perennials, with flowers in axillary pairs, with evident pedicels. Calyx with 2 entire lips, the upper with a hollow, scale-like protruberance on its back. Corolla more than twice as long as calyx, 2-lipped; lips nearly closed, upper concave, narrow; lower flat, 3-lobed; corolla-tube lacking a small ring of hairs inside, near the base. Stamens 4, in 2 unequal pairs, visible beneath the upper lip of the corolla. Anthers hairy.

1. Flowers blue, about 15 mm long .. .. **1. S. galericulata**
   Flowers pink, less than 10 mm long .. .. .. **2. S. minor**

1. Scutellaria galericulata. 7-8. Almost hairless or downy, with erect, but weak stems 20-45 cm high. Leaves oblong-lanceolate, somewhat cordate, slightly toothed or crenate, shortly stalked. Flowers about 15 mm long, blue, forming a sparse, 1-sided spike. *Lake-shores; occasional and largely in the North.*

2. S. minor. 7-8. Similar but much smaller (15 cm high or less), with stalkless leaves, entire or slightly toothed at the base, and pink flowers 8 mm long. *Bogs and marshes; locally frequent in the South-west, rarer in the South-east, very rare elsewhere.*

4. Galeopsis

Annuals, with leaves somewhat tapered at the base, usually serrate. Calyx with 5, equal, strong, long teeth. Corolla 2-lipped; upper lip hooded, laterally compressed, lower lip flat, 3-lobed. Anthers hairy.

1. Hairs soft and downy, stem smooth .. .. **1. G. angustifolia**
   Hairs stiff and bristly, stem rough 2

2. Corolla mainly yellow, at least 25 mm long .. **2. G. speciosa**
   Corolla usually purple or white, less than 25 mm long **3. G. tetrahit**

1. † Galeopsis angustifolia (*Galeopsis ladanum*). **8-9.** Stem softly downy, 15-50 cm high with spreading branches. Leaves usually lanceolate, slightly toothed, tapered to a short stalk. Flowers reddish-purple, sometimes spotted with white, 20 mm long, in axillary whorls. *Calcareous gravels, especially on eskers in the East-Centre; rare.*

2. * G. speciosa. 7-8. Stem rough with stiff, bristly downwardly pointing hairs, 25-70 cm high. Leaves oval-lanceolate, pointed, toothed. Flowers in short terminal spikes. Corolla 25-35 mm long, yellow, with a purple spot on the lower lip. *Arable land on peaty soils; occasional and mainly in the North.*

3. † **G. tetrahit. 7-9.** Stem rough with stiff, bristly downwardly pointing hairs, some glandular, 15-40 cm high. Corolla 12-20 mm long, mauve or white; centre of lower lip mottled mauve and white, margin broad, mauve. *Arable land on peaty soils; occasional, more frequent in the North.*

† *G. bifida* differs in having the lower lip of the corolla almost entirely purple, turned down and notched at the end. Apparently rare and more or less confined to the North-east, though probably under-recorded.

5. Lamium. Deadnettle

Annuals or perennials similar to *Galeopsis* but differing in the more or less cordate leaves and nutlets which are flattened on top.

1.	Flowers pure white	..	..	.. **1. L. album**
	Flowers reddish-purple	..	..	.. 2
2.	Upper leaves stalkless	..	..	.. 3
	Upper leaves stalked	..	..	.. 4
3.	Calyx about 6 mm long; calyx-teeth not spreading in fruit		**4. L. amplexicaule**
	Calyx about 10 mm long; calyx-teeth spreading in fruit		**5. L. confertum**
4.	Leaves bluntly and regularly toothed	..	..	**2. L. purpureum**
	Leaves deeply and irregularly toothed	..	..	**3. L. hybridum**

1. * **Lamium album. White deadnettle. 4-9.** A hairy perennial with stems 25-50 cm high, mainly erect but creeping at the base. Leaves stalked, oval, cordate, pointed, strongly toothed. Flowers 20-25 mm long, pure white, in crowded axillary whorls. Calyx-teeth longer than tube, slender. *Roadsides, hedges and waste-places, ruins; locally frequent in the East half, very rare in the West.*

2. L. purpureum. Red deadnettle. *Neanntóg chaoch.* **3-10.** A slightly downy annual, 10-20 cm high, branched from the base. Leaves all stalked, usually oval and cordate, crenate or bluntly toothed. Flowers reddish-purple, 12-15 mm long, in a usually congested terminal spike; bracts often purplish. Calyx-teeth longer than tube. Corolla with a distinct line of hairs near the base of the tube. *Waste places and field margins; frequent.*

3. † **L. hybridum. 4-10.** Similar to *L. purpureum*, but with more deeply and irregularly toothed leaves; the base of the corolla-tube with, at best, a weak line of hairs. *Waste places and field margins; occasional, and mainly around the coasts.*

4. * **L. amplexicaule. Henbit. 5-8.** A slightly downy annual 10-20 cm high, branched from the base. Leaves nearly round, crenate, the lower stalked, the upper stalkless and clasping the stem. Flowers reddish-purple and 15 mm long or inconspicuous and 3-4 mm long, in whorls which form a rather lax spike. Calyx very hairy, about 6 mm long; calyx-teeth about as long as tube, converging in fruit. *Waste and sandy places, usually near the coast; rare and declining.* Two types of flower are produced; one has a very long, conspicuous corolla-tube whilst the corolla in the other type does not open and is very small and inconspicuous.

5. * **L. confertum** (*L. mollucellifolium, L. intermedium*). **3-10.** Similar to *L. amplexicaule* but with the calyx about 10 mm long, less hairy and the calyx-teeth spreading in fruit. *Similar habitats; but rarer in the South.*

6. Lamiastrum

Lamiastrum galeobdolon (*Lamium galeobdolon, Galeobdolon luteum*). **Archangel. 4-7.** A hairy perennial with creeping barren stems and erect flowering

ones, 20-45 cm high. Leaves oval, toothed, shortly stalked, somewhat tapered at the base. Flowers bright yellow, sometimes spotted orange-brown, 20-25 mm long, in distant axillary whorls. Calyx-teeth triangular and short. Corolla 2-lipped; upper lip hooded, lower lip flat, 3-lobed. Stamens 4, unequal. Anthers hairless. *Woods and hedges; mainly in the South-east; rather rare but sometimes locally abundant.*
Two sub-species occur:
Subsp. *argentatum* has conspicuous white blotches on the leaves and is mainly found in cultivation though it is sometimes naturalised
Subsp. *montanum.* Lacks white blotches on the leaves and is native.

7. Ballota
* Ballota nigra. Black horehound. 7-8. A dark green, hairy, unpleasant-smelling, erect perennial, 20-90 cm high. Leaves stalked, broadly oval, usually cordate, irregularly crenate. Flowers in axillary whorls, or clusters, all turned to one side. Calyx funnel-shaped with 5 short, broadly triangular teeth. Corolla purplish-pink, 15 mm long, 2-lipped; upper lip somewhat hooded, lower lip flat, 3-lobed. Stamens 4 unequal. Anthers hairless. *Roadsides and waste-places, mainly in the East half; rare and decreasing.*

8. Stachys. Woundwort
Leaves cordate or cut-off square at the base. Flowers reddish, in axillary whorls, forming a terminal spike. Calyx regularly 5-toothed. Corolla 2-lipped; upper lip slightly hooded, entire, erect and nearly straight; lower flat, 3-lobed. Stamens 4, unequal; anthers hairless.

1. Corolla pale pink, less than 10 mm long; stems weak and straggling
   5. S. arvensis
   Corolla deep purplish-red, more than 10 mm long; stems erect .. 2
2. Leaves almost stalkless .. .. .. **3. S. palustris**
   Leaves distinctly stalked 3
3. Spike short and compact; leaves crenate .. **1. S. officinalis**
   Spike long and interruputed; leaves toothed 4
4. Few, if any fruits ripening; upper leaves with short stalks **4. S. x ambigua**
   Most fruits ripening; upper leaves with distinct stalks **2. S. sylvatica**

1. Stachys officinalis (*S. betonica, Betonica officinalis*). **Betony. 7-8.** An erect, more or less hairy perennial, 25-50 cm high. Leaves oblong-lanceolate, lower ones cordate, with long stalks, very regularly crenate; upper ones nearly stalkless and more toothed. Flowers purplish-red, 18-20 mm long, in a short, ovoid, terminal spike. *Woods and bushy places; very rare, local and apparently decreasing.*

2. S. sylvatica 7-8. A hairy, erect, rhizomatous, unpleasant-smelling perennial up to 1 m high. Leaves all stalked, oval, cordate, strongly toothed. Flowers deep reddish-purple, 15 mm long in axillary whorls which form a loose, leafy spike. *Hedges and wood-margins; very frequent.*

3. S. palustris. 7-8. Similar to *S. sylvatica,* but less strongly smelling; leaves oblong-lanceolate, often slightly cordate, finely toothed and more or less stalkless; flowers a lighter, dull red. *Ditches, river-banks and damp arable fields; frequent.*

4. S. x ambigua. 8. Intermediate between the parents, *S. sylvatica* and *S. palustris,* in most characters. Leaves stalked, oblong-lanceolate. Fruits not forming. Often found in the absence of one or both parents. *Woods, hedges, damp ground; occasional.*

5. S. arvensis. 8-9. A hairy annual, with straggling, though sometimes upright, branches 8-40 cm long. Leaves small, oval, crenate; at least the lower stalked. Flowers pale pink, 7-9 mm long, in axillary whorls forming a loose, leafy spike; corolla scarcely longer than calyx. *Arable land; occasional in the South-east, very rare elsewhere.*

9. Nepeta

* Nepeta cataria. Catmint. 7-8. An erect perennial, 40-80 cm high. Leaves stalked, triangular-oval, somewhat cordate, coarsely toothed, covered with whitish-grey down, aromatic. Flowers small, white spotted with purple, in numerous, shortly stalked clusters, forming a compact spike. Calyx 5-toothed, teeth more or less equal. Corolla 2-lipped; upper lip flat; lower lip somewhat concave, with a large central lobe with a toothed margin and 2 very small lateral lobes. Stamens 4, unequal; anthers hairless. *Banks and roadsides, mainly in the North and West; rare.*

10. Glechoma

Glechoma hederacea. Ground ivy. 4-6. A slightly hairy perennial with trailing or creeping stems; feebly aromatic. Leaves round, deeply cordate, stalked, deeply crenate, up to 25 mm across. Flowers violet, 20-25 mm long, in axillary whorls. Calyx 5-toothed, teeth more or less equal. Corolla 2-lipped; upper lip flat; lower 4-lobed, the central lobes the largest; tube much longer than calyx. Stamens 4; unequal; anthers hairless. *Woods, hedges and grassy places; frequent.*

11. Prunella

Prunella vulgaris. Self-heal. 6-8. A slightly hairy perennial with creeping stems. Leaves 20-35 mm long, oval-oblong, toothed or entire, all stalked except the uppermost. Flowers purple, 12 mm long, in short, compact, cylindrical, terminal spikes. Calyx 2-lipped; upper lip almost entire, lower deeply 2-lobed. Corolla 2-lipped; upper lip slightly hooded, entire, lower 3-lobed, flat, the middle lobe the largest and often toothed. Stamens 4; unequal. *Damp pastures, roadsides, woods, heaths, gardens, and in waste-ground; abundant.*

12. Melissa

Melissa officinalis. 7-9. Erect perennial up to 120 cm high. Leaves broadly oval, crenate, sparsely hairy above, hairless beneath, lemon-scented. Flowers in axillary whorls, forming elongated spikes. Calyx 2-lipped, upper lip bent backwards, 3-toothed, lower 3-toothed, forward pointing. Corolla 10-12 mm long, pale yellow, tinged with pink, 2-lipped; tube slightly curved; upper lip slightly hooded, notched, lower 3-lobed. Stamens 4; unequal; anthers hairless. *Roadsides and bushy places; rare.*

13. Clinopodium

Leaves oval-lanceolate, base somewhat tapering. Flowers in axillary whorls, forming an elongated spike. Calyx 2-lipped, upper lip with 3 broad teeth, lower with 2 longer, narrower teeth. Corolla 2-lipped; upper lip spreading, 2-lobed, lower 3-lobed, spreading. Stamens 4, unequal; anthers hairless.

1. Most stems creeping; corolla less than 10 mm long ..	..	**1. C. acinos**
Most stems erect; corolla more than 10 mm long ..	..	2
2. Flower stalks long, easily visible, flowers forming an open head		**2. C. ascendens**
Flower stalks very short, not easily visible, flowers in dense, compact whorls		**3. C. vulgare**

1. * Clinopodium acinos (*Acinos arvensis, Calamintha acinos*). **Basil thyme. 7-8.** A branched, spreading, downy annual, 8-25 cm high, slightly aromatic. Leaves small, oval, stalked, feebly toothed. Flowers violet, in axillary whorls of about 6, less than 10 mm long. *Field margins and sandy or gravelly places in the Centre and South-east; rare.*

2. C. ascendens (*Calamintha sylvatica* subsp. *ascendens, C. sylvatica*). **7-9.** A straggling perennial with erect, unbranched stems 30-60 cm high; aromatic. Leaves oval, hairy, feebly toothed. Flowers pinkish-purple, in stalked, axillary cymes, forming an open head, more than 10 mm long. *Rocky places and dry banks; rare and mainly in the South half.*

3. * C. vulgare (*Calamintha officinalis*). **Basil. 7-9.** Similar to *C. ascendens*, differing in the oval-lanceolate leaves and almost stalkless flowers which form dense whorls at each node of the inflorescence. *Roadsides and dry banks; formerly occasional and mainly in the South-east, now very rare.*

14. Origanum
Origanum vulgare. Marjoram. 7-9. An erect, downy, branched perennial, 40-70 cm high, often tinged with red. Leaves oval, stalked, nearly entire, 20-30 mm long. Flowers pinkish-purple, in compact clusters arranged in a terminal, corymbose panicle. Bracts often red or purple. Calyx with 5 nearly equal teeth. Corolla somewhat 2-lipped; upper lip notched, lower 3-lobed. Stamens 4; unequal; anthers hairless. *Dry, usually calcareous banks, roadsides and stony places; rare in the North and South-west, locally frequent elsewhere.*

15. Thymus
Thymus praecox (*T. drucei, T. polytrichus, T. serpyllum*). **Thyme. 6-8.** A low, aromatic perennial with creeping barren stems and erect flowering ones 3-7 cm high; the latter are 4-angled with 2 sides very hairy and 2 nearly hairless. Leaves 6-8 mm long, oval, entire, rather hairy. Flowers small, purple, in compact, ovoid heads. Calyx 2-lipped; upper lip 3-toothed, lower 2-toothed. Corolla, stamens and nutlets as in *Origanum. Heaths, dry banks, rocky places and seaside pastures; very frequent near the coast, local inland.*

* *T. pulegioides*, which has flowering stems up to 30 cm long which are hairy only on the angles, has been recorded as a casual in the past.

16. Lycopus
Lycopus europaeus. Gipsywort. 7-8. A rather stiff, erect, nearly hairless perennial, 25-90 mm high, not aromatic. Leaves large, oblong-lanceolate, very shortly stalked, pinnatifid or coarsely toothed. Flower small and numerous, stalkless, white spotted with a few purple dots, in dense, widely separated, axillary whorls. Calyx 5-toothed. Corolla white, spotted with reddish-purple, somewhat 2-lipped; upper lip notched, lower 3-lobed. Stamens 4, markedly unequal in size; 2 large and easily visible and 2 tiny, vestigial and indistinct. *Dry banks, roadsides and stony places; occasional in the North and South-west, locally frequent elsewhere.*

17. Mentha. Mint. *Mismín*
Aromatic perennials, with numerous, small, mauve or pink flowers in dense whorls. Calyx regularly 5-toothed. Corolla nearly regular, not 2-lipped, somewhat bell-shaped, with 4 short lobes, of which one is broader than the rest and often notched. Stamens 4, equal in length.

Many plants of this genus have been cultivated for centuries as aromatic herbs; some have escaped here and there. In many cases the origin of these cultivated forms is obscure; some are sterile hybrids which can multiply by vegetative means. Not all plants will key out easily and some may be impossible to name with certainty.

1. Stems creeping, forming a dense mat; leaves 2-4 mm across;
    flowers 6 or fewer at each node   ..   ..   **1. M. requienii**
    Stems not creeping, not mat-forming; leaves more than 5 mm
    across; flowers more than 6 at each node   2

2. Whorls of flowers spread out along stem   3
    Whorls of flowers aggregated together into a spike or head   ..   7

3. Leaves 20 mm long or less, nearly entire   **2. M. pulegium**
    Leaves over 25 mm long, distinctly toothed or crenate   ..   4

4. Calyx-teeth about 1 mm long; much longer than broad   **4. M. x gracilis**
    Calyx-teeth either more than 1 mm long, or if 1 mm long then
    about ^{2}/3rds as broad as long   5

5. Plant almost hairless; stamens usually protruding from the
    flower   ..   ..   ..   **7. M. x smithiana**
    Plant hairy; stamens usually hidden within the flower   ..   6

6. Calyx 2.5 mm long or less; plant with good (swollen) seeds   **3. M. arvensis**
    Calyx more than 2.5 mm long; plant sterile   ..   **6. M. x verticillata**

7. Leaves distinctly stalked   8
    Leaves stalkless   9

8. Calyx-tube and upper surface of leaves hairy; always with good
    (swollen) seeds   ..   ..   ..   **5. M. aquatica**
    Calyx-tube and upper surface of leaves almost hairless; always
    without good seeds   ..   ..   ..   **8. M. x piperita**

9. Leaves almost hairless   ..   ..   ..   **10. M. spicata**
    Leaves evidently pubescent   11

10. Leaves usually less than 4 cm long, strongly wrinkled; almost
    round   ..   ..   **9. M. suaveolens**
    Leaves usually more than 4 cm long   11

11. Leaves smooth, almost hairless; plant with good (swollen)
    seeds   ..   ..   ..   **10. M. spicata**
    Leaves wrinkled, hairy; plant without good seeds   ..   **11. M. x villosa**

1. * Mentha requienii. 5-7. A much branched, slender, creeping and mat-forming, strongly aromatic, perennial. Leaves round, 2-4 mm across, entire. Flowers in well-separated whorls of 6 or fewer, minute. Corolla scarcely longer than calyx. *Naturalised on damp rocks or roadsides near the coast; infrequent.* Native of the Mediterranean.

2. M. pulegium. Penny-royal. 8-9. Stems spreading; leaves stalked, oval, nearly entire, slightly hairy, 10-20 mm long. Flowers pinkish-mauve, in distinct axillary whorls. *Damp, sandy places; occasional in Kerry, very rare elsewhere.*

3. M. arvensis. Corn mint. 8-9. Stems erect or spreading, 15-40 cm long. Leaves stalked, varying from lanceolate to nearly round, feebly toothed, rather hairy. Flowers pinkish-mauve, in distinct, widely spaced whorls, in the axils of leaves which are much longer than the flowers. Calyx-teeth triangular. *Fields and waste-places; occasional.*

4. * M. x gracilis (*M.* x *gentilis*). **7-11.** The hybrid between *M. arvensis* and *M. spicata*. Similar to *M. arvensis*, differing mainly in the short, narrow, awl-shaped calyx-teeth, often red stems, and sterility. *Scattered throughout; occasional.*

5. M. aquatica (*M.* x *gentilis*). **7-9.** Stems up to 90 cm high, often reddish. Leaves stalked, oval, pointed, coarsely toothed, somewhat hairy. Flowers in compact ovoid or globular heads, often with 1 or 2 additional whorls lower down the stem. Calyx-teeth slender, pointed. *Marshes, ditches and lake-shores; frequent.*

6. M. x verticillata (*M.* x *gentilis, M. sativa*). **7-11.** The hybrid between *M. aquatica* and *M. arvensis*. Similar to *M. aquatica*, differing mainly in the elongated inflorescence with well separated whorls of sterile flowers and shorter and more broadly triangular calyx-teeth. *Fields, marshes, ditches; frequent and often in the absence of both parents.*

7. * M. x smithiana (*M. rubra*). **7-11.** The hybrid between *M. aquatica, M. arvensis* and *M. spicata*. Almost hairless, red-stemmed, erect, up to 1.5 m high. Leaves oval, distinctly toothed. Flowers in well separated whorls, with exserted stamens. Calyx-teeth variable in shape; some broadly triangular, others narrowly so. *Damp places, woods; seemingly absent from the Centre, otherwise rare and scattered throughout.*

8. * M. x piperita. Peppermint. 8-9. The hybrid between *M. aquatica* and *M. spicata*. Stem erect, 30-80 cm high, often reddish. Leaves stalked, oval to lanceolate, usually toothed, nearly hairless. Flowers in a somewhat interrupted terminal spike. *Riverbanks and ditches; occasional.*

9. * M. suaveolens (*M. rotundifolia*). **8-9.** Stem erect, branched, 35-80 cm high. Leaves stalkless, broadly oval or almost round, crenate, wrinkled, hairy, especially underneath, rounded at the tip. Flowers in dense terminal spikes, forming a panicle. *River-banks, roadsides and waste-places; occasional in the South and East, rare elsewhere.*

10. * M. spicata (*M. viridis, M. longifolia*). **Spearmint. 8-9.** Stem erect, branched, 30-90 cm high. Leaves stalkless, lanceolate, pointed, toothed. Flowers in terminal spikes, often clustered. *The commonest Mint in gardens; naturalised in waste places in a few districts.*

11. * M. x villosa. Applemint. 8-9. The hybrid between *M. spicata* and *M. suaveolens*. Differing from *M. spicata* in its sterility and leaves which are often hairy, wrinkled and oval. *Fairly frequent in gardens; very rarely naturalised.*

18. Salvia

Salvia verbenaca (*S. horminioides*). **6-9.** A hairy, erect, somewhat aromatic perennial, 30-70 cm high. Leaves oval-oblong, wrinkled, irregularly toothed or pinnatifid, 5-10 cm long; lower ones stalked, upper stalkless. Flowers bluish-purple, 10-12 mm long, in whorls of about 6, arranged in a long, loose spike. Calyx strongly 2-lipped, upper lip almost entire, lower lip 2-toothed. Corolla 2-lipped; upper lip hooded, lower spreading and 3-lobed. Stamens 2, peculiarly shaped, with a short filament and the anther greatly elongated transversely and fertile only at one end. *Dry banks, sand-dunes and roadsides near the coast; rare and almost confined to the South half.*

XCIV.   SOLANACEAE

Herbs or shrubs. Leaves alternate, stalked, without stipules. Flowers more or less regular, hermaphrodite. Sepals 5, united to form a funnel-shaped, sometimes 2-lipped calyx. Corolla 5-lobed. Stamens 5, attached to the corolla-tube. Ovary superior, 2-celled; style solitary. Fruit a berry or a capsule.

To this family belong the Potato (*Solanum tuberosum*) and Tomato (*Lycopersicon esculentum*), the Red, Green and Chilli peppers (*Capsicum annuum*) as well as Tobacco (*Nicotiana tabacum*); also *Petunia* x *hybrida* and species of *Physalis* (Japanese-lantern) are grown for ornament. Many members of the family are poisonous.

Tomato plants are frequent casuals often found on rubbish-dumps and on the coast where seed has been washed-ashore from sewage outfalls.

1. Anthers cohering to form a cone in the centre of the flower   ..   **4. Solanum**
   Anthers separate   2

2. Shrub   ..   ..   **1. Lycium**
   Herb   3

3. Leaves entire, not toothed or pinnatifid ..   ..   ..   **2. Atropa**
   Leaves strongly toothed or pinnatifid   4

4. Corolla at least 5 cm long, uniformly white, rarely purple; calyx
   not enclosing the usually spiny fruit ..   ..   **5. Datura**
   Corolla less than 3 cm long, yellowish with purple veins; calyx
   enclosing the smooth fruit   ..   ..   **3. Hyoscyamus**

1. Lycium
* Lycium barbarum. Duke of Argyll's tea plant. 6-8. A hairless, usually spiny, straggling shrub, with arching branches up to 2 m. Leaves, undivided, entire, lanceolate, slightly bluish-green, shortly and indistinctly stalked, 4-8 cm long. Flowers axillary, solitary or in small clusters. Calyx c. 4 mm, 2-lipped. Corolla purplish, 7-12 mm long; lobes slightly longer than tube. Stamens projecting beyond the corolla; anthers on long filaments. Fruit an oblong, red berry. *Seashores, track-sides and waste places; rare*. Native of China.

Easily confused with * *L. chinense*, which reputedly differs in its leaves which are widest below the middle, its slightly shorter calyx, and slightly longer corolla and corolla-lobes (5-8 mm). The occurrence, relative frequency and status of *L. barbarum* and *L. chinense* in Ireland requires investigation.

2. Atropa
* Atropa belladonna. Deadly nightshade. 6-8. An erect, large, downy or hairless perennial 60-150 cm high. Leaves up to 20 cm, undivided, entire, oval, stalked. Flowers solitary, axillary. Calyx c. 15 mm. Corolla bell-shaped, 20-30 mm long; corolla-lobes slightly spreading, apex acute, 5-6 mm. Stamens slightly shorter than the corolla. Fruit a spherical, shining black berry about 15 mm across. *Waste-places; rare and often casual*.

3. Hyoscyamus
Hyoscyamus niger. Henbane. 6-9. An erect, coarse, usually downy, sticky and smelly biennial herb, 60-150 cm tall. Leaves oval, undivided, strongly toothed or pinnately lobed, rarely almost undivided, up to 20 cm long; the basal ones stalked, the upper ones stalkless and sometimes clasping the stem. Flowers numerous, in two rows on the upper part of the stem. Calyx funnel-shaped, c. 15 mm, persistent and enlarging in fruit. Corolla broadly funnel-shaped; 25-35 mm across, with broad, rounded lobes; dull yellow with purple veins. Stamens projecting beyond the corolla. Fruit a capsule, enclosed in the calyx. Seeds, flat, pale brown, rough. *Rare on sandy or stony shores throughout; often impermanent*.

4. Solanum
Leaves stalked. Flowers in cymes. Calyx small, lobed to at least half-way. Corolla with a very short tube and star-shaped, spreading lobes. Stamens with very

short filaments and anthers converging so as to form a cone in the centre of the flower. Fruit a berry.

* *Solanum rostratum* an erect, spiny annual with glandular and non-glandular hairs and white or purplish flowers and the similar * *S. sisymbrifolium* which has yellow flowers and no glandular hairs are casual in Cork and Wexford.

1.   Perennial, woody at base; petals purple; berry red   ..   **1. S. dulcamara**
    Annual herb; petals white; berry black or green   ..   **2. S. nigrum**

1. Solanum dulcamara. Bitter-sweet. *Dréimire gorm.* **6-9.** A perennial, with slender, trailing or twining stems up to 200 cm, woody at the base. Leaves entire, the lower usually undivided, oval; the upper with 3-leaflets, the central much the largest. Inflorescence usually with more than 10 flowers. Corolla purple (rarely white), 15 mm across. Berries bright red, ovoid, 10 mm long. *Hedges, ditches, woodland margins, waste-places, walls and stony sea-shores; occasional, commoner in the North and East.*

2. * S. nigrum. Black nightshade. 7-9. A bushy, hairy annual with branched, angular stems, up to 60 cm high. Leaves oval, sometimes coarsely toothed. Inflorescence with 5-10 flowers. Corolla white, 10 mm across. Berries globular, black, rarely green, *c.* 8 mm across. *Arable ground and waste places; mostly in the South and East; an occasional casual, perhaps naturalised in a few places.*

Two sub-species, of uncertain occurrence in Ireland, may occur: subsp. *nigrum* has hairs which are neither glandular or spreading and subsp. *schultesii* has glandular, spreading hairs.

5. Datura
* **Datura stramonium. Thorn apple. 6-9.** A stout, erect, more or less hairless annual, up to 100 cm high. Leaves long-stalked, broadly oval, undivided, strongly toothed, up to 30 cm long. Flowers solitary. Calyx 3-5 cm long, tubular, shortly lobed, splitting after flowering and not persistent around the fruit. Corolla trumpet-shaped, 5-10 cm long, usually white or sometimes purple; lobes with long-pointed tips. Stamens sometimes projecting beyond the corolla. Fruit an ovoid, erect, usually spiny capsule. Seeds flat, heart-shaped, dark brown, slightly rough. *Amongst root-crops; mainly in the South near the coasts (Wexford, Waterford and Cork), sporadic, sometimes forming large colonies.* Native of North America.

XCV. BUDDLEJACEAE

* **Buddleja davidii. Butterfly-bush. 6-9.** Shrub to 4 m high with arching branches topped with showy, conical panicles of lilac flowers. Leaves 10-20 cm, lanceolate, pointed, toothed, with felted white hairs beneath. Flowers more or less regular, hermaphrodite. Calyx tubular, with 4 teeth. Corolla with a long tube and 4 short lobes, lilac with an orange centre. Stamens 4, attached to the corolla and hidden within its tube. Ovary superior; 2-celled; style single. Fruit a capsule with numerous very small seeds. *Walls and waste-ground; very frequent in and around Cork and Dublin, occasional elsewhere.* Native of China.

XCVI. SCROPHULARIACEAE

Herbs (rarely shrubs); flowers usually irregular, solitary or in spikes or racemes. Calyx of 4 or 5 sepals, united at least at the base. Corolla of 4 or 5 united petals, sometimes 2-lipped. Stamens 4 (rarely 2 or 5), inserted on the corolla. Ovary superior, usually 2-celled; style single. Fruit a capsule.

Many ornamental garden plants belong to this family, including species or cultivars of *Penstemon, Mimulus, Calceolaria, Nemesia, Antirrhinum, Veronica* and *Hebe*.

1. Plant without green colour; leaves reduced to fleshy or papery scales   2
   Plant green in parts; most of the leaves not scale-like   ..   3

2. Flowers very shortly stalked, in a 1-sided raceme; scale leaves
   white or pale pink   **22. Lathraea**
   Flowers stalkless, pointing in all directions; scale-leaves
   brownish   ..   ..   **23. Orobanche**

3. Stamens 2   4
   Stamens 4 or 5   5

4. Herb   ..   ..   **13. Veronica**
   Shrub   ..   ..   **14. Hebe**

5. Corolla regular, 2-3 mm across   6
   Corolla irregular, or, if regular, more than 5 mm across   ..   7

6. Leaves entire, hairless   ..   ..   ..   **1. Limosella**
   Leaves crenate, hairy   ..   ..   ..   **15. Sibthorpia**

7. Corolla mainly yellow   8
   Corolla mainly of some other colour, though sometimes with a
   yellow patch   14

8. Corolla almost regular; stamens 5   ..   ..   **3. Verbascum**
   Corolla irregular; stamens 4   9

9. Corolla with a spur at the base; leaves alternate or whorled   ..   10
   Corolla without a spur; leaves opposite   11

10. Leaves ovate or hastate, shortly stalked, hairy   ..   **10. Kickxia**
    Leaves linear, stalkless, hairless   ..   ..   **8. Linaria**

11. Calyx 5-toothed   ..   ..   ..   **2. Mimulus**
    Calyx 4-toothed   12

12. Leaves (except for the upper bracts) not toothed   ..   **16. Melampyrum**
    Leaves toothed   13

13. Calyx inflated, at least in fruit, hairless or sparsely hairy but
    not sticky   ..   ..   ..   **21. Rhinanthus**
    Calyx not inflated, sticky with numerous glandular hairs   **19. Parentucellia**

14. Corolla with a spur or pouch at the base   15
    Corolla without a spur or pouch at the base   19

15. Corolla with a fairly narrow spur or a pouch at its base   ..   16
    Corolla with a broad pouch   18

16. Leaves stalked, at least as broad as long   ..   **9. Cymbalaria**
    Leaves stalkless, much longer than broad   ..   17

17. Annual; flowers in the axils of ordinary leaves   ..   **7. Chaenorhinum**
    Perennial; flowers in racemes, with bracts much smaller than
    the foliage-leaves   ..   ..   ..   **8. Linaria**

18. Corolla 30-35 mm long; calyx-lobes oval, much shorter than the
    corolla   ..   ..   ..   **5. Antirrhinum**
    Corolla c. 15 mm long; calyx-lobes linear, almost as long as the
    corolla   ..   ..   ..   **6. Misopates**

19. At least the lower leaves alternate   20
    All leaves opposite   22

20. Leaves deeply divided pinnately into toothed segments; calyx
    inflated in fruit   ..   ..   ..   **20. Pedicularis**

Leaves slightly crenate or toothed, but not deeply divided; calyx
  not inflated   21

21. Not more than 20 cm high; corolla with short, slender tube and
  spreading lobes   ..   ..   **12. Erinus**
  Up to 150 cm high; corolla with long and wide tube and more or
  less erect lobes   ..   ..   **11. Digitalis**

22. Calyx with 5 broad, obtuse lobes; plant perennial   ..   **4. Scrophularia**
  Calyx with 4 narrow, acute to subacute lobes; plant annual   ..   ·   23

23. Corolla pink, its upper lip arched, not lobed   ..   **18. Odontites**
  Corolla white or purple; upper lip flat, 2-lobed   ..   **17. Euphrasia**

1. Limosella

Limosella aquatica. 6-9. A small, hairless annual, with weak stems, usually
rooting at the nodes. Leaves basal, stalked, oval to broadly linear, entire. Flowers
axillary, regular; peduncles shorter than leaf-stalks. Corolla *c.* 3 mm across, 5-lobed,
scarcely longer than calyx, lilac-pink or white. Stamens 4. *In small pools, or on wet
mud on the margins of lakes; only in the West half (Cork to Fermanagh) and very
local.*

2. Mimulus

* Mimulus guttatus. Monkey-flower. 6-9. Perennial, hairless below, but with a
sticky down on the upper parts of the plant. Leafy stems prostrate or spreading;
flowering stems erect, up to 35 cm high. Leaves opposite, round or broadly oval,
toothed, the lower ones shortly stalked. Flowers 25-40 mm across, in leafy, terminal
racemes. Calyx tubular, 5-toothed. Corolla bright yellow, with red spots, with a
wide tube and 5 spreading lobes. Stamens 4. *Streamsides and other wet places, mainly in
mountain districts; frequent in the North, occasional elsewhere.* Native of western
North America.

Plants generally similar to *M. guttatus* but with very short glandular hairs and
more numerous and larger red spots on the corolla, are occasionally found. They are
hybrids (* *M.* x *robertsii*) with *M. luteus* (the latter has not been recorded reliably
from Ireland).

* *M. moschatus*, also from western North America, with smaller, pale yellow
flowers without red spots, is a rare casual.

3. Verbascum. Mullein

Verbascum thapsus. 6-8. A stout, erect biennial 70-120 cm high; stem and
leaves densely covered with whitish wool. Leaves up to 30 cm long, oval-oblong,
entire or crenate, tapered at the base or shortly stalked. Flowers 20-25 mm across, in
groups in the axils of bracts in a long, dense, terminal spike. Calyx deeply 5-lobed.
Corolla yellow, with a very short tube and 5 more or less equal, spreading lobes.
Stamens 5; filaments woolly with white hairs. *Gravelly banks, waste places and
seashores; locally frequent in the South half, rarer in the North.*

* *V. virgatum*, which is sparingly naturalised in Cork and Kerry, has rather
smaller flowers in a more open spike, often branched at the base, and purple hairs on
the filaments.

4. Scrophularia. Figwort. *Fothram*

Perennials, hairless except for the somewhat downy inflorescence. Stems erect,
square in section. Flowers in terminal panicles. Leaves opposite. Calyx with 5 short,
rounded lobes. Corolla small, purplish-brown, obscurely 2-lipped, with a wide,
almost globular tube and 5 short, rounded lobes. Normal stamens 4; the fifth is represented by a staminode in the form of a scale on the inside of the upper lip of the
corolla. Capsule almost globular.

1. Leaves acute; stem scarcely winged on the angles; membranous
    margin of sepals very narrow and inconspicuous .. .. **1. S. nodosa**
    Leaves obtuse or subacute; stem distinctly winged on the angles;
    membranous margin of sepals conspicuous 2
2. Leaves mostly obtuse; staminode rounded, not lobed
    [Fig. XCVIa] .. .. .. **2. S. auriculata**
    Leaves subacute; staminode distinctly 2-lobed [Fig. XCVIb] **3. S. umbrosa**

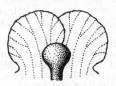   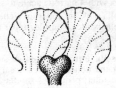

Fig. XCVIa   Fig. XCVIb

1. Scrophularia nodosa. 7-8. Up to 100 cm high. Stem sharply 4-angled, but not or scarcely winged. Leaves acute, fairly sharply toothed. Rhizome with numerous tuber-like swellings. Bracts small. Sepals with a very narrow membranous border (less than 1 mm wide). *Hedges, ditches and waste ground; very frequent.*

2. S. auriculata (*S. aquatica*). **7-8.** Generally similar to *S. nodosa*, but often more robust, and with smooth rhizome without tuber-like swellings. Stem distinctly winged on the angles. Leaves usually obtuse, crenate or bluntly toothed; small, leaflet-like lobes sometimes present at the base. Bracts small. Sepals rounded, obtuse, with a conspicuous membranous border about 1 mm wide. Staminode rounded at tip [Fig. XCVIa]. *Ditches, river-banks and other damp places (but often on drier ground in the West); frequent in the South and West, occasional elsewhere.*

3. S. umbrosa. 7-8. Like *S. auriculata*, but leaves subacute, without lobes at the base; bracts sometimes large and leafy; sepals subacute, with membranous margin wide at the tip, but narrower at the sides; staminode distinctly 2-lobed at tip [Fig. XCVIb]. *River-banks (mainly of the Rivers Liffey and Bann); very rare.*

5. Antirrhinum
* **Antirrhinum majus. Snapdragon. 7-9.** Perennial, woody at the base. Stems branched, 30-50 cm high. Leaves lanceolate, entire, the lower opposite, the upper alternate. Flowers in terminal racemes. Calyx hairy, with 5 short, rounded, equal lobes. Corolla 30-35 mm long, purplish-pink (rarely white), with a broad tube, prolonged at the base into a short, wide pouch, and 2 lips, the lower with a ridge which closes the mouth of the tube. Stamens 4. *Old walls; occasional.* Native of the Mediterranean.

6. Misopates
† **Misopates orontium** (*Antirrhinum orontium*). **7-9.** Annual, with erect stem 20-45 cm high, glandular-hairy above. Leaves opposite, linear-lanceolate, tapered at the base but not stalked. Flowers in leafy, terminal racemes. Calyx with 5 linear, somewhat unequal lobes up to 25 mm long. Corolla white or pink, shaped as in *Antirrhinum*, but only 10-15 mm long, shorter than calyx. Stamens 4. *Arable fields; established in Co. Cork, though rare and declining, a rare casual elsewhere in the South-east.*

7. Chaenorhinum

* Chaenorhinum minus (*Linaria minor*). **6-9.** A small, bushy annual up to 15 cm high, downy all over. Leaves linear-oblong, opposite below, alternate above. Flowers numerous, axillary, on slender pedicels. Calyx with 5 oblong lobes. Corolla 6-8 mm long, with a wide tube prolonged at the base into a short, narrow, straight spur, mostly purple, but with a yellow band on the lower lip. Stamens 4. *Dry bare ground, mostly on or near railway-tracks; formerly frequent, now rather rare.*

8. Linaria. Toadflax

Perennials; leaves opposite or whorled below, alternate above, linear, entire. Flowers in terminal, spike-like racemes. Calyx with 5 long, narrow lobes. Corolla 2-lipped; upper lip with 2 lobes, the lower with three; tube closed at the mouth by a ridge on the lower lip, and prolonged at the base into a slender, acute spur. Stamens 4.

1.	Corolla yellow	.. ..	**3. L. vulgaris**
	Corolla white, violet or pink	.. ..	2
2.	Flowers deep violet or pink; spur curved, at least half as long as the rest of the corolla		**1. L. purpurea**
	Flowers white or pale lilac; spur straight, much shorter than the rest of the corolla		**.. 2. L. repens**

1. * Linaria purpurea. 6-8. Hairless; stems erect, 30-80 cm high. Leaves 2-4 cm long. Flowers numerous, in long, dense racemes; pedicels shorter than the bracts. Corolla deep violet; spur curved, more than half as long as the rest of the corolla. Seeds angular, not winged. *Walls and waste ground in the South and East; rare.* Native of the Mediterranean.

2. * L. repens. 6-9. Stems creeping at the base, then erect, usually freely branched. Leaves 2-4 cm long. Flowers in fairly lax racemes; pedicels equalling or longer than the bracts. Corolla white or pale lilac with deeper veins; spur straight, much shorter than the rest of the corolla. Seeds angular, not winged. *Walls and dry waste places, mainly in the East; rather rare.*

3. † L. vulgaris. 7-9. Hairless below, often glandular-downy in the inflorescence. Stems erect, 30-75 cm high, arising from a creeping rhizome. Leaves up to 7 cm long. Corolla *c.* 15 cm long (excluding spur), yellow with an orange band on the lower lip. Spur almost as long as the rest of the corolla, slightly curved. Seeds disc-shaped, surrounded by a broad, membranous wing. *Roadsides, railways and waste ground, mainly in the South and East; occasional.*

9. Cymbalaria.

* Cymbalaria muralis. Ivy-leaved toadflax. 5-9. A delicate, hairless perennial, with slender, creeping or trailing stems, rooting at the nodes. Leaves mostly alternate, kidney-shaped, 15-35 mm wide, palmately lobed, with 5 short, rounded lobes. Flowers solitary in the leaf-axils, on long pedicels. Corolla shaped as in *Linaria*, lilac, 8-10 mm long (excluding spur); spur short, slightly curved. Seeds wrinkled, not winged. *Limestone or mortared walls, rarely on rocks or shingle; very frequent.*

10. Kickxia

* Kickxia elatine. 7-9. A rather hairy annual with prostrate or spreading stems. Leaves alternate, stalked, oval or hastate. Flowers solitary in the leaf-axils, on slender pedicels. Calyx with 5 acute lobes. Corolla shaped as in *Linaria*, yellow, with the inside of the upper lip violet; spur acute, nearly straight, as long as the rest of the corolla. *Arable fields and open waste ground; occasional in County Cork, a rare, though sometimes locally frequent, casual elsewhere in the South and East.*

11. Digitalis

Digitalis purpurea. Foxglove. *Méaracán púca.* **6-8.** A robust, downy biennial, with a stout, erect, unbranched stem up to 150 cm high. Leaves up to 30 cm long, alternate, oval, crenate, m ostly stalked, but the uppermost stalkless. Flowers drooping, in a long, terminal raceme. Calyx 5-lobed with acute lobes. Corolla 40-50 mm long, with a long, wide tube and 5 short lobes, purple. Stamens 4, concealed in the corolla-tube. *Woods, heaths and rocky ground on acid soils (very rarely on limestone); rare in the Centre, very frequent and locally abundant elsewhere.*

12. Erinus

* Erinus alpinus. 6-9. A small, tufted perennial, with spreading or semi-erect stems up to 20 cm long. Leaves alternate, variably hairy, the lower ones stalked, toothed, 10-25 mm long. Flowers 6 mm across, in short, terminal racemes. Calyx deeply 5-lobed; corolla purple (less often white), nearly regular, with a slender tube and 5 spreading lobes. Stamens 4, concealed in the corolla-tube. *Walls and vertical rock-faces; rare.* Native of western and Central Europe.

13. Veronica. Speedwell. *Seamar chré*

Small herbs with undivided leaves. Flowers nearly regular, solitary in the leaf-axils, or in axillary or terminal, bracteate racemes. Calyx deeply 4-lobed. Corolla usually blue (less often pink or white), with a very short tube and 4 slightly unequal lobes. Stamens 2. Capsule 2-lobed, usually flattened in a plane at right angles to that of the septum.

1. Flowers solitary in the axils of ordinary leaves 2
   Flowers in axillary or terminal racemes; bracts differing from the foliage-leaves in size or shape 6
2. Perennial, with creeping and rooting stems .. **14. V. filiformis**
   Annual; stems not rooting 3
3. Flowers 10-12 mm across; style 3 mm long; capsule much broader than high, with divergent lobes .. **13. V. persica**
   Flowers 5-7 mm across; style not more than 1.5 mm long; capsule about as broad as high, with more or less parallel lobes .. 4
4. Leaves at least as broad as long; capsule with 2-4 seeds **15. V. hederifolia**
   Leaves longer than broad; capsule with 8-20 seeds 5
5. Corolla bright blue except for a white eye; capsule with 14-20 seeds .. .. .. **12. V. polita**
   Corolla mainly pale blue, white or pink; capsule with 8-12 seeds **11. V. agrestis**
6. Main stem ending in a raceme [Fig. XCVIc] 7
   Main stem ending in a tuft of leaves; all flowers on side-branches [Fig. XCVId] 9
7. Perennial, with prostrate stems rooting at the nodes; styles 2.5 mm in fruit .. .. .. **1. V. serpyllifolia**
   Annual; stems erect, not rooting; style less than 1 mm in fruit .. 8
8. Leaves downy, crenate or bluntly toothed .. **9. V. arvensis**
   Leaves hairless, more or less entire .. .. **10. V. peregrina**
9. Leaves downy or hairy; plant of fairly dry places 10
   Leaves hairless; plant of wet places 12
10. Leaves tapered at base; pedicels shorter than bracts or calyx **2. V. officinalis**
    Leaves cordate or truncate at base; pedicels longer than bracts and calyx 11
11. Leaves mostly stalkless; capsule shorter than calyx; main stem with two lines of hairs .. .. .. **3. V. chamaedrys**
    Leaves stalked; capsule longer than calyx; main stem hairy all round .. .. **4. V. montana**

Fig. XCVIc   Fig. XCVId

12. Leaves all shortly stalked, about twice as long as broad   **6. V. beccabunga**
    At least the upper leaves stalkless, about 4 times as long as broad   13

13. All racemes arising singly, one at each node, on alternate sides of
    the stem   ..   ..   ..   **5. V. scutellata**
    Most of the racemes arising in opposite pairs   14

14. Corolla blue; pedicels at least as long as the bracts at
    flowering   ..   ..   **7. V. anagallis-aquatica**
    Corolla pink; pedicels usually shorter than the bracts at
    flowering   ..   ..   **8. V. catenata**

1. Veronica serpyllifolia. 5-7. A hairless or slightly downy perennial with shortly creeping stem and erect flowering branches 5-20 cm high. Leaves opposite, oval, very shortly stalked, entire or slightly toothed. Calyx-lobes oblong. Flowers in lax, terminal racemes. Corolla 6 mm across, white or pale blue, with darker veins. Capsule slightly shorter than the calyx. *Roadside verges, waste or cultivated ground and lawns; abundant in most districts.*

2. V. officinalis. 6-8. A hairy perennial; stems prostrate, rooting, 10-35 cm long. Leaves opposite, oval, bluntly toothed, shortly stalked. Flowers 6-8 mm across, in short, dense, erect, axillary racemes; pedicels very short. Corolla violet-blue. Capsule flat, about as broad as long. *Heathy grassland, open woods and walls; very frequent.*

3. V. chamaedrys. Germander speedwell. 4-8. Perennial with straggling stems up to 50 cm long. Main stem with two lines of hairs. Leaves opposite or very shortly stalked, oval, coarsely toothed, downy. Flowers 10-12 mm across, in lax, axillary racemes. Calyx-lobes oblong, acute. Corolla bright blue. Capsule somewhat flattened, shorter than the calyx. *Hedges, roadsides, field-margins and meadows; abundant.*

4. V. montana. 4-7. Like *V. chamaedrys*, but with main stem hairy all round, leaves clearly stalked, flowers of a paler lilac-blue, and capsule strongly flattened, longer than the calyx. *Woods and thickets, mainly on base-rich soils; occasional.*

5. V. scutellata. 6-8. A delicate, usually hairless perennial, with slender, more or less erect stems up to 50 cm high. Leaves opposite, stalkless, linear-lanceolate, shortly and distantly toothed, up to 50 mm long. Flowers 6 mm across, in loose, axillary racemes, which arise alternately on either side of the stem, one at each node. Corolla pale lilac or white. Capsule notched at the tip, longer than the calyx. *Bogs, ditches, marshes and lake-margins; frequent in most districts.*

6. V. beccabunga. Brooklime. 6-8. A hairless, rather fleshy perennial, with stout, spreading stems up to 50 cm long. Leaves opposite, shortly stalked, oval, bluntly toothed, 20-30 mm long. Flowers in short, opposite, axillary racemes. Corolla bright blue, 7 mm across. Capsule not strongly flattened, scarcely notched at tip. *Streams, ditches and marshes; abundant.*

7. V. anagallis-aquatica. 6-8. An erect, almost hairless perennial up to 30 cm high. Leaves opposite, oblong-lanceolate, stalkless, entire or very shortly toothed. Flowers 6 mm across, in opposite, axillary racemes. Corolla pale blue. Pedicels at least as long as the bracts at flowering time, semi-erect in fruit. Capsule not strongly flattened, scarcely notched at tip. *Streams and other wet places; frequent.*

8. V. catenata. 6-8. Very like *V. anagallis-aquatica,* but with a pale pink corolla, and pedicels shorter than the bracts at flowering time and projecting horizontally in fruit. *Similar situations; occasional.*

9. V. arvensis. 4-7. A small, downy, branched, erect annual, 5-15 cm high. Leaves opposite, triangular, oval, coarsely and bluntly toothed, the lower stalked, the upper stalkless. Flowers numerous, in slender, rather dense racemes; pedicels very short; bracts narrow, entire. Calyx-lobes oblong, unequal. Corolla 4 mm across, bright blue. Capsule heart-shaped, about as long as the calyx. *Walls, cultivated ground and waste places; very frequent and locally abundant.*

10. * V. peregrina. 4-7. Like *V. arvensis,* but hairless; leaves almost entire; corolla whitish; calyx-lobes equal. *Cultivated ground; more or less naturalised in the North-west; a rare casual elsewhere in the North half.* Native of America.

11. † V. agrestis. 4-9. A downy annual with prostrate or semi-erect stems up to 20 cm long. Leaves triangular-oval, shortly stalked, bluntly toothed, the lower opposite, the upper alternate. Flowers 4-7 mm across, solitary in the axils of the upper leaves. Corolla white or pale blue or pink. Capsule inflated, slightly broader than long, with 8-12 seeds. *Cultivated ground, roadsides and walls; formerly frequent, now rare.*

12. † V. polita. 4-9. Like *V. agrestis,* but leaves of a dull, greyish green; corolla bright blue; capsule with 14-20 seeds. *Similar situations; formerly fairly frequent, now very rare.*

13. * V. persica. 3-9. A downy annual with prostrate or semi-erect stems up to 50 cm long. Leaves oval, coarsely toothed, the lower opposite, the upper alternate. Flowers solitary in the axils of the upper leaves, on slender pedicels longer than the adjacent leaf. Corolla bright blue, with a white eye, 10-12 mm across. Capsule flattened, with divergent lobes, containing 8-16 seeds. *Arable fields, roadsides and waste ground; abundant in most districts.* Native of South-west Asia.

* *V. crista-galli,* similar to *V. persica* in general habit, but with pale blue corolla, much shorter than the large calyx, of which the lobes are united in pairs almost to the tip, and with only 2 large seeds in the capsule, is sparingly naturalised in similar habitats in Co. Cork, and occurs as a rare casual elsewhere in the South.

14. * V. filiformis. 4-5. A shortly downy perennial, with slender stems creeping and rooting. Leaves *c.* 5 mm wide, round or kidney-shaped, crenate. Flowers solitary in the leaf-axils, on long, slender, erect pedicels. Corolla 9-12 mm across, clear, pale blue. Capsule not formed in Ireland. *A frequent weed of garden lawns, occasionally naturalised in pastures, grassy banks or riversides.* Native of Turkey and the Caucasus.

15. * V. hederifolia. 4-6. A shortly hairy annual with straggling stems 10-40 cm long. Leaves mostly alternate (but some of the lowest opposite), semi-circular in outline, 5-lobed, shortly stalked. Flowers solitary in the axils of the upper leaves.

Corolla pale blue or lilac, 4-5 mm across, slightly shorter than the calyx. Capsule hairless, inflated, with 2-4 seeds. *Cultivated and waste ground; occasional to frequent in the East half; rather rare in the West.*

14. Hebe

Evergreen shrubs with entire, opposite leaves and naked buds (without scale-leaves). Flowers as in *Veronica*, except that the capsule is flattened in the plane of the septum, borne in dense, axillary spikes

1. Leaves not more than 2.5 cm long, mucronate; flowers white or
       pale lilac ..   ..   ..   **1. H. elliptica**
    Leaves 5-6 cm long, not mucronate; flowers deep violet   **2. H. x franciscana**

1. * Hebe elliptica. 5-7. A bushy shrub up to 150 cm high, very shortly downy on the twigs and leaf-margins but otherwise hairless. Leaves crowded, 20-25 x 9-12 mm, oval, mucronate, stiff. Racemes confined to the uppermost leaf-axils of each branch, appearing subterminal, short, dense. Flowers 15 mm across, white, variably tinged with lilac. *Walls and rocky ravines in Kerry and Galway; rare.* Native of New Zealand.

2. * H. x franciscana (*H. elliptica* x *H. speciosa*). Like *H. elliptica*, but hairless; leaves 50-60 x 20-25 mm, not mucronate, softer. Racemes longer, extending further down the twigs from the tip. Flowers 20 mm across; corolla deep violet. *Widely grown for garden hedges and locally naturalised, mainly on walls and sea cliffs; rather rare.* A hybrid of garden origin.

Often mistaken for * *H. speciosa*, which is, however, rarely cultivated. Some other species are rarely self-sown from gardens, including * *H. salicifolia*, also from New Zealand, a taller shrub with long, narrow leaves and white flowers.

15. Sibthorpia

Sibthorpia europaea. 7-9. A delicate, somewhat hairy perennial, with slender, prostrate stems rooting at the nodes. Leaves alternate, round or kidney-shaped, crenate, stalked, 8-18 mm wide. Flowers solitary in the leaf-axils, very shortly stalked, minute. Calyx-lobes 4 or 5. Corolla nearly regular, 2-4 mm across, with 4 or 5 lobes, pale yellow flushed with pink. Stamens 3, 4 or 5 (variable on the same plant). Capsule globular; seeds few. *Streamsides and damp grassland; occasional in the Dingle peninsula (Kerry), unknown elsewhere.*

16. Melampyrum. Cow-wheat

Hemiparasitic annuals with opposite, mostly entire leaves. Flowers in pairs in the upper leaf-axils, forming loose, one-sided terminal spikes. Calyx with 4 acute lobes. Corolla 2-lipped, the upper lip entire, the lower shortly 3-lobed. Stamens 4, concealed in the corolla-tube.

1. Corolla-tube longer than calyx; lower lip of corolla horizontal;
       capsule with 4 seeds   ..   ..   ..   **1. M. pratense**
    Corolla-tube about equalling calyx; lower lip of corolla turned
       downwards; capsule with two seeds ..   ..   **2. M. sylvaticum**

1. Melampyrum pratense. 5-9. Usually freely branched, with thin, wiry stems; usually hairless. Leaves stalkless or very shortly stalked, oval to lanceolate, acute, entire except for the uppermost, which have usually a few large, acute teeth near the base. Corolla 12-18 mm long, varying from bright to very pale yellow; lower lip horizontal. Capsule drawn out to a long apical point, containing 4 seeds. *Woods, bog-margins, stony lake-shores and mountain slopes; frequent.*

2. M. sylvaticum. 6-8. Like *M. pratense*, but with narrower leaves, usually all entire; corolla 8-10 mm, deep yellow tinged with brown with lower lip bent downwards; capsule with a short point, containing 2 seeds. *Woods and mountain glens in Antrim and Derry; rare.*

17. Euphrasia. Eyebright. *Roisín radhairc*

Small, usually erect, hemiparasitic annuals. Lower leaves opposite, the upper often alternate, stalkless, toothed. Flowers stalkless in the axils of the upper leaves, forming usually loose, terminal spikes. Calyx with 4 finely pointed lobes. Corolla 2-lipped, with a slender tube; upper lip shortly 2-lobed; lower lip deeply 3-lobed, with notched lobes, white, to a variable extent veined or tinged with purple, and with a yellow patch on the lower lip. Stamens 4; anthers prolonged at the base into slender points. Capsule about twice as long as broad.

A very difficult genus, in which doubts as to the limits of species are complicated by frequent hybridization. For identification several, well-grown, undamaged plants are necessary.

The leaves bearing flowers in their axils are referred to as bracts, though they do not differ greatly in shape or size from the lower leaves. Corolla-length is measured from the base of the tube to the tip of the upper lip.

1. Bracts and calyx bearing gland-tipped hairs *c.* 0.5 mm long, easily
    visible to the naked eye as a greyish down   2
    Bracts and calyx without gland-tipped hairs, or with gland-tipped
    hairs less than 0.2 mm long, scarcely visible to the naked eye ..   3

2. Stem stiffly erect, 15-40 cm high, usually with a few slender, erect
    branches from near the base; lower lip of corolla 8-10 mm wide
                                                    1. E. rostkoviana
    Stem straggling, not more than 20 cm long, with irregularly disposed,
    flexuous branches; lower lip of corolla 7-8 mm wide   .. **2. E. anglica**

3. Leaves somewhat fleshy; bracts crowded and overlapping, forming
    a dense, 4-sided spike   ..   ..   ..   **4. E. tetraquetra**
    Leaves not fleshy; bracts not crowded and seldom overlapping;
    spike not obviously 4-sided   4

4. Bracts and calyx bearing very short gland-tipped hairs, visible under
    a lens   ..   .. **3. E. arctica**
    Gland-tipped hairs absent   5

5. Capsule fringed with hairs at the tip; leaves green, mostly 1.1 - 1.3
    times as long as broad, usually with 5 teeth on each side   ..   6
    Capsule hairless; leaves often bronze-coloured, 1.5 - 2 times as
    long as broad, with 2-3 (rarely 4) teeth on each side   **11. E. salisburgensis**

6. Stem prostrate, or very short (not more than 3 cm high)   .. **7. E. confusa**
    Stem erect, at least 10 cm high   7

7. Lower lip of corolla 7-9 mm wide   8
    Lower lip of corolla 4-6 mm wide   9

8. Corolla 7-8 mm long; capsule about as long as calyx   **5. E. nemorosa**
    Corolla 9-10 mm long; capsule considerably shorter than
    calyx   ..   ..   **6. E. pseudokerneri**

9. Corolla mainly purple   ..   ..   ..   **9. E. micrantha**
    Corolla mainly white   10

10. Upper leaves and bracts about twice as long as broad   **10. E. scottica**
    Upper leaves and bracts not more than 1.5 times as long as broad   **8. E. frigida**

In view of the difficulties of identification in this genus, it has been thought more helpful to give, instead of a systematic description of each species organ by organ, an indication of the characteristic and 'eye-catching' characters of each, by which they are most likely to be recognised.

1. Euphrasia rostkoviana. 7-8. Tall, stiffly erect; branches, if present, few, slender, erect, arising from near the base. Bracts and calyx covered with relatively long gland-tipped hairs, visible to the naked eye as a greyish down. Corolla large, white. *Mainly in meadows or among long grass; frequent but local.*

2. E. anglica. 6-8. Like *E. rostkoviana* in its covering of hairs, but stem shorter, less erect, and often more branched, and corolla rather smaller. *Pastures and rough grassland; occasional.*

3. E. arctica (*E. brevipila*). **6-9.** Fairly tall and robust, usually with several spreading branches. Leaves fairly large, the lower ones rather bluntly toothed. Bracts and calyx bearing fairly numerous, very short gland-tipped hairs (visible with a lens against the light). Corolla fairly large, mainly white. *Disturbed grassland, as on roadside verges and field-margins; abundant in most districts.*
Nearly everywhere the commonest species.

4. E. tetraquetra (*E. occidentalis*). **6-8.** Usually with numerous, more or less erect branches. Leaves usually rather fleshy. Corolla medium-sized, mainly white. Usually recognizable by its dense, 4-sided inflorescence, suggestive of a church tower. Intermediates with *E. arctica* and *E. nemorosa* (perhaps hybrids) are, however, fairly frequent. *Cliff-tops, stabilized dunes and other habitats near the sea; frequent. Also rarely inland.*

5. E. nemorosa. 7-9. Medium-sized, usually rather bushy with numerous short, spreading branches. Leaves, even the lowest, with teeth more acute than in most other species. Corolla medium-sized, usually mainly purple. *Pastures and heaths; very frequent.*

6. E. pseudokerneri. 6-8. Like *E. arctica* in several features, but rather less robust and without the gland-tipped hairs. Corolla moderately long, but with very wide lower lip, white. Capsule considerably shorter than calyx (in most other species it is nearly equal). *Short grassland overlying limestone rock; occasional, but local, in the West (Clare to Donegal), unknown elsewhere.*

7. E. confusa. 5-8. Stem prostrate or very short, sparingly branched. Corolla fairly small, white. Normally the only species to flower in May. *Heathy grassland and stabilized sand-dunes; occasional.*

8. E. frigida. 7-9. Fairly short, sparingly branched. Flowers extending low down the stem, the internode below the lowest flower being usually conspicuously longer than the others. Corolla fairly small, white or lilac. *Mountain cliffs and exposed places near the sea, mainly in the West; rare.*

9. E. micrantha. 7-9. Fairly small; stem slender, unbranched or with a few branches near the middle. Whole plant usually tinged with purple. Leaves small (seldom more than 7 mm). Corolla small, usually purple. Capsule scarcely notched. *Moorland and heathy ground, nearly always among* Calluna; *frequent in the North and West, occasional elsewhere.*

10. E. scottica. 7-8. Moderately tall; slender and sparingly branched. Like *E. micrantha*, but leaves slightly larger, not tinged with purple, corolla white and capsule shortly but distinctly notched. *Fens, usually with* Schoenus, *and occasionally on wet mountain slopes; occasional in West and Centre, rare elsewhere.*

11. E. salisburgensis. 7-9. Stem fairly short, usually freely branched so as to give a bushy outline. Leaves narrower than in other species (at least 1.5 times as long as broad), hairless and jaggedly toothed, with 2-4 long teeth on each side. Leaves sometimes green, but often bronze-coloured. Corolla small, white with purple veins. *Rocky ground, sand-dunes and mountain cliffs, usually associated with* Thymus praecox*; locally frequent in the West (Limerick to Donegal); unknown elsewhere.*

18. Odontites

Odontites vernus. 7-8. An erect, downy, hemiparasitic annual 15-30 cm high, with a hard, freely branched stem. Leaves opposite, stalkless, lanceolate, toothed. Flowers in terminal leafy spikes; bracts similar to the leaves but smaller, mostly alternate. Calyx bell-shaped, with 4 short teeth. Corolla 8-10 mm long, dull pinkish-red, strongly 2-lipped; upper lip entire, the lower 3-lobed, shorter than the upper. Capsule flattened. *Pastures, roadsides and stony places; abundant.*

Two subsecies are usually recognized:

Subsp. *vernus*, with rather few, suberect, straight branches and bracts longer than the flowers

Subsp. *serotinus*, with more numerous, nearly horizontal branches, often turned up at the tip, and bracts shorter than the flowers or equalling them. A considerable number of Irish plants appear to be intermediate between the sub-species.

19. Parentucellia

Parentucellia viscosa (*Bartsia viscosa*). **6-9.** An erect, hemiparasitic annual covered with sticky down. Stem 15-45 cm high, usually unbranched. Leaves stalkless, opposite (though upper bracts sometimes alternate) oblong-lanceolate, coarsely toothed. Flowers in a terminal, leafy spike. Calyx tubular, with 4 long teeth. Corolla 17-20 mm long, bright yellow, showy, 2-lipped; upper lip hooded, entire; lower lip with 3 broad lobes, longer than the upper. Stamens 4, concealed below the upper lip. Capsule shorter than calyx, not compressed. *Damp grassland; frequent in the South-west, rare elsewhere in the West and North, but apparently spreading.*

20. Pedicularis. Lousewort

Hemiparasitic herbs; leaves mostly alternate, deeply divided pinnately, with small, toothed or pinnately lobed segments. Flowers in leafy, terminal spikes. Calyx broadly tubular, inflated especially in fruit, with 4 short, irregularly toothed lobes at the mouth. Corolla reddish-pink, strongly 2-lipped; upper lip hooded and laterally compressed, very shortly 2-lobed; lower lip with 3 short, broad lobes. Stamens 4, concealed under the upper lip.

1. Erect annual, with a single stem with short branches; upper lip of corolla with 2 teeth on each margin [Fig. XCVIe] ..   ..   **1. P. palustris**
    Perennial, with several more or less prostrate stems; upper lip of corolla with only one tooth on each margin, near the top [Fig. XCVIf]   **2. P. sylvatica**

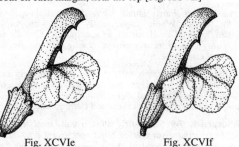

Fig. XCVIe   Fig. XCVIf

1. Pedicularis palustris. 5-9. An erect annual; stem up to 60 cm high, freely branched. Leaves 30-50 mm long. Calyx hairy. Upper lip of corolla with 2 teeth on each margin, one near the top, the other half-way down [Fig. XCVIe]. *Marshes, fens and wet meadows; frequent, and locally abundant in the North and West.*

2. P. sylvatica. 5-7. Perennial, with several more or less prostrate stems 7-20 cm long. Leaves 15-20 mm long. Upper lip of corolla with only one tooth on each margin, near the top [Fig. XCVIf]. *Damp or heathy upland pastures, moorland and drier parts of bogs; very frequent.*

Two subspecies may be distinguished:
Subsp. *sylvatica*, with hairless calyx, found mainly in the East
Subsp. *hibernica*, with hairy calyx (like that of *P. palustris*), found in the West and on moorland in the East. A few plants are intermediate, with short or sparse hairs on the calyx.

21. Rhinanthus

Rhinanthus minor. Yellow rattle. 5-8. An erect, more or less hairless annual; stem hard, angular, often blackish, 10-30 cm high, usually branched. Leaves opposite, stalkless, linear to oblong-lanceolate, toothed. Flowers in loose, leafy terminal spikes. Calyx inflated but flat; mouth narrow, with 4 short teeth. Corolla *c.* 15 mm long, strongly 2-lipped, yellow, sometimes with blue teeth on upper lip, which is hooded, laterally compressed, shortly 2-toothed; lower lip shorter than the upper, 3-lobed. Stamens 4. Capsule flat, about as broad as long; seeds flat, usually winged. *Meadows and pastures; abundant.*

Very variable; a number of different schemes have been proposed for subdivision of the species, but in the present state of our knowledge it does not seem to be possible to assign names to the Irish variants.

22. Lathraea

Lathraea squamaria. Toothwort. 4-5. A parasitic perennial without any green colour; rhizome underground, covered with whitish, fleshy, scale-like leaves. Flowering stem erect, above ground, 10-20 cm high, bearing similar fleshy, alternate leaves, white or pale lilac. Flowers in a dense, one-sided raceme; pedicels very short. Calyx with 4 short, broad, hairy lobes. Corolla 12-15 mm long, 2-lipped, pale lilac; upper lip entire, the lower indistinctly 3-lobed. Stamens 4. *On roots of various trees and shrubs, especially* Corylus; *widespread but rare.*

23. Orobanche. Broomrape

Parasitic plants without chlorophyll, probably mostly perennial. Stems erect, often swollen at the base but without rhizomes. Leaves lanceolate, acute, brownish, dry and papery. Flowers fairly numerous, in a terminal spike with bracts. Calyx deeply cleft into 4 acute lobes. Corolla 2-lipped, somewhat curved; upper lip shortly 2-lobed, the lower 3-lobed. Stamens 4, inserted on the corolla near the base; filaments often hairy. Fruit a capsule; seeds minute.

1.	Lower lip of corolla fringed with small, gland-tipped hairs			..	2
	Lower lip of corolla not fringed with gland-tipped hairs				3
2.	Stigma yellow	..	..	..	**4. O. rapum-genistae**
	Stigma red or purple	..	..	..	.. **1. O. alba**
3.	Stigma red or purple	..	..	..	.. **2. O. minor**
	Stigma yellow..	..	..	..	.. 4
4.	Corolla narrowed just below the mouth; parasitic on Ivy			**3. O. hederae**
	Corolla not narrowed below the mouth; parasitic on various herbs		**2. O. minor**

1. Orobanche alba (*O. rubra*). **6-8.** Stems 10-25 cm high, purplish-red. Flowers rather few, in a short spike. Corolla creamy-yellow, flushed with dull red. Lower lip fringed with short, gland-tipped hairs. Filaments hairy, at least in lower half. Stigma reddish-purple. *On roots of* Thymus, *near the North and West coasts; very local.*

2. * O minor. 6-10. Stems 15-60 cm, yellowish-brown, often tinged with purple. Flowers in a spike which is rather lax below but dense above. Corolla 12-18 mm long, dull yellow, usually tinged with purple. Filaments sparsely hairy at the base. Stigma usually purple, rarely yellow. *On roots of a wide variety of plants, perhaps most commonly* Trifolium spp. *Frequent in the South and East, rather rare elsewhere.*

3. O. hederae. 6-8. Stem 12-50 cm high, usually purple. Flowers in a long but rather lax spike. Corolla 10-20 mm, cream tinged with reddish-purple, somewhat constricted just below the mouth; middle lobe of lower lip acute, sometimes appearing truncate. Filaments usually hairless. Stigma yellow. *On roots of* Hedera; *frequent in the South half, rather rare in the North.*

4. O. rapum-genistae. 6-8. Stem stout, yellowish-brown, 25-80 cm high. Flowers nearly straight, unpleasant-smelling, in a long, fairly dense spike. Corolla 20-25 mm long, yellow or brown, sometimes tinged with red; upper lip almost entire; lower lip fringed with gland-tipped hairs. Filaments hairy above, hairless at the base. Stigma yellow. *On roots of* Ulex *and* Cytisus; *formerly fairly frequent near the South and East coasts; now very rare.*

XCVII.   LENTIBULARIACEAE

Perennial herbs. Flowers irregular, solitary or in slender racemes, on long leafless peduncles. Calyx 2- or 5-lobed. Corolla united, 2-lipped; tube short and broad, with a spur at the base. Stamens 2, attached to the base of the corolla-tube. Fruit a many-seeded capsule.

1. Leaves in a basal rosette, entire and undivided   ..   **1. Pinguicula**
    Leaves not in a basal rosette, highly divided   ..   **2. Utricularia**

1. Pinguicula. Butterwort. *Liath uisce*
Leaves arranged in a basal rosette, stalkless, broadly oblong, entire, with incurved margins, thick, very glandular. Flowers solitary. Calyx 2-lipped; upper lip 3-lobed, lower 2-lobed. Corolla-tube open at the mouth; upper lip 2-lobed, lower 3-lobed. Stamens inserted at the base of the corolla-tube next to the ovary.

1. Corolla small, pale violet or yellow, more or less regular, with
        5 nearly equal lobes   ..   ..   ..   **1. P. lusitanica**
    Corolla medium to largish, deep violet, irregular, 2 lipped;
        lower lip much longer than upper   ..   ..   ..   **2.**
2. Corolla 20-25 mm across; lobes of the lower lip with wavy margins,
        overlapping   ..   ..   ..   **2. P. grandiflora**
    Corolla 10 mm across; lobes of the lower lip flat, not overlapping **3. P. vulgaris**

1. Pinguicula lusitanica. 6-8. Leaves 15-20 mm long, dull greyish-green. Flowering stem 4-12 cm high. Corolla pale lilac, often tinged with yellow in the centre, 5-7 mm across, nearly regular, with 5 short, broad, nearly equal lobes; spur short, blunt, and curved sharply downwards. Capsule globular. *Bogs, flushes and by mountain streams; frequent in the extreme West, rather rare elsewhere.*

2. P. grandiflora. 5-7. Leaves 25-70 mm long. Flowering stems 7-13 cm high. Corolla violet, 20-25 mm across, strongly 2-lipped; lower lip the longer, its lobes broad and overlapping with wavy margins; spur slender and nearly straight. Capsule nearly globular. *Bogs, fens, wet rocks and mountain heaths; very frequent in Kerry and Cork, rare in Limerick and Clare, unknown elsewhere.*

3. P. vulgaris. 5-7. Leaves 20-55 mm long. Flowering stems 6-18 cm high. Corolla as in *P. grandiflora* but about 10 mm across with the lobes of the lower lip narrow, flat and not overlapping. Capsule ovoid. *Similar situations; frequent in the North, West and Centre, rare elsewhere.*

Hybrids (*P.* x *sculyi*), intermediate in form, between the two latter species but usually sterile, are occasionally found.

2. Utricularia. Bladderwort

Rootless aquatics with submerged leaves finely divided into linear segments. The submerged stems also bear small, transparent bladders which act as traps for small aquatic animals. Inside the bladders are microscopic, 2- and 4-armed hairs. The relative length of the arms of the 4-armed hairs and their degree of spread are important distinguishing features. Flowers borne above the surface of the water, in a few-flowered raceme. Calyx deeply 2-lobed. Corolla yellow; lower lip with a palate that closes the mouth of the tube. Stamens attached to the very top of the corolla-tube.

1. Bladders borne on separate leafless branches [Fig. XCVIIa]   **2. U. intermedia**
    Bladders borne at the base of the leaves [Fig. XCVIIb]   ..   2
2. Leaves without bristle-like teeth [Fig. XCVIIc]; spur of corolla
    very short and blunt   ..   ..   .. **1. U. minor**
    Leaves with bristle-like teeth [Fig. XCVIId]; spur of corolla half
    as long as lower lip   3
3. Lower lip of the corolla with broadly-spreading margins; inner
    surface of spur of corolla glandular all round   ..   **4. U. australis**
    Lower lip of corolla with downturned margins; inner surface of
    spur of corolla glandular on one side only   ..   **3. U. vulgaris**

1. Utricularia minor. 7-8. Stems rather slender, 8-25 cm long. Leaves 6-8 mm long, with few segments; teeth usually absent, if present then lacking a bristle-like point. Bladders borne at the base of the leaves; 4-armed hairs with the arms similar in

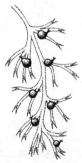

Fig. XCVIIa   Fig. XCVIIb   Fig. XCVIIc   Fig. XCVIId

length, all pointing the same way. Corolla 7 mm long, pale yellow; spur blunt and very short [Fig. XCVIIe]. *Ditches, bog-holes, pools and lake-margins; fairly frequent in the West, rare elsewhere.*

Fig. XCVIIe

2. U. intermedia. 8-9. Stems rather slender. Leaves 6-10 mm long with fairly numerous, toothed segments; teeth with a bristle-like point. Bladders borne on separate branches from the leaves, often buried in the mud; 4-armed hairs with the arms similar in length and arranged so as to form a line or narrow cross-shape. Flowers rarely produced. Corolla pale yellow, 12 mm long, with a long, pointed spur, the inside of which is glandular all round; lower lip of corolla with upturned margins. *Similar situations, though perhaps mainly on bare wet acid peat; very rare in the East half, frequent in the West half.*

U. ochroleuca has been reported from Ireland. According to some authors, it differs from *U. intermedia* in having acute leaf-tips, broadly spreading 4-armed-hairs in the bladders and the lower-lip of the corolla with a downturned margin. However much sterile Irish material, usually assigned to *U. intermedia,* also has acute leaf tips and slightly spreading 4-armed hairs. Further study of this complex of species is required.

3. U. vulgaris. 6-8. Submerged stems fairly stout, 15-40 cm long. Leaves up to 25 mm long, with numerous, toothed segments; teeth with a bristle-like point. Bladders borne at the base of the leaves; 4-armed hairs with arms of two distinct lengths, forming an open cross. Corolla 25 mm long, deep yellow; spur long and rather pointed, the inside glandular on one side only; lower lip of corolla with downturned margins [Fig. XCVIIf]. *Similar situations, more frequent in base-rich habitats; rather rare.*

4. U. australis (*U. neglecta, U. major*) **6-8.** Similar to *U. vulgaris* but differing in its corolla which has spreading margins, glands all round the inside of the spur and a relatively deeper palate. *Similar situations; probably about as frequent.*

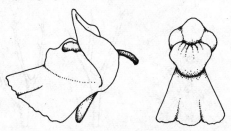

Fig. XCVIIf

XCVIII. PLANTAGINACEAE

Herbs, usually perennial, with basal rosettes of undivided leaves and small, regular flowers, usually in dense spikes. Sepals 4, free or slightly united at base. Corolla membranous and united, with the tube at least as long as the 4 spreading, triangular lobes. Stamens 4, attached at the base of the corolla-tube. Ovary superior, 1-4 celled. Fruit a few-seeded capsule. *Littorella* differs in having solitary flowers lacking a corolla, and a fruit which is a minute nut.

1. Flowers hermaphrodite, in spikes; plant terrestrial; without stolons **1. Plantago**
   Flowers monoecious, solitary; plant often submerged; spreading by
   stolons so as to form a dense mat ..   ..   .. **2. Littorella**

1. Plantago. Plantain

Flowers hermaphrodite, in dense spikes. Sepals membranous, with a green or brown midrib, shorter than the corolla. Corolla membranous, whitish or brownish, with 4 spreading, triangular lobes and a short tube. Filaments usually white.

1. Flowering stem furrowed ..   ..   .. **5. P. lanceolata**
   Flowering stem not furrowed   2
2. Leaves narrow (more than 3 times as long as broad) without
   prominent veins   3
   Leaves oval (less than 3 times as long as broad) with prominent veins   4
3. Leaves undivided; spikes usually more than 4 cm long **3. P. maritima**
   Leaves pinnatifid; spikes usually less than 4 cm long **2. P. coronopus**
4. Filaments white; peduncle usually much shorter than leaves;
   capsule usually with more than 4 seeds ..   ..   .. **1. P. major**
   Filaments lilac; peduncle usually much longer than leaves;
   capsule usually with 4 seeds   ..   ..   .. **4. P. media**

1. Plantago major. 6-8. Leaves spreading, often closely pressed to the ground, broadly oval with 5-9 veins; the base almost truncate, with a broadly winged leaf-stalk as long as the blade; the tip blunt. Peduncles about as long as leaves; rounded in cross-section. Spike usually slightly shorter than its peduncle, 2-10 cm long, often with the lowest couple of flowers well separated from the rest. Anthers lilac. Capsules with 4-12 seeds, 0.9-1.7 mm long. *Roadsides, path-sides, waste-places and pastures, often on muddy ground; abundant.*

Two subsp. are distinguishable: the above description applies to subsp. *major*; plants of the rarer, largely maritime subsp. *intermedia* are usually smaller with leaves with 3-5 veins, a base which gradually tapers to the leaf-stalk and an acute tip, the capsules usually contain more than 13-15 seeds and have a rougher surface.

2. P. coronopus. Buck's horn plantain. 6-8. Leaves usually hairy, spreading, very variable in shape and deeply pinnatifid with short oblong segments; occasionally entire. Peduncles about as long as leaves; rounded in cross-section. Spike shorter than its peduncle, 1-4 cm long. Anthers yellow. Capsule with 2-4 light brown, usually shortly winged seeds about 1 mm long. *Salt-marshes, banks, rocks, waste places by the sea; very frequent.*

3. P. maritima. 6-9. Leaves somewhat erect, linear, entire, fleshy, up to 20 cm long. Peduncles often much longer than the leaves; rounded in cross-section. Spike shorter than its peduncle, 3-11 cm long. Anthers yellow. Capsule with 2 dark brown seeds, 1.5-2.2 mm long. *Sea-shores and salt marshes; very frequent and widespread. Also inland, on mountains, rocks and lake-shores in the West and North.*

Plants from the seaward side of salt marshes have small leaves of circular cross-section whilst those from the landward side are usually larger and flat in cross-section.

4. * P. media. 6-8. Plant densely hairy. Leaves spreading, oval with a short, very broad stalk. Peduncles often much longer than the leaves; rounded in cross-section. Spike much shorter than its peduncle, 2-6 cm long. Filaments lilac, anthers white to lilac. Capsule with 4, black, slightly shining seeds about 1 mm long. *Lawns and waste-places; widespread but rare.*

5. P. lanceolata. Ribwort plantain. *Slánlus.* **5-8.** Leaves spreading to somewhat erect, lanceolate, with a few scattered hairs. Peduncles longer than leaves; clearly furrowed in cross-section. Spike much shorter than its peduncle, 1-3 cm long. Anthers pale yellowish-white. Capsule with 2 dark brown, shining seeds about 3 mm long. *Pastures, meadows and waste-places; abundant.*

2. Littorella
Littorella uniflora. 6. Plant sometimes with stolons. Leaves all basal, tufted, bright green, linear, erect, 2-10 cm long. Monoecious. Female flowers stalkless, borne at the base of the male pedicel, with a small calyx but no corolla. Male flowers on long pedicels at least $^1/2$ as long as the leaves, with a whitish corolla with a long tube and spreading, triangular lobes, and stamens protruding on very long, slender filaments. Fruit a minute nut, surrounded by the brown, membranous, persistent pericarp. *Lake-shores. Frequent in the North and West; rare elsewhere.*

XCIX. CAPRIFOLIACEAE

Usually shrubs, occasionally herbs. Leaves opposite. Flowers variable in form; regular or irregular, axillary or terminal, in cymes, pairs or whorls. Calyx-tube united to ovary; surmounted by 5 small, triangular teeth. Corolla united, 5-lobed or 2-lipped. Stamens 5, attached to the corolla. Ovary inferior. Fruit a berry or berry-like drupe.

1. Leaves pinnate .. .. **1. Sambucus**
    Leaves undivided 2
2. Corolla-tube much longer than lobes .. .. .. **5. Lonicera**
    Corolla-tube much shorter than lobes 3
3. Style absent .. .. **2. Viburnum**
    Style well developed 4
4. Flowers in the axils of conspicuous purple bracts; fruit purple-brown
    4. Leycesteria
    Bracts small and inconspicuous; fruit white .. **3. Symphoricarpos**

1. Sambucus
Leaves pinnate with a terminal leaflet. Flowers regular, in dense, many flowered, corymbose cymes. Corolla white, with a very short tube and 5 spreading lobes. Style absent; stigma 3-lobed. Fruit a drupe.

1. Large perennial herb; stipules large .. .. .. **1. S. ebulus**
    Shrub or small tree with greyish bark; stipules small or absent .. **2. S. nigra**

1. * Sambucus ebulus. 6-8. A large perennial herb with thick, erect, pithy stems, 50-180 cm high. Leaves with 7-11 lanceolate, sharply saw-toothed leaflets, 6-11 cm long. Corolla about 5 mm across; creamy white with its outer surface and that of the anthers tinged with pink. *Banks, waste-places and by ruins; scattered and occasional.*

2. S. nigra. Elder. *Trom.* **6-7.** A small deciduous tree with greyish bark and pithy stems. Leaves with 5-9 oval leaflets, 5-15 cm long; with stipules minute or absent. Flowers similar to *S. ebulus* but scented and with neither the corolla or anthers tinged with pink. *Hedges and woods throughout; especially frequent near houses.*

2. Viburnum

Deciduous trees or shrubs. Leaves lobed or entire, stalked. Flowers in dense, many flowered, corymbose cymes. Corolla white, with a short tube and 5 rounded, spreading lobes. Style absent; stigma obscurely 3-lobed. Fruit a berry.

1. Leaves lobed; fruit bright red when ripe .. .. **1. V. opulus**
    Leaves not lobed; fruit black when ripe .. .. .. **2. V. lantana**

1. Viburnum opulus. Guelder rose. 6-7. A large shrub to 4 m with leaves palmately 3-5-lobed, irregularly toothed, 4-12 cm long and reddening in autumn. Petiole at least 1.5 cm long with stalkless glands near the top. Flowers in dense corymbose cymes: inner 4-7 mm across, fertile, with both stamens and a carpel; outer 15-20 mm across, sterile, lacking stamens or carpels. Stigma 3-lobed. Fruit a 1-seeded, bright red, berry-like drupe. *Thickets, hedgerows, woodland margins, river-banks and lake-shores; occasional throughout.*

2. * V. lantana. Wayfaring tree. 5-6. A medium-sized shrub to 3 m with oval, sharply toothed leaves, distinctly hairy on the lower surface. Petiole about 1 cm long, without glands. Flowers all alike and fertile. Corolla 4-7 mm across. Fruit compressed, ridged, green then red turning black. *Occasionally planted and persisting in hedges in the East half; rare, though occasionally locally frequent elsewhere.*

3. Symphoricarpos

* Symphoricarpos albus (*S. rivularis*). **Snowberry. 6-9.** A deciduous shrub, spreading extensively by means of suckers. Leaves hairless, small (2-4 cm long), oval usually entire. Flowers in groups of 3-7 in small terminal spikes. Calyx-teeth small, spreading, persistent in fruit. Corolla 5-6 mm across, pinky, funnel-shaped. Fruit a globular, white, berry-like drupe with 2 seeds. *Hedges; frequent and widespread.* Native of western America.

4. Leycesteria

* Leycesteria formosa. 7-9. A tall, deciduous shrub; often somewhat herbaceous; with erect branches and large, entire or shallowly toothed, oval to lanceolate leaves with an acuminate tip and a distinct leaf-stalk. Flowers borne in whorls in the axils of conspicuous red bracts; drooping. Bracts with white hairs on the margins. Corolla white or purplish, regular, funnel-shaped. Style clearly protruding. Fruit a globular, purple-brown berry. *Hedges; frequent and widespread.* Native of the Himalayas.

5. Lonicera

Lonicera periclymenum. Woodbine, Honeysuckle. *Féithleog, Taith-fhéith-leann.* **6-8.** A tall, deciduous shrub; often somewhat herbaceous; with erect branches and large, entire or shallowly toothed, oval to lanceolate leaves with an acuminate tip and a distinct leaf-stalk. Flowers borne in terminal heads. Bracts with white hairs on the margins. Corolla white or yellow, variably tinged with purplish-red on the outside, 2-lipped and funnel-shaped. Style clearly protruding. Fruit a globular, purple-brown berry. *Hedges; frequent and widespread.*

A number of species of *Lonicera* are commonly planted in gardens and beside roads: of these * *L. xylosteum* with oval leaves about 5-6 cm long, densely hairy young shoots and yellow flowers, and * *L. nitida*, a rarely flowering, low-growing shrub to 1 m, with small oval leaves, 6-14 mm long, commonly cultivated as a hedge are the most common. * *L. ledebourii* with dark green, hairy leaves upto 10 cm long and regular, orange-red flowers about 17 mm long, borne in pairs on short axillary branches is planted and has spread in hedges in a few places in the West. It is often confused with * *L. involucrata* which is similar but hairless and with smaller flowers.

C. ADOXACEAE

† **Adoxa moschatellina. 4-5.** A delicate, hairless perennial herb, 7-18 cm high. Leaves twice to thrice ternate all basal except for one pair half-way up the stem. Flowers small, green in crowded, cuboidal, 5-flowered heads. The top, terminal flower of each head with 4 petals, 8 stamens and 4 styles; the surrounding 4 flowers with 5 petals, 10 stamens and 5 styles. Ovary inferior. Fruit, rarely formed, a dry drupe. *Scrubby woodland. Known only from two localities. Doubtfully native at Cave Hill, near Belfast. Certainly introduced at Leopardstown, Dublin.*

CI. VALERIANACEAE

Herbs with opposite leaves without stipules. Flowers small and numerous, in terminal or axillary cymes. Sepals united; calyx-teeth minute or forming a bumpy ring in flower. Petals united, sometimes irregular, with a long tube and 5 lobes. Stamens 1 or 3, attached to the corolla. Ovary inferior, 1-celled; style solitary. Fruit achene-like.

1. Small, slender plant 10-30 cm high. Fruit without a pappus   **1. Valerianella**
   Tall, robust plant 50-150 cm high. Fruit with a feathery pappus on top   2

2. Leaves pinnate. Stamens 3   ..   ..   .. **2. Valeriana**
   Leaves undivided. Stamen 1   ..   ..   **3. Centranthus**

1. Valerianella. Cornsalad

Annual; stems repeatedly (apparently dichotomously) branched. Leaves undivided, oblong. Corolla funnel-shaped, regular, not spurred at the base; pale bluish mauve. Calyx absent or represented by a small scale, persistent in fruit. Stamens and stigmas 3. Fruit with two small, sterile, empty cells next to the fertile cell, visible in cross-section.

Ripe fruits and a strong hand-lens are essential for confident determination.

1. Calyx absent or rudimentary in fruit   2
   Calyx clearly visible in fruit   3

2. Fruit ovoid; almost as wide as long; with a shallow grove on one
   side [Fig. CIa]   ..   .. **1. V. locusta**
   Fruit oblong; longer than wide; with a deep,wide groove on one side
   [Fig. CIb]   ..   ..   ..   **2. V. carinata**

3. Fruit smooth, hairless; sterile cells of ovary large in cross-section
   [Fig. CIc]   ..   .. **3. V. rimosa**
   Fruit with 2 distinct ribs, sometimes hairy; sterile cells of ovary not
   obvious in coss-section [Fig. CId]   ..   ..   **4. V. dentata**

1. Valerianella locusta. 4-6. Hairless or slightly hairy; stems spreading, 10-30 cm high. Leaves oblong to weakly spoon-shaped, entire or weakly toothed, 10-35 mm long. Calyx minute or absent. Fruit hairless, ovoid, almost as wide as long, with a shallow groove on one side; with the sterile cells about the same size as the fertile cell in cross-section and the outer wall of the fertile cell swollen and spongy [Fig. CIa]. *Sandy ground, dry banks and tilled fields; frequent near the coast, rare inland.*

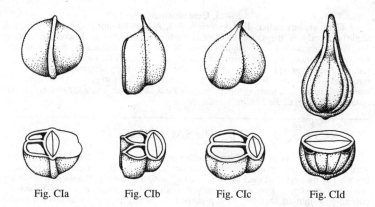

Fig. CIa   Fig. CIb   Fig. CIc   Fig. CId

2. † V. carinata. 4-6. Similar to *V. locusta* but with oblong fruits, longer than wide with a deep, wide groove on one side and with the outer wall of fertile cell not spongy [Fig. CIb]. *Similar habitats to V. locusta but much rarer; seemingly rather rare, though probably underrecorded.*

3. † V. rimosa. 4-6. Similar to *V. locusta* but more erect and taller (15-40 cm) with the flowers on longer stalks and so in more open cymes; the fruits smooth, not grooved, clearly crowned by a single calyx tooth, the fertile cell smaller than the sterile cells and with the outer wall of fertile cell not spongy [Fig. CIc]. *Tilled fields, mainly in the South and East; rare and declining.*

4. † V. dentata. 4-6. Similar in general appearance to *V. locusta* but more erect and taller; the calyx with distinct, persistent teeth, one of which is much larger than the others; the fruit sometimes smooth but often distinctly hairy, with 2 small ribs incorporating the 2, very small, sterile cells [Fig. CId]. *Tilled fields; very rare and declining.*

2. Valeriana

Valeriana officinalis. Valerian. 5-8. Perennial, with unbranched, erect stems 50-125 cm high. Leaves pinnate, with 9-13, lanceolate, usually toothed leaflets. Flowers 5 mm across in large terminal corymbs. Calyx-teeth minute in flower, developing into a feathery pappus in fruit. Corolla pink, regular. Stamens 3; styles 3 lobed; both clearly protruding. Fruit achene-like. *Ditches, riversides and damp woods; very frequent and widespread.*

The great variability in leaflet size and shape which this species shows is, to some extent, related to variability in chromosome number. Small plants with narrow leaves and with twice the normal number of chromosomes are found on dry, calcareous ground whereas larger plants with broader leaves and four times the normal number of chromosomes occur in damper places: however intermediates abound and Irish material requires further investigation.

* *V. pyrenaica*, a tall perennial with undivided and broadly heart-shaped, toothed, basal leaves borne on long stalks and a few dense, bright pink, corymbs of flowers is naturalised, usually in woods, in a few places.

3. Centranthus
* Centranthus ruber. Red valerian. 5-6. A hairless, upright, bushy perennial, slightly woody at the base, 25-60 cm high. Leaves oval to lanceolate, usually undivided, untoothed and slightly pale bluish-green, the upper ones stalkless. Flowers in dense, elongated panicles. Calyx as in *Valeriana*. Corolla usually bright red, rarely pink or white; with one lobe of the corolla widely separated from the other four, and with a long, slender spur at the base. Stamen and stigma 1, protruding. *Old walls and rocks and waste-ground; mainly near the South and East coasts; locally abundant*. Native of the Mediterranean.

CII. DIPSACACEAE

Erect biennial or perennial herbs with opposite leaves without stipules. Flowers small and numerous, in dense, terminal heads surrounded by a common involucre of bracts. The true calyx of each flower is small, with the lower part united to the ovary and the free, upper part cup-shaped or toothed; this, the true calyx, is usually concealed within another, larger, cup-shaped structure (epicalyx) which consists of a united whorl of bracteoles. Corolla united, slightly irregular, with a long tube and 4 lobes. Stamens 4, attached to the corolla, anthers free and clearly protruding. Ovary inferior, 1-celled; style solitary. Fruit an achene.

1. Stems and bracts prickly .. .. **1. Dipsacus**
   Stems and bracts not prickly 2
2. All flowers in a head about the same size .. .. **2. Succisa**
   Outer flowers in each head distinctly larger than the inner .. **3. Knautia**

1. Dipsacus. Teasel
Dipsacus fullonum. 7-8. Biennial with erect, prickly stems 1-2 m high. Leaves large, lanceolate, stalkless, prickly underneath on the midrib. Leaves on the stems united at their bases to form a water-collecting cup. Flowers accompanied by long-pointed scales; in large, ovoid to conical heads surrounded by an involucre of long, narrowly lanceolate, upward-curving, undivided bracts some of which overtop the flower-head. True calyx hairy; margin more or less entire; slightly longer than the oblong epicalyx. Corolla pink, purple or lilac. *Roadsides, quarries, open ground and waste-places; occasional, and usually not far inland, in the East and North, very rare elsewhere.*

2. Succisa
Succisa pratensis. Devil's bit. *Urach bhallach.* **7-9.** Biennial with erect, usually sparsely hairy stems 40-120 cm high. Leaves 5-20 cm long, mostly towards the base of the plant; oval to lanceolate, stalked, entire or shallowly toothed. Flowers accompanied by small, hairy green scales; in hemispherical heads surrounded by an involucre of lanceolate bracts which are about as long as the flowers. True calyx with 4 bristle-like teeth, clearly protruding from the oblong to funnel-shaped epicalyx. Corolla violet-purple. Anthers usually protruding. *Hedgebanks, heaths, cut-away bogs and marshes, pastures; widespread and abundant.*

3. Knautia
Knautia arvensis. Field scabious. 6-8. Hairy, upright perennial 40-100 cm high. Leaves 10-18 cm long, usually pinnate or pinnatifid. Flowers without accompanying scales; in flat-topped heads surrounded by an involucre of lanceolate bracts which are shorter than the outermost flowers. Outer flowers distinctly larger and more irregular than the inner. True calyx with 8 fine, long bristle-like teeth, clearly protruding from

the oblong epicalyx which is densely hairy at the tip. Corolla bluish lilac. *Dry pastures and banks, fairly frequent in the East, South and Centre; rare in the West and North.*

CIII. CAMPANULACEAE

Herbs with milky latex and alternate leaves with stipules. Flowers shortly stalked; axillary or in racemes or heads. Calyx-tube fused with the ovary, surmounted by 5 teeth. Corolla of 5 fused petals, 5-lobed. Stamens 5, forming a tube around the style. Ovary inferior; style single; stigma 2- or 3-lobed. Fruit a many seeded capsule.

Many species of *Campanula, Lobelia* and a few other genera in this family are grown as garden plants.

1. Aquatic; leaves all basal, hollow; flowers irregular .. .. **4. Lobelia**
   Terrestrial; both basal and stem-leaves present, not hollow;
   flowers regular 2
2. Flowers aggregated together into a compact head .. .. **3. Jasione**
   Flowers solitary or in racemes .. .. .. 3.
3. Stems prostrate .. .. .. **2. Wahlenbergia**
   Stems erect .. .. **1. Campanula**

1. Campanula. Bellflower

Perennials with flowers in racemes or panicles. Corolla bell-shaped, with 5 short lobes. Stigmas 3.

1. Stem-leaves narrow, almost linear; calyx teeth very narrow **1. C. rotundifolia**
   Stem-leaves triangular or oval; calyx-teeth lanceolate or triangular 2
2. Calyx-teeth spreading or turned back .. .. **4. C. rapunculoides**
   Calyx-teeth erect and pressed against the corolla 3
3. Lower stem leaves stalkless; stem rounded or bluntly ridged **2. C. latifolia**
   Lower stem-leaves stalked; stem sharply 4-angled .. **3. C. trachelium**

1. Campanula rotundifolia. Harebell. *Méaracán gorm.* **7-8.** Stems very slender. Basal leaves round or heart-shaped, crenate; lower stem leaves lanceolate, upper linear. Flowers drooping, blue, solitary or in a short raceme, shortly pedicelled. Calyx-teeth very slender. *Pastures, heaths, sand-hills and mountain cliffs; locally abundant in parts of the North and West, rare elsewhere.*

2. * C. latifolia. 7-8. Stems rounded or bluntly ridged, erect, usually softly hairy, 50-120 cm high. Leaves broadly lanceolate, shallowly toothed with a tapering base. Flowers erect or slightly spreading, on very long pedicels. Calyx-teeth spreading in flower and turned-back in fruit. Corolla violet-blue, 40-50 mm across. *Known only from shady river banks in Down, Antrim & Londonderrry.*

3. * C. trachelium. 7-8. Similar to *C. latifolia* but with sharply 4-angled stems up to 100 cm, shortly stalked and coarsely toothed stem-leaves, cut-off square at the base; calyx-teeth which are not spreading in flower or turned back in fruit and a corolla 25-35 mm across. *Wooded river-banks in the South-east (mainly in the Nore Valley); very rare.*

4. * C. rapunculoides. 7-9. Stems rounded, erect, sparsely hairy, 30-60 cm high. Leaves oval or triangular, toothed, stalkless. Flowers drooping. Calyx-teeth erect and held against the corolla, turning back soon after flowering. Corolla violet-blue, 20-30 mm across. *Roadsides, waste places and as a garden weed, mainly in the East; rather rare.* Native of Eurasia.

2. Wahlenbergia

Wahlenbergia hederacea. Ivy-leaved bellflower. 7-8. A delicate perennial with slender, prostrate stems. Leaves broadly triangular or nearly round, palmately lobed, stalked. Flowers solitary, borne opposite the leaves, on very long, slender pedicels. Corolla bell-shaped, pale blue. Stigmas 3. *River banks and damp grassy places, mostly in the South-east and South-west; rare.*

3. Jasione

Jasione montana. Sheep's bit, Sheep's scabious. 6-8. Usually biennial, 5-50 cm high. Leaves oblong-lanceolate or spoon-shaped, undulate and hairy; the basal ones narrowing towards the base and forming a rosette. Flowering stems leafy and unbranched in the upper half, leafy and often branched in the lower. Flowers small and numerous, bright blue, stalked, in terminal heads 10-20 mm across, surrounded by a series of toothed, green bracts. Calyx-teeth narrow; corolla very deeply cut into 5 narrow lobes. Stigmas 2. *Heaths, walls, rocky and sandy places in the mountains or by the coast; very rare in the Centre; frequent elsewhere.*

Easily mistaken for a composite or scabious, but the flowers are stalked, have a 5-toothed calyx and the fruits are capsules containing several seeds. Material from coastal cliffs and walls is often rather robust with larger than normal bracts.

4. Lobelia

Lobelia dortmanna. Water lobelia. 7-8. A submerged, aquatic perennial with a rosette of linear, blunt, thick basal leaves 3-7 cm long, hollow and with a partition down the centre, forming two longitudinal tubes. Flowering stem leafless and unbranched, erect, rising 15-25 cm above the water surface. Flowers pale violet, drooping, in a graceful raceme. Corolla irregular, with a long, slender tube, slit along the top, and 2 lips, the upper with 2 narrow, erect lobes, the lower with 3 broader, spreading lobes. Stamens concealed within the corolla-tube. *Lake-margins; frequent in the extreme West (Kerry to Donegal), very rare elsewhere.*

Isoetes lacustris though rarer, looks vegetatively similar and is found in-similar situations. It differs in possessing 4 longitudinal air-canals in its leaves, which also contain easily-visible, horizontal partitions.

CIV. COMPOSITAE (ASTERACEAE)

Herbs, rarely shrubs or small trees, with usually alternate leaves without stipules. In some species a white, milky liquid (*latex*) will issue from the cut surface of the stem or leaf. Flowers small and numerous, massed together in compact heads, each head being surrounded by an *involucre* of numerous bracts and looking like a single flower. Florets stalkless on the common receptacle, sometimes with small, chaffy scales between the florets. Calyx usually represented by a *pappus* of silky or feathery hairs crowning the ovary, more conspicuous in fruit than in flower; sometimes reduced to small scales or absent altogether. Corolla fused, regular or irregular; in one type of floret (*tubular*) it is regular, tubular or bell-shaped, with 5 short lobes or teeth (Fig. CIVa); in the other type (*ligulate*) it is irregular, flat, linear or oblong, usually with 5 small teeth at the end, and with a very short tube at the base (Fig. CIVb). (The florets in a head may be all ligulate; or all tubular; or the outer ligulate, usually forming a peripheral circle of rays, and the remainder tubular. In this last case the ligulate or *ray-florets* lack stamens, and sometimes a pistil as well.) Stamens 5, attached to the corolla; filaments free, but anthers united into a tube, through which the style eventually protrudes carrying the pollen with it. Ovary inferior, 1-celled; style single; stigma forked. Fruit an achene, crowned by a pappus, if present. (In some species the achenes become prolonged at the top, forming a distinct *beak* (Fig.

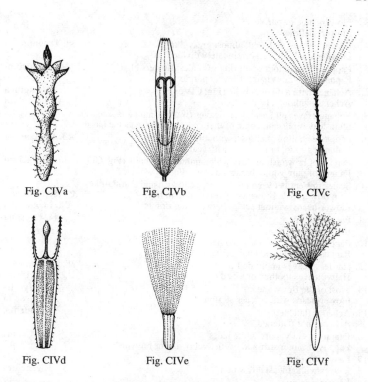

Fig. CIVa   Fig. CIVb   Fig. CIVc

Fig. CIVd   Fig. CIVe   Fig. CIVf

CIVc). Pappus, if present, rarely of bristles (Fig. CIVd) usually of hairs, which in some species are simple or unbranched (Fig. CIVe) whilst in others they are branched and appear somewhat feathery (use a hand-lens) (Fig. CIVf).

One of the largest families of flowering plants, with many representatives commonly cultivated. Vegetables include Lettuce (*Lactuca*), Jerusalem artichoke (*Helianthus*) and Globe artichoke (*Cynara*); ornamental plants include species of *Dendranthema,* (Chrysanthemum), *Aster* (Michelmas daisies), *Helichrysum* (Everlasting), *Dahlia, Cosmos, Callendula* (Marigold), *Rudbeckia*, many varieties of *Callistephus chinensis* (Aster), and species of some of the genera dealt with below, etc.

The occasionally encountered casuals * *Galinsoga ciliata*, which has oval, almost stalkless, opposite, coarsely hairy, green leaves and very small, (3-5 mm across) flower-heads, the outer florets white, ligulate and 3 toothed, the inner yellow and tubular; and * *Conyza canadensis* which has a similar, though smaller flower-head, with the corolla-limb of the ligulate florets very short and not obviously 3 toothed and the leaves narrowly oval and alternate; appear, at present, not to be naturalised.

1.	Shrub or tree ..	..	..	..	.. **21. Olearia**
	Herb ..	..	..	..	2
2.	Florets all ligulate; latex present	..		..	.. 3
	At least some florets tubular; latex absent		..	..	18

3. Flowers blue or purple 4
   Flowers yellow 7

4. Leaves narrow, unlobed, almost grass-like .. **38. Tragopogon**
   Leaves broad, toothed or pinnately divided 5

5. Pappus reduced to a small ring of scales; flowers blue **34. Cichorium**
   Pappus of obvious hairs; flowers purple 6

6. Achenes with a distinct beak (Fig. CIVc) .. .. **40. Lactuca**
   Achenes without a beak .. .. .. **41. Cicerbita**

7. Foliage-leaves all basal; stem leaves (if any) small and scale-like 8
   Stem-leaves present; some of them nearly as large as the basal .. 11

8. Peduncles hollow, hairless, without scale-leaves .. **43. Taraxacum**
   Peduncles solid, or hairy, or with scale-leaves 9

9. Pappus of brownish or dirty white, unbranched hairs (Fig. CIVe) **46. Hieracium**
   Pappus of pure white, branched hairs (Fig. CIVf) 10

10. Scales present between the florets, yellowish and corolla-like
    in flower, pale brown or silvery-white in fruit .. **35. Hypochoeris**
    Flower-heads without scales between the florets .. **36. Leontodon**

11. Pappus absent .. .. **44. Lapsana**
    Pappus present 12

12. Pappus feathery, of branched hairs (Fig. CIVf) 13
    Pappus of unbranched hairs (Fig. CIVe) 14

13. Hairless; leaves undivided .. .. .. **38. Tragopogon**
    Hairy; leaves toothed or lobed .. .. .. **37. Picris**

14. Most of the flower-heads with only 5 florets .. .. **42. Mycelis**
    Flower-heads with at least 10 florets 15

15. Achenes flattened .. .. **39. Sonchus**
    Achenes not flattened 16

16. Pappus of silky, pure white hairs .. .. .. **45. Crepis**
    Pappus of rather stiff and brittle, yellowish or brownish hairs .. 17

17. Leaves hairless .. .. **45. Crepis**
    Leaves with at least a few hairs .. .. **46. Hieracium**

18. Leaves prickly 19
    Leaves without prickles 22

19. Outer involucral bracts with prickly margins 20
    Outer involucral bracts prickly only at tip 21

20. Inner row of involucral bracts long and narrow, shining, straw-
      coloured, spreading horizontally at maturity: leaves not veined
      with white .. .. **27. Carlina**
    Inner row of involucral bracts not as above: leaves with
      conspicuous white veins.. .. **32. Silybum**

21. Hairs of pappus not feathery (Fig. CIVe) .. .. **30. Carduus**
    Hairs of pappus branched or feathery (Fig. CIVf) .. **31. Cirsium**

22. Some of the leaves divided, or deeply and conspicuously lobed
      or toothed 23
    All leaves undivided, if toothed or lobed then not deeply .. 39

23. Outer florets ligulate, forming conspicuous rays 24
    Outer florets tubular, though sometimes these are larger and
      more conspicuous than the inner 32

24. Ray-florets yellow 25
    Ray-florets white or lilac-pink 27

25. Pappus altogether absent; involucral bracts with broad,
    membranous, pale brown margins   ..   ..   **18. Chrysanthemum**
    Achene crowned by a pappus of hairs or bristles; involucral
    bracts sometimes with black tips, otherwise green   ..   26

26. Pappus of hairs   ..   .. **26. Senecio**
    Pappus of 2-4 bristles   ..   .. **11. Bidens**

27. Leaf-segments more than 1 mm wide, not hair-like   28
    Leaf-segments hair-like, 1 mm wide or less   29

28. Flower-heads 10-20 mm across; leaves deeply dissected   **19. Tanacetum**
    Flower-heads 40-50; leaves undivided or shortly pinnatifid **20. Leucanthemum**

29. Flower-heads 5-7 mm across, numerous, in crowded corymbs .. **13. Achillea**
    Flower heads 10-50 mm across, solitary or few, not crowded ..   30

30. Flower-heads with florets only; scales absent   .. **15. Tripleurospermum**
    Flower-heads with both scales and florets   31

31. Point of attachment of corolla of tubular-florets to top of achene
    obscured by a prolongation of the base of the corolla which
    envelops the top of the achene (Fig. CIVg)   ..   **14. Chamaemelum**
    Point of attachment of corolla of tubular-florets to top of achene
    visible (Fig. CIVh)   ..   ..   ..   **12. Anthemis**

Fig. CIVg   Fig. CIVh

32. Leaves opposite   ..   .. **11. Bidens**
    Leaves alternate   33

33. Pappus absent; foliage often scented   34
    Pappus present; foliage not scented   36

34. Flower-heads 3-5 mm across   ..   ..   **22. Artemisia**
    Flower-heads 8-10 mm across   35

35. Bushy annual, seldom more than 25 cm high; flowers greenish-
    yellow   ..   ..   **16. Matricaria**
    Erect perennial 70-100 cm high; flowers bright golden yellow **19. Tanacetum**

36. Flowers yellow   ..   .. **26. Senecio**
    Flowers pink or purple   37

37. Flower-heads 4-5 mm across, each with 5-6 florets ..   **1. Eupatorium**
    Flower-heads at least 20 mm across, with numerous florets ..   38

38. Involucral bracts with brown, fringed apex   ..   **33. Centaurea**
    Involucral bracts green or purple, untoothed, with an acute tip .. **32. Cirsium**

39. Flowering stems completely leafless; all leaves basal   ..   **3. Bellis**
    Flowering stems bearing at least some scale-leaves   40

40. Leaves hairless   41
    Leaves with some hairs, at least on the lower surface   ..   46

41. Pappus present   42
    Pappus absent   45

42. Ray-florets white, mauve or absent; leaves not toothed   ..   **4. Aster**
    Ray-florets yellow; leaves usually toothed, at least at the tip   ..   43

43. Flower-heads mostly less than 12 mm across, in a long and
        narrow inflorescence   ..   ..   ..   **2. Solidago**
    Flower-heads mostly more than 12 mm across, solitary or in a
        corymbose inflorescence   44

44. Bracts of the involucre in several overlapping rows ..   ..   **9. Inula**
    Bracts of involucre mostly in 1 row, with a few much shorter bracts
        at the base ..   ..   **26. Senecio**

45. Flower-heads 15 mm across, in corymbs   ..   .. **13. Achillea**
    Flower-heads 40-60 mm across, solitary   .. **20. Leucanthemum**

46. Outermost achenes with a pappus of white, silky hairs (sometimes
        together with small scales)   47
    Outermost achenes with a pappus of stiff bristles, or pappus absent   57

47. Leaves large, round, arising from an underground rhizome; flowering-
        stem bearing only scale-leaves   48
    Flowering-stem leafy, with leaves more or less similar to the basal ones   49

48. Flowers yellow; leaves with black-tipped teeth   ..   **23. Tussilago**
    Flowers purplish; leaves usually without black-tipped teeth   .. **24. Petasites**

49. Ray-florets yellow   50
    Ray florets purple, pink or absent   52

50. Flower-heads not more than 15 mm across   ..   ..   **2. Solidago**
    Flower-heads 25 mm or more across   51

51. Leaves hairier underneath than above; mature achenes without a
        minute collar of fused scales surrounding the base of the pappus
        (use hand-lens)   ..   ..   **9. Inula**
    Leaves densely downy on both sides; mature achenes with a minute
        collar of fused scales surrounding the base of the pappus (use
        hand-lens) ..   ..   **10. Pulicaria**

52. Flower-heads on stalks at least 20 mm long   53
  · Flower-heads stalkless, or on stalks less than 8 mm long   ..   54

53. Leaves not toothed; disc-florets yellow, ray-florets lilac-blue;
        achenes hairy   ..   ..   **5. Erigeron**
    Leaves toothed; all florets tubular, purple; achenes hairless   .. **31. Cirsium**

54. Flower-heads 8-15 mm across, on short but distinct stalks   ..   55
    Flower-heads 2-4 mm across; stalkless   56

55. Leaves untoothed; flowers reddish-pink or white   ..   **8. Antennaria**
    Leaves toothed; flowers purple   ..   ..   **29. Sausserea**

56. Leaves erect, pressed close to the stem ..   ..   ..   **6. Filago**
    Leaves diverging somewhat from the stem   ..   **7. Gnaphalium**

57. Ray-florets present   ..   ..   .. **20. Leucanthemum**
    Ray-florets absent   58

58. Involucral bracts with hooked tip   ..   ..   .. **28. Arctium**
     Involucral bracts not hooked at tip   59
59. Plant densely covered in white, woolly hairs   ..   **.. 17. Otanthus**
     Plant hairless or somewhat hairy but not white and woolly   ..   60
60. Outer florets ligulate, yellow   ..   .. **25. Doronicum**
     Outer florets tubular, purple   ..   .. **33. Centaurea**

1. Eupatorium

Eupatorium cannabinum. Hemp agrimony. 7-8. Perennial; stems up to 120 cm high, scarcely branched. Leaves mostly opposite, slightly downy, usually divided into three segments (rarely undivided, or pinnate with 5 leaflets; leaflets lanceolate, coarsely toothed, 5-10 cm long. Flower-heads very small and numerous, in terminal corymbs. Involucral bracts few, unequal in length. Florets pale pink, all tubular, 5 or 6 in each head. Pappus of unbranched hairs. *Marshes, streamsides and rocky ground; frequent in South half, occasional in North.*

2. Solidago

Solidago virgaurea. Golden rod. 7-9. An erect, almost hairless perennial, 15-60 cm high. Leaves alternate, oblong-lanceolate, slightly toothed. Flower-heads 6-10 mm across, numerous, in an oblong, terminal panicle. Involucral bracts few, overlapping. Florets yellow; inner tubular; outer ligulate and radiating. Pappus of simple hairs. *Heaths and rocky ground; locally abundant, but absent from large areas of the Centre and North-east.*

Various American species of this genus cultivated in gardens are sometimes long-persistent or naturalised. The species most widely grown are * *S. canadensis*, 90-125 cm high, with rough or hairy leaves about 12 mm wide, and inflorescence with horizontal branches; and * *S. gigantea*, often taller, with leaves 15-20 mm wide, smooth and shining on the upper surface, and with hairy stems.

3. Bellis

Bellis perennis. Daisy. *Nóithín.* **3-10.** Perennial, Leaves all basal, rather fleshy, oval, untoothed or with blunt teeth, with a wide, flat stalk. Flower-heads solitary on leafless peduncles, 20 mm across. Involucral bracts numerous, overlapping, in about 2 rows. Ray-florets white, sometimes tipped with pink. Inner florets tubular, yellow. No pappus. *Short-grassland, pastures, roadsides, banks, etc; abundant.*

The double form, often grown in gardens, is persistent.

4. Aster

Perennials, with erect stems. Leaves alternate. Ray-florets purple or white, usually in 1-2 rows, sometimes absent; inner florets tubular, yellow. Pappus of unbranched hairs.

1. Coastal; leaves fleshy, plant totally hairless   ..   **1. A. tripolium**
     Usually not coastal; leaves not fleshy, usually with at least a
     few hairs on the stems   ..   ..   .. **2. A. x salignus**

1. Aster tripolium. Sea aster. 8-9. Hairless, 20-100 cm high. Leaves oblong-lanceolate, or the upper ones linear-oblong, untoothed, rather fleshy with no lateral veins or 3 obscure ones. Flower-heads 12-20 mm across, in a small, compact corymb. Involucral bracts few, oblong. Ray-florets sometimes absent. *Salt-marshes, estuary banks, and rocks by the sea; very frequent.*

2. * A. x salignus. Michaelmas daisy. 8-10. Similar but usually slightly hairy and taller, with the lateral veins of the leaf obvious. *Waste places and abandoned gardens; often persisting but rather rarely naturalised.*

* *A. novi-belgii*, with broader, clasping leaves, also known as Michlemas daisy, and one of the parents of *A. x salignus*, may be naturalised in some places.

5. Erigeron

Similar to *Aster* but sometimes annual and with ray-florets usually in more than 2 rows.

1. Stems upright; lower leaves unlobed ..   ..   .. **1. E. acer**
    Stems spreading; lower leaves often with 3 lobes .. **2. E. karvinskianus**

1. Erigeron acer. Blue fleabane. 7-8. A hairy, slender annual or biennial, with an erect, often red or purple stem 10-35 cm high. Basal leaves stalked, oblong-lance-olate, withering early; stem-leaves small, stalkless. Flower-heads 12 mm across, in a small, loose panicle. Involucral bracts numerous, narrow and pointed, hairy. Outer florets purple, ligulate, but slender and nearly erect; inner florets tubular, yellow. pappus of unbranched hairs, long and reddish. *Dry pastures and sandy or gravelly places, chiefly in Centre and South-east; rare, local and declining.*

2. * E. karvinskianus (*E. mucronatus*). **7-8.** Similar but perennial, less hairy, spreading, with at least the basal leaves with 3 lobes, the flower-heads on rather long stalks and the ray-florets spreading. *Walls and stony banks; rare.*

6. Filago. Cudweed

Annuals covered with white, woolly hairs. Leaves greyish-white. Flower-heads small, stalkless, in crowded clusters intimately surrounded by leaves. Involucral bracts brownish or yellowish. Florets small, yellow, all tubular.

1. Flower-heads in clusters of 15 or more; each cluster 12-15 mm
    across ..   .. **1. F. vulgaris**
    Flower-heads in clusters of 3-8; each cluster 5-8 mm across **2. F. minima**

1. Filago vulgaris (*F. germanica*). **7-8.** 15-30 cm high, leaves linear-lanceolate, erect, 10-20 mm long, stalkless, overlapping. Involucral bracts with a bristle-like tip, concealing the florets. *Dry banks and sandy ground; rather rare.*

2. F. minima (*Logfia minima*). **6-8.** Similar, but smaller and slenderer, with leaves narrower, only 5-7mm long and more widely spaced, flower-heads in clusters of 3-8, less obviously yellow. Involucral bracts acute but lacking a bristle-like tip. *Sandy and gravelly places, mainly in South and East; rare.*

7. Gnaphalium

Stems and leaves covered with white, woolly hairs. Leaves linear-lanceolate, alternate. Flower-heads very small, almost stalkless. Involucral bracts brownish. Florets small, all tubular.

1. Perennial; flowering-stems unbranched, erect; flower-heads
    often pinkish (sometimes brown) in elongated, long narrow
    spikes ..   .. **1. G. sylvaticum**
    Annual; stems branched from the base; flower-heads in brown,
    dense, terminal clusters ..   ..   .. **2. G. uliginosum**

1. Gnaphalium sylvaticum (*Omalotheca sylvatica*). **7-8.** Perennial, with erect, leaf flowering stems up to 25 cm high. Leaves 3-6 cm long. Flower-heads in a leafy, spike-like inflorescence; each head rather small, with brownish-white or pink florets, concealed by blunt involucral bracts (Fig. CIVi). *Upland pastures and damp, sandy places; rare and apparently decreasing.*

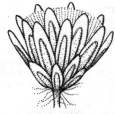

Fig. CIVi   Fig. CIVj

2. G. uliginosum (*Filaginella uliginosa*). **7-9.** A bushy annual up to 20 cm high, but often much less, branched from near the base. Leaves 15-30 mm long. Flower-heads very small, in terminal clusters of 3-10. Involucral bracts pointed (Fig. CIVj). *Damp, shady or peaty ground; frequent, except in Centre.*

8. Antennaria

Antennaria dioica. Cat's foot, Mountain everlasting, Mountain cudweed. 6-7. Perennial, with tufted and creeping stems. Leaves mostly basal, oval or oblong, untoothed, shortly stalked, white and silky beneath; stem-leaves linear, erect. Flower-heads in crowded clusters of 3-5. Dioecious, (male florets have a style and ill-formed achene; the female are fluffier in appearance and lack anthers). Involucral bracts numerous, especially in females, overlapping, those of the inner row large, pink or white, resembling ray-florets, especially in the male. Florets all tubular, pink or white; female ones very slender and more numerous than the male. Pappus of unbranched hairs. *Rocky or mountain pastures, heaths and sandhills; very local, abundant in parts of the West and Centre, rare elsewhere.*

9. Inula

Erect, scarcely branched perennials, with alternate, undivided leaves. Flower-heads large, solitary or in small corymbs. Involucral bracts numerous, overlapping, in several rows. Florets all yellow; outer ones ligulate and radiating, with styles, inner ones tubular. Pappus of unbranched hairs.

1. Leaves thick and succulent . . . . **1. I. crithmoides**
   Leaves flat, not succulent 2
2. Plant at least 100 cm; leaves 25 cm or more in length, surface
      hairy on underside . . . . . . **3. I. helenium**
   Plant about 50 cm; leaves about 5 cm long, surface (excluding
      veins) almost hairless on underside . . . . **2. I. salicina**

1. Inula crithmoides. Golden samphire. 7-8. Hairless, 30-50 cm high; branched from the root-stock. Leaves 25-50 mm long, yellowish-green, thick and fleshy, narrow, usually with 3 blunt teeth at tip. Flower-heads 25 mm across, solitary or in a loose corymb; peduncles long, with many small bracts. Achenes hairy. *Rocky shores and cliffs on South and East coasts; rare and local.*

2. I. salicina. 7-8. Almost hairless, 30-50 cm high, widely spreading by underground stolons. Leaves stalkless, lanceolate, toothed, almost hairless (except on the veins underneath), 5-7 cm long. Flower-heads about 35 mm across. Achenes hairless. *Stony, limestone shores and islands of Lough Derg, unknown elsewhere.*

3. * I. helenium. 7-8. Stem stout, up to 175 cm high. Leaves very large (up to 50 cm long), toothed, softly hairy on the lower side; the lower oblong and stalked, the upper oval, and clasping the stem. Flower-heads solitary, 50-70 mm across. Achenes hairless. *Roadsides and bushy places near houses and ruins; rather rare.*

10. Pulicaria

Pulicaria dysenterica. Fleabane. 8-9. An erect, branched, leafy perennial, 25-60 cm high, covered with soft, downy hairs. Leaves oblong, wavy and somewhat toothed, clasping the stem. Flower-heads 25 mm across, in small corymbs; involucral bracts numerous, overlapping, in several rows. Florets all yellow; outer ones ligulate, radiating, slender, with style; inner ones tubular. Pappus of unbranched hairs, surrounded, at the base, by a minute collar of fused scales. Achenes hairy. *Damp pastures and roadsides; fairly frequent in the South half, occasional in North.*

11. Bidens. Bur-marigold

Hairless, erect annuals with opposite leaves. Involucral bracts numerous, in 2 or 3 rows, the outer ones long and leafy. Florets greenish-yellow, in medium-sized heads; usually all tubular, sometimes a few of the outer ones ligulate and radiating, without styles. Receptacles bearing chaffy scales between the florets. Pappus of 2-4 rigid, tough, barbed bristles.

1. Lower leaves with distinct lobes, shortly stalked; flower-heads
    never with ray-florets   ..   ..   ..   **1. B. tripartita**
    Lower leaves toothed but unlobed, unstalked; flower-heads
    sometimes with ray-florets   ..   ..   **2. B. cernua**

1. Bidens tripartita. 8-9. Stem fairly stout, 35-70 cm high. Leaves lanceolate, stalked, at least the basal 3 or 5 lobed, the segments lanceolate and coarsely toothed. Flower-heads nearly erect, without ray-florets, 15-25 mm across. *Marshes, bog-holes and river-banks; rather rare and mainly in the South half.*

2. B. cernua. 8-9. Similar but more robust with coarsely toothed, stalkless, linear-lanceolate leaves and drooping flower-heads 25-40 mm across, with or without ray-florets. *Similar situations; occasional.*

12. Anthemis

* Anthemis cotula. 7-9. An upright, hairless annual with a strong unpleasant smell, about 50 cm high. Leaves alternate, divided into very fine, hair-like segments. Flower-heads solitary, 15-25 mm across; involucral bracts with a broad, membranous margin. Outer florets ligulate, white, the style minute or absent; inner tubular, yellow. Achene rough on margins. Pappus absent. *Waste and cultivated ground; very rare, largely in the East; formerly widespread but declined due to changes in farming pratices.*

13. Achillea

Perennials with alternate leaves. Flower-heads small and numerous, in corymbs; involucral bracts overlapping, in several rows, with a dark margin. Outer florets ligulate and radiating, with style, usually white; inner florets tubular. No pappus.

1. Leaves toothed but not highly divided; flower-heads 12-15 mm
    across   ..   ..   **1. A. ptarmica**
    Leaves highly divided into fine, linear segments; flower-heads
    6-9 mm across   ..   ..   ..   **2. A. millefolium**

1. Achillea ptarmica. Sneezewort. 7-8. Hairless; stems erect, rigid, 30-80 cm high. Leaves stalkless, linear-oblong, toothed, 4-7 cm long. Flower-heads 12-15 mm across; ray-florets white, 10-12, 4-5 mm long; inner florets white or greenish. *Ditches, lake-shores and damp waste places; very frequent in North half, occasional and local in South.*

2. A. millefolium. Yarrow. 7-9. Stem creeping, with numerous, short, leafy shoots and erect flowering stems 10-40 cm high. leaves rather woolly, oblong in outline, twice pinnate, with numerous very fine, linear segments, which are crowded and do not lie in one plane. Flower-heads numerous, 6-9 mm across, white or mauve; ray-florets about 6, short and broad. *Pastures, roadsides and waste places; abundant.*

14. Chamaemelum

Chamaemelum nobile (*Anthemis nobilis*). **Chamomile. 7-9.** A slightly downy perennial with creeping stems and alternate, sweet-smelling leaves pinnately dissected into very fine, hair-like segments. Flower-heads solitary, 25 mm across; involucral bracts in 2 or 3 rows, with pale membranous margin. Outer florets ligulate, radiating, white; inner florets tubular, yellow; oblong, chaffy scales present on the receptacle between the florets. Pappus absent. *Roadsides, pastures, heaths, lake-shores and waste-grounds; frequent in the South-west, rare elsewhere.*

15. Tripleurospermum

Leaves alternate, finely dissected into hair-like segments, with a faint, pungent smell. Flower-heads solitary; involucral bracts in several rows, with dark brown, membranous margin. Outer florets ligulate, radiating, white, with style; inner florets tubular, yellow. No scales present on the receptacle between the florets. Pappus represented by a short membranous ring; achenes with 3 smooth ribs on one side and 2 dark oil-glands on the other.

1.   Ribs on achene almost contiguous, oil-glands elongated
    (Fig. CIVk)   ..   ..   ..   **1. T. maritimum**
    Ribs on achene well-separated, oil-glands almost round
    (Fig. CIVl) ..   ..   **2. T. inodorum**

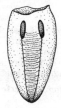

Fig. CIVk   Fig. CIVl

1. Tripleurospermum maritimum (*Matricaria maritima*). **7-8.** Biennial or perennial, with semi-prostrate stems; hairless or sparsely hairy. Leaf-segments rather fleshy, with a short point. Flower-heads 30-45 mm across. Achenes with ribs almost contiguous and oil-glands elongated (Fig. CIVk). *Rocky and shingly seashores and waste ground near the sea; very frequent.*

2. † T. inodorum (*Matricaria perforata*). **6-8.** Erect annual, 30-80 cm high, branched above; young leaves slightly hairy, hairless later. Leaf segments narrow, not fleshy, with a long point. Flower-heads 30-45 mm across. Achenes with the ribs well separated and the oil-glands nearly round (Fig. CIVl). *Disturbed ground; occasional.*

* *Matricaria recutita*, a rare casual, is very similar but the receptacle is hollow and the achenes have 4-5 faint ribs and no oil-glands.

16. Matricaria

Matricaria discoidea (*M. matricariodes, Chamomilla suaveolens*). **Pineapple-weed. 6-9.** A bushy annual, hairless or sparsely hairy, 5-30 cm high. Leaves finely dissected into hair-like, pointed segments, with a pleasant fruity scent. Flower-heads numerous, conical, 8-12 mm across; involucral bracts with a colourless, membranous margin. Florets all tubular, greenish-yellow. Achenes smooth, with 3-4 fine ribs; pappus represented by a low membranous ring or scale. *Farm-yards, roadsides and waste places; abundant.*

17. Otanthus

Otanthus maritimus (*Diotis maritima*). **7-9.** Perennial, about 25 cm high, with stem, leaves and bracts densely covered with a felt of white hairs. Leaves oblong, slightly crenate. Flower-heads 8 mm across, with broad, overlapping bracts. Florets yellow, all tubular. *Sand and shingle beaches on South coast of Wexford; unknown elsewhere.*

18. Chrysanthemum

* **Chrysanthemum segetum. Corn marigold.** *Liathán.* **6-8.** A hairless, rather erect annual up to 50 cm high. Leaves alternate, often with a whitish bloom, oblong-lanceolate, the lower pinnatifid and stalked, the upper stalkless and nearly undivided. Flower-heads solitary, 50 mm across; involucral bracts with a broad, pale brown, membranous margin. Florets all yellow, the outer ligulate, radiating. Achenes ribbed, those of the ray-florets with 2 broad wings. No pappus. *Cultivated fields and disturbed ground; locally frequent in the North and East, rather rare elsewhere.*

19. Tanacetum

Perennials. Leaves alternate, pinnate, aromatic, with toothed or lobed segments. Flower-heads numerous, in corymbs; involucral bracts largely or wholly membranous. Achenes ribbed; pappus represented by a low ring.

1. Florets all yellow, all usually tubular .. .. .. **1. T. vulgare**
   Outer florets white, ligulate .. .. **2. T. parthenium**

1. * Tanacetum vulgare (*Chrysanthemum vulgare*). **Tansy. 7-8.** Stems erect, 50-90 cm high. Leaves pinnate, hairless or sparsely hairy, with jaggedly toothed or pinnatifid, linear-oblong pinnae. Flower-heads 8-10 mm across, in dense corymbs. Florets all bright yellow, all tubular, rarely the outer very shortly ligulate, not radiating. *Roadsides, ditches and waste places, usually near houses; occasional.*

2. * T. parthenium (*Chrysanthemum parthenium*). **Feverfew. 7-8.** Stems erect, 25-60 cm high. Leaves pinnate, usually slightly downy, the segments variously pinnatifid. Flower-heads 12-20 mm across, in loose corymbs. Outer florets white, ligulate, radiating; inner florets yellow, tubular. *Similar habitats; occasional.*

20. Leucanthemum

Leucanthemum vulgare (*Chrysanthemum vulgare*). **Ox-eye daisy, Dog daisy.** *Nóinín mór.* **6-8.** An erect perennial 25-70 mm high, hairless or sparsely hairy. Leaves alternate, pinatifid or almost untoothed, the lower oval, stalked, the upper oblong-lanceolate, stalkless. Flower-heads 50 mm across, solitary; involucral bracts with brown, membranous margin. Outer florets white, radiating, the inner tubular, yellow. Achenes ribbed. No pappus. *Meadows and dry grassland; abundant.*

21. Olearia

* **Olearia macrodonta. Daisy-bush. 6-8.** A shrub or small tree up to 6 m in height with hairy branches and opposite, oval, rigid, coarsely toothed leaves, white with hairs beneath and large, flattish heads of flowers, with white ligulate florets and yellow disc florets is planted in a number of areas, especially in the West. Native of New Zealand.

22. Artemisia

Perennials, often slightly woody at the base. Leaves alternate, pinnately divided, with linear or oblong segments, white underneath. Flower-heads small, in terminal, somewhat leafy racemes or panicles. Involucral bracts usually cottony, with membranous margins. Florets few, all tubular. Outer florets female, inner hermaphrodite (except in *A. maritima* where all florets are hermaphrodite). No pappus.

1. Leaves green on the upper surface .. .. **1. A. vulgaris**
   Leaves white on the upper surface 2
2. Leaves strongly aromatic; segments 3-4 mm wide; flower-heads
     hemispherical, 2-3 mm across .. .. **2. A. absinthium**
   Leaves scarcely aromatic; segments 1 mm wide or less; flower-
     heads ovoid, 1-2 mm across .. .. **3. A. maritima**

1. Artemisia vulgaris. Mugwort. 7-9. Stems erect, reddish, hard, 50-120 cm high. Leaves oval in outline, pinnate, with deeply toothed or lobed segments, green and hairless on the upper surface, white underneath, not aromatic. Flower-heads ovoid, usually erect, 2-3 mm across; involucral bracts very cottony, with a green midrib; florets 20 or less, yellow tinged with red. *Dry banks and waste places; rare and declining.*

2. * A. absinthium. Wormwood. 7-8. Stems erect, hard, 30-80 cm high. Leaves strongly aromatic, twice pinnate; segments oblong, whitish with silky hairs on both sides. Flower-heads hemispherical, 3-4 mm across; florets fairly numerous, dull yellow. *Waste places, walls and by ruins; occasional in South-east; rare and declining elsewhere.*

3. A. maritima (*Seriphidium maritimum*). **7-8.** Stems woody, branched, spreading, up to 50 cm high. Leaves scarcely aromatic, twice pinnate with narrow, linear segments, white all over with cottony hairs. Flower-heads ovoid, 1-2 mm across; inner involucral bracts brownish or chaffy at the top; florets about 5, yellow or red. *Muddy or rocky sea-shores on East and West coasts; rare and very local.*

23. Tussilago

Tussilago farfara. Colt's foot. *Gallán greanchair.* **2-5.** Perennial. Leaves 8-15 cm across, cordate, round in outline, but produced into short angles and somewhat toothed, white and cottony, especially below. Flower-heads solitary, 25-40 mm across, appearing before the leaves, on long peduncles bearing numerous scale-leaves. Involucral bracts linear, in a single row, with a few shorter outer ones. Florets all yellow; outer row ligulate, radiating, narrow, with style; inner ones tubular, male. Pappus white and silky, of unbranched hairs. *Clay and gravel banks, damp fields and roadsides; abundant.*

24. Petasites

Leaves round, cordate, all basal. Flowering-stems with scale-leaves and an erect raceme of flower-heads with scale-like bracts. Florets all tubular, or the outer very short and not radiating. Dioecious or imperfectly so. Involucral bracts and pappus as in *Tussilago*.

1. Outer florets shortly ligulate; leaves and flowers appearing at the
     same time .. .. .. **2. P. fragrans**
   Outer florets tubular; flowers appearing before the leaves .. 2
2. Lobes at base of leaf convergent (Fig. CIVm), with 2 veins in
     each lobe nearby; flowers pinkish-mauve .. **1. P. hybridus**
   Lobes at base of leaf divergent (Fig. CIVn), with 1 vein in each
     lobe nearby; flowers white .. .. .. **3. P. albus**

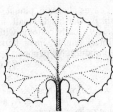

Fig. CIVm   Fig. CIVn

1. Petasites hybridus. Butterbur. *Gallán mór.* **4-5.** Leaves very like those of *T. farfara*, but much larger, up to 90 cm across, with the lobes at the base of the leaf somewhat convergent (Fig. CIVm). Flower-heads numerous, in a dense raceme; involucral bracts oblong and blunt. Florets dull purple, not scented, all tubular. *Riversides and damp places; frequent but local.*

This species is imperfectly dioecious; a few female florets are usually to be found at the edge of the male heads, and a few male in the centre of the female heads. Most Irish plants are predominantly male; the female (which has a more open inflorescence) is very rare.

2. * P. fragrans. Winter heliotrope. 12-1. Leaves large, nearly round, regularly toothed but not angled, green and hairless above, downy and greyish beneath. Flower-heads in a short and rather loose raceme; involucral bracts linear. Florets pinkish-mauve, very sweet smelling; the outer very shortly ligulate the inner tubular. *Shady banks and roadsides; occasional and locally abundant.*

3. * P. albus. 3-5. Very similar to *P. hybridus* but with white flowers, divergent leaf-lobes with only 1 vein close to their margin (Fig. CIVn). Leaves very like those of *T. farfara*, but usually larger and with more prominent marginal teeth which are not black tipped. *Streamsides, roadsides and shrubberies in the North; very rare.*

25. Doronicum

* Doronicum pardalianches. Leopard's bane. 6-7. Rhizomatous perennial, with erect stems up to 100 cm. Leaves alternate, the basal with a long stalk, deeply cordate, their stalks densely hairy. Flower-heads 3-5 cm across, long-stalked, in small clusters. Florets yellow; outer ligulate; inner tubular. Outer achenes hairless, without pappus; inner achenes hairy with pappus of unbranched hairs. *Woods and plantations; rather rare.*

26. Senecio

Leaves alternate, toothed or pinnatifid. Flower-heads in corymbs or panicles. Involucral bracts linear, in a single row, with usually a few much shorter outer ones. Florets all yellow, the outer ones usually ligulate and radiating, the inner tubular. Pappus of unbranched hairs.

1.	Mature leaves whitish- or greyish-hairy on the underside ..	2
	Mature leaves green on the underside	3
2.	Creeping rhizome present; hairs loose and cottony ..	**5. S. erucifolius**
	Rhizome absent; hairs forming a dense, white felt ..	**1. S. cineraria**
3.	Leaves finely toothed, but not lobed	**2. S. fluviatilis**
	Leaves pinnately lobed, or coarsely and deeply toothed ..	4

4. Outer involucral bracts with dark tips 5
   Outer involucral bracts without dark tips 8
5. Plant, most obviously the inflorescence, conspicuously covered
   in sticky, glandular hairs, which often 'catch' debris .. **8. S. viscosus**
   Plant without glandular hairs, or with a few scattered glandular hairs 6
6. Flower-heads 15-20 mm across; involucre weakly bell-shaped;
   ray-florets large and conspicuous .. .. **6. S. squalidus**
   Flower-heads 4-10 mm across; involucre tubular; ray-florets
   small or absent 7
7. Ray-florets small, strongly rolled back; young flower-heads
   stalked; involucral bracts brownish-purple at tip .. **7. S. sylvaticus**
   Ray-florets absent or rarely small and spreading; young flower-
   heads stalkless; involucral bracts tipped with black **9. S. vulgaris**
8. Inflorescence with some glandular hairs; ray-florets soon rolled back 9
   Inflorescence without glandular hairs; ray-florets not rolled-back,
   rarely absent 10
9. Plant with rather few glandular hairs; achenes minutely hairy
   (lens) .. .. **7. S. sylvaticus**
   Plant with many glandular hairs; achenes hairless .. **8. S. viscosus**
10. Achenes of disc-florets hairy; lowest leaves usually withered at
    flowering time .. .. .. **3. S. jacobaea**
    Achenes of disc-florets hairless; lowest leaves usually persisting
    till flowering time .. .. .. **4. S. aquaticus**
    Hybrids are rather common in this genus.

1. Senecio cineraria (*S. bicolor*). **8.** Stems branched, 30-60 cm high, woody at the base, covered, like the underside of the leaves, with a dense mat of white hairs. Leaves deeply pinnatifid with blunt, oblong segments; the midrib more or less flush with the upper surface of the leaf. Flower-heads 12 mm across, in dense corymbs; ray-florets conspicuous. Achenes hairless. *Naturalised on banks and cliffs at Killiney, Dublin.*

Hybrids with *S. jacobaea* (*S. x albescens*), which have more jaggedly toothed, less hairy leaves, with a slightly depressed midrib and minutely hairy achenes occur at Killiney and in West Cork.

2. * S. fluviatilis (*S. sarracenisis*). **8-9.** A stout, erect, hairless perennial, 80-150 cm high. Leaves lanceolate, stalkless, regularly toothed but not lobed, about 15 cm long. Flower-heads numerous, 25-30 mm across, in a compact corymb, each with 6-7 large ray-florets. Outer involucral bracts fairly long, black-tipped. Achenes almost hairless. *Roadsides; waste ground and river-banks; rare.*

3. S. jacobaea. Ragwort, Ragweed. *Buachalán bui.* **6-9.** A stout perennial, 30-140 cm high, hairless or slightly woolly. Leaves deeply pinnatifid, the lower ones usually with the terminal lobe the largest; segments toothed. Flower-heads 18-25 mm across, in a dense corymb. Ray-florets numerous, spreading; rarely absent. Involucral bracts narrow-elliptical; outer ones few and small. Achenes of ray-florets hairless, remainder hairy. *Pastures and waste places, sandhills, etc; abundant. The variety without ray-florets is very local, but abundant in some coastal districts.*

4. S. aquaticus. Marsh ragweed. 7-8. Very similar to *S. jacobaea* but the leaves, especially the basal, have an obvious, large terminal lobe, the flower-heads are larger (25-30 mm diameter), in a looser corymb, the ray-florets are longer, with wider spaces between them, and all the achenes are hairless. *Wet marshes, pastures and ditches; common especially in West.*

Hybrids with *S. jacobaea* (*S.* x *ostenfeldii*) are not uncommon where both parents occur. They are intermediate in most respects, often produce fresh, vigorous flowering branches, in early Autumn and are almost sterile with few, well-developed fruits.

5. S. erucifolius. 8-9. Perennial with creeping rhizome and erect stems, 50-100 cm high. Leaves regularly and deeply pinnatifid, with slender, coarsely toothed segments; white or greyish-white, especially beneath, with cottony hairs. Flower-heads 15-25 mm across, in a dense corymb. Outer involucral bracts several, narrower but almost as long as the inner. All achenes hairy. *Roadsides, dry banks, waste grounds, pastures, generally on dry soils of glacial drift; only near the East coast around Dublin; locally very frequent.*

6. * S. squalidus. Oxford ragwort. 5-10. A rather stout annual up to 30 cm high, hairless or nearly so. Leaves variable but usually deeply pinnatifid. Flower-heads 15-20 mm across, in an irregular corymb; involucral bracts tipped with black. Outer florets ligulate, radiating. *Walls and waste places, mainly in the larger cities, especially Cork, Dublin and Belfast; very rare elsewhere.*

7. S. sylvaticus. 6-8. Annual, 25-70 cm high, hairless or slightly woolly. Leaves narrow, lower irregularly and deeply pinnatifid; lobes jagged and toothed. Flower-heads cylindrical, about 10 x 4 mm, clearly stalked, in a somewhat corymbose panicle; involucral bracts green or sometimes brownish-purple at tip, the outer ones very small or absent. Outer florets ligulate, but short and rolled back and therefore inconspicuous. *Sandy places, heaths and dry banks; widespread but occasional.*

8. † S. viscosus. 4-10. Similar to *S. sylvaticus* but densely covered in glandular hairs, which trap air-blown debris, so giving the plant a characteristic 'grubby' appearance, with the outer bracts usually brown-tipped, and the ray-florets initially spreading but quickly rolling back as the flowers wither. *Waste places, road and railway margins and railway ballast; widespread, sometimes locally abundant. The distribution of this plant in Ireland appears closely related to that of the railway network.*

9. S. vulgaris. Groundsel. *Gronnlus.* **1-12.** Annual, 10-35 cm high, hairless or slightly woolly. Leaves narrow, irregularly but seldom deeply pinnatifid; lobes jagged and toothed. Flower-heads cylindrical, about 12 x 4 mm, almost stalkless at first, but the stalk lengthens as the fruit ripens. Involucral bracts linear, tipped with black, with several small outer ones below the main series. Florets usually all tubular. *Open, disturbed ground; abundant.*

A form with short, broad ray-florets, usually less than 8 mm long, occurs rather rarely on railway tracks and in waste ground.

27. Carlina
Carlina acaulis. Carline thistle. 7-9. A dry, stiff, erect biennial, 15-40 cm high, thinly covered with white cottony hairs. Leaves lanceolate, pinnatifid, very prickly. Flower-heads solitary or in groups of 2-4, rather flat, 20-35 mm across. Outer involucral bracts similar to the leaves; inner row straw-coloured, linear, entire, shining, spreading in dry weather, erect when moist. Florets all tubular, purple, interspersed with long, chaffy scales. Achenes silky; pappus of long, feathery hairs. *Dry pastures, sandhills and gravel banks; very frequent in Centre; rare in South and North where it is declining.*

28. Arctium. Burdock
Stout, erect biennials with large, alternate, undivided leaves, nearly hairless above, but covered with white down beneath. Flower-heads globular; involucral bracts numerous, linear, ending in stiff, hooked points. Florets purple, all tubular; styles white. Receptacle bearing stiff, spine-like scales between the florets. Pappus of unbranched, short, stiff hairs.

1.   Petioles of lower leaves solid   ..   ..   .. **1. A. lappa**
     Petioles of lower leaves hollow   ..   ..   .. **2. A. minus**

1. Arctium lappa (*A. majus*). **8.** Up to 150 cm high. Leaves broadly oval or triangular, cordate, with rounded apex; petioles of at least the lower leaves solid. Flower-
heads 30-40 mm across, on long stalks, in a loose, somewhat corymbose
inflorescence. Involucral bracts hairless, equalling or overtopping the florets. Heads
hemispherical in fruit, open at top. *Roadsides and waste places; rare.*

2. A. minus. 7-8. Leaves heart-shaped, toothed or crenate, with pointed tip;
petioles of at least the lower leaves hollow. Flower-heads 15-35 mm across, usually
stalkless or almost so, in a raceme or panicle. Involucral bracts usually with cottony
hairs, shorter than or equalling the florets. Heads ovoid to hemispherical in fruit.
Roadsides and waste places; frequent in most districts.

3 subspecies are commonly recognised:

Subsp. *nemorosum* has virtually stalkless flower-heads 30-35 mm across, with
erect involucral bracts in fruit, is common everywhere and the only subsp. recorded
in the North.

Subsp. *minus* with similar but smaller flower-heads 15-25 mm across and involucral bracts about the same length as the florets is apparently absent in the North,
though present at low frequency in the rest of the country.

Subsp. *pubens* with flower-heads on stalks of 10-40 mm, 30-35 mm across and
with the involucral bracts spreading in fruit may also occur in Ireland.

However some Irish material does not fit neatly into these categories, possessing
a mixture of characters, and further investigation of *A. minus* is desirable.

29. Sausserea

Sausserea alpina. 8. Perennial, usually rather cottony. Stem stout, erect, 10-25
cm high. Leaves oblong-lanceolate, toothed; the upper stalkless. Flower-heads cylindrical or ovoid, shortly stalked, in a small dense corymb. Involucral bracts overlapping, oblong, obtuse. Florets all tubular, purple. Pappus of feathery hairs. *Mountain
cliffs and ledges, above 300 m; very rare and local, largely in the West half.*

30. Carduus. Thistle

Biennials with stiff, erect stems, and narrow, pinnatifid, very prickly leaves.
Involucral bracts numerous, overlapping in several rows, undivided, some or all with
prickly tips. Florets all tubular. Achenes hairless; pappus of long, silky, unbranched
hairs.

1.   Flower-heads nodding, hemispherical ..   ..   .. **1. C. nutans**
     Flower-heads erect, cylindrical or globular   2
2.   Involucre nearly hairless; flower-heads cylindrical, not constricted
        at the top (Fig. CIVo) ..   ..   ..   **2. C. tenuiflorus**
     Involucre with cobwebby hairs, globular; flower-heads constricted
        at the top with the florets spreading above it (Fig. CIVp) **3. C. acanthoides**

1. * Carduus nutans. 5-8. Robust. Stem spiny but spines absent beneath the
flower-heads. Leaves sparsely hairy and with cottony hairs on the veins. Flower-
heads hemispherical, usually nodding, up to 40 mm across. All except the inner
involucral bracts strongly bent out and back; inner erect. Florets purple. *Pastures,
heaths and roadsides; abundant.*

2. C. tenuiflorus (*C. pycnocephalus*). **6-8.** Rather slender, 40-120 cm high.
Stems and lower-side of leaves whitish with cottony hairs. Stems with continuous
prickly wings running down from the leaf bases. Flower-heads erect, cylindrical,

Fig. CIVo   Fig. CIVp

long, stalkless in small clusters of 3-10. Involucral bracts erect, linear-oblong, nearly hairless, with prickly tips. Florets pinkish-mauve or white, scarcely spreading beyond the diameter of the involucre (Fig. CIVo). *Sandy banks and dry ground; occasional in Centre and South-east, rare elsewhere; declining.*

3. C. acanthoides (*C. crispus*). **5-8.** Stem 40-100 cm high, somewhat cottony, with prickly wings, the prickles often well over 5 mm long. Leaves rather sparsely cottony on the lower side. Flower-heads 25 mm across; involucre globular, constricted at top, the florets spreading out above it (Fig. CIVp). Bracts very narrow, with cobwebby hairs, erect or slightly spreading, the inner scarcely prickly. Florets purple or white. *Dry banks and waste places, mainly in the East and Centre; rare.*

31. Cirsium. Thistle. *Feochadán*

Biennials or perennials; leaves usually pinnatifid and prickly. Involucral bracts numerous, overlapping, in several rows, usually spine-tipped. Florets all tubular, usually purple. Achenes hairless; pappus of long, soft, feathery hairs.

1. Involucres very prickly, with spreading bracts. Upper surface of
   leaves rough, almost prickly .. .. **1. C. vulgare**
   Involucres scarcely prickly, with erect bracts. Leaves often with
   prickly margins, but smooth on upper surface 2
2. Flower-heads clustered, 15-25 mm across 3
   Flower-heads solitary, 25-50 mm across 4
3. Stem with spiny wings; leaves often purple tinged .. **4. C. palustre**
   Stem not winged; leaves usually green .. .. **5. C. arvense**
4. Flower-heads 25-30 mm across .. .. **2. C. dissectum**
   Flower-heads 30-45 mm across .. .. **3. C. heterophyllum**

1. Cirsium vulgare (*Cnicus lanceolata*). **Spear thistle. 7-8.** Biennial; stem stout, 70-150 cm high, with prickly wings. Leaves wavy and deeply pinnatifid, rough with small prickles on the upper surface, rather white and cottony below; leaves not toothed, ending in a stout prickle. Flower-heads few, erect, 25-30 mm across; involucre rather cottony, globular, with spreading, prickly bracts; florets deep purple, spreading out above it. *Pastures and waste-places; abundant.*

2. C. dissectum (*Cnicus pratensis*). **Bog thistle. 6-8.** Perennial, with shortly creeping rhizome. Stems unbranched, 20-60 cm high, not winged or prickly. Leaves mostly basal, only slightly pinnatifid, with weak marginal prickles, whitish with cottony hairs on the lower side. Flower-heads solitary, 25-30 mm across. Involucre ovoid or cylindrical, rather cottony; bracts erect and scarcely prickly. Florets deep purple. *Damp or peaty pastures; very frequent in the North-west, West and Centre, rarer elsewhere and declining.*

3. C. heterophyllum (*C. helenioides*). **7-8.** Like *C. dissectum* but larger in all its parts, up to 160 cm high. Leaves varying from almost untoothed to finely toothed to deeply pinnatifid, scarcely prickly, almost flat, white with felted hairs on the underside. Flower-heads 30-50 mm across. *Wet grassland near Lough Gill and Fermanagh; very rare.*

4. C. palustre (*Cnicus palustris*). **Marsh thistle. 6-8.** Biennial; stem 70-140 cm high, with prickly wings. Leaves often purple-tinged, deeply pinnatifid, somewhat cottony below and hairy above; lobes with toothed and very prickly margins. Flower-heads 15-20 mm across, stalkless, in clusters. Involucre somewhat cottony, nearly globular; bracts erect, pointed, lanceolate, tipped with purple or black. Florets usually deep purple, occasionally white. *Marshy places and wet meadows and pastures; abundant.*

Hybrids between *C. palustre* and *C. dissectum* (*C.* x *forsteri*) occur occasionally with the parents; they are intermediate in most features with discontinuous wings on the stems and flower-heads solitary or in clusters of 2-3.

5. C. arvense (*Cnicus arvensis*). **Creeping thistle. 7-8.** Perennial, spreading by creeping roots; stems simple, up to 100 cm high, not winged. Leaves deeply pinnatifid with toothed lobes, very prickly on the margins, pale green above, white beneath. Dioecious, but with abortive ovary in male flower and abortive stamens in female. Flower-heads shortly stalked, 15-25 mm across, the male rather larger than the female; bracts erect, spine-tipped. Florets dull lilac. *Dry pastures and roadsides; abundant.*

32. Silybum

* **Silybum marianum. Milk thistle. 7-9.** An erect biennial 50-150 cm high, hairless and shining. Leaves pinnatifid and prickly, veined with white; upper ones clasping the stem with rounded auricles. Flower-heads solitary, 25-40 mm across, usually drooping. Involucre globular; bracts leafy, with prickly, toothed margins and long, spreading, prickly tips. Florets purple, all tubular. *Sandy banks and waste-places, usually near houses; rare.*

33. Centaurea

Leaves alternate, not prickly. Involucre hard, globular; bracts numerous, overlapping, green, short and broad with a mainly oval or crescentic, brown top, fringed with long, flexible teeth. Florets all tubular, but the outer ones sometimes much larger, and without stamens or pistil. Receptacle with bristles between the florets. Pappus of short, stiff, scaly bristles or rarely absent.

1. Outer florets bright blue .. .. .. **3. C. cyanus**
    All the florets purple 2
2. Leaves undivided or pinnatifid. Involucre appearing entirely
    dark brown .. .. **2. C. nigra**
    Leaves deeply pinnatifid. Involucre partly green .. **1. C. scabiosa**

1. Centaurea scabiosa. 7-8. Leaves all deeply pinnatifid, segments lanceolate. Flower-heads 30-50 mm across; outer florets enlarged, neuter, without anthers or style. Involucral bracts green, with the apex blackish and finely toothed. *Dry banks and pastures; frequent, though local, in South and Centre, rare elsewhere.*

2. C. nigra. Blackheads, Knapweed. *Mullach dubh.* **7-9.** A slightly hairy perennial, with hard, branched stems 35-80 cm high. Leaves oblong; lower ones stalked and somewhat pinnatifid, upper ones stalkless and undivided. Flower-heads 25 mm across. involucral bracts with the apex oval, narrow based, blackish-brown, the green part being overlapped by the appendages of the next row and invisible. Florets deep purple, usually all similar; occasionally those of the outer row enlarged and neuter. *Pastures, banks, meadows and roadsides; abundant.*

Narrow-leaved plants, smaller in most of their parts, with pale apical portions to the involucral bracts are occasional; they have been separated as subsp. *nemoralis* but probably do not justify their status as they are not consistently distinguishable.

3. C. cyanus. Cornflower. 7-8. A slender annual, 30-60 cm high, covered with grey, cottony hairs. Leaves linear, the lower ones slightly pinnatifid. Flower-heads 30-40 mm across; involucral bracts with silvery-white teeth. Outer florets large, neuter, bright blue; inner ones bluish-purple. *Roadsides; very rare, only in the East.* Formerly a weed of Corn- or flax-fields; now almost extinct.

34. Chicorium

* **Chicorium intybus. Chicory. 7-8.** A rigid perennial, 40-60 cm high. Leaves rather hairy, oblong-lanceolate; lower ones pinatifid, upper untoothed and clasping the stem. Flower heads 35 mm across, stalkless in clusters of 2-4, or rarely solitary. Involucre of two rows; inner of 8 oblong bracts, outer of 5 much shorter ones. Florets all ligulate, bright blue. Pappus very minute. *Roadsides and waste-places; mainly in South and East, very rare.*

35. Hypochoeris

Foliage leaves all in basal rosettes; stem leaves very small, reduced to scales. Involucre nearly hairless; bracts numerous, overlapping, in several rows, the outer ones very short. Florets all ligulate, bright yellow. Scales present between the florets. Achenes crowned by a feathery pappus, the central usually with a long beak.

1. Leaves hairy; flower-heads at least 25 mm across; all achenes
   usually beaked   ..   ..   ..   **1. H. radicata**
   Leaves hairless; flower-heads about 15 mm across; peripheral
   achenes without beaks   ..   ..   ..   **2. H. glabra**

1. Hypochoeris radicata. Cat's ear. 6-9. Perennial. Leaves 10-20 cm long, covered with stiff hairs, oblong-lanceolate, pinnatifid with blunt lobes, the terminal lobe broad and usually blunt. Flowering stems hairless, up to 50 cm high, leafless but with a few small scales, usually branched, swollen at the top. Flower-heads 1-4 on a stem, 25-35 mm across. *Pastures, heaths and roadsides; abundant.*

2. H. glabra. 6-8. Like *H. radicata* but annual, with almost hairless leaves and smaller flower-heads which often remain closed and the peripheral achenes in a head unbeaked. *Sand-dunes on the North coast; rare.*

36. Leontodon

Perennials; leaves all basal. Florets all ligulate, bright yellow. Receptacle without scales. Involucre of a single row of long, equal bracts, and several small, outer ones. Achenes with a short beak or none.

1. Stems usually branched, with 2 or 4 flower-heads; hairless or
   with simple hairs   ..   ..   ..   **1. L. autumnalis**
   Stems unbranched, with only 1 flower-head; leaves hairy, with
   hairs forked at the tip   2

2. Flower-heads usually at least 25 mm across; peduncle very hairy;
    all achenes with a pappus of feathery hairs   ..   **3. L. hispidus**
  Flower-heads usually less than 25 mm across; peduncle sparsely
    hairy; outermost achenes with a pappus of short scales   **2. L. taraxacoides**

1. Leontodon autumnalis. 7-10. Leaves hairless or sparsely hairy with unbranched hairs, linear-oblong, varying from untoothed to deeply pinnatifid. Flowering-stems few, up to 35 cm high, hairless, usually branched, with 2-7 flower-heads, bearing a few scale-leaves. Flower-heads 20-30 mm across. Achenes without beaks, all with a pappus of dirty white, feathery hairs. *Damp grassland, frequent.*

2. L. taraxacoides (*L. leysseri*). **6-8.** Leaves with stiff, forked hairs, linear-oblong, pinnatifid with short, blunt, triangular lobes. Peduncles unbranched, quite leafless, numerous, 10-20 cm high, usually hairy only at base. Flower-heads 15-25 mm across. Outer achenes without a beak, and with a pappus of small scales; inner ones shortly beaked, with a pappus of white feathery hairs. *Pastures and dry banks; very frequent in the South and Centre, rather rare in the North.*

3. L. hispidus. 6-8. Like *L. taraxacoides*, but larger, coarser and hairier, especially on the peduncle; flower-heads 25-35 mm across; all achenes with a pappus of dirty white hairs, scarcely beaked. *Similar habitats; though rarer and absent from the North.*

37. Picris. Ox-tongue
Coarse biennials with stiff, often hooked hairs. Flower-heads in irregular corymbs; florets all ligulate, yellow. Achenes reddish-brown; pappus of white, feathery hairs.

1. Achenes without a beak; leaves usually pinnatifid   ..   **1. P. hieracioides**
  Achenes with a beak; leaves with the margins waved or toothed,
    not pinnatifid   ..   ..   **2. P. echioides**

1. * Picris hieracioides. 7-9. Up to 100 cm high. Hairs hooked and clinging. Leaves narrow-lanceolate, slightly pinnatifid; lower ones stalked. Flower-heads 25-35 mm across; involucral bracts numerous, the outer short and spreading, covered with black hairs. Achenes not beaked. *Railway banks and gravel-pits in the South-east Centre; very rare.*

2. † P. echioides. 7-9. Hairs stiff, almost prickly. Leaves oblong-lanceolate, with waved or coarsely toothed margins; upper ones clasping the stem with rounded auricles. Flower-heads 20-25 mm across, on stout peduncles; outer involucral bracts leafy and heart-shaped, as long as the inner ones. Achenes with a long, slender beak bearing the pappus. *Waste-places and fields, mainly in the East half, and usually not far inland; very rare.*

38. Tragopogon
Hairless biennials with almost unbranched, erect, leafy flowering stems and alternate, long, narrow leaves. Flower-heads solitary. Florets all ligulate. Achenes with a long beak and widely spreading, feathery pappus.

1. Flowers yellow; peduncles swollen beneath the head   **1. T. pratensis**
  Flowers dull purple; peduncles not swollen beneath the
    head   ..   ..   **2. T. porrifolius**

1. Tragopogon pratensis. Goat's beard. 6-7. Stems 35-60 cm high. Leaves almost grass-like, tapering gradually from base to tip. Involucre of about 8 equal bracts, 25 mm or more in length. Florets usually shorter than the bracts. Achenes rather rough. *Dry banks and pastures, mainly in Centre; occasional.*

2. * T. porrifolius. Salsify. 6-8. Like *T. pratensis*, but with involucral bracts 30-50 mm long, peduncles swollen beneath the flower-heads and dull purple florets. *Dry banks and waste-places; persisting from cultivation, rare.*

39. Sonchus. Sow-thistle. *Bainne muice*

Sappy and rather brittle herbs with hollow stems, hairless except in the inflorescence. Leaves alternate; lower ones stalked, the upper clasping the stem. Flower-heads numerous, in corymbs or umbels. Involucral bracts overlapping in several rows. Florets all ligulate, yellow. Achenes flattened, not beaked; pappus of unbranched, white hairs.

1. Pedicels covered with dark hairs .. .. **3. S. arvensis**
   Pedicels hairless 2
2. Auricles rounded (Fig. CIVq); achenes with no transverse wrinkles **1. S. asper**
   Auricles pointed (Fig. CIVr); achenes with fine transverse wrinkles
   (hand-lens) .. .. **2. S. oleraceus**

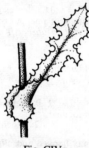 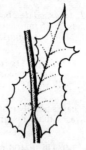 

Fig. CIVq   Fig. CIVr   Fig. CIVs

1. Sonchus asper. 6-9. A hairless annual, 30-80 cm high. Leaves pinnatifid, usually wavy, with numerous, prickly marginal teeth; auricles of the upper leaves rounded in outline (Fig. CIVq). Flower-heads numerous, 20-25 mm across, in a crowded corymb or irregular umbel. Involucres conical and closed at top during ripening of the fruit. Achenes with faint longitudinal ribs but no transverse wrinkles. *Waste-places, roadsides; very frequent.*

2. S. oleraceus. 6-10. Similar to *S. asper* except for the leaves, which are slightly bluish-green, almost flat and have pointed auricles (Fig. CIVr) and the achenes, which have fine transverse wrinkles. *Similar situations, about as common.*

3. S. arvensis. 7-9. Perennial, 70-150 cm high, with creeping rhizome; hairless below, but inflorescence covered with dark hairs. Leaves usually pinnatifid with few, widely-spaced segments, and toothed, slightly prickly margins; auricles of the upper ones short and rounded. Flower-heads deeper yellow, 35-40 mm across, in a corymbose panicle; involucre not closed at the top after flowering. Achenes as in *S. oleraceus*. *River-banks, field- and bog-margins and sea-shores; fairly frequent.*

40. Lactuca

* Lactuca tatarica. 8-9. A smallish, creeping perennial with linear, shallowly toothed basal leaves; stems with more or less untoothed leaves, branched towards the top; florets all ligulate, purple; achenes with a long beak and pappus of simple hairs.

Known only from one stretch of shore, East of Galway, where it has persisted from the early part of this century.

41. Cicerbita

* Cicerbita macrophylla. 7-9. A tall perennial with far-creeping rhizome. Leaves mostly pinnatifid with the terminal lobe the largest, large, with winged petiole and clasping base, the upper toothed and often not pinnatifid, with an oval somewhat cordate blade and broadly-winged petiole. Flower-heads numerous, in a glandular-hairy panicle. Florets all ligulate, purple. Achenes not beaked. Pappus of simple hairs. *A garden escape, occasionally naturalised in hedges and waste-places in the West.*

42. Mycelis

* Mycelis muralis (*Lactuca muralis*). **7-8.** A slender, hairless herb, usually biennial, 40-80 cm high; the stem and leaves sometimes dark purple. Leaves alternate, pinnatifid with the terminal lobe the largest, the lobes angular and the upper ones clasping the stem. Flower-heads numerous, 12 mm across, in a loose panicle; involucre of 5 long, equal bracts, and a few very small outer ones. Florets ligulate, yellow, usually 5 in each head. Achenes black, with a short beak and a delicate pappus of unbranched, white hairs. *Occasional on rocks, walls and cultivated ground; rare in woodland; locally abundant on open limestone pavement in Clare.*

43. Taraxacum. Dandelion. *Caisearbhán*

Perennial; leaves all basal. Flower-heads solitary, on hollow, hairless peduncles. Involucre of an inner row of long, equal bracts, and numerous shorter outer ones. Florets all ligulate, bright yellow. Receptacle without scales. Achenes rough, usually with short spines in their upper half, and bearing, at the end of a very long beak, a white pappus of unbranched hairs. The area of the achene at the base of the beak is called the *cone.* Pollen sometimes altogether absent.

A very difficult genus, consisting in Ireland, like *Hieracium*, of a multitude of forms, which set seed without pollination, and never, therefore, interbreed. A very large number of microspecies have been described; over 70 species are recorded for County Dublin alone; however many still await discovery. The distribution of *Taraxacum* micro-species within Ireland is poorly known, records for some counties being almost totally lacking. The genus may be divided into a number of sections (here referred to as groups) which are sometimes rather difficult to distinguish.

1. Leaves scarcely lobed; involucral bracts with wide, membranous
    edges   ..   ..   ..   **Group III**
    Leaves usually deeply lobed; involucral bracts usually without
    broad, membranous edges   2

2. Involucral bracts with a small protruberance on the back, near the
    tip, making them appear forked (Fig. CIVs)   ..   **Groups I & II**
    Involucral bracts without a protruberance on the back   ..   3

3. Leaves with dark blotches or spots   ..   ..   **Groups IV & V**
    Leaves more or less unspotted (sometimes with spots between
    the lobes) ..   .. **Groups VI, VII & VIII**

Group I (Erythrosperma). Leaves strongly lobed. Heads usually less than 3 cm across. Bracts with an apical protruberance. Achenes with a long, cylindrical, narrow cone, often reddish. *Dry places, especially sand-dunes; occasional to frequent.*

Group II. (Obliqua). Similar to **Group I**, but with brownish achenes and the cone pyramidal and about 0.5 mm long. *Sandy grassland by the sea; very rare.*

Group III (Palustria). Leaves very narrow, almost unlobed, without dark spots. Outer bracts with wide, membranous edges, erect and pressed close to inner bracts. *Fens, turloughs and wet meadows; largely in the West; rare.*

Group IV. (Spectabilia). Leaves usually moderately lobed, often with dark spots. Outer side of ligules often reddish tinged. Achenes about 4.5 mm long. Pollen absent. *Wet, acidic grassland, roadsides; occasional.*

Group V. (Naevosa). Similar to **Group IV**, but the blotches on the leaves merge together, the achenes are only 4 mm long, and the ligules do not have a reddish tinge. *Similar habitats but largely in the North; occasional.*

Group VI. (Celtica). Petioles and midribs usually reddish, the red colouration not forming stripes; leaves with no or few spots or blotches. Involucral bracts spreading or erect but not curved backwards. *Damp grassland, roadsides; occasional.*

Group VII. (Hamata). Similar to **Group VI,** but with the pink or red colouration on the midrib forming lines separated by a green band and the involucral bracts bent backwards. *Roadsides, grassland, frequent.*

Group VIII. (Ruderalia) (*Vulgaria*). By far the largest group, containing many micro-species. Similar to **Group VI** but the leaves are often rather highly and three-dimensionally lobed and lack red colouration and the involucral bracts are bent backwards. *Waste ground, roadsides, grassland; abundant.*

44. Lapsana

Lapsana communis. Nipplewort. *Duilléog mhaith.* **7-8.** A slender, branched, nearly hairless annual, 30-90 cm high. Lower leaves pinnatifid with the terminal lobe the largest, with few segments; upper leaves lanceolate, toothed, stalkless. Flower-heads 6-8 mm across, on slender stalks, in a loose panicle. Involucre of 8-10 long bracts and a few very short ones. Florets yellow, all ligulate, rather few. No pappus. *Woods and hedges; very frequent.*

45. Crepis

Leaves pinnatifid, mostly basal; stems sometimes reddish at base. Flower-heads rather small, in a loose, corymbose panicle. Florets all ligulate, yellow. Involucre of a single row of equal bracts, with a few small outer ones. receptacle flat, without scales. Achenes rarely beaked; pappus of unbranched hairs, white except in *C. paludosa.*

1. Ripe achenes with a long, slender beak (Fig. CIVc) ..	**3. C. vesicaria**
Achenes not beaked	.. 2
2. Involucral bracts downy on the <u>inner</u> surface ..	.. **4. C. biennis**
Involucral bracts hairless on the <u>inner</u> surface ..	.. 3
3. Achenes 4-5 mm. Pappus brownish or dirty yellowish-white, stiff and brittle. Hairs on outside of involucre obvious, 1-2 mm long..	**1. C. paludosa**
Achenes less than 3 mm. Pappus pure white, silky. Hairs on outside of involucre less than 1 mm long or absent	**2. C. capillaris**

1. Crepis paludosa. 6-9. Perennial, 30-70 cm high, hairless except for inflorescence. Leaves oval or lanceolate, with a few triangular teeth in the lower half, sometimes almost pinnatifid with the terminal lobe the largest; upper ones clasping the stem with toothed or angled auricles. Pedicels and involucres hairy; hairs on involucre 1-2 mm. Flower-heads 15-20 mm across. Achenes 5 mm, not beaked;

pappus off-white, brittle. *Wet meadows, wet rocky places and by streams in mountains; frequent in the North-west, rather rare elsewhere.*

2. C. capillaris. 6-9. Annual or biennial, rather slender, up to 75 cm high, hairless or slightly hairy. Leaves linear-oblong, pinnatifid or toothed. Flower heads 12-20 mm across. Involucral bracts hairless on their inner surface. Achenes 2.5 mm long, without a beak; pappus white and silky. *Pastures, banks and walls; frequent.*

3. C. vesicaria (*C. taraxacifolia*). **5-7.** A hairy biennial, 30-75 cm high. Basal leaves deeply pinnatifid, usually with the terminal lobe the largest. Upper leaves few, small, often untoothed. Flower-heads 15-20 mm across; involucral bracts slightly hairy. Achenes with slender beaks nearly as long as themselves (Fig. CIVc); pappus white and silky. *Dry banks, roadsides and gravel-pits; frequent in Centre, rare elsewhere.*

4. * C. biennis. 7-9. Similar to *C. vesicaria* but taller, with more numerous stem-leaves, larger flower-heads 20-35 mm across, and achenes without a beak. *Roadsides and waste-places; occasional but locally abundant, spreading.*

46. Hieracium. Hawkweed
Perennials, very similar to *Crepis*, but as a rule hairier, the leaves more nearly untoothed, the flower-heads sometimes solitary, or the pappus always brown, or dirty white and brittle.

This is an extremely difficult genus, as, like Irish *Taraxacum*, it does not form species in the normal sense. Seed is set without pollination, so that each plant preserves indefinitely in its decendents its individual characteristics, without any of the mixing which cross-fertilisation would bring. Hence an enormous number of species have been described (about 50 for Ireland). An attempt has been made to enable the reader to name tentatively the more widespread or notable Irish forms; but the key (which omits many local plants and places the species into groups) must be used with caution and reserve. Indeed, the delimitation of some of the groups is unclear and the placement of certain species within them therefore uncertain. All, except for the *H. pilosella* group flower rather late, usually in July-August.

These remarks do not apply to *H. pilosella*, which (in Ireland, though not elsewhere) is constant, distinct and easily recognised.

1.	Flowering stem quite leafless; leafy runners arising from its base	**Group 1**
	Flowering stem with at least 1 or more scale-leaves; plant without runners	2
2.	Basal leaves all or mostly withered at flowering	3
	Basal leaves present, forming a rosette, when flowers open	6
3.	Outer involucral bracts with out-turned tips; leaves with the margins rolled-over	**Group 2**
	Outer involucral bracts without out-turned tips; leaves usually without their margins rolled-over	4
4.	Middle stem leaves clasping the stem	**Group 3**
	None of the stem-leaves really clasping, though sometimes broad based	5
5.	Usually more than 15 stem-leaves present	**Group 4**
	Usually less than 15 stem-leaves present	**Group 5**
6.	Stem-leaves more or less clasping the stem	**Group 8**
	Stem-leaves not clasping the stem	7

7. Leaves scarcely bristly on margins; bracts of involucre incurved
      in bud, with dense, small, star-shaped hairs, usually densely
      woolly   ..   ..   **Group 6**
    Leaves with stout bristly hairs on margins; bracts of involucre erect
      in bud, with few or no star-shaped hairs and not densely woolly   **Group 7**

Group 1 (Pilosella). **Hieracium pilosella** (*Pilosella vulgaris, Pilosella offici-narum*). **Mouse-ear hawkweed. 5-8.** Leaves all basal, in a rosette, oblong-lanceolate, hairy, white beneath. Long, leafy, creeping runners arise from the rosette. Peduncles leafless, 15-25 cm high, hairy, with a single or few flower-heads. Florets lemon-yellow, flushed with red on the lower side. *Dry banks, walls, pastures, eskers and dunes; very frequent.*

Divided into a number of species, 3 of which occur in Ireland.

H. pilosella with a single, yellow flower-head per flowering stem is the most common. Sometimes itself divided into 7 sub-species, largely on the basis of the types, distribution and lengths of hairs present on the involucral bracts. However, the distinctions are not clear-cut, the forms not well separated geographically or ecologically and they, therefore, do not warrant sub-specific status. The most widespread form (subsp. *micradenium*) has the involucral bracts evenly covered in short (0.5 mm) glandular hairs of more or less equal length; a form with a mixed covering of unbranched non-glandular and glandular hairs on the bracts is also frequent and is the commonest form in the North (subsp. *trichosoma*); plants whose bracts are only covered in short (2 mm or less) non-glandular hairs are occasional (subsp. *melanops*).

* **H. caespitosum**, only found on the River Lee at Cork, has many (up to 50), yellow flower-heads per stem.

* **H. aurantiacum** (*H. brunneocroceum*) also has fairly numerous flower-heads but the outer florets are orange-brown to red and turn purplish on drying; widespread, though rather rare.

Group 2 (Umbellata). **H. umbellatum** is the only Irish representative of the group. Rosette absent; stem leaves numerous, narrow, tapered at base but not really stalked, very shallowly toothed, with the margins rolled-over; outer involucral bracts with out-turned tips. *Riversides and other shady situations; occasional; declining, at least in the North.*

Subsp. **bichlorophyllum** (*H. bichlorophyllum*) has bright green, broader, oblong lanceolate leaves. *Occasional in the West.*

Rather rare plants, from river-banks in Donegal, Mayo and Clare (Lough Derg), somewhat intermediate between Groups 2 & 4, with very broad, lanceolate involucral bracts have been called **H. maritimum**.

Group 3 (Foliosa) (*Inuloides*). No rosette; stem leaves fairly numerous, pale beneath, the lower ones tapered at base, the middle and upper clasping the stem. Involucral bracts dark with a pale margin. **H. subcrocatum**, known only from upland streamsides in Wicklow and Antrim, has a blackish style and stem leaves gradually tapering to the base. **H. strictiforme**, from acidic rocks, river banks and walls, is more widespread, and frequent in the North and East, it also has blackish stigmas and nearly untoothed leaves which are rounded at the base. **H. latobrigorum**, from upland streamsides, is similar but has yellow stigmas; fairly frequent in Wicklow, Down and Antrim.

H. prenanthoides, a very rare species of boulder clay by the coast at Red Bay, Antrim is the only Irish representative of the closely related group **Prenanthoidea**. It differs, most obviously, in its densely glandular peduncles and pale brown, not purplish or blackish-brown achenes.

Group 4 (Sabauda). H. sabaudum (*H. perpropinquum, H. bladonii*) is the only Irish representative of the group. No rosette; stem leaves numerous, usually at least 15, crowded below, decreasing in size upwards, lanceolate, finely toothed; the lower ones stalked, the uppermost with a rounded base. Involucral bracts with appressed tips. *Heaths, woodland, shady river banks, walls; fairly frequent in the South-east.*

Group 5 (Tridentata) (*Laevigata*). About 7 very local species of the North and West belong here. All are similar to *H. sabaudum* but have fewer than 15 stem-leaves, the uppermost of which taper, somewhat, to their base: **H. stewartii**, from woods and river banks, mainly in the North-west, is the most widespread and probably the most frequent.

Group 6 (Vulgata) (*Glandulosa*). The largest group, comprising about 17 species, mostly rather rare, local and in the North. Rosette-leaves persistent, more or less hairy, but without stiff marginal bristles; stem-leaves few or none stalked or stalkless, but never clasping the stem. Involucral bracts more or less incurved in bud, usually densely woolly, sometimes glandular. **H. vulgatum** has broadly lanceolate basal-leaves, usually obviously toothed and purple beneath, and about 3 stem-leaves; it is the second commonest *Hieracium* (after *H. pilosella*) in North-east Ireland, but is very rare and scattered elsewhere. **H. euprepes**, is probably the next most frequent, though with the exception of one record for Glencar, Kerry, it is confined to coasts in the North-east (mainly Antrim). It has rather few glandular hairs and 1-2 stem-leaves (usually the upper are very small and scale-like).

Group 7 (Oreadea) (*Suboreadea*). About 10 species, mainly of mountain districts in the North half, but also scattered in the South belong here. Rosette-leaves persistent, stalked, bluish-green, often purple-spotted, more or less bristly, especially at margin; stem-leaves few or none, the lowest usually stalked. Flower-heads rather few. Involucral bracts usually erect in bud. **H. basalticum**, probably the most common, is frequent on basalt in Antrim and occasional on limestone in Sligo and Leitrim; has spotted, oval rosette-leaves, at most 1 stem-leaf and sometimes a few scattered star-shaped hairs on the involucral bracts. **H. caledonicum** is similar but usually has 2 stem-leaves, the inflorescence is somewhat glandular and the tips of the involucral bracts are somewhat incurved in bud; mainly in the far North (especially Donegal). **H. scoticum**, also largely found in Donegal, also somewhat glandular has 3-7 stem-leaves. **H. argenteum**, absent from the South-east, but otherwise widespread though rather rare, has almost lanceolate rosette-leaves and 2 stem leaves.

Group 8 (Cerinthoidea) (*Alatum*). About 7 species in Ireland; 3 of which are fairly frequent. Rosette leaves persistent, bluish-green, stalked, the petiole clothed with woolly, white or yellowish-white hairs. Stem-leaves one or several, usually narrow, clasping the stem. Flower-heads large (35-50 mm across). **H. anglicum** is fairly frequent on rocky ground in the West, where it is fairly frequent on limestone, and North, where it is especially frequent on the mountains of Antrim and Derry; it has 1-2 stem-leaves and lemon-yellow flowers. **H. iricum**, often found on calcareous rocks, is occasional in the West, often taller (more than 30 cm), has 3-7 stem-leaves and deeper yellow flowers but is otherwise fairly similar; small specimens can be easily confused with *H. anglicum*. **H. ampliatum**, rare and almost exclusively on basalt in the North-east, has petiolate stem-leaves and rosette-leaves with 2-3 large, coarse teeth at their base; its flowers are lemon-yellow.

MONOCOTYLEDONS

CV. ALISMATACEAE

Hairless aquatic or marsh perennials with basal leaves. Flowers regular, hermaphrodite or monoecious, with 3 green sepals and 3 white or lilac petals. Stamens 6 or more. Pistil superior, consisting of numerous free carpels. Fruit a collection of achenes.

1. Flowers unisexual; stamens more than 6; some leaves sagittate   **1. Sagittaria**
    Flowers hermaphrodite; stamens 6; leaves oval to linear, not sagittate   2
2. Flowers in a panicle with several whorls; carpels in a regular ring   **4. Alisma**
    Flowers in an umbel, sometimes with a single whorl below it; carpels
    in a more or less globular head   3
3. Aerial leaves, if present, linear-lanceolate, acute   ..   .. **2. Baldellia**
    Aerial or floating leaves oval, obtuse   ..   ..   .. **3. Luronium**

1. Sagittaria
Sagittaria sagittifolia. Arrowhead. 7-8. Most of the leaves sagittate, erect, 5-8 cm wide, borne above the surface on long stalks; a few leaves, however, are ribbon-like and submerged. Stem up to 40 cm, emerging above the surface and bearing numerous shortly stalked flowers in whorls of 3. Monoecious; stamens in male flowers about 12; anthers purple. Carpels very numerous, in a globular head; achenes winged. Petals in both types of flower 10-15 mm, white with a purple patch at the base. *Lakes, canals and other slow-moving waters, mainly in the Centre and East; rather rare.*

2. Baldellia
Baldellia ranunculoides (*Alisma ranunculoides*). **6-7.** Stem erect, or sometimes creeping and rooting at the nodes, from which arise umbels of flowers. Leaves linear-lanceolate, stalked, projecting above the water; linear, submerged leaves are sometimes also present. Flowers 10-15 mm across, in a terminal umbel, sometimes with a single whorl of flowers below it. Petals white or pale lilac. Stamens 6. Carpels forming a globular head. *Shallow water on the margins of freshwater-bodies (especially lakes); frequent.*

3. Luronium
Luronium natans (*Alisma natans*). **7-8.** Stems slender, floating, though rooted at the base. Lower leaves submerged, linear; upper leaves floating, long-stalked, oval, obtuse. Flowers in small umbels, rarely solitary. Stamens 6. Carpels in an irregular head. *Shallow water at lake-margins; very rare. Recently discovered in West Galway; possibly overlooked elsewhere.*

4. Alisma. Water-plantain
Flowers hermaphrodite, in a panicle with several whorls. Stamens 6. Carpels arranged in a ring.

1. Leaves 2-4 times as long as wide, truncate or cordate at the
    base   ..   .. **1. A. plantago-aquatica**
    Leaves 6-8 times as long as wide, tapered to the stalk   **2. A. lanceolatum**

1. Alisma plantago-aquatica. 7-8. Stem up to 75 cm high. Leaves erect, long-stalked, oval, pointed, 2-4 times as long as wide, cordate or truncate at the base. Flowers in a terminal panicle of several whorls, open mainly in the afternoon. *Ditches, pools, canals and lake-margins; very frequent.*

2. A. lanceolatum. 7-8. Very like *A. plantago-aquatica* but with narrower leaves (6-8 times as long as wide), tapered to the stalk at the base and flowers open mainly in the morning. *Similar habitats; occasional.*

CVI.   BUTOMACEAE

Butomus umbellatus. Flowering rush. 6-8. Aquatic herb with leaves all basal, very long, erect, narrowly linear and 3-angled. Stem unbranched, 70-150 cm high, bearing a large, terminal umbel of regular, pink flowers 20-25 mm across. Perianth segments 6, all coloured, in two whorls of 3, the outer, smaller and tinged with green; stamens 9. Ovary superior, composed of 6 free carpels which become follicles in fruit. *Rivers, canals and lakes; rare.*

CVII.   HYDROCHARITACEAE

Aquatic perennials, with submerged or floating leaves and regular, dioecious flowers. Sepals 3, small and green; petals 3; stamens 6 or more, ovary fused, inferior.
   * *Lagarosiphon major* with untoothed, stalkless, narrow, spirally arranged, densely crowded, strongly bent-back, submerged leaves has been found on a few occasions some distance from habitation but is not, yet, naturalised.

1. Leaves circular, floating, with a distinct, long petiole   **1. Hydrocharis**
   Leaves linear or lanceolate, without a distinct petiole   . .   2
2. Leaves at least 15 cm long, in dense basal tufts with sharp teeth, not
      translucent . .   . . **2. Stratiotes**
   Leaves no more than 2 cm long, produced along the stem, not
      obviously toothed, translucent   3
3. Upper leaves dark green, mostly in whorls of 3   . .   . . **3. Elodea**
   Upper leaves pale green, mostly in whorls of 3-5   . .   . . **4. Hydrilla**

1. Hydrocharis
Hydrocharis morsus-ranae. Frogbit. 7-8. Stems submerged or floating, producing at the nodes tufts of roots, leaves and flowers. Leaves floating, long-stalked, round, entire, deeply cordate, rather thick, 25-50 mm across. Flowers 20 mm across, white with a yellow eye; female ones solitary, male ones 2-3 on a peduncle. Stamens 12, some without anthers. Styles 6, each with a forked stigma. *Ditches, bog-holes, marshes, slow-streams and canals; occasional in the East & Centre, very rare elsewhere.*

2. Stratiotes
   * **Stratiotes aloides. Water soldier. 7.** Leaves linear-lanceolate, pointed, strongly toothed, rather fleshy, 15-30 cm long, in dense basal tufts. Flowers as in *Hydrocharis*, but 30-45 mm across, and with numerous stamens in the male. *Shallow water; naturalised in Upper Lough Erne and near Cork.*

3. Elodea. Pondweed
Stem and leaves submerged. Leaves minutely toothed, stalkless, dark translucent green, mostly in whorls of 3. Male flowers unknown in Ireland. Female inconspicuous, 3-4 mm across, raised to the surface by a very long beak to the ovary, of which the lower, fertile part is enclosed in a tubular, 2-lipped bract.

1. Leaves more or less flat; leaf-apex rounded   . .   **1. E. canadensis**
   Leaves usually twisted or bent-back; leaf-apex sharply pointed   **2. E. nuttallii**

1. * **Elodea canadensis. Canadian pondweed. 7-8.** Leaves 5-15 mm long, usually flat, linear or oblong with a rounded tip. *Rivers, canals, ponds and ditches; frequent in the lowlands, rare in mountain districts.* Native of North America.

2. * **E. nuttallii. 7-8.** Similar to *E. canadensis* but usually with twisted or bent-back, linear or lanceolate, longer leaves with a sharply pointed tip. *Similar habitats; known only from the Lough Neagh basin and Dublin, but spreading.* Native of North America.

4. Hydrilla

Hydrilla verticillata (*H. lithuanica*). **8.** Stem and leaves submerged. Leaves pale translucent green, in whorls of 3-5, 10-15 mm long, minutely toothed, stalkless, with an acute tip. Male flowers unknown in Ireland; female very rarely produced, axillary, with a long ovarian beak as in *Elodea*. *Known only from one lake near Renvyle, Co. Galway.*

For some years plants from Renvyle were confused with *E. nuttallii.*

CVIII.   JUNCAGINACEAE

Triglochin

Hairless marsh perennials of Rush-like habit. Leaves all basal, linear, rather fleshy. Flowers small, greenish, regular, hermaphrodite, in a long slender spike. Perianth segments 6; stamens 6, with very short filaments; carpels 3 or 6, united at first but separating in fruit.

1. Carpels 6; leaves not furrowed at the base; plant of salt-marshes
    and muddy shores only; never inland   ..   **1. T. maritima**
    Carpels 3; leaves deeply furrowed at the base; plant of fresh-
    water marshes and wet pastures, occasionally at the back of
    salt-marshes   ..   ..   ..   **2. T. palustris**

1. Triglochin maritima. 6-8. Leaves 8-40 cm long, deeply furrowed on one side, rounded on the other. Flowering stem 15-50 cm high, the upper half occupied by the dense spike. Fruit ovoid-oblong of 6 carpels, usually diverging slightly from the stem. *Salt-marshes and muddy shores by the coast; very frequent.*

2. T. palustris. 7-8. Very similar to *T. maritima* but with smaller, less fleshy leaves, a laxer spike and a linear-oblong fruit of 3 carpels, pressed closely against the stem. *Marshes and wet pastures; very frequent.*

CIX.   POTAMOGETONACEAE

Aquatic perennials. Leaves submerged or floating (rarely aerial on marshy ground). Flowers in spikes or heads, usually borne above the water-surface. Perianth of 4 free, greenish segments. Stamens 4; anthers stalkless, attached to the base of the adjoining perianth-segment. Carpels usually 4, free; fruit of one or more drupes or achenes.

1. Leaves mostly alternate (occasionally opposite below the
    inflorescence)   ..   ..   ..   **1. Potamogeton**
    Leaves all opposite   ..   ..   ..   **2. Groenlandia**

1. Potamogeton. Pondweed. *Duileasc na abhann*

Leaves mostly alternate. Fruit a drupe. Hybrids are rather frequent in this genus. Three of the most widespread are described below and accounted for in the key. Some others are briefly noted. They are all sterile, except *P.* x *zizii*, but can reproduce by vegetative means, and in consequence can be found in the absence of one or both parents.

Like many aquatic plants, species of this genus can vary greatly in accordance with the depth of the water and the speed of its motion.

1. Floating or aerial leaves present 2
   All leaves submerged 8

2. Submerged leaves absent, or reduced to narrow stalks less than
   5 mm wide; larger stipules more than 45 mm long .. **1. P. natans**
   Submerged leaves present, with distinct blade at least 10 mm wide;
   stipules not more than 40 mm long 3

3. Submerged leaves stalked 4
   Submerged leaves stalkless 5

4 . Floating leaves opaque and somewhat leathery, contrasting strongly
   with the translucent, membranous submerged leaves; fruits reddish
   brown .. .. **2. P. polygonifolius**
   Floating leaves translucent, not very different from the submerged
   leaves, both of them with a conspicuous network of opaque veins;
   fruits green .. .. **3. P. coloratus**

5. Submerged leaves ribbon-like, at least 15 times as long as
   wide .. .. .. **7. P. x sparganifolius**
   Submerged leaves not ribbon-like, not more than 10 times as long as
   wide 6

6. Submerged leaves obtuse; peduncles of uniform thickness .. **9. P. alpinus**
   Submerged leaves with a short, fine point; peduncles thickened in
   upper part 7

7. Submerged leaves mostly less than 15 mm wide; stipules less
   than 20 mm long .. .. .. **5. P. gramineus**
   Submerged leaves mostly more than 15 mm wide; stipules
   mostly more than 20 mm long .. .. .. **6. P. x zizii**

8. Leaf-blades at least 5 mm wide, not parallel-sided or grass-like .. 9
   Leaf-blades not more than 4 mm wide, parallel-sided and grass-like 18

9. Leaves at least 15 times as long as wide .. **7. P. x sparganifolius**
   Leaves not more than 10 times as long as wide 10

10. Some leaves stalked 11
    Leaves all stalkless 13

11. Leaf-stalks mostly at least 12 mm long .. .. **3. P. coloratus**
    Leaf-stalks mostly less than 12 mm long 12

12. Larger leaves more than 25 mm wide, all shortly stalked .. **4. P. lucens**
    Leaves not more than 25 mm wide, many of them stalkless .. **6. P. x zizii**

13. Leaf-margin undulate and sharply toothed, the teeth easily visible
    to the naked eye .. .. .. **16. P. crispus**
    Leaf-margin flat, entire or very minutely toothed 14

14. Leaves clasping the stem, with cordate base 15
    Leaves tapered to a fairly narrow base 16

15. Leaves mostly less than 4 times as long as wide; fruits less than
    4 mm long .. .. **11. P. perfoliatus**
    Leaves mostly more than 4 times as long as wide; fruits more
    than 4 mm long .. .. .. **10. P. praelongus**

16. Leaves obtuse .. .. **9. P. alpinus**
    Leaves acute 17

17. Fruits numerous, 2.5 - 3 mm long .. .. **5. P. gramineus**
    Fruits not developed .. .. **8. P. x nitens**

18. Stipule united with leaf-base, forming a sheath 19
    Stipule free from leaf-base, arising from the node, beside the leaf 20

19. Leaves mostly acute; fruit 4 mm long, with a conspicuous
    beak .. .. .. **17. P. pectinatus**
    Leaves with a fine but rounded tip; fruit 2.5 - 3 mm long,
    scarcely beaked .. .. .. **18. P. filiformis**

20. Many of the leaves more than 2 mm wide 21
    Most of the leaves not more than 2 mm wide 22

21. Leaves mostly obtuse; stipules obscurely veined, with free
    (though often overlapping) margins [Fig. CIXa] .. **12. P. obtusifolius**
    Leaves mostly mucronate; stipules prominently veined, with
    margins united so as to form a tube [Fig. CIXb] .. .. **13. P. friesii**

22. Lateral veins of leaf conspicuous; glands at base of leaf well
    developed; stipules with margins free (though often
    overlapping) [Fig. CIXc] .. .. **14. P. berchtoldii**
    Lateral veins of leaves faint; glands at base of leaf small and
    inconspicuous; stipules with margins united so as to form a
    tube [Fig. CIXd] .. .. .. **15. P. pusillus**

Fig. CIXa   Fig. CIXb   Fig. CIXc   Fig. CIXd

1. Potamogeton natans. 6-7. Floating leaves numerous, long-stalked, broadly oval or oblong, entire, opaque, thick and rather leathery, 50-100 mm long. Submerged leaves absent or reduced to stalks less than 5 mm wide. Stipules mostly 5-8 cm long. Spike dense, 35-50 mm long; peduncle twice as long, stout. *Lakes, ponds, ditches and slow streams; abundant.*

2. P. polygonifolius. 6-8. Floating leaves as in *P. natans*, but somewhat narrower; submerged leaves lanceolate, long-stalked, thinner and more membranous, sometimes absent. Stipules 25-35 mm long. Spike 25-35 mm long, dense; peduncle much longer, slender. *Bog-holes, drains, lakes and wet, peaty ground; abundant except on limestone soils.*

3. P. coloratus. 6-7. Floating and submerged leaves similar in texture, thin and translucent, with a conspicuous network of opaque veins, often tinged with brownish-red, the uppermost broadly oval, the lower narrower. Stipules 20-50 mm long. Spike 15-40 mm long, slender; peduncle 2-4 times as long. *Shallow, calcareous water in pools and ditches; frequent in Centre, rather rare elsewhere.*

4. P. lucens. 6-7. Leaves all submerged, thin, translucent, rather wavy, oblong-lanceolate, subacute, 25-70 mm wide, tapered to a short stalk. Spike dense, 50 mm long; peduncle stout, thickest below the spike, slightly longer than the spike. Fruits 3-4.5 mm long, brown. *Pools, lakes and streams, usually in rather deep water; frequent in the North half, rather rare in the South.*

In addition to *P.* x *zizii*, described below, two other hybrids of this species are known from Ireland. *P.* x *salicifolius* (*P. decipiens*) is the hybrid with *P. perfoliatus*; it differs from *P. lucens* chiefly in its stalkless leaves. *P.* x *nerviger* is the hybrid with *P. alpinus*; it is known only from the R. Fergus in Co. Clare.

5. P. gramineus. 6-7. Floating leaves stalked, thick, oval, rather small; often absent. Submerged leaves membranous, oblong to narrowly lanceolate, mostly less than 15 mm wide, acute, tapered at the base but not stalked. Spike dense, 25-35 mm long; peduncle much longer, stout, thickest below the spike. Fruits 2.5-3 mm long, dark green. *Rivers and lakes, mainly in the North half; occasional.*

6. P. x zizii (*P. gramineus* x *P. lucens*). **6-7.** Floating leaves 55-100 x 20-40 mm, dark green, thick, opaque; sometimes absent. Submerged leaves 50-130 x 11-30 mm, narrowly elliptical, stalkless or very shortly stalked. Stipules 25-45 mm. Spikes 20-50 mm, rather rarely produced; peduncle 30-50 mm, stout, thickest below the spike. Fruits c. 3 mm long, green, often few. *Rivers and lakes, mainly in the North and West; occasional.*

The only fertile hybrid in the genus.

7. P. x sparganifolius (*P. gramineus* x *P. natans*). **6-7.** Floating leaves elliptical, usually absent in fast-flowing water. Submerged leaves linear to narrowly lanceolate, translucent or opaque, 3-10 mm wide, often ribon-like. Stipules 20-70 mm long. Spikes 25-45 mm long, dense; peduncle 30-100 mm long, scarcely thickened at the top. Fruits not formed. *Rivers and canals, from Westmeath and Galway northwards; rather rare.*

8. P. x nitens (*P. gramineus* x *P. perfoliatus*). **6-7.** Intermediate between the parent species, but usually closer to *P. gramineus*. Floating leaves elliptical, shortly stalked, rather rarely produced. Submerged leaves translucent, oblong, 4-8 times as long as wide, stalkless, slightly clasping at the base, acute. Stipules 15-20 mm long. Spike 10-20 mm long, sterile; peduncle slightly thickened below it. *Rivers and lakes; widespread but rather rare.*

9. P. alpinus. 6-7. Floating leaves stalked, broadly lanceolate, somewhat leathery, often absent. Submerged leaves oblong-lanceolate, membranous, tapered at the base, stalkless, obtuse. Often reddish. Stipules 20-40 mm. Spike dense, 20-35 mm long; peduncle 2-4 times as long, not swollen below the spike. Fruits c. 3 mm, reddish-brown. *Lakes and slow rivers, usually in fairly shallow water; occasional in the North half, rather rare in the South.*

10. P. praelongus. 6-7. Leaves all submerged, oblong, with an obtuse, hooded tip, stalkless and slightly clasping the stem, 25-40 mm wide. Stipules up to 60 mm long. Spike rather lax, 35-50 mm long; peduncle at least twice as long, not swollen at the tip. Fruits c. 5 mm, dark green. *Lakes and rivers, often in fairly deep water; rather rare.*

11. P. perfoliatus. 6-7. Leaves all submerged, usually triangular-oval, but sometimes lanceolate, acute or obtuse, clasping the stem with a broad, deeply cordate base. Stipules small, decaying early. Spike 15-25 mm; peduncles longer, scarcely swollen at the top. Fruits c. 3 mm, brownish-green. *Lakes, streams, ditches and canals; frequent.*

12. P. obtusifolius. 6-8. Leaves all submerged, broadly linear, 2.5-3.5 mm wide, obtuse, stalkless, often somewhat crowded near the tip of the stem. Stipules 10-30 mm, with free, but usually overlapping margins [Fig. CIXa]. Spikes 5-10 mm long; peduncles twice as long, slender. Fruits *c.* 3 mm, brownish-green. *Ditches, pools and bog-drains; occasional.*

13. P. friesii. 6-8. Very like *P. obtusifolius*, but with leaves often mucronate; stems more strongly flattened; stipules with margins united so as to form a tube [Fig. CIXb], and peduncles up to 4 times as long as the spike. *Lakes and canals in the Centre and West; rare.*

14. P. berchtoldii. 6-8. Leaves all submerged, linear, grass-like, 1-2 mm wide. 3-veined, usually acute, not bordered by a marginal vein at the tip. Stipules 5-15 mm, with free, but often overlapping margins [Fig. CIXc]. Spike few-flowered, very short; peduncle slender. Fruits 2-3 mm, green. *Still or slowly moving water of all kinds; very frequent.*
Hybrids with *P. coloratus* and *P. natans* are known. The former (*P.* x *lanceolatus*) is locally frequent in the Caher River, Co. Clare.

15. P. pusillus (*P. panormitanus*). **6-8.** Very like *P. berchtoldii*, but with a marginal vein bordering the tip of the leaf; stipules tubular, though often splitting with age [Fig. CIXd], and slightly smaller fruits (not more than 2.5 mm). *Similar situations; rather rare.*

16. P. crispus. 6-7. Leaves all submerged, linear-oblong, 7-15 mm wide, obtuse; margin strongly waved and finely toothed, with teeth easily visible to the naked eye. Stipules small, soon decaying. Spike small and rather lax, with about 8 flowers. Peduncle slender, about 50 mm long. Fruits 4-6 mm, including the beak, which is nearly as long as the body of the fruit. *Still or slowly moving water; very frequent in most districts.*

17. P. pectinatus (*P. interruptus*). **6-7.** Leaves all submerged, linear or thread-like, usually less than 2 mm wide, but occasionally wider, obtuse or acute, stalkless. Stipules united with the leaf-base to form a sheath with free margins, wrapped around the stem. Spike consisting of 4-5 whorls of flowers; peduncle very slender and flexuous. Fruits 3-5 mm, brown, with a short but distinct beak. *Lakes and ponds; more rarely in rivers or canals, usually in base-rich and sometimes brackish water; frequent near the coast, occasional inland.*

18. P. filiformis. 6-8. Like *P. pectinatus*, but with leaves always very narrow and thread-like, obtuse; stipular leaf-sheath without free margins, but forming a closed tube around the stem; fruits not beaked, with a stalkless stigma. *Lakes, mostly in the North half; rather rare.*

2. Groenlandia
Leaves all opposite. Fruit an achene.

Groenlandia densa (*Potamogeton densus*). **6-7.** Leaves all submerged, opposite, stalkless and somewhat clasping the stem, arranged in two opposite rows, usually recurved, lanceolate to oval; margin minutely toothed. Stipules absent. Inflorescence consisting of two flowers, each with 4 carpels, forming a compact head on a short, slender peduncle, which is curved downwards in· fruit. Fruits 3-4 mm, greenish brown, with a very short beak. *Rivers and canals; very rare, and apparently declining.*

CX. RUPPIACEAE

Ruppia

Aquatic submerged perennials with slender stems and almost hair-like leaves. Most leaves alternate, but often some opposite. Flowers hermaphrodite, in pairs on a peduncle which is short and erect in flower but longer and turned downwards in fruit. Perianth absent. Stamens minute, 2; anthers stalkless, each with 2 distinct, well separated lobes. Carpels free. Fruits pear-shaped, borne on long slender stalks, forming a kind of umbel.

1. Sheath at base of leaf not swollen; peduncle less than 30 mm;
    fruits assymmetrical [Fig. CXa]   ..   ..   **1. R. maritima**
    Sheath at base of leaf swollen; peduncle more than 40 mm;
    fruits symetrical [Fig. CXb]   ..   ..   **2. R. cirrhosa**

1. Ruppia maritima (*R. rostella*). **7-8.** Base of leaves sheathing but not inflated. Carpels 4. Fruits distinctly assymmetrical [Fig. CXa]. *Tidal mudflats and brackish pools and ditches; frequent in the South-west; rather rare elsewhere.*

2. R. cirrhosa (*R. spiralis*). **7-8.** Similar to *R. maritima* but with the sheath at the base of the leaves swollen, sometimes more than 4 carpels in each flower and the fruits more or less symmetrical [Fig. CXb]. *Similar situations; rare, mainly in the North-east and South-east.*

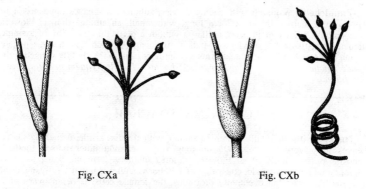

Fig. CXa   Fig. CXb

CXI. ZOSTERACEAE

Zostera. Grass wrack, Eel grass

Marine plants with creeping underground stems and alternate grass-like leaves. Flowers submerged, monoecious, inconspicuous, in a yellowish-green spike enclosed in the sheathing leaf-base, each consisting of a single anther or a fused ovary formed from 2 carpels with a forked style.

1. Leaves 6 mm or more wide   ..   ..   .. **1. Z. marina**
    Leaves no more than 3 mm wide   2

2. Leaf-sheaths forming a tube around the stem; flowering stems
    branched   ..   ..   **2. Z. angustifolia**
    Leaf-sheaths enclosing the stem but split and not forming a tube   **3. Z. noltii**

1. Zostera marina. 6-8. Leaves of sterile shoots about 50 cm long and 5-8 mm broad, sometimes more; sheaths fused into a tube. Flowering shoots freely branched with somewhat smaller leaves. Inflorescence about 10 cm long. *Muddy, sandy shores, only uncovered at low spring tides, locally frequent.*

2. Z. angustifolia (*Z. hornemanniana*). **7-8.** Very similar to *Z. marina* and often confused with it but with smaller, narrower, leaves about 25 cm long by no more than 3 mm wide, sometimes with a small apical notch, with the sheaths forming a tube around the stem. Flowering shoots branched. Inflorescence about 10 cm long. *Tidal estuaries and mud-flats, from mid-tide downwards; apparently rare, but distribution still not yet known.*

3. Z. noltii (*Z. nana*). **7-9.** Usually clearly creeping and rooting with long, slender underground stems. Leaves of sterile shoots about 15 cm long by no more than 2 mm wide, with the sheaths enclosing the stem but split and not forming a tube. Flowering stems usually unbranched. Inflorescence usually about 5 cm long. *Similar situation to* Z. angustifolia; *widespread, rare, though sometimes locally abundant.*

CXII. ZANNICHELLIACEAE

Zannichellia palustris. 6-8. Stems slender, submerged. Leaves opposite, or in whorls of 3, narrow-linear, 2-7 cm long, with small, sheathing stipules. Flowers monoecious, solitary or in pairs, axillary, without a perianth, consisting of a single stamen or pistil of 4-6 stalkless or stalked, free carpels, each with a large peltate stigma and persistent style which forms a prominent beak to the slightly winged fruit. *Ponds, ditches and lakes, in fresh or brackish water; locally frequent near the coast, rare inland.*

CXIII. NAJADACEAE

Najas flexilis. 8. Small submerged annual, with slender, brittle, branching stems. Leaves linear, very delicate, 10-25 mm long, very finely and rather sparsely toothed, opposite or in whorls of 3. Flowers minute, submerged, monoecious, axillary, without a perianth; the male, consisting of 1 stalkless anther is initially fully enclosed in a sac-like bract but eventually protrudes, the female consists of an ovary of 2 carpels. Fruit a very small ovoid drupe, stalkless. *Lakes in the West; rare. Grows in deep water, and is usually seen as fragments washed ashore.*

CXIV. MELANTHIACEAE

Narthecium ossifragum. Bog asphodel. 7-8. Herb with a slender, not bulbous, rootstock. Leaves up to 25 cm long, grass-like, pointed, curved and flattened, hairless, mostly basal, erect and arranged in two rows. Flowering stem 15-30 cm high, with a few small, scale-like leaves, bearing a compact, terminal raceme of erect, regular, bright yellow flowers, 12 mm across. Perianth segments 6, free, persistent in fruit. Stamens 6. Filaments densely hairy. Ovary superior. Capsule orange-red with numerous elongated seeds. *Bogs; very frequent.*

CXV. ASPHODELACEAE

Simethis planifolia. Kerry lily. 5-7. Herb with a rhizomatous, not bulbous, rootstock. Leaves up to 40 cm long, grass-like, pointed, basal, hairless, erect. Flowering stem 25-30 cm high, bearing a lax panicle of rather few, regular flowers. Perianth segments 6, free, white (purplish outside). Stamens 6. Filaments densely hairy. Ovary superior. Fruit a small, subglobular capsule. *Dry heathy ground near the sea; occasional near Derrynane in Kerry, unknown elsewhere.*

CXVI. ' COLCHICACEAE

Colchicum autumnale. Autumn crocus. 8-9. Perennial herb with a stout corm. Leaves oblong, 15-25 cm long, withering early, before the flowers appear in Autumn. Flowers solitary, pinkish-purple, 4-7 cm across; perianth with 6 spreading segments and a very long and slender tube of which the lowest part, surrounding the ovary, is underground. Stamens 6. Fruit an aerial capsule. *Meadows and river-banks; very rare, only known from the Nore valley and one site in Limerick, unknown elsewhere.*

CXVII. HYACINTHACEAE

Perennial herbs with a bulbous rootstock and linear, hairless basal leaves. Perianth of 6 similar segments. Stamens 6. Ovary superior. Fruit a capsule.

In addition to Spanish bluebell, *Chinodoxa* and various species of *Muscari* (Grape hyacinth) are commonly grown in gardens.

1. Perianth segments united at the base; flowers bell-shaped and
        nodding   ..   ..   **2. Hyacinthoides**
    Perianth segments free; flowers star-shaped and erect   ..   2

2. Flowers blue ..   ..   **1. Scilla**
    Flowers white   ..   ..   ..   **3. Ornithogalum**

1. Scilla

Scilla verna. Squill. 4-5. Leaves few, usually at least as long as the flowering stem, 5-20 cm long. Stem 5-40 cm, bearing a compact, flat-topped raceme of erect, bright blue (rarely white) flowers 15 mm across. Perianth segments free, spreading. *Locally frequent on rocky or sandy places on the East and North-east coasts (from Wexford to Derry).*

2. Hyacinthoides

Leaves rather fleshy. The upper half of the flowering stem with a loose raceme of bell-shaped flowers.

1. Flowers in a one-sided raceme   ..   ..   **1. H. non-scriptus**
    Flowers not in a one-sided raceme   ..   ..   **2. H. hispanicus**

1. Hyacinthoides non-scriptus (*Endymion non-scriptus, Scilla non-scripta*). **Bluebell. 4-5.** Stem 25-50 cm high, bearing a loose, one-sided raceme of drooping, tubular, purplish-blue flowers 25 mm long. Perianth with the segments united at the base and strongly curled back at the tip. *Woods, thickets, heaths and grassy banks; very frequent.*

2. * H. hispanicus (*Endymion hispanicus*). **Spanish bluebell. 4-5.** Differing from *H. non-scriptus* in its broader leaves, more numerous, erect flowers, which are larger and darker in colour, in a raceme which is not one-sided and with the perianth segments weakly curved back at the tip. *Grown in gardens and naturalised in a number of localities.* Native of South-west Europe and North Africa.

3. Ornithogalum
* Ornithogalum umbellatum. Star-of-Bethlehem. 4-6. Stem 10-20 cm high. Leaves few, usually at least as long as the flowering stem, grooved, with a white stripe down the middle. Flowers about 3 cm across; forming a flat-topped raceme of about 6 flowers. Perianth segments white, with a green stripe on the back. *Naturalised in a few sites in sand-dunes at Brittas Bay, Co. Wicklow.*

CXVIII. ALLIACEAE

Allium
Rootstock bulbous. Leaves basal, but some of them sheathing the base of the stem and appearing to arise from it. Flowers in an umbel, subtended by 1-2 papery bracts. Perianth-segments free. Plants with a strong smell of garlic.

This genus combines the inflorescence of the Amaryllidaceae with the superior ovary of the Liliaceae, and some authors assign it to the former family.

Various species are cultivated as Onions, Leeks, Chives and Garlic (The latter is well naturalised at one site in Sligo).

1.	Stems 3-angled	..	..	..	**1. A. triquetrum**
	Stem cylindrical	..	..	..	2
2.	Leaves oblong-oval, with a distinct leaf-stalk	..	**2. A. ursinum**
	Leaves linear, without a leaf-stalk	..	..	..	3
3.	Stamens of 2 kinds, 3 with filaments ending in 3 points, of which the central bears the anther	..	..	..	4
	Stamens all alike, with undivided filaments	..	..	6
4.	Leaves cylindrical, hollow, 3-4 mm wide	..	..	**7. A. vineale**
	Leaves flat, 6-30 mm wide ..	..	..	..	5
5.	Stem 70-175 cm; bract single; pedicels sometimes branched	..	..	..	**5. A. ampeloprasum**
	Stem not more than 80 cm; bracts 2; pedicels unbranched ..	..	..	..	**6. A. scorodoprasum**
6.	Stamens much longer then perianth	..	..	**4. A. carinatum**
	Stamens about the same length as perianth	..	**3. A. oleraceum**

1. * Allium triquetrum. 4-6. Stem sharply 3-angled, about 30 cms high. Leaves linear, keeled, 5-10 mm wide, bright green. Flowers nodding, in a small, 1-sided umbel; perianth bell-shaped, white with a green line along each segment. Stamens without appendages. *Hedges and waste places, mainly in the South and East; local but abundant in some districts.*

2. A. ursinum. Wild garlic, Ramsons. *Gairleóg.* **4-6.** Bulb very small. Stem slender, 15-35 cm high. Leaves basal, usually only 2 to each stem, oval, pointed, stalked, 4-7 cm wide. Flowers white, star-like, in a loose umbel of 8-12. Stamens without appendages. *Woods, hedges and damp, shady places; frequent, locally abundant.*

3. * A. oleraceum. 7-8. Stem up to 80 cm. Leaves 2-4 mm wide, sheathing the stem, cylindrical or flat. Flowers dull pink, greenish or brown, usually few, sometimes mixed in with stalkless bulbs. Stamens without appendages, shorter than or equalling the perianth. *Shores of Lough Neagh, and seemingly naturalised elsewhere (Cork, Wexford, Dublin); rare and easily confused with the next species.*

4. * A. carinatum. 8. Like *A. oleraceum*, but flowers pinkish-purple, with stamens longer than the perianth. *Roadsides, scrubland in the North-east (especially around Lough Neagh); occasional.* Native of Europe and Turkey.

5. A. ampeloprasum (*A. babingtonii*). **Wild leek. 6-7.** Stem stout, up to 150 cm high, its lower half sheathed by leaf-bases. Leaves grass-like, keeled, 10-30 mm wide. Flowers mauve or greenish, in a rather shaggy, globular umbel, mixed in with numerous, small, stalkless bulbs; pedicels unequal in length, some of them branched with a bulb at the point of forking. Stamens longer than perianth, 3 of them with long, slender, lateral appendages. *Rocky and sandy ground and waste places on the West coast; (Clare to Donegal); rare and very local.*

6. * A. scorodoprasum. Sand leek. 5-7. Stem slender, 30-80 cm high, its lower half sheathed by leaf-bases. Leaves linear, flat, 6-15 mm wide. Umbel consisting of numerous, purple, stalkless bulbs, and usually a few mauve or purple flowers. Stamens as in *A. ampeloprasum*, but shorter than the perianth. *Woods and sandy ground in Cork, Kerry and near Portstewart (Derry); rare.*

7. A. vineale. Crow garlic. 6-7. Stem slender, 30-75 cm high, its lower part sheathed by leaf-bases. Leaves rather few, hollow, nearly cylindrical, very long and slender. Flowers few, pink or green, intermixed with bulbs; usually the flowers are suppressed and the umbel is replaced by a head of bulbs. Stamens as in *A. ampeloprasum*. *Pastures, sandhills, banks and bushy places; rather rare and local and almost confined to the South half.*

CXIX.   PHORMIACEAE

* Phormium tenax. New Zealand flax. 7. A robust, shortly rhizomatous perennial with stiff, more or less erect, sword-like leaves, over 1 m long, which arise at ground level from a large rosette 1-2 m across. Flowering stem up to 4 m high with a panicle of tubular, dark red-orange flowers, each 3-5 cm long. Perianth free, almost to base; segments with their tips bent back and inner surface greenish-red. Stamens 6, anthers orange. Ovary superior. Fruit a capsule. *Planted and persistent by the sea in the South-west.* Native of New Zealand.

CXX.   ASPARAGACEAE

Asparagus officinalis. Asparagus. 6-8. Perennial herb with a creeping rhizome. Stems usually somewhat prostrate, branched, about 30 cm high. Leaves reduced to small scales, which bear in their axils tufts of short, bluish-green, stiff, needle-like branches. Flowers solitary, dioecious, small, on short pedicels usually less than 6 mm long. Perianth segments whitish, free. Fruit a red berry. *Sandhills on the South-east coast (Wicklow to Tramore); very rare.*

The edible Asparagus, usually considered as a distinct sub-species (subsp. *officinalis*), has green, needle-like branches and bears flowers on long pedicels (more than 6 mm long). It has long been naturalised on sand-dunes in Dublin and also occurs in Fermanagh.

CXXI. AMARYLLIDACEAE

Hairless perennials with a bulbous rootstock. Leaves basal. Flowers regular, in pairs or umbels on leafless peduncles, subtended by 1 or 2 papery bracts. Perianth-segments 6, all alike, free or united into a tube at the base. Stamens 6. Ovary 3-celled, inferior. Fruit a capsule.

Very many species and hybrids of *Narcissus*, including all kinds of Daffodil and Jonquil, are commonly cultivated and persist in long-abandoned gardens. The Snowdrop (*Galanthus*) and *Nerine* belong to this family, and a number of other genera, mainly from South Africa, including *Hippeastrum* and *Clivea*, are often grown as pot plants.

1. Flowers 35-40 mm across, with a distinct trumpet-like centre   **2. Narcissus**
    Flowers 15 mm across, without a distinct trumpet-like centre   **1. Leucojum**

1. Leucojum

Leucojum aestivum. Summer snowflake. 5. Stem and leaves 30-60 cm high, greyish-green; leaves linear. Flowers white, drooping, cup-shaped, 15 mm across, in a terminal umbel of about 5. Stamens epigynous; filaments short. Marshes and damp meadows; rare. *Often an escape from cultivation, but native in Limerick, Clare and Wexford and possibly elsewhere in the South.*

2. Narcissus

* Narcissus x medioluteus (*N.* x *biflorus*). **5.** Stem and leaves 35-40 cm high; leaves linear, fleshy. Flowers white with a yellow centre, 35-40 mm across, 2 on each stem. Perianth with a long narrow tube and 6 spreading lobes; at the mouth of the tube is a shortly projecting, yellow, circular frill, the corona. Stamens inserted on the perianth-tube and scarcely projecting from its mouth. *Grassy places and thickets in the South-west.* An old-established hybrid of garden origin.

CXXII. DIOSCOREACEAE

* Tamus communis. Black bryony. 6-8. Climbing, hairless perennial herb with a large underground tuber. Stems up to 4 m long, angled. Leaves heart-shaped, with a long, slender tip. Leaf-stalks slender, with small stipules; at least half as long as the blade. Flowers yellowish-green, very small, dioecious; in loose, axillary racemes of about 15-20 flowers. Petals 6. Male flowers stalked, with 6 stamens; female flowers, stalkless, with an inferior ovary bearing 1 style topped by 3, 2-lobed stigmas. Fruit a pale red berry, 10-13 mm across. *Known only from woodlands around Lough Gill and hedges near Armagh, Cookstown and Ballyvaughan.*

CXXIII. IRIDACEAE

Hairless perennials with erect stems and erect, mainly basal, sword-shaped leaves arranged in two ranks. Flowers regular or slightly irregular; perianth of 6 petal-like segments united at the base. Stamens 3, inserted on the perianth or on top of the ovary. Ovary inferior, 3-celled; style single, 3-branched above. Fruit a capsule.

Members of this family widely cultivated for ornament include species and hybrids of *Iris, Gladiolus, Crocus* and *Freesia.*

1. Flowers orange, slightly irregular; rootstock a corm . .   **3. Crocosmia**
    Flowers blue, yellow or dull purple, regular; rootstock a rhizome   2

2. Flowers 7-10 cm across; the three outer perianth-segments
        drooping, the three inner smaller and erect   ..   ..   **2. Iris**
    Flowers not more than 3 cm across; perianth-segments
        spreading, all alike   ..   ..   ..   **1. Sisyrhinchium**

1. Sisyrhinchium

1. Sisyrhinchium bermudiana (*S. angustifolium*). **Blue-eyed grass. 6-7.**
Rhizome short and slender. Stems up to 40 cm, more or less erect, narrowly winged.
Leaves 7-15 cm x 2-5 mm, rather pale bluish-green. Flowers in small, umbel-like
cymes of 2-5; usually two of these cymes on each stem, each subtended by two
bracts. Flowers 15-20 mm across, open only in sunshine. Perianth-segments oblong,
violet-blue, united at the base to form a very short tube. Filaments united, forming a
tube around the style. Capsule bluntly 3-angled, drooping, blackish. *Damp grassland
and stony lake-shores in the West and Centre; occasional in Kerry, rare elsewhere.*
    Believed to be native, though otherwise known only from North America;
confusion has been caused, however, by the occurrence of another, very similar
American species as an introduction in many parts of Europe.
    * *S. californicum*, naturalised from gardens in County Wexford and by Lough
Corrib, is similar, but more greyish-green, larger in all its parts, and with yellow
flowers 25-30 mm in diameter.

2. Iris

Rootstock a thick, fleshy rhizome. Flowers in short, terminal and axillary cymes.
Outer perianth-segments broad, drooping, the inner narrower, erect. Style-branches
broad, petal-like, concealing the stamens.

1. Flowers dull yellow or purplish; inner perianth segments nearly
        as long as the outer   ..   ..   ..   **1. I. foetidissima**
    Flowers bright yellow; inner perianth-segments less than half as
        long as the outer   ..   ..   ..   **2. I. pseudacorus**

1. * Iris foetidissima. Gladdon, Stinking iris. 6-7. Leaves dark green, unpleasant-smelling when bruised. Flowers 8 cm across, dull purple tinged with dull yellow
(rarely entirely pale yellow). Erect perianth-segments nearly as long as the outer,
drooping ones, but much narrower. Seeds bright orange, remaining long in dehisced
capsule before falling. *Banks, thickets and sandy shores; rather rare.* Usually, and
perhaps always, an escape from cultivation.

2. I. pseudacorus. Yellow flag. *Feileastram.* **6-7.** Leaves rather pale green,
odourless, up to 100 cm long. Flowers 8-10 cm across, bright yellow. Erect perianth-
segments only half as long as the outer, drooping ones. Seeds dull brown. *Ditches,
marshes and wet fields; abundant.*

3. Crocosmia

* **Crocosmia x crocosmiflora** (*Tritonia crocosmiflora*). **Montbretia. 7-9.** Stems
simple, up to 100 cm high, swollen at the base to form a corm, often with persistent
corms of previous years below it. Leaves shorter than the stem, arising from its lower
part. Flowers stalkless, in terminal, one-sided spikes or panicles. Perianth bright
orange, funnel-shaped, slightly curved downwards; lobes spreading, slightly unequal,
about as long as the tube. *Woods, river-banks and roadside verges; locally abundant
in the South and West, occasional elsewhere, mainly on acid soils.* A hybrid of
garden origin between two species, both native of South Africa.

CXXIV. JUNCACEAE

Herbs, usually perennial. Leaves alternate or basal, sometimes reduced to scale-like sheaths. Flowers hermaphrodite, regular, in often crowded cymes. Perianth inconspicuous, membranous, whitish or brownish, consisting of 6 free segments in two whorls of 3. Stamens 6, rarely 3. Ovary superior, 1- or 3-celled. Style single; stigmas 3. Fruit a small capsule.

1. Plant hairless. Capsule with more than 3 seeds   ..   ..   **1. Juncus**
    Leaves fringed with long, white, silky hairs. Capsule with 3 seeds   **2. Luzula**

1. Juncus. Rush. *Luachair*

Leaves hairless, seldom flat and grass-like, often cylindrical and stiff, resembling the stems. Capsule with numerous seeds.

1. Normal green leaves absent; all leaves reduced to short, brown
     sheaths at the base of the stems   2
    Some green leaves present (sometimes cylindrical and looking like
     the stems   4

2. Stems bluish-green, hard and tough, the pith in their centre
     interrupted by air-spaces   ..   ..   .. **3. J. inflexus**
    Stems not bluish-green, soft and easily broken, the pith in their
     centre continuous   3

3. Stem immediately below the inflorescence glossy and smooth,
     with more than 30 low, inconspicuous ridges; inflorescence
     diffuse (rarely compact) [Fig. CXXIVa]   ..   **4. J. effusus**
    Stem immediately below the inflorescence with about 30
     conspicuous ridges, not glossy; inflorescence compact
     [Fig. CXXIVb]   ..   ..   **5. J. conglomeratus**

4. Leaves cylindrical, similar to the stems in general appearance   ..   5
    Leaves with two distinct surfaces, though sometimes the upper
     is deeply channelled   10

5. Leaves solid, with stiff, spinous points   6
    Leaves hollow, with internal partitions; points neither spinous nor
     very stiff   7

6. Perianth-segments greenish-brown, slightly shorter than the capsule
     [Fig. CXXIVc]   ..   ..   ..   **1. J. maritimus**
    Perianth-segments reddish-brown, only half as long as the capsule
     [Fig. CXXIVd]   ..   ..   ..   **2. J. acutus**

7. Leaves less than 1 mm wide, soft and flexible, without conspicuous
     internal partitions; rhizome absent, but base of stem usually
     swollen   ..   ..   **15. J. bulbosus**
    Leaves at least 1.5 mm wide, fairly stiff, with conspicuous internal
     partitions, giving them a jointed appearance when dry; creeping
     rhizome present   8

8. Perianth-segments straw-coloured, all obtuse   ..   **14. J. subnodulosus**
    Perianth-segments brown or black, at least the outer ones pointed   9

9. Perianth-segments medium brown, all sharply pointed, the points
     often incurved [Fig. CXXIVe]   ..   ..   **16. J. acutiflorus**
    Perianth-segments very dark brown or black, the outer sharply
     pointed, with straight points, the inner obtuse or moderately
     acute [Fig. CXXIVf]   ..   ..   ..   **17. J. articulatus**

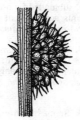

Fig. CXXIVa   Fig. CXXIVb

Fig. CXXIVc   Fig. CXXIVd   Fig. CXXIVe   Fig. CXXIVf

10. Leaves flat, soft and grass-like, 3-7 mm wide .. **13. J. planifolius**
    Leaves less than 3 mm wide, often channelled 11

11. Annual; inflorescence very diffuse, occupying much of the stem .. 12
    Perennial; inflorescence fairly compact 14

12. Leaves at least 1.5 mm wide; anthers longer than filaments; seeds
    with conspicuous longitudinal ridges.. .. **11. J. foliosus**
    Leaves less than 1.5 mm wide; anthers shorter than filaments or
    equalling them; seeds not or obscurely ridged 13

13. Capsule shorter than the inner perianth-segments .. **10. J. bufonius**
    Capsule at least as long as the inner perianth-segments **12. J. ranarius**

14. Leaves all basal (except for a bract at the base of the inflorescence),
    forming a dense rosette .. .. **6. J. squarrosus**
    Some stem-leaves present; basal leaves not forming a rosette .. 15

15. Inflorescence overtopped by at least two bracts; perianth-segments
    sharply pointed .. .. **9. J. tenuis**
    Inflorescence overtopped by one bract or none; perianth-segments
    obtuse, often with hooded tip 16

16. Capsule only slightly longer than perianth-segments **7. J. gerardii**
    Capsule about twice as long as perianth-segments .. **8. J. compressus**

1. Juncus maritimus. 7-8. Stems 40-90 cm high, densely tufted, stiff and wiry, ending in a sharp point. Leaves all basal, similar to the stems, except a few of the lowest which are reduced to membranous sheaths. Flowers greenish-brown, in a fairly diffuse panicle, subtended by a bract which looks like the continuation of the stem. Perianth-segments acute, about as long as the capsule [Fig. CXXIVc]. *Salt-marshes and sandy shores; very frequent.*

2. J. acutus. 6-7. Like *J. maritimus*, but taller (up to 150 cm); stems stouter, stiffer, and with a sharp, spinous point; flowers dark brown, in a rather more compact panicle; perianth-segments obtuse, only half as long as the capsule [Fig. CXXIVd]. *Sandy and muddy sea-shores in the South and East (West Cork to Dublin Bay); rather rare.*

3. J. inflexus. 6-8. Stems bluish-green, densely tufted, wiry and tough, not more than 1.5 mm in diameter, ridged, with interrupted pith. Leaves all reduced to glossy, dark brown sheaths. Inflorescence terminal (but subtended by a bract looking like the continuation of the stem, and therefore appearing lateral), consisting of a slender, rather diffuse panicle with suberect branches. Perianth-segments pale brown, acute, about as long as the capsule. *Wet fields and ditches, usually on limestone or heavy clay soils; abundant in the Centre; local elsewhere.*

4. J. effusus. Common rush. 7-8. Stems tufted, dark green, glossy, up to 100 cm high and 3-4 mm in diameter, with numerous very fine ridges, soft and easily broken; pith continuous. Leaves reduced to reddish-brown sheaths at the base of the stems. Inflorescence as in *J. inflexus*, but usually more widely spreading, rarely compact and more or less spherical. Perianth-segments brown, usually tinged with green, acute, about as long as the capsule [Fig. CXXIVa]. *Ditches, marshes, streamsides, damp fields and roadsides; abundant.*

Hybrids with *J. inflexus* (*J.* x *diffusus*) are occasionally found.

5. J. conglomeratus. 7-8. Very like *J. effusus*, but with stems somewhat shorter and more slender, and much more obviously ridged (especially just below the inflo-rescence), not glossy, and with a characteristic limp and dry feel; inflorescence usually very compact and more or less spherical, more rarely of several stalked heads [Fig. CXXIVb]. *Moorland and damp, upland pastures, mainly on acid, rather poor soils; frequent.*

6. J. squarrosus. 6-7. Stems stiff, slender, 10-30 cm high, leafless, arising from a rosette-like tuft of numerous horizontal, basal leaves, which are short, stiff, shining and channelled. Flowers in small clusters in a lax inflorescence. Perianth-segments brown, with whitish margins, subacute, slightly longer than the capsule. *Moors and other moist, peaty places; very frequent in mountain districts, rather rare elsewhere.*

7. J. gerardii. 6-8. Stems slender, up to 60 cm high, arising from a creeping rhizome. Leaves narrow, channelled, partly basal, but some from higher on the stem. Flowers in a slender, rather lax panicle; lowest bract usually shorter than the inflores-cence. Perianth-segments pale brown, obtuse, nearly as long as the capsule. *Wet places by the sea; very frequent.*

8. J. compressus. 6-7. Very like *J. gerardii*, but with a broader panicle, which is usually shorter than the lowest bract, and with the perianth-segments only half as long as the capsule. *Damp grassland; known only from two stations in Louth and Roscommon, but perhaps overlooked elsewhere.*

9. * J. tenuis (*J. macer*). **7-8.** Stems very slender and wiry, up to 60 cm high. Leaves all basal or nearly so, very narrow, channelled. Flowers greenish, in a loose, terminal panicle, overtopped by two or three slender, leaf-like bracts. Perianth-segments slender, pointed, longer than the more or less spherical capsule. *Damp roadsides, tracks and paths; widespread but very local.* Native of North America. Very intermittent in its appearances in different districts.

10. J. bufonius. Toad rush. 7-8. A small, pale green annual with fibrous roots and numerous slender, erect or spreading, tufted stems up to 35 cm high. Leaves mainly, but not entirely basal, very slender, channelled. Flowers in a much-branched, leafy panicle occupying much of the plant. Perianth-segments 6-8 mm, green, pointed, somewhat longer than the capsule. Anthers usually shorter than the filaments. Seeds smooth or very faintly ridged. *Damp, muddy places; abundant.*

11. J. foliosus. 7-8. Very like *J. bufonius*, but often stouter; perianth-segments about equalling the capsule, usually with a dark line on either side of the midrib; anthers much longer than the filaments; seeds with conspicuous longitudinal ridges. *Similar habitats; frequent in the South and West, rare elsewhere.*

12. J. ranarius (*J. ambiguus*). **7-8.** Like *J. bufonius*, but rather smaller; perianth-segments 4-6 mm, obtuse, slightly shorter than the capsule. *Salt-marshes and other damp habitats, usually near the coast; occasional.*

13. * J. planifolius. 6-7. Stems slender, erect, 20-45 cm. Leaves all basal, 3-7 mm wide, shorter than the stem, flat and grass-like. Flowers in numerous stalked, compact heads, disposed in a lax inflorescence. Perianth-segments shorter than the capsule, the outer acute, the inner obtuse. Stamens 3. *Streamsides, ditches and wet bogs; locally frequent in a restricted region of South Connemara.* Native of Australia and South America; introduced by unknown means.

14. J. subnodulosus. 8-9. Stems erect, about 100 cm high, arising singly from a creeping rhizome. Lowest leaves reduced to brown sheaths; above these are 1 or 2 cylindrical stem-leaves, similar to the stems but hollow, and with transverse internal partitions, which gives them a jointed (bamboo-like) appearance when dry. Flowers pale brown, in a diffuse inflorescence with widely spreading branches. Perianth-segments obtuse, slightly shorter than the capsule. *Fens and calcareous marshes; also more rarely on acid blanket-bog; frequent in the West and Centre, rare elsewhere.*

15. J. bulbosus. 6-8. Stems spreading, prostrate or floating, more rarely erect, swollen at the base, without rhizome. Leaves slender, usually channelled, often with inconspicuous internal partitions, but not appearing jointed. Flowers dark brown, in compact clusters, arranged in a diffuse, terminal cyme. Perianth-segments acute, equalling or shorter than the capsule. Stamens 3 or 6. *Bogs, pools, ditches and lake-margins, usually on peaty soils; frequent to abundant.*

When growing submerged in water, the stem is very long, often rooting at the nodes, the leaves are very slender, and the plant is often viviparous, with some of the flowers replaced by leafy buds.

16. J. acutiflorus. 7-9. Stems erect, 60-90 cm high, from a creeping rhizome. Lower leaves reduced to brown sheaths; above these are 2-3 cauline leaves, cylindrical, hollow, with internal transverse partitions, giving a jointed appearance, as in *J. subnodulosus*. Flowers medium brown, in compact heads arranged in a loose inflorescence with suberect branches. Perianth-segments sharply pointed, about as long as the capsule, which is tapered gradually to a long point [Fig. CXXIVe]. *Bog-margins, acid marshes and wet fields and woods; very frequent.*

17. J. articulatus. 7-8. Like *J. acutiflorus*, but stems seldom more than 50 cm high, tufted, from a very short rhizome; cauline leaves more numerous, somewhat flattened, hollow and with internal partitions, but with a less obviously jointed appearance; perianth-segments dark brown, the outer pointed, the inner obtuse to subacute, all shorter than the capsule, which is glossy, black and suddenly narrowed to a short point [Fig. CXXIVf]. *Marshes, wet fields, lake-shores and roadsides; abundant.*

Hybrids between the last two species are fairly common. They are usually sterile, but capable of vigorous vegetative growth.

2. Luzula. Wood-rush

Perennials, with flat, soft, grass-like leaves edged with long, fine, silky hairs, growing in drier places than most species of *Juncus*. Perianth-segments brown, acute. Stamens 6. Ovary 1-celled, containing 3 seeds, which often bear a white, soft appendage.

1. Flowers borne singly, most of them on long pedicels .. **4. L. pilosa**
   Flowers in clusters, on very short pedicels 2
2. Lower leaves up to 20 mm wide .. .. **3. L. sylvatica**
   Leaves not more than 6 mm wide 3
3. Filaments usually much shorter than anthers; seeds nearly
   spherical .. .. **1. L. campestris**
   Filaments almost as long as anthers; seeds nearly twice as long
   as broad .. .. **2. L. multiflora**

1. Luzula campestris. 4-5. Plant with a shortly creeping rhizome; stems 10-25 cm high. Leaves shorter than stem, 3-5 mm wide. Flowers in dense clusters of 3-8, arranged to form a small, more or less umbel-like inflorescence. Perianth-segments 2.5-3.5 mm long. Filaments usually much shorter than anthers. Seeds (including appendage) more or less globular. *Dry pastures and banks; very frequent.*

2. L. multiflora. 5-6. Like *L. campestris*, but rhizome absent and stems densely tufted; leaves slightly broader; filaments almost as long as the anthers, and seeds considerably longer than broad. *Moors, upland heaths and bog-margins; very frequent.*

At least two subspecies occur:

Subsp. *hibernica*, in which the flower-clusters are all clearly stalked, the basal leaves usually less than 3 mm wide and the seeds up to 1.1 mm long with an appendage 0.25 mm long is widespread in western Ireland. The occurrence of subsp. *multiflora*, which is very similar but has basal leaves more than 3 mm wide, somewhat larger capsules and seeds with an appendage about 0.5 mm long awaits confirmation.

Subsp. *congesta*, in which the flower-clusters are stalkless, forming a compact, lobed head, and the seeds are at least 1.2 mm long.

L. pallescens (*L. pallidula*), similar but with smaller flowers, the petals of which are of distinctly different sizes, known only from one locality in Antrim, appears extinct.

3. L. sylvatica. 5-6. Larger than the two preceeding species, with stems up to 75 cm high and leaves 15-30 cm long and up to 20 mm wide. Inflorescence large and diffuse, with numerous mostly long-stalked clusters of 2-5 flowers. Filaments very much shorter than anthers. Appendage of seeds very small and inconspicuous. *Woods, thickets, glens and mountain-ledges; frequent.*

4. L. pilosa. Stems fairly densely tufted, 20-25 cm high. Basal leaves 6 mm wide, about as long as the stem; stem-leaves similar but narrower. Flowers borne singly, not in clusters, on long, slender pedicels, forming a lax, terminal panicle. Filaments somewhat shorter than the anthers. Perianth-segments shorter than the capsule. Seeds with basal appendage more than 1 mm long. *Woods and other shady places; fairly frequent in the North and East, rare elsewhere.*

CXXV.   ERIOCAULACEAE

Eriocaulon aquaticum (*Eriocaulon septangulare*). **Pipewort. 7-8.** A submerged perennial, with a dense basal rosette of linear, pointed, soft, translucent leaves 5-8 cm long and white, transversely banded, worm-like roots. Flowering stems erect, simple, leafless, ridged, bearing, above the surface, a terminal, button-like head, about 12 mm across, of numerous, minute, whitish-grey. monoecious flowers; interspersed with black, chaffy bracts often covered in short, white hairs. Usually with the male flowers in the centre of the head and the female at the margin. Perianth of 4 segments (sometimes partly fused), often fringed with short hairs; stamens 4; ovary 2-lobed; styles 2. *Bog-pools and lakes near the West coast; very local, but frequent in some districts.*

CXXVI.   GRAMINEAE   (POACEAE).   GRASSES

Herbs, mostly perennial, of characteristic habit, with hollow, cylindrical, usually unbranched stems, swollen and solid at the nodes. Leaves alternate, in 2 ranks, narrow-linear, undivided, the lower part sheathing the stem. This sheath is usually split for its whole length down the side opposite the origin of the blade, but remains intact in some species. At the junction of the blade and sheath is usually present on the inner side, pressed against the stem, a small membranous appendage, the *ligule* (Fig. CXXVIa). At its base the blade may be clasping in the form of an *auricle* [Glos. Fig. 3]. Flowers small, mostly hermaphrodite, in small *spikelets*, which are arranged in terminal spikes, racemes or panicles. Each spikelet consists of 1-10 (rarely more) flowers, arranged in 2 ranks, each enclosed between 2 small, chaffy bracts, of which the inner (next to the axis of the spikelet), called the *palea*, is usually smaller and more membranous than the outer, known as the *lemma* (Fig. CXXVIb). Often, arising from the back, or sometimes the tip, of the lemma is a bristle-like projection, the *awn* (Fig. CXXVIb). At the base of the spikelet, below the flowers, or sometimes enclosing them, are usually 2 *glumes* (Fig. CXXVIb); the glumes may also, on occasion, bear awns. Perianth reduced to minute, scarcely visible scales; stamens 3 (fewer in *Anthoxanthemum* and some species of *Vulpia*), with long, slender filaments; ovary 1-celled, superior; styles 2, ending in long, very feathery stigmas. Fruit a *caryopsis*, i.e. an achene in which the pericarp is fused with the seed-coat; it is usually enclosed in the persistent lemma and palea.

Cultivated members of this family include all the cereals, such as Wheat (*Triticum*), Barley (*Hordeum*), Oats (*Avena*), Rye (*Secale*) and Maize (*Zea*); also the Pampas-grass, (*Cortederia*), grown for decoration.

1. Ligule represented by a line of hairs only (with no membranous
        portion at all)   2
    Ligule entirely or almost entirely membranous, or absent   ..   5
2. Spikelets stalkless or nearly so; plants of mud-flats only   ..   **46. Spartina**
    Spikelets distinctly stalked   3

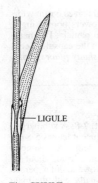

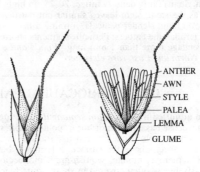

LIGULE

ANTHER
AWN
STYLE
PALEA
LEMMA
GLUME

Fig. CXXVIa

Fig. CXXVIb

Fig. CXXVIc   Fig. CXXVId   Fig. CXXVIe

3. Tall reed, with leaves more than 10 mm wide   ..   **42. Phragmites**
    Leaves not more than 10 mm wide   4
4. Inflorescence narrow but freely branched and open with numerous
        spikelets; glumes shorter than lemmas   ..   ..   **44. Molinia**
    Inflorescence unbranched or very slightly branched but still not open;
        glumes as long as lemmas and enclosing them   ..   **43. Danthonia**
5. Spikelets stalkless, or with very short stalks, in a simple spike, or a
        crowded and compact spike-like panicle (Fig. CXXVIc)   ..   6
    Spikelets distinctly stalked, or if stalkless, arranged in a distinctly
        branched inflorescence (Fig. CXXVId)   25
6. Spikelets with only 1 flower containing stamens or ovary (sometimes
        lemmas or other sterile rudiments of other flowers are present)   7
    Spikelets with 2 or more flowers containing stamens, and usually
        an ovary as well   16
7. Spikelets without awns   8
    Awns present on the lemmas or glumes or both   10

8. Robust, rhizomatous perennial; leaves with inrolled margins,
    up to 50 cm long; plant of sandy areas by the coast only   **34. Ammophila**
   Small annual; leaves flat, not more than 7 cm long   9
9. Inflorescence cylindrical but slightly bushy; spikelets very shortly
    stalked   ..   ..   **37. Phleum**
   Inflorescence very narrowly cylindrical; spikelets stalkless,
    embedded in an excavation in the axis   ..   **39. Parapholis**
10. Inflorescence dense, egg-shaped, white and fluffy; lemmas with
    two apical bristles and a long, very obvious awn   ..   ..   **35. Lagurus**
   Inflorescence not white and fluffy; lemmas not as described above   11
11. Lower leaves hairy, at least on the sheaths   12
   All leaves hairless   14
12. Awn arising from the back of the lemmas (from noticably below
    their tip)   ..   ..   ..   **31. Anthoxanthum**
   Glumes (and lemmas) tapered to an awn-like tip   13
13. All spikelets fertile, inserted in groups of 3 on the axis   **21. Hordelymus**
   Only the central spikelet of each group of 3 fertile; lateral
    spikelets consisting of 2 glumes and a lemma, all very narrow   **20. Hordeum**
14. Spikelets distinct, in a slender, 1-sided, comb-like spike; glumes
    absent   ..   ..   **45. Nardus**
   Spikelets crowded and overlapping, in a dense cylindrical spike;
    all spikelets with glumes   15
15. Glumes with a terminal (sometimes rather short) awn; lemma obtuse **37. Phleum**
   Glumes without an awn; lemma with a long awn, arising from near
    the base   ..   ..   **38. Alopecurus**
16. Spikelets less than 10 mm long (excluding awns)   17
   Spikelets more than 10 mm long (excluding awns)   21
17. Spikelets distinct, scarcely overlapping   18
   Spikelets crowded, overlapping, not easily seen as units without
    dissection   19
18. Plant not more than 15 cm high; leaves without auricles; all
    spikelets with 2 glumes   ..   ..   **4. Catapodium marinum**
   Plant usually more than 15 cm high; leaves with auricles; inner
    glume missing from all spikelets except the terminal one   ..   **2. Lolium**
19. Leaves downy   ..   ..   **26. Koeleria**
   Leaves hairless   20
20. Inflorescence slender, one-sided, forming a half-cylinder, green;
    leaves gradually tapered to the long, fine tip; ligule entirely
    membranous   ..   ..   ..   **8. Cynosurus**
   Inflorescence ovoid, symmetrical, bluish at flowering time; leaves
    abruptly narrowed to the tip; ligule membranous but capped with
    a minute fringe of hairs   ..   ..   **11. Sesleria**
21. Lemmas with awn inserted on back, some distance from tip   **25. Gaudinia**
   Lemmas without an awn, or with awn arising from the tip   ..   22
22. Spikelets very shortly stalked   ..   ..   **17. Brachypodium**
   Spikelets stalkless, set in a notch in the spike-axis (Fig. CXXVIe)   23
23. Spikelets arranged with the narrow-side of each spikelet against the
    spike-axis; inner glumes missing from all spikelets except the
    terminal one   ..   ..   **2. Lolium**
   Spikelets arranged with the flat side of each spikelet next to the
    spike-axis; all spikelets with 2 glumes   24

24. Spikelets inserted singly on the spike-axis; glumes and lemmas
   hairless   ..   ..   **19. Agropyron**
   Spikelets inserted on the spike-axis in groups of 2 or 3; glumes
   and lemmas downy   ..   .. **18. Leymus**

25. Spikelets with tufts of silky hairs between the glumes and the
   flower   ..   ..   **36. Calamagrostis**
   Hairs between glumes and flowers minute or absent   ..   26

26. Awns present (on lemmas or glumes)   27
   Awns absent   37

27. Awns arising from tip of lemmas   28
   Awns arising someway down the back of lemmas   29

28. Spikelets not crowded in dense clusters ..   ..   **1etc. Festuca-group**
   Spikelets in lower part of panicle crowded in dense clusters at the
   ends of bare branches   ..   ..   **7. Dactylis**

29. Spikelets 1-flowered   30
   Spikelets with 2-4 flowers   31

30. Panicle compact and spike-like; spikelets 6-10 mm long; glumes
   very unequal   ..   ..   ..   **32. Anthoxanthum**
   Panicle open and diffuse; spikelets not more than 4 mm long;
   glumes nearly equal   ..   ..   ..   **33. Agrostis**

31. Spikelets at least 8 mm long (excluding awns)   32
   Spikelets no more than 7 mm long (excluding awns)   ..   34

32. Annual; larger glume at least 20-25 mm long   ..   **22. Avena**
   Perennial; larger glume not more than 15 mm long   33

33. Leaves hairy, at least on the sheaths   ..   ..   **23. Avenula**
   Leaves hairless   ..   ..   **24. Arrhenatherum**

34. Leaves hairless   35
   Leaves hairy, at least on the sheaths   36

35. Annual, not more than 25 cm high   ..   ..   **29. Aira**
   Perennial, at least 30 cm high   ..   ..   **28. Deschampsia**

36. Glumes hairy, pink or whitish-green, not shining. Ligule often fairly
   large and conspicuous   ..   ..   ..   **32. Holcus**
   Glumes hairless, shining, yellowish. Ligule small and
   inconspicuous   ..   .. **27. Trisetum**

37. Leaves hairy, at least on the sheaths   38
   Leaves hairless   39

38. Leaf-sheaths not split at the top; ligule prolonged at the tip into a
   sharp point on the opposite side to the leaf-blade; spikelets very
   widely spaced in a very open panicle   ..   ..   **12. Melica**
   Leaf-sheaths split; ligule not as described above; spikelets crowded,
   in a dense panicle   ..   ..   **32. Holcus**

39. Spikelets 1-flowered   40
   Spikelets with 2 or more flowers   43

40. Glumes less than half as long as the lemma   ..   .. **9. Catabrosa**
   Glumes equalling or exceeding the lemma and enclosing it   ..   41

41. Spikelets crowded in a dense panicle; stem stout, 75-200 cm high   **40. Phalaris**
   Spikelets well spaced-out, in a diffuse panicle; stem slender, seldom
   over 75 cm high   42

42. Glumes keeled (spikelets compressed from side to side), firmer than
    the lemma ..   .. **33. Agrostis**
    Glumes flat or rounded (spikelets weakly compressed from the
    front to the back), more delicate than lemma   ..   .. **41. Milium**

43. Spikelets blue at flowering-time; leaves abruptly narrowed to the
    tip; ligule membranous but capped with a minute fringe of hairs **11. Sesleria**
    Spikelets not blue at flowering-time; leaves tapered more or less
    gradually to the tip; ligule entirely membranous 44

44. Spikelets about as broad as long   45
    Spikelets distinctly longer than broad 46

45. Spikelets with 3 flowers, of which 2 (the lower 2) are male; leaves
    up to 10 mm wide; (Lough Neagh only)   .. **30. Hierochloë**
    Spikelets with 4-10 flowers, all hermaphrodite; leaves 2-3 mm wide;
    widespread..   ..   .. **10. Briza**

46. Glumes and lemmas acute ..   ..   .. **1etc. Festuca-group**
    Glumes and lemmas rounded or truncate at tip   47

47. Glumes much shorter than lemmas   ..   .. **.. 9. Catabrosa**
    Glumes about as long as lemmas   ..   .. **1etc. Festuca-group**

1 etc. Festuca-group

(In this group of grasses the distinctive features of each genus are rather technical
and difficult for the beginner; it is simplest therefore to provide a unified key for
them all. For each species in this key the generic number is followed by the species
number (1.1 therefore indicates the first species in the first grass genus - in this case
Festuca altissima). However for those who feel more confident, at the head of the
account for each genus in this group is also provided a key to the species.)

Key to species of *Festuca, Vulpia, Catapodium, Poa, Puccinellia, Glyceria, Bromus, Bromopsis and Anisantha.*

1. Spikelets viviparous   2
    Spikelets not viviparous 3

2. Leaves very narrow and bristle-like   ..   .. **1.7 Festuca vivipara**
    Leaves broad and flat   ..   ..   .. **5.8 Poa alpina**

3. Stem or leaves hairy or downy, at least towards the base   .. 4
    Plant hairless throughout 14

4. Basal leaves very narrow and bristle-like   .. **1.5 Festuca rubra**
    All leaves flat and fairly broad   5

5. Spikelets ovoid, turgid, with rather broad, closely packed glumes 6
    Spikelets slender, with narrow, loosely packed glumes   .. 10

6. Lemmas not more than 6.5 mm long   7
    Lemmas at least 6.5 mm long   8

7. Panicle rather open, with some branches (peduncles) longer
    than their spikelets; lemmas wrapped tightly around the
    caryopsis in fruit and so not obscuring the axis of the
    spikelet   ..   ..   .. **14.5 Bromus pseudosecalinus**
    Panicle fairly compact, with all branches (peduncles) shorter than
    their spikelets; lemmas not wrapped around the caryopsis in
    fruit and so obscuring the axis of the spikelet   .. **14.2 Bromus lepidus**

8. Panicle compact, with some of the spikelets almost
    stalkless   ..   ..   .. **14.1 Bromus hordeaceus**
    Panicle long and loose; all peduncles longer than their spikelet .. 9

9. Lemmas more than 8 mm long; anthers 1-1.5 mm
    long   ..   ..   ..   **14.3 Bromus commutatus**
    Lemmas less than 8 mm long; anthers 2-3 mm long   **14.4 Bromus racemosus**
10. Lower lemmas shorter than their awn   11
    Lower lemmas longer than their awn   13
11. Awns 30 mm or more in length; lemmas more than
    20 mm   ..   ..   ..   **16.3 Anisantha diandra**
    Awns less than 30 mm long; lemmas 10-20 mm   12
12. Panicle lax, the branches spreading or drooping   ..   **16.1 Anisantha sterilis**
    Panicle dense, the branches sub-erect to erect   **16.2 Anisantha madritensis**
13. Spikelets nodding, at the ends of long branches   ..   **15.1 Bromopsis ramosa**
    Spikelets erect, in a compact panicle   ..   ..   **15.2 Bromopsis erecta**
14. Lemmas or glumes with awns   15
    Lemmas or glumes without awns   20
15. Awns at least as long as lemmas   16
    Awns shorter than lemmas   19
16. Stem usually more than 70 cm high   ..   ..   **1.2 Festuca gigantea**
    Stem less than 50 cm high   17
17. Lower glume minute (1 mm) or absent. Lemma distinctly
    keeled   ..   ..   ..   **3.3 Vulpia fasciculata**
    Both glumes present, the smaller at least $^1/5$ the length of
    the larger. Lemma with poorly-defined midrib   18
18. Flowering stem ridged. Lower glume 2.5-5 mm, half to $^3/4$ as
    long as upper   ..   ..   ..   **3.1 Vulpia bromoides**
    Flowering stem almost smooth. Lower glume 0.4- 2.5 mm,
    about $^1/3$ as long as upper   ..   ..   **3.2. Vulpia myuros**
19. Lower leaves flat when fresh; plant usually at least 100 cm
    tall   ..   .. **1.4 Festuca arundinacea**
    Lower leaves very narrow and bristle-like; plant usually less
    than 100 cm tall   46
20. Annuals with hard, rigid stems, seldom over 15 cm high   ..   21
    Plant either exceeding 15 cm, or else with stem and leaves
    fairly soft and flexible   22
21. Inflorescence usually branched, some spikelets clearly
    stalked. Lemma 2-2.5 mm   ..   **4.1 Catapodium rigidum**
    Inflorescence usually unbranched, spikelets stalkless or
    very shortly stalked. Rachis stout, flattened, shiny.
    Lemma 2.5-3.5 mm   ..   ..   **4.2 Catapodium marinum**
22. Leaf-sheaths not split-open for most of their length   23
    Leaf-sheaths split-open for most of their length   30
23. Lower leaves narrow and bristle-like   ..   ..   **1.5 Festuca rubra**
    Lower leaves flat and fairly broad, though sometimes folded   ..   24
24. Spikelets 12-30 mm long   25
    Spikelets 3-12 mm long   27
25. Tip of lemma distinctly 3-toothed   ..   ..   **13.3 Glyceria declinata**
    Tip of lemma not toothed or only slightly lobed   26
26. Lemma 6-7 mm long   ..   ..   ..   **13.1 Glyceria fluitans**
    Lemma 4-5 mm long   ..   ..   ..   **13.2 Glyceria notata**

27. Spikelets usually with 5 or more flowers, 6-12 mm long   **13.4 Glyceria maxima**
    Spikelets with 2-5 flowers, 3-5 (rarely -6) mm long   ..   28

28. Plant rhizomatous, far-creeping; ligule of flowering shoot
    very short, usually cut-off square at top   ..   **5.4 Poa pratensis**
    Plant tufted, not rhizomatous; ligule of flowering shoot 2-5 mm
    long, pointed or somewhat rounded at tip   29

29. Ligule of flowering shoot 4 mm long or more; leaf-sheaths
    somewhat rough   ..   ..   ..   **5.2. Poa trivialis**
    Ligule of flowering shoot less than 4 mm long; leaf-sheaths
    smooth   ..   ..   ..   **5.3 Poa palustris**

30. Stem distinctly flattened   ..   ..   ..   **5.6 Poa compressa**
    Stem cylindrical   31

31. Annual, seldom over 25 cm high, with soft, bright green leaves
    often transversely wrinkled   ..   ..   **5.1 Poa annua**
    Perennial; either 30 cm high or more, or else forming a close turf
    or dense tufts   32

32. Plants of woods, meadows or grassy slopes   33
    Sea-shore plants   40

33. All leaves flat when fresh   34
    Lower leaves very narrow and bristle-like   46

34. Spikelets 3-8 mm long   35
    Spikelets 10-20 mm long   39

35. Ligule very short or absent   36
    Ligule conspicuous   37

36. Plant rhizomatous, far-creeping; lemmas pointed, with distinct
    veins; ligule more than 1 mm long   ..   ..   **5.4 Poa pratensis**
    Plant tufted, not far-creeping; lemmas blunt, scarcely veined;
    ligule less than 0.5 mm long   ..   ..   **5.7 Poa nemoralis**

37. Panicle branches arising in pairs or groups of 3; ligule ragged
    at tip   ..   ..   **1.1 Festuca altissima**
    Panicle branches arising in groups of 3-7; ligule pointed at tip   ..   38

38. Ligule of flowering shoot 4 mm long or more; leaf-sheaths
    somewhat rough   ..   ..   **5.2 Poa trivialis**
    Ligule of flowering shoot less than 4 mm long; leaf-sheaths
    smooth   ..   ..   **5.3 Poa palustris**

39. Branches of panicle arising in pairs, one bearing only 1 spikelet
    (Fig. CXXVIf)   ..   ..   ..   **1.3 Festuca pratensis**
    Branches of panicle arising in pairs; each bearing several
    spikelets (Fig. CXXVIg)   ..   ..   .. **1.4 Festuca arundinacea**

40. Lemmas blunt   41
    Lemmas sharply pointed   43

41. Plants spreading by extensive stolons; lemmas 3-5 mm
    long   ..   ..   ..   **6.1 Puccinellia maritima**
    Plants tufted; lemmas 2-2.5 mm long   42

42. Panicle branches spreading to deflexed, bare in their lower
    half. Midrib of lemma not reaching tip   ..   **6.2 Puccinellia distans**
    Panicle branches spreading to suberect, some with spikelets
    almost to the base. Midrib of lemma reaching tip **6.3 Puccinellia fasciculata**

43. Lower leaves flat when fresh   44
    Lower leaves very narrow and bristle-like   46

Fig. CXXVIf

Fig. CXXVIg

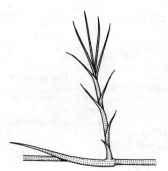

Fig. CXXVIh

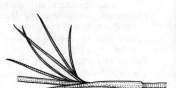

Fig. CXXVIi

44. Plant rhizomatous, far-creeping 45
   Plant tufted, not rhizomatous and not far-creeping though
      sometimes with short stolons .. .. **5.2 Poa trivialis**

45. Panicle branches often in groups of 3-4; leaf base hairless;
      glumes very unequal in size, the lower usually with 1 vein
      only (use hand-lens) .. .. .. **5.4 Poa pratensis**
   Panicle branches often in groups of 2-3; leaf base often hairy;
      glumes almost equal in size, both with 3 veins
      (use hand-lens) .. .. .. **5.5 Poa humilis**

46. Upper stem-leaves flat; plant spreading by rhizomes; tillers with
      sheaths fused up to the mouth, side shoots extravaginal that is
      arising at right angles from the parent shoot and immediately
      breaking through the sheath of the parent shoot
      (Fig. CXXVIh) .. .. .. **1.5 Festuca rubra**

All leaves bristle-like; plant in compact tufts; upper third of non-
flowering leaf-sheaths split and overlapping; all side shoots
intravaginal that is running parallel to the parent shoot, and
therefore enclosed within its sheath for some distance (Fig. CXXVIi) 47

47. Leaves hairless at base; awns absent or minute; spikelets less than
5.5 mm long; mainly Northern .. .. **1.8 Festuca filiformis**
Leaves often hairy at base; awns up to 1.5 mm; spikelets usually
more than 5.5 mm; ubiquitous .. .. **1.6 Festuca ovina**

1. Festuca

Perennials, usually hairless, without stolons. Infloresence composed of many-
flowered spikelets in a panicle. Glumes subequal. Lemmas pointed or awned, 3- to 5-
veined, rounded but not keeled.

1. Spikelets viviparous .. .. .. **7. F. vivipara**
   Spikelets not viviparous 2

2. Lower leaves very narrow and bristle-like 3
   All leaves flat when fresh 5

3. Upper stem-leaves flat; plant spreading by rhizomes; tillers with
   sheaths fused up to the mouth, side shoots extravaginal that is
   arising at right angles from the parent shoot and immediately
   breaking through the sheath of the parent shoot (Fig. CXXVIh) **5. F. rubra**
   All leaves bristle-like; plant in compact tufts; upper third of non-
   flowering leaf-sheaths split and overlapping; all side shoots intravaginal that is running parallel to the parent shoot, and therefore
   enclosed within its sheath for some distance (Fig. CXXVIi) .. 4

4. Leaves hairless at base; awns minute or absent; spikelets less than
   5.5 mm long; mainly Northern .. .. **8. F. filiformis**
   Leaves often hairy at base; awns up to 1.5 mm; spikelets usually
   more than 5.5 mm; ubiquitous .. .. .. **6. F. ovina**

5. Awns on lemma longer than lemma itself; stem usually more than
   70 cm high; nodes dark in colour .. .. **2. F. gigantea**
   Awns on lemma short or absent; stem usually less than 70 cm high;
   nodes not dark in colour 6

6. Spikelets 3-8 mm long .. .. .. **1. F. altissima**
   Spikelets 10-20 mm long 7

7. Branches of panicle arising in pairs, one bearing only 1 spikelet
   (Fig. CXXVIf) .. .. .. **3. F. pratensis**
   Branches of panicle arising in pairs; each bearing several
   spikelets (Fig. CXXVIg) .. .. **4. F. arundinacea**

1. Festuca altissima (*F. sylvatica*). **7.** A hairless tufted perennial. Stems stout,
erect, 70-130 cm high with scale-like sheaths at base. Leaves 6-12 mm broad, keeled,
tapered towards the sheaths, rough on the edges, lacking auricles; ligule *c.* 4 mm, tip
ragged. Spikelets yellowish green, 6 mm long, with 3-5 flowers, in a loose, open,
drooping panicle 10-15 cm long, with slender branches arising in pairs or groups of
3. Glumes small, slightly unequal; lemmas finely pointed, but awnless. *Woods and
shady glens; rare.*

2. F. gigantea (*Bromus giganteus, Lolium giganteum*). **7-8.** A hairless tufted
perennial, with smooth stems 60-150 cm high with dark patches on the nodes. Leaves
bright green, glossy, up to 50 cm long, harsh but limp, ridged, 8-15 mm broad,
drooping, with conspicuous auricles; ligule short. Panicle long and loose, slightly

nodding; spikelets pale green, lanceolate, 10-15 mm long, with 3-8 flowers; the branches arising in pairs. Awns as long as or longer than the lemmas, wavy. *Woods and thickets; widespread and locally frequent.*

3. F. pratensis (*Lolium pratense*). **6-7.** Stems 30-90 cm high. Leaves flat, ridged, up to 4 mm broad; ligule short; auricles hairless. Spikelets green or purple, 12-15 mm long, with 5-10 flowers, in a narrow panicle on paired branches, one bearing a single spikelet, the other several (Fig. CXXVIf). Spikelets 10-12 mm, linear to lanceolate. Glumes small, unequal; lemmas pointed, not awned. *Damp meadows and shady roadsides; frequent in the North-East and Centre, rarer elsewhere.*

x *Festulolium loliaceum*, a sterile hybrid between *Festuca pratensis* and *Lolium perenne*, occurs occasionally in damp meadows and on roadsides. It resembles the former in its hairless auricles, branched inflorescence, at least in the lower section and longer, laxer spikelets, the uppermost stalkless, the lower very shortly stalked with 2 unequal glumes. x *Festulolium braunii* (*F. pratensis* x *Lolium multiflorum*) which differs in its short-awned lemmas has been recorded on a few occasions.

4. F. arundinacea (*F. elatior, Lolium arundinaceum*). **6-7.** Stems 80-170 cm high, forming strong, dense tufts. Leaves stiff, rough, flat, 8-10 mm wide, hairless; auricles hairy, ligule short. Panicle broad with branches spreading in flower and fruit, bearing 3 or more spikelets on the shorter of each panicle branch (Fig. CXXVIg). Spikelets 10-12 mm, lanceolate to ovate. Lemmas pointed, sometimes shortly awned. *Meadows, roadsides and damp ground; very frequent.*

x *Festulolium holmbergii* (*F. arundinacea* x *Lolium perenne*) resembles x *Festulolium loliaceum*, from which it may be distinguished by its minutely hairy auricles.

5. F. rubra. Creeping red fescue. 6. Plants with slender creeping rhizomes, often forming loose mats. Tillers with sheaths fused up to the mouth, extravaginal (Fig. CXXVIh). Basal leaves bristle-like, sometimes hairy on the sheaths; stem leaves flat, 1-3 mm wide, without auricles; lower sheaths often reddish. Ligule very short. Spikelets 6-13 mm long, with 3-9 flowers. Lemmas 5-6 mm long. *Walls, sandy ground, salt marshes and dry waste places; abundant.*

A number of taxa usually treated as subspecies have been recorded from Ireland. Subsp. *rubra* with a well-developed rhizome system, forms loose patches with culms up to 75 cm and has green, usually folded leaves. Its spikelets are 7-10 mm long and it is widespread and common in a variety of inland and coastal habitats. Subsp. *juncea* (subsp. *pruinosa*) with short rhizomes forming tight clumps and strongly bluish green, narrow (less than 2.4 mm), rigid leaves and spikelets 7-10 mm, is locally frequent on sea cliffs and rocky shores. Subsp. *arenaria* with larger, hairy spikelets (8-14 mm) has extensive rhizomes and bluish-green leaves. Its upper leaf-ribs are minutely but densely hairy and their lower surfaces are rounded (keeled in subsp. *rubra*). It has been recorded from coasts in Dublin and Clare. Subsp. *commutata*, a densely tufted, usually hairless plant with upper glumes 3.5-6 mm and lemmas 5-6.5 mm is now widely sown in amenity grassland, especially on drier soils.

* *F. heterophylla*, similar but densely tufted, non-rhizomatous and with the ovary minutely hairy on top, is well-naturalised in deciduous woodland, at a single site in Co. Limerick and may be so elsewhere.

6. F. ovina. Sheep's fescue. 6-7. Plants densely tufted, lacking rhizomes, forming a close turf; stems usually 12-40 cm high. Leaves all alike, less than 4 mm wide with very small rounded auricles; ligule very short. Upper third of non-flowering leaf-sheaths split and overlapping; all tillers intravaginal (Fig. CXXVIi). Spikelets 4-9 mm long, with 3-8 flowers, arranged in a narrow panicle. Glumes slightly unequal, pointed; lemmas ending in a point or short awn less than a third of their length. *Heaths, dry pastures, mountains and sea-shores; abundant.*

At least two subspecies have been recognised from Ireland. Subsp. *ophioliticola* has larger spikelets (5.5-7.5 mm), lemmas (3.6-4.9 mm) and leaves with usually 7 veins. Subsp. *hirtula* has shorter spikelets, (5.3-6.3 mm), lemmas (3.1-4.2 mm) and the leaves have 5-7 veins.

The 2 records for *F. indegesta*, with stiffer, sharply pointed leaves and a longer awn to the lemma, from the Burren (Poulsallagh & Mullaghmore), require confirmation as recent authorities indicate they are an error.

7. F. vivipara. 6-7. Similar to *F. ovina* in leaves and habit, but with viviparous flowers is considered by some authors to be a variety of *F. ovina*. Other *Festuca* taxa also produce proliferous flowers. *Mainly on mountains, but descending to sea-level in the West; locally abundant.*

8. F. filiformis (*F. tenuifolia*). **6-7.** Resembles *F. ovina* but its leaves are narrower, hairless, and usually long in proportion to the culms and the ligule minute. The spikelets (less than 5.4 mm) and lemmas (less than 3.2 mm) are shorter and the awns may be very short or absent. Recorded mainly from the North; some of these records may refer to *F. ovina* subsp. *hirtula.*

2. Lolium. Rye-grass

Tufted, hairless annuals or perennials. Leaves flat, keeled or folded, with split often reddish sheaths, auricles and a short, obtuse ligule. Inflorescence a long slender spike, with the spikelets in 2 ranks, flattened, each seperately inset in an excavation in the axis, with its narrower edge adjoining the axis. Spikelets with several flowers; glumes usually 1, two on the terminal spikelet.

1.	Annual or biennial. Lemmas awned	..	..	.. 2
	Perennial. Lemmas awnless	..	..	**1. L. perenne**
2.	Lemmas remaining soft when mature	..	..	**2. L. multiflorum**
	Lemmas hardening at maturity	..	..	**3. L. temulentum**

1. Lolium perenne. Perennial rye-grass. 6-7. Perennial, with strong, tufted stems, 20-65 cm high. Leaves mostly basal, 2-5 mm broad, folded down the middle in bud. Spike 10-25 cm long; spikelets 10-20 mm long, tough, with 5-15 flowers pressed close against the spike-axis. Lemmas obtuse, awnless. *Meadows, roadsides and waste places; widely sown in amenity and agricultural grassland; abundant.*

2. * L. multiflorum (*L. italicum*). **Italian rye-grass. 6-7.** Annual or biennial, 35-80 cm high. Leaves 4-8 mm wide, spirally rolled in bud. Spike and spikelets longer and laxer than *L. perenne*, each lemma with a long, terminal awn. *Widely sown in meadows and occasionally naturalised at field-margins.*

3. * L. temulentum. 6-8. A stiff annual with prominently awned lemmas and glumes as long as or longer than the uppermost lemma. These are elliptic to ovate, and harden in fruit. *Formerly widespread throughout Ireland as a cornfield weed. Recently known only from the Aran Islands and East Mayo.*

3. Vulpia

Hairless, erect annuals with short, very narrow leaves with inrolled margins and a minute ligule. Inflorescence a narrow, shortly-branched panicle. Glumes unequal, pointed or awned, sometimes exceedingly short; lemmas tapered gradually to a long awn. Stamens often reduced to 2 or 1.

1. Lower glume minute (1 mm) or absent. Lemma distinctly
      keeled   ..   ..   **3. V. fasciculata**
   Both glumes present, the smaller at least $^1/_5$ the length of the
      larger. Lemma with poorly-defined midrib   2
2. Flowering stem ridged. Lower glume 2.5-5 mm, half to $^3/_4$ as
      long as upper   ..   ..   ..   **1. V. bromoides**
   Flowering stem almost smooth. Lower glume 0.4- 2.5 mm, about
      $^1/_3$ as long as upper   ..   ..   ..   **2. V. myuros**

1. Vulpia bromoides (*Festuca bromoides*). **6.** Stems 10-40 cm high, ridged.
Uppermost leaf 3 cm or more below the base of the inflorescence. Panicle rather
sparse, usually branched, up to 8 cm long. Spikelets shortly stalked, green, turning
brown, 10 mm long, with 4-6 flowers. Glumes pointed but not awned; the larger 1.5
to twice as long as the smaller, strongly nerved. Lemma with an awn twice its own
length. *Walls, dry banks, dry heathland and gravelly places; frequent in the South
and West, occasional elsewhere.*

2. † V. myuros (*Festuca myuros*). **6.** Stem smooth, 10-50 cm high. Panicle
sometimes lax, often curved or nodding, sometimes branched towards the base, and
often partly sheathed by the uppermost leaf. Larger glume 2.5-5 times as long as the
smaller and weakly nerved. *Walls and dry gravelly places; occasional in South half,
very rare in North.*

3. V. fasciculata (*V. membranacea, Festuca uniglumis*). **6.** 15-30 cm high.
Uppermost leaf usually well separated from the panicle, which is very narrow and
often reduced to a spike-like raceme. Spikelets 12-15 mm long, with 5-7 flowers, the
uppermost sterile and reduced. Lower glume minute (1 mm) or absent. Upper glume
10-14 mm long, excluding awn. Fertile lemmas 10-15 mm long, with 1 strong nerve
and an awn 20-25 mm long. *Bare sandy ground in dunes on the East coast (Louth to
Wexford); rare.*

4. Catapodium
Small, hairless annuals, with hard stiff stems. Ligule very short to short. Spikelets
many-flowered, in a spike or panicle. Glumes nearly equal; lemmas obtuse, not
keeled.
1. Inflorescence usually branched, some spikelets clearly stalked.
      Lemma 2-2.5 mm   ..   ..   ..   **1. C. rigidum**
   Inflorescence usually unbranched, spikelets stalkless or very
      shortly stalked. Rachis stout, flattened, shiny. Lemma
      2.5-3.5 mm ..   ..   **2. C. marinum**

1. Catapodium rigidum (*Desmazeria rigida, Festuca rigida*). **5-7.** Stems erect,
5-10 cm high. Leaves narrow, flat or with inrolled margins; ligule oval, ragged.
Spikelets narrow, 4-6 mm long, with 5-9 flowers, in a rather narrow stiff panicle
arranged in 1 plane. *Rocks, walls and dry places; very frequent in S. half, rare and
mainly coastal in North.*
Taller plants (to 20 cm) branching pyramidally have been named subsp. *majus.*

2. C. marinum (*Desmazeria marina, Festuca rottboellioides*). **6-7.** Stems
spreading-erect, wiry, 5-15 cm long. Leaves short, narrow but flat. Spikelets broadly
ovoid, 6 mm long, with 5-10 flowers, stalkless in a 1-sided spike, sometimes
branched towards the base. *Sea-shores, walls and dry waste places near the sea;
frequent but local.*

5. Poa. Meadow grass

Hairless, usually perennial. Spikelets flattened, with 2-9 flowers, arranged in a panicle. Glumes slightly unequal, keeled, pointed. Lemmas keeled, rather obtuse.

1. Spikelets viviparous .. .. **8. P. alpina**
   Spikelets not viviparous 2

2. Stem distinctly flattened; panicle often dark purple .. **6. P. compressa**
   Stem cylindrical; panicle usually not dark purple 3

3. Annual, seldom over 25 cm tall; with soft, bright green leaves
   often transversely wrinkled .. .. .. **1. P. annua**
   Perennial, either 30 cm tall or more, or else forming close turf or
   dense tufts; leaves not transversely wrinkled 4

4. Plant rhizomatous, far-creeping 5
   Plant tufted, not rhizomatous and not far-creeping though
   sometimes with short stolons 6

5. Panicle branches often in groups of 3-4; leaf base hairless;
   glumes very unequal in size, the lower usually with 1 vein
   only (use hand-lens) .. .. .. **4. P. pratensis**
   Panicle branches often in groups of 2-3; leaf base often hairy;
   glumes almost equal in size, both with 3 veins (use hand-lens) **5. P. humilis**

6. Ligule minute or absent, if present then usually cut-off square
   at the tip .. .. **7. P. nemoralis**
   Ligule 2-5 mm long, usually pointed or somewhat rounded at the tip 7

7. Ligule of flowering shoot 4 mm long or more; leaf-sheaths
   somewhat rough .. .. .. **2. P. trivialis**
   Ligule of flowering shoot less than 4 mm long; leaf-sheaths
   smooth .. .. **3. P. palustris**

1. Poa annua. 1-12. Annual, with smooth, rather weak, spreading stems, 5-20 cm high. Leaves soft, flat, often transversely wrinkled, 3-5 mm broad, pale green; sheaths split; ligule medium, 2-5 mm long, tip pointed. Spikelets oblong, 4 mm, with 3-7 flowers. Panicle loose, pyramidal, 5-8 cm long. Lemmas obtuse. *Pastures, tilled ground, roadsides and waste places; abundant.*

2. P. trivialis. 6-7. Rootstock not creeping; stems tufted, erect, 30-60 cm high, rough, especially at the top. Ligule long (4-6 mm), narrow, pointed (much shorter on non-flowering stems). Spikelets green or purple, 3-4 mm long, with 2-4 flowers, in a loose feathery panicle 5-10 cm long. Lemmas pointed with distinct veins. *Meadows, pastures and damp roadsides; abundant.*

3. * P. palustris 6-7. Resembles *P. trivialis*, but is taller, slenderer, with smooth leaf-sheaths. The ligule is shorter (2-4 mm) and less pointed. The panicle is much larger and more open with relatively few spikelets. *A fodder plant naturalised in damp places, especially in North half.*

4. P. pratensis. 6-7. Tufted or with rootstock shortly creeping; stems erect, smooth, cylindrical, fairly stout, 30-60 cm high. Leaves flat, rather stiff, about 3 mm broad, the blade of the uppermost shorter than its sheath, leaf-bases hairless. Sheaths entire, at least in lower part, smooth; ligule short. Spikelets green or purple, oval, 4-6 mm long with 3-5 flowers. Panicle usually pyramidal, loose, feathery, with the branches arising in groups of 3-6. Glumes somewhat unequal. Lemmas pointed, with fairly distinct veins. *Pastures, sandhills, banks and waste places; very common.*

5. P. humilis (*P. subcaerulea*). **6-7.** Similar to *P. pratensis* but smaller (to 30 cm), with more extensive rhizomes, leaf-bases usually minutely, though sometimes sparsely, hairy at the mouth of the sheath, glumes more or less equal and sharply pointed and panicle branches arising in pairs or in groups of 3 (rarely up to 5). *Damp ground, especially near the sea; common.*

6. * P. compressa. 6-7. Plant with distinct rhizomes; stems stiff, erect, smooth, 25-50 cm high, flattened, especially at the base. Leaves short, hairless, slightly bluish-green, 2-3 mm broad; sheaths split; ligule short. Panicle purplish or green, 1-sided, narrow, dense, stiff, 2-7 cm long. Spikelets oblong-lanceolate, 3-6 mm long, with 3-7 flowers. Lemmas somewhat pointed, faintly veined. *Old walls, dry stony places and roadsides; rare.*

7. † P. nemoralis. 6-7. Stems erect, loosely tufted, smooth and slender, 30-80 cm high. Leaves soft, thin, long, narrow (less than 2 mm), the blade of the uppermost longer than its sheath, often held at right-angles to the stem. Sheaths split; ligule very short. Spikelets pale green, oval, 3 mm long, with 2-5 flowers. Panicle sparse, rather narrow, with very slender branches. Lemmas obtuse, scarcely veined. *Woods and dry shady places, mainly in the East; occasional.*

8. P. alpina. 7-8. Tufted perennial. Leaves arising from a stout, shortly creeping, fibrous rootstock, 3-4 mm broad, short; ligule medium, blunt or pointed. Spikelets green, in an open or nodding panicle; usually viviparous. *Mountain cliff-edges in West (Brandon Mt. and Ben Bulben range); very rare.*

6. Puccinellia

Seashore plants with narrow leaves; sheaths split; ligule short, obtuse. Spikelets with 3-10 flowers, arranged in a panicle. Glumes unequal, bluntly keeled, obtuse. Lemmas obtuse, not keeled.

1.	Plants spreading by extensive stolons; lemmas 3-5 mm long	**1. P. maritima**
	Plants tufted; lemmas 2-2.5 mm long ..	2
2.	Panicle branches spreading to deflexed, bare in their lower half.	
	Midrib of lemma not reaching tip	**2. P. distans**
	Panicle branches spreading to suberect, some with spikelets	
	almost to the base. Midrib of lemma reaching tip ..	**3. P. fasciculata**

1. Puccinellia maritima (*Glyceria maritima*). **6-7.** Tufted, but with creeping stolons which sometimes form a close sward; stems erect, 15-30 cm high. Leaves usually with inrolled margins, slightly bluish-green. Panicle slender, with erect branches, especially after flowering, the lower ones normally arising in pairs. Spikelets green or purple, 7-11 mm long, with 5-10 flowers, distributed all along the branches; lemmas 3-5 mm, blunt or slightly pointed. *Salt-marshes and muddy or rocky seashores; very frequent.*

2. P. distans (*Glyceria distans*). **6-7.** Stems closely tufted, without stolons, 20-50 cm high. Leaves narrow, flat. Panicle broad, with long spreading branches deflexed in fruit, the lower ones bare towards the base. Spikelets green or purple, 4-6 mm, with 3-6 flowers; lemmas 2-2.5 mm, very blunt at the tip, the midribs not reaching the apex. *Salt-marshes and open ground near the sea; locally frequent on South, East and North-east coasts, very rare in North-west and West.*

3. P. fasciculata (*Glyceria borreri, P. pseudodistans*). **6-8.** Resembles *P. distans*, but its panicle is narrow or spreading, with at least some branches densely furnished with spikelets to the base. Lemmas 1.8-2.3 mm, with the midrib reaching the apex and forming a short point. *Muddy inlets and edges of saline pools and drains on the South and East coasts and perhaps elsewhere; very rare.*

7. Dactylis

Dactylis glomerata. Cock's-foot. 6-7. Hairless; stems densely tufted, up to 120 cm high. Tillers densely compressed. Leaves bluish green, flat but folded and keeled when young, 5-12 mm broad, rough on the edges; sheaths split at the top but undivided in lower part; ligule long, ragged. Spikelets green or purple-tinged, 7 mm long, with about 4 flowers; in dense clusters in a flattened and triangular, 1-sided panicle, whose lower branches are usually long and bare at the base. Glumes and lemmas alike, downy, keeled, usually with a short terminal awn. *Meadows, pastures and waste places; abundant.*

8. Cynosuros

Cynosuros cristatus. Dog's-tail, Thraneen grass. 7-8. Hairless, with tufted, wiry stems 30-60 cm high. Leaves mostly basal, flat, ridged, 2-3 mm broad; ligule very short; sheaths usually split about half-way down. Inflorescence a narrow, compact, 1-sided spike, 25-50 mm long, with the spikelets separated by a clear longitudinal partition. Spikelets flattened, green, arranged in groups of 2 or 3, the outermost of each group being flowerless and reduced to a comb-like row of glumes. Fertile spikelets with 3-6 flowers; glumes equal, shorter than the flowers; lemmas pointed or shortly awned. *Pastures, meadows and roadsides; abundant.*

9. Catabrosa

Catabrosa aquatica. 6-7. Hairless, stems 20-50 cm high, extensively creeping and rooting at the base. Leaves short, flat, soft, smooth, blunt, 4-9 mm broad, sweet-tasting, greenish-purple; sheaths split; ligule medium-long, acute. Spikelets usually 2-flowered, sometimes 1 or 3, purple, ovoid, 4 mm long, in a very open, feathery panicle 8-25 cm long. Glumes broad, irregularly truncated at the top, unequal, much shorter than the awnless lemma. *Ditches, pools and open muddy ground; occasional.*

10. Briza

Briza media. Quaking grass. 6-7. Hairless, with slender wiry stems 25-50 cm high. Leaves short, flat, rough on the edges, 3-5 mm broad; sheaths for the most part entire; ligule very short. Spikelets shining green or purple, somewhat flattened, about 6 mm long and about as broad with 6-9 flowers, hanging from slender pedicels in a graceful, very open panicle. Glumes and lemmas similar, oval and obtuse. *Sand-dunes, dry pastures and banks, more rarely in wet grassland; very frequent in Centre, local elsewhere.*

11. Sesleria

Sesleria caerulea (*S. albicans*). **4-5.** Hairless, 12-40 cm high. Leaves mostly basal, 3-5 mm broad, bluish-green; apex rounded, but with a fine hair-like point. Sheaths split for a short distance at the top, but entire for most of their length; ligule very short, fringed with hairs. Spikelets glistening, bluish, 5-7 mm long, each with 2 or 3 flowers, in a very compact, ovoid, spike-like panicle 1-3 cm long. Glumes nearly equal, very membranous, about as long as the flowers. Lemmas ending in 3-5 teeth. *Pastures and rocky places on limestone; locally abundant in the West, (Clare to South Donegal) rare in Centre, unknown elsewhere.*

12. Melica

Melica uniflora. 5-6. Hairless or slightly hairy. Rhizome creeping; stems leafy, 30-50 cm high. Leaves flat, 4-6 mm broad, tapered towards the sheath, rather rough with ridges on the lower side; sheaths entire; ligule short, prolonged into a bristle-like point opposite the leaf blades. Spikelets usually purple, ovoid, 6 mm long, each borne separately on a slender pedicel in a sparse, fairly long, narrow panicle or raceme. Spikelets with 1 fertile and a second infertile floret. Glumes nearly equal, as long as the flowers; lemmas obtuse. *Woods and shady banks; occasional.*

13. Glyceria

Aquatic hairless perennials; sheaths entire. Panicles branched, spikelets flattened, with 6-14 flowers, arranged in a panicle or raceme. Glumes and lemmas obtuse, convex not keeled; glumes unequal, shorter than the flowers, 3-veined, lemmas 7-veined.

1.	Spikelets 12-30 mm long	..	..	..	2
	Spikelets 3-12 mm long	..	..	..	**4. G. maxima**
2.	Tip of lemma distinctly 3-toothed	..	..		**3. G. declinata**
	Tip of lemma not toothed or only slightly lobed	..		..	3
3.	Lemma 6-7 mm long	..	..	..	**1. G. fluitans**
	Lemma 4-5 mm long	..	..	..	**2. G. notata**

1. Glyceria fluitans. 6-8. Stems 40-100 cm, creeping or floating at the base, the upper part erect. Leaves often floating, soft, ridged and keeled, 4-8 mm broad; sheaths smooth, entire; ligule long, narrowly triangular, pointed. Spikelets green, linear-oblong, 20-30 mm long, with 8-14 flowers, breaking up at maturity beneath the lemmas. Panicle rather 1-sided, slender, with erect or spreading branches, sometimes reduced to a raceme. Lemmas rounded and entire at the tip, 6-7 mm long. Anthers 2-3 mm long. *Ditches, pools and slow streams; very frequent.*

2. G. notata (*G. plicata*). **6.** Very similar to *G. fluitans*, but with rougher sheaths; smaller spikelets, more spreading and freely branched panicles and shorter, rounded ligules. The spikelets also break up at maturity beneath each lemma but have shorter anthers (1-1.5 mm). The lemmas are shorter (4-5 mm), and sometimes slightly 3-lobed at the tip. *Ditches and slow streams; frequent.*

G. x pedicellata, a hybrid between the last two species is fairly common. It is intermediate in most characters and is best recognised by the failure of the glumes and lemmas to fall off the panicle after flowering. The anthers fail to open, good pollen is lacking and fruits are not produced. It can form large stands, often in the absence of one or both parents.

3. G. declinata. 6-8. Similar to *G. fluitans*, but seldom over 35 cm high, often prostrate at the base, the stem curving upwards and the ligule shorter. Panicle usually narrow and less branched; spikelets greenish or greenish purple, lemmas 4-5 mm long, clearly 3-lobed at the tip. Anthers very short (less than 1 mm). *Muddy situations, often on acid ground, mainly in the South and West; occasional.*

4. G. maxima (*G. aquatica*). **7-8.** Rootstock creeping; stems erect, stout, reed-like, leafy, 1-2 m high. Leaves long, rather rough, without ridges or keel, 8-12 mm broad; sheaths entire; ligule medium, obtuse, drawn to a central point. Spikelets green or purple, oblong, 5-10 mm long, with 4-9 flowers. Panicle very spreading, 15-35 cm long. Anthers 1.5 - 2 mm. *Canals, ditches and riversides; fairly frequent in Centre and South-east, very rare elsewhere.*

14. Bromus

Annuals with ovoid spikelets. Inflorescence a panicle or shortly-stalked raceme. Lower glume 3 or 5-veined; upper glume 5-7 veined; lemmas awned, 7-11 veined, longer than the awns.

1.	Spikelets less than 13 mm long; lemmas not more than 6.5 mm long	2
	Spikelets more than 15 mm long; lemmas more than 6.5 mm long	3
2.	Panicle rather open, with some branches (peduncles) longer than their spikelets; lemmas wrapped tightly around the caryopsis in fruit and so not obscuring the axis of the spikelet	**5. B. pseudosecalinus**

Panicle fairly compact, with all branches (peduncles) shorter
than their spikelets; lemmas not wrapped around the caryopsis
in fruit and so obscuring the axis of the spikelet .. .. **2. B. lepidus**
3. Panicle compact, with some of the spikelets almost stalkless **1. B. hordeaceus**
Panicle long and loose; all peduncles longer than their spikelet .. 4
4. Lemmas less than 8 mm long; anthers 2-3 mm long .. **4. B. racemosus**
Lemmas more than 8 mm long; anthers 1-1.5 mm long **3. B. commutatus**

1. Bromus hordeaceus (*B. mollis*). **6-7.** A very variable softly downy annual 5-80 cm high. Leaves thin, soft, 4-6 mm broad. Spikelets pale green, hairy, erect, ovoid, turgid, 18 mm long, with about 6 closely packed flowers; almost stalkless or shortly stalked in a narrow, compact, erect panicle 3-10 cm long. Lemmas soft, 7-11 mm long; awns as long as the lemmas. *Meadows, roadsides and waste places; common.*

Plants, usually less than 10 cm high, with hairless lemmas from sandy-coasts have been separated as subsp. *thominei*; however the frequency (or even occurrence) in Ireland of this subspecies is uncertain as the hybrid between *B. hordeaceus* and *B. lepidus* is very similar, differing in its larger caryopsis (which is as long as, and not shorter than, the palea) and appears common. Other, taller, maritime material with hairy lemmas less than 8.5 mm long has been called subsp. *ferronii*. Thorough investigation of the variation and distribution of this species and its hybrids in Ireland is needed.

2. * B. lepidus (*B. britannicus*). **6-7.** Like *B. hordeaceus* but with spikelets mostly 7-13 mm and lemmas, 5.5-6.5 mm, shorter than its caryopsis and usually hairless. *Meadows and roadsides; occasional.*

3. B. commutatus. **6.** A softly downy annual 30-70 cm high. Leaves thin, limp, 6-8 mm wide. Spikelets pale green, nearly hairless, spreading or slightly nodding, ovoid, turgid, 15-20 mm long, with 5-8 closely packed flowers; on rather long stalks in a loose but narrow usually nodding panicle 10-15 cm long. Lemmas hard, somewhat rhombic, 8-11 mm wide, with similarly-sized awns. *Meadows and roadsides; rare.*

4. * B. racemosus. **6-7.** Similar to *B. commutatus*, but with a smaller, narrower, erect panicle and oval lemmas, 6-8 mm long. *Similar situations; very rare.*

5. * B. pseudosecalinus, is rather similar, but with even smaller lemmas (5-6 mm) with short awns, in rather shaggy spikelets.

15. Bromopsis
Erect perennials. Spikelets narrowly oblong, more than 15 mm (excluding awns). Lower glume usually 1-veined, upper 3-veined. Lemmas 5-7 veined, acute and very shortly forked at tip.
1. Spikelets nodding, at the ends of long branches .. .. **1. B. ramosa**
Spikelets erect, in a compact panicle .. .. .. **2. B. erecta**

1. Bromopsis ramosa (*Bromus ramosus, Zerna erecta*). **6-7.** A hairy perennial, 100-175 cm high. Leaves harsh but limp, 6-12 mm broad; leaf-sheaths with prominent, pointed auricles at mouth. Ligule long, obtuse. Spikelets green or purplish, nodding, narrow, 25 mm long, with 5-9 flowers; panicle very loose and open, 1-sided, with long drooping branches arising in pairs or groups of 3. Awns about as long as the lemmas. *Woods, thickets and shady roadsides; frequent.*

2. B. erecta (*Bromus erecta*). **6.** A densely tufted perennial with very short rhizomes, 40-80 cm high. Leaves mostly basal, stiff, seldom over 3 mm broad, slightly hairy or hairless, auricle rounded; ligule short. Spikelets green or purple, erect, narrow lanceolate, 25 mm long, with 5-9 loosely packed flowers. Panicle rather narrow and compact, 8-15 cm long, with erect branches arising in pairs or groups of 3. Anthers deep orange. Awns about as long as the lemmas. *Dry banks, sand-dunes and old pastures, and railway embankments in South and Centre; locally frequent near Dublin, rare elsewhere.*

16. Anisantha

Annuals. Spikelets distinctly compressed. Lowest glume usually 1-veined; upper glume 3-veined. Lemmas 7-veined, drawn to a fine, minutely-forked point.

1. Lemmas more than 20 mm   ..   ..   **3. A. diandra**
   Lemmas 10-20 mm   2
2. Panicle lax, the branches spreading or drooping   ..   **1. A. sterilis**
   Panicle dense, the branches sub-erect to erect   ..   **2. A. madritensis**

1. Anisantha sterilis (*B. sterilis*). **6-7.** Annual, or rarely perennial; 30-70 cm high, hairless but downy towards the base, procumbent in fruit. Leaves limp, 4-6 mm broad; ligule medium. Spikelets green or purplish, nodding, 25-40 mm long, solitary, with 7-11 loosely packed flowers. Panicle very loose, with long spreading or drooping branches arising in whorls of 3 or 4. Awns longer than their lemmas. *Dry banks, ruins and urban waste places; fairly frequent in East, South and Centre, rare and local in North.*

2. * A. madritensis (*Bromus madritensis*). **5-7.** Is naturalised on walls and waste places around Carrick-on-Suir. It is smaller, with a narrow erect panicle and short branches bearing 1-2 longer (25-40 mm) spikelets.

3. * A. diandra (*Bromus diandrus*). **5-7.** Similar but taller and more robust, up to 80 cm high, with stems hairy to the top, often procumbent in fruit and longer, blunter ligules. The inforesence is a spreading or nodding panicle with solitary spikelets 30-50 mm and very long (30-50 mm) awns. *Naturalised on sandy ground near the sea in Dublin and Wexford; casual elsewhere.*

17. Brachypodium

Perennials; sheaths split. Spikelets stalkless or with very short pedicels, linear-lanceolate, in 2 ranks in a spike-like raceme; each with 8-10 flowers. Glumes unequal, pointed but not awned; lemmas larger, with terminal awns.

1. Tufted. Raceme drooping. Leaf-sheaths hairy. Leaves more
   than 6 mm wide. Awns 7-12 mm.   ..   ..   **1. B. sylvaticum**
   Rhizomatous. Raceme erect. Leaf sheaths hairless. Leaves less
   than 6 mm wide. Awns 1-6 mm.   ..   ..   **2. B. pinnatum**

1. Brachypodium sylvaticum. **7-8.** Stems tufted, slender, 50-100 cm high, usually leafy to the top. Leaves long, 8-12 mm broad, hairy, thin and dry, drooping, yellowish-green; ligule medium-sized, obtuse. Spike slender, with about 8 or 10 drooping green spikelets, 25-40 mm long, compact and cylindrical in flower, flattened and shaggy in fruit. Uppermost awns in each spikelet as long as the lemmas or longer. *Hedges, woods and shady banks; common.*

2. B. pinnatum. **7-8.** Similar to *B. sylvaticum* but with a creeping rootstock; sometimes nearly hairless; leaves narrower (less than 8mm), often with inrolled margins, absent from upper half of stem; ligule small, fringed with hairs. Spikelets erect with the awns only half as long as the lemmas. *Occasional on railway banks, mostly in the Southern half, but also, very rarely, in dry grassland.*

18. Leymus

Leymus arenarius (*Elymus arenarius*). **Lyme-grass. 7.** Stems stiff, 100-130 cm high, forming large tufts arising from a creeping rootstock. Leaves firm, bluish-green, flat, 8-12 mm broad, prominently ribbed, ending in stiff, sharp points; sheaths split; ligule very short. Spikelets purplish, 20-25 mm long, usually 3-flowered, stalkless in opposite pairs (with the flat side of each spikelet) in notches in the axis of a stout, dense spike 12-25 mm long. Glumes lanceolate, pointed, slightly unequal, nearly as long as the spikelet. Lemmas slightly smaller and less pointed. *Sandy shores in North and East; very local.*

19. Elymus

Perennial, usually rhizomatous. Sheaths split; ligule short or absent; leaf constricted at junction between blade and sheath; ligules very short. Inflorescence a 2-ranked spike with the flat side of each spikelet (the edges of the glumes and lemmas) next to the spike-axis. Spikelets many-flowered, firm, laterally compressed.

1. Lemmas long-awned .. .. **1. E. caninus**
   Lemmas awnless 2
2. Leaves flat, not ribbed on upper surface .. .. **2. E. repens**
   Leaves often inrolled, prominently ribbed on upper surface .. 3
3. Axis of spike brittle, with smooth angles; leaves minutely but
   densely downy on upper surface .. .. .. **4. E. juncea**
   Axis of spike tough, with rough angles; leaves hairless. **3. E. atherica**

1. Elymus caninus (*Agropyron caninum*). **7.** Stems tufted, slender, 50-100 cm high. Leaves flat, thin and dry, rather harsh, not strongly ribbed, 5-10 mm broad, usually downy, at least on the sheaths. Spike 6-18 cm long, very slender, often nodding. Spikelets green, 12 mm long (excluding awns), with 3-5 flowers. Glumes long-pointed or shortly awned; lemmas with a terminal awn at least as long as themselves. *Shady and rocky places; rare.*

2. E. repens (*Elymus repens, Agropyron repens*). **Scutch, Couch-grass. 7.** Rhizome long and creeping, flowering stems stiffly erect, 30-100 cm high. Leaves flat, 5-10 mm broad, rough on the upper surface with fine ridges, hairless or very sparsely hairy. Spike stiff, 7-20 cm long; axis tough. Spikelets green, 10-20 mm long, with 4-7 flowers, half their length or more apart. Glumes pointed or very shortly awned; lemmas similar. *Tilled fields and waste places; abundant.*

3. E. atherica (*Elymus pycnanthus, Agropyron pungens*). **7-8.** Like *E. repens* but leaves often inrolled, bluish-green and with prominent broad ribs on the upper surface. Spikelets closely overlapping, one-fifth to half their length apart. Glumes and lemmas 7-10 mm long, acute or subobtuse. Axis of spike tough, rough on the angles. *Sandy shores and upper parts of salt-marshes, mainly in South half; rather rare.*

4. E. juncea (*Elymus farctus, Agropyron junceiforme, A. junceum*). **7-8.** Rhizome far-creeping, producing prostrate leafy branches and erect flowering stems 30-50 cm high. Leaves stiff, bluish-green, inrolled, with the upper surface minutely downy and finely but conspicuously ridged. Spike stout, rigid. 5-12 cm long; axis smooth, brittle. Glumes and lemmas obtuse, 11-20 mm long. *Sandy seashores; very frequent.*

Hybrids within this genus are common, but often overlooked. All are sterile. *Elymus* x *obtusicula (E. atherica* x *E. juncea)* often forms large stands on the east coast and was recorded in the past as *Agropyron acutum* or *Triticum acutum*. It resembles *E. atherica* but the spikelets are further apart, sometimes larger (up to 25 mm) and the prominent leaf-ribs are minutely hairy. *E. repens* x *E. juncea (E.* x *laxa)* is also occasional close to the sea. Like *E. juncea* the axis of the spike is fragile and the leaves resemble *E. repens. E. repens* x *E. atherica* also occurs.

20. Hordeum. Barley

Leaves somewhat hairy, with split sheaths and a very short, obtuse ligule. Spikelets 1-flowered, arranged in groups of 3, each group in an excavation in the axis of a compact, flattish spike; the flower in the two lateral spikelets of each group abortive. Glumes very narrow, sometimes reduced to an awn; lemmas broader, with a long terminal awn.

Two casuals are fairly frequently encountered, neither persist; in * *H. distichon*, the common cultivated or 2-row Barley, only the central spikelet at each node is fertile whereas in * *H. vulgare* either 2 or 3 spikelets at each node are fertile, producing 4- and 6-row Barley respectively.

1. Upper leaf sheaths inflated. Some glumes hairy at base   **1. H. murinum**
    Upper leaf-sheaths not inflated. All glumes hairless   **2. H. secalinum**

1. Hordeum murinum. 6-8. Annual; stems tufted, leafy, 15-50 cm high, somewhat creeping at the base. Leaves short, flat, 3-5 mm broad, thin and dry, rough and usually omewhat hairy; sheaths loose. Spike green, slightly broadened at the base; lemmas 20-25 mm long, including the very long awn. *Roadsides and waste places, chiefly near towns in the East half; common around Dublin, rare elsewhere.*

2. H. secalinum (*H. nodosum*). **6-7.** Annual or perennial, with slender tufted nearly erect stems, 30-60 cm high. Leaves flat or in-rolled, 3 mm broad or less, rough on the upper surface, usually hairy on the lower surface and sheaths. Leaf-sheaths tight. Spike yellow-green, slender, 25-50 mm long. Glumes of all the spikelets reduced to awns. Lemmas of fertile spikelets 15 mm long, including the awn, which is about as long as the rest of the lemma; those of the lateral spikelets smaller. *Damp grasland, chiefly near the sea in South half; rare.*

21. Hordelymus

Hordelymus europaeus (*Hordeum europaeum*). **6-7.** Stems tufted, 60-100 cm high. Leaves flat, about 8 mm broad, usually downy on the sheaths; ligules very short. Spikelets 1-flowered, 12 mm long, arranged as in *Hordeum*, but all with fertile flowers; spike 5-10 cm long. Glumes fused at base, lemmas as in *Hordeum*. *Known from only one shady river-glen in the Glens of Antrim.*

In * *Hordeum vulgare* either 2 or 3 spikelets at each node are fertile, but the glumes are not fused at the base.

22. Avena. Oat

Tall, hairless or slightly hairy annuals. Leaves flat, with split sheaths; ligule fairly long. Spikelets large, hanging from slender stalks in a 1-sided panicle, each with 2-3 flowers. Glumes nearly equal, pointed. Lemma with a long, dark brown, bent awn arising from its beak.

1. Lemma with 2 distinct bristly points, each 4-7 mm long   **1. A. strigosa**
    Lemma with 2 very short points, less than 2 mm long   ..   2
2. Lemmas with distinct tufts of reddish-brown hairs at base   ..   **2. A. fatua**
    Lemmas lacking such hairs   ..   ..   ..   **3. A. sativa**

1. * Avena strigosa. 7-8. 60-120 cm high. Leaves 5-10 mm wide. Glumes 20 mm long, about as long as the flowers. Lemma bearing at the tip two bristle-like points each 4-7 mm long. *A persistent weed, especially of cereal crops.*

2. * A. fatua. 6-8. Like *A. strigosa*, but with slightly longer glumes, considerably longer than the flowers; teeth of lemma short but with a dense tuft of orange-brown hairs at the base. *Cultivated ground; frequent and increasing.*

3. * A. sativa. 6-8. The cultivated Oat, has long glumes and a shortly toothed lemma, but without the tuft of orange hairs and is often seen on country roadsides as a casual, but seldom persists.

23. Avenula

Avenula pubescens *(Helictotrichon pubescens, Avena pubescens).* **5-6.** 30-70 cm high, downy at least on the lower sheaths. Leaves flat, short, 4 mm broad; sheaths split; ligule long, acute. Spikelets few, pale, shining, 12-15 mm long (excluding awns), usually 3-flowered (sometimes 2), erect, in a narrow panicle or simple raceme up to 20 cm long. Glumes slightly unequal, almost as long as the flowers. Lemmas with long, dark, bent awns, arising from their backs. *Sand-dunes, dry banks and limestone pastures, locally frequent in Centre, occasional elsewhere.*

24. Arrhenatherum

Arrhenatherum elatius. False oat. 6-7. Hairless; rootstock creeping; stems 60-150 cm high, sometimes with tuberous swellings at the base (var. *bulbosum*). Leaves 5-8 mm broad, few, rather harsh; sheaths split; ligule short, obtuse. Spikelets 8-10 mm across, pale and shining, in a loose but narrow panicle, 15-25 cm long; each with an upper hermaphrodite flower and a lower male one. Glumes unequal, pointed, the larger as long as the flowers. Lower lemma with a long, bent awn inserted on its back near the base; upper lemma with a short awn or none. *Hedges, roadsides and waste places; abundant.*

25. Gaudinia

* Gaudinia fragilis. 6-8. A softly hairy annual up to 75 cm high. Leaves 2-3 mm wide; ligule short, truncate. Spikelets pale yellowish green, 15 mm long, each with 4-9 flowers, arranged in a long slender shaggy spike. Glumes unequal. Lemma with a long awn inserted on its back. *Introduced occasionally with imported grass-seed; naturalised in Limerick and perhaps elsewhere.*

26. Koeleria

Koeleria macrantha *(K. cristata, K. gracilis).* **6-7.** Stems tufted, 15-40 cm high. Leaves short, mostly basal, ridged, hairy or downy, less than 2.5 mm broad; sheaths split; ligule very short. Spikelets pale silvery green or purplish, flattened, 5 mm long, each with 2 or 3 flowers; arranged in clusters on a spike or compact spike-like panicle 2-7 cm long. Glumes unequal, slightly longer than the flowers. Lemmas pointed but not awned. *Dry often calcareous pastures, banks, sand-dunes and rocky places; frequent near West coast, widespread but local elsewhere.*

27. Trisetum

Trisetum flavescens. 7. Stems loosely tufted, 30-60 cm high. Leaves flat, short, 3 mm broad, somewhat ridged, downy on both blade and sheath. Sheaths split; ligule short, often fringed with hairs. Spikelets numerous, shining, initially green, turning yellowish, about 5 mm long (excluding awns), each with 3 or 4 flowers, in an open oblong panicle 8-15 cm long. Glumes unequal, pointed, shorter than the flowers. Lemmas lanceolate, forked at the tip, each with a fine, long awn inserted on its back. *Dry banks, sand dunes and limestone pastures; locally frequent in the South; rarer in the North.*

28. Deschampsia

Hairless perennials with tufted stems. Sheaths split. Spikelets 2-flowered, in a panicle. Glumes nearly equal, lanceolate, pointed, membranous, barely as long as the flowers. Lemmas obtuse and toothed at the apex, each with an awn inserted on its back.

1. Leaves flat , strongly ridged on upper side   ..   **1. D. caespitosa**
   Leaves very narrow, with inrolled margins   2
2. Ligule wider than blade of leaf, rounded at tip, not more than
   3 mm long ..   ..   **2. D. flexuosa**
   Ligule very narrow, acutely pointed, up to 8 mm long   .. **3. D. setacea**

1. Deschampsia caespitosa. 7-8. Stems 70-150 cm high, densely tufted in large tussocks. Leaves long, flat, harsh, very strongly ridged on upper side, 3-5 mm broad; ligule long, lanceolate. Spikelets silvery green or purple, 5 mm long, in a very loose, spreading feathery panicle 20-40 cm long. Lemmas with awns arising from near the base. *Woods, damp meadows and streamsides; very frequent.*

Subsp. *alpina*, from Kerry and West Mayo differs in its awn which arises from the upper half of the lemma.

2. D. flexuosa. 6-7. Stems 30-60 cm high, smooth and slender. Leaves nearly all basal, very narrow, with inrolled margins. Ligule obtuse, 1-3 mm long. Spikelets shining, silvery grey or brown, 5 mm long. Panicle 6-15 cm long; branches slender, wavy, spreading in flower but erect in fruit. Awns of lemmas protruding beyond glumes. *Heaths and dry moors; locally frequent in mountain districts, rare in lowlands.*

3. D. setacea. 7-8. Like *D. flexuosa*, but with a very long and narrow, acutely pointed ligule, 3-8 mm long, shorter, less wavy pedicles, and with a gap of about 1.5 mm between the bases of the two flowers in each spikelet. *Wet bogs and lake-margins; frequent in South-west Connemara, very rare elsewhere.*

29. Aira

Small hairless annuals with very narrow, hairless bristle-like leaves. Sheaths split; ligule medium to long, lanceolate. Spikelets small, 2-flowered, in a panicle. Glumes nearly equal, membranous, longer than the flowers. Lemmas each with a very fine awn, which projects beyond the glumes, inserted on its back.

1. Panicle diffuse, clearly branched   ..   ..   **1. A. caryophyllea**
   Panicle compact, very shortly branched   ..   **2. A. praecox**

1. Aira caryophyllea. 5-6. 7-20 cm high. Sheaths slightly rough. Spikelets 3mm long, silvery brown, solitary at the ends of the branches of a loose spreading panicle. *Banks, walls and sand dunes; frequent except in parts of the Centre.*

2. A. praecox. 5. Similar to *A. caryophyllea*, but with smooth sheaths, and the spikelets silvery green, and crowded together in a narrow, dense panicle 1-3 cm long. *Heaths, sand dunes walls and dry waste places; frequent.*

30. Hierochloë

Hierochloë odorata. 5-6. Hairless, with tufted stems 30-50 cm high. Leaves flat; ligule rather long, pointed. Spikelets 3-flowered, the two lower flowers male, the uppermost hermaphrodite; arranged in a small, 1-sided, open panicle. Glumes pointed, nearly equal, shining and rather membranous. Lemma similar but hairy. *Known only from one marsh at the South-east corner of Lough Neagh.*

31. Anthoxanthum

Anthoxanthum odoratum. Vernal grass, Sweet-scented grass. 5-6. Sometimes rather hairy, but often nearly hairless; sweet-scented (due to coumarin) when drying. Stems loosely tufted, rather slender, 30-50 cm high. Leaves flat, pointed, short, 4-5 mm broad. Spikelets 1-flowered, in clusters in a compact but rather shaggy, oblong, spike-like panicle. Glumes pointed but scarcely awned, very unequal, the larger about 7 mm long. Between them and the flower are two further hairy lemmas (representing abortive flowers) each with a long awn inserted on the back. Lemma (of fertile flower) and palea smaller, without awns. Stamens 2. *Pastures, meadows, heaths and woods; abundant.*

32. Holcus

Leaves flat, more or less downy, with split sheaths. Spikelets numerous, in a panicle, each containing 2 flowers, of which the upper is male, the lower hermaphrodite. Lemma of the upper flower with a fine awn inserted on its back.

1. Tufted. Leaf-sheaths evenly clothed with soft hairs. Awn of upper
   lemma hooked   ..   ..   .. **1. H. lanatus,**
   Rhizomatous. Stem-nodes hairy contrasting with the otherwise
   hairless sheaths. Awn of upper lemma slightly curved   ..   **2. H. mollis**

1. Holcus lanatus. Yorkshire fog. 6-7. Stems 30-70 cm high, usually tufted and forming tussocks. Leaves soft, pale green, 6-8 mm broad; lower sheaths veined with reddish-purple; ligule short (1-4 mm), obtuse. Stem and leaves evenly clothed in a fine soft down. Spikelets 4 mm long, downy, pink or pale green, in a feathery, dense, pyramidal panicle 7-13 cm long. Glumes slightly unequal, oval lanceolate, scarcely pointed. Awn of upper flower short, hooked at tip, not protruding beyond the glumes. *Meadows, pastures and waste places; abundant.*

2. H. mollis. 6-8. Similar to *H. lanatus* but with stems arising singly from a creeping rhizome, and the nodes very much hairier than the internodes; ligule usually longer, 3-5 mm; spikelets slightly larger; and the awn of the upper flower curved, protruding beyond the sharply pointed glumes. *Woods, heaths and waste places; locally frequent except in parts of West.*

33. Agrostis. Bent grass

Leaves hairless; sheaths split. Spikelets 1-flowered, very small, numerous, in a panicle which is diffuse and feathery at least at flowering time. Glumes nearly equal, pointed; lemma smaller, membranous, obtuse, sometimes awned; palea very small or absent.

1. Ligule on flowering stems usually sharply pointed; lemma usually
   awned   ..   ..   **1. A. canina**
   Ligule on flowering stems obtuse; lemma very seldom awned   ..   2
2. Plant spreading by conspicuous leafy stolons; ligule on flowering
   stems rounded at tip   ..   ..   ..   **2. A. stolonifera**
   Plant tufted, or spreading by underground rhizomes; ligule on
   flowering stems not rounded at tip   3
3. Ligule on sterile shoots broader than long   ..   **4. A. capillaris**
   Ligule on sterile shoots longer than broad   4
4. Plant usually over 50 cm high; palea clearly visible ..   **3. A. gigantea**
   Plant usually over 50 cm high; palea minute   ..   ..   **1. A. canina**

1. Agrostis canina. 7-8. Stems slender, smooth, usually tufted, 20-60 cm high. Basal leaves very narrow, with inrolled margins, or almost cylindrical. Upper leaves short, narrow but flat, ridged. Ligule fairly long, acute. Spikelets purplish or greenish brown. Lemma usualy with a fine awn inserted on its back, projecting beyond the glumes. Panicle contracted before and after flowering. *Heaths and moors; frequent.*

Now considered to consist of 2 taxa. *A. canina* has stolons but lacks rhizomes and has a ligule 1.5 times as long as wide and is usually associated with damper acid soils. *A vinealis* has rhizomes but lacks stolons and has often obtuse ligules less than 1.5 times as long as wide and is associated with drier, acid soils. Their respective geographical distributions are not known.

2. A. stolonifera *(A. alba).* **Fiorin-grass. 6-7.** Very variable. Stems 30-120 cm high with numerous leafy stolons from the base. Leaves flat, ridged, dry and rather harsh, 3-6 mm broad; ligule medium, more or less rounded. Spikelets usually pale green. Lemma with a very short awn or none. Panicle contracted before and after flowering. *Damp meadows, ditches, waste places, and rocky sea-shores; abundant.*

3. A. gigantea. 6-8. Stems 50-100 cm., spreading by underground rhizomes which bear only scale-leaves. Ligule medium, longer than broad, at least on sterile shoots. Panicle large, remaining open and feathery in fruit. *Tilled fields and waste ground; occasional in East, rare in West.*

4. A. capillaris *(A. tenuis).* **6-8.** Stems 20-45 cm high; tufted or with short underground rhizomes. Leaves narrow but flat; ligule short. Panicle remaining open and feathery in fruit. *Dry pastures, sand dunes, heaths and mountain grassland; abundant.*

34. Ammophila

Ammophila arenaria. Marram, Bent. 7. Rhizome creeping; flowering stems 60-120 cm high. Leaves long, rigid, ending in a stiff point; margins inrolled, the outer side being green and polished, the inner white and ridged. Sheaths split; ligule very long, acute. Spikelets straw-coloured, 1-flowered, narrow but 10-15 mm long, each with a tuft of short, silky hairs at its base; arranged in a dense cylindrical spike-like panicle about 15 cm long, tapered at both ends. Glumes nearly equal, narrow, pointed; lemma and palea slightly shorter. *Sandhills and sandy shores; abundant.*

35. Lagurus

* Lagurus ovatus. 6-7. A softly hairy annual with stems to 50 cm. Leaf sheaths inflated, rounded on the back. Ligules short. Inflorescence a dense egg-shaped panicle, white and fluffy. Spikelets 1-flowered. Lemmas with long (15 mm) white bent awns. *Naturalised in sand dunes in Wexford, casual elsewhere.*

36. Calamagrostis

Perennials. Spikelets 1-flowered, in panicles. Glumes nearly equal, with numerous silky hairs between them and the flower, persistent. Lemma with an awn inserted on its back.

1. Lemma smooth, shorter than the tuft of hairs at its base. Awn
    arising from the tip of the lemma   ..   ..   **1. C. epigejos**
    Lemma rougher, longer than the ring of hairs. Awn arising from
    the back of the lemma   ..   .. **2. C. stricta**

1. Calamagrostis epigejos. 7-8. Leaf-blades hairless, with stout stems up to 150 cm high and long rather rough leaves; ligule long, fraying at the tip. Panicle 15-30 cm long, purple-brown. Lemma much shorter than glumes and slightly shorter than the hairs at its base; awn arising from its tip. *Damp rocky places in West and North; very rare.*

2. C. stricta *(C. neglecta).* **6-7.** 30-80 cm high, hairless or slightly hairy. Leaves short, narrow, sometimes with inrolled margins; ligule short. Panicle 15 cm long, narrow, green or purple. Lemma longer than the hairs at its base; awn arising from its back. *Shores of Lough Neagh; rare.*

37. Phleum
Leaves flat, hairless, somewhat ridged, rough on the edges; sheaths split. Spikelets 1-flowered, very numerous, in a dense, regular, cylindrical spike. Glumes equal, keeled, pointed; lemma and palea much shorter, membranous, without awns.

1.	Annual. Glumes gradually narrowed to the tip ..	**3. P. arenarium**
	Perennial. Glumes obtuse	2
2.	Spikelets 4-5.5 mm. Panicle 6-9 mm wide. Ligule blunt	**1. P. pratense**
	Spikelets 2-3.5 mm. Panicle 2-6 mm wide. Ligule pointed	**2. P. bertolonii**

1. Phleum pratense *(P. nodosum).* **Cat's tail, Timothy-grass. 7-8.** Perennial, with somewhat tufted stems up to 30-120 cm high. Leaves about 5-8 mm broad, rather soft. Ligule usually medium, obtuse. Spike green or purple, up to 15 cm long, longer and proportionally slenderer than in *Alopecurus pratensis*, and without its silky sheen. Spikelets 4-5.5 mm. Glumes 3-4 mm long, somewhat hairy, tapered to long, diverging, stiff, awn-like points. *Meadows, pastures and roadsides.*

2. P. bertolonii. 7-8. Resembles *P. pratense* and is sometimes treated as a subspecies, but is usually shorter (less than 40 cm), with narrower leaves (2-6 mm), a more pointed ligule, narrower panicle (3-6 mm) and the spikelets 2-3.5 mm. *Similar habitats; occasional.*

3. P. arenarium. 5-6. Annual, 7-20 cm high. Leaves very short, the uppermost with an inflated sheath; ligule medium, pointed. Spike bluish-green, 1-4 cm long, tapered at both ends. Glumes lanceolate, 3 mm long, hairy in upper part, with short, awn-like points. *Thin, stable sand-dune grassland; occasional.*

38. Alopecurus
Leaves flat, hairless, ridged on the upper surface and on the sheaths; sheaths split. Spikelets 1-flowered, very numerous, in a dense, regular, cylindrical spike. Glumes equal, hairy, not awned. Lemma shorter, with a slender awn inserted on its back, projecting beyond the glumes. Palea absent.

1.	Stems simply erect. Ligule short, truncate ..	**3. A. pratensis**
	Stems strongly bent upwards. Ligule medium, pointed	..
2.	Awns conspicuous, protruding beyond the glume ..	**1. A. geniculatus**
	Awns inconspicuous, not protruding beyond the glume	**2. A. aequalis**

1. Alopecurus geniculatus. 6-7. A small perennial or annual, with stems 15-40 cm long, creeping and often rooting at the base, and then turning upwards at one of the nodes. Glumes obtuse. Ligule fairly long. Spike green or purple, slender, 2.5-4 cm long. Glumes obtuse, 2.5 mm long, scarcely united at the base. Anthers yellow or purple. *Marshes and ditches; frequent.*

2. A. aequalis has recently been recognised from muddy areas near the South coast. It differs from *A. geniculatus* in having awns that do not extend beyond the tip of the glume and in its bright-orange anthers.

3. A. pratensis. Foxtail. 5-6. Perennial; stem 40-100 cm high, not creeping at base. Lower leaf-sheaths usually tinged with brownish purple. Ligule short, truncate. Spike 4-8 cm long and 5-10 mm wide, greenish, very silky with the projecting awns of the lemmas. Glumes pointed, united at base. *Meadows and pastures; frequent.*

39. Parapholis

Hairless annuals. Leaves short, narrow. Sheaths split, swollen, ligule minute. Spikelets 1-flowered, in 2 ranks in a slender spike, each embedded in an excavation in the axis. Glumes equal, positioned side by side in front of the spikelet. Lemma and palea membranous, pointed, shorter than the glumes.

1. Anthers 1.5-4 mm. Flowering stems straight, usually more than
   15 cm .. .. **1. P. strigosa**
   Anthers 0.5-1 mm. Flowering stems curved, less than 10 cm **2. P. incurva**

1. Parapholis strigosa (*Lepturus filiformis*). **6-9.** A hairless annual with tufted straight, erect stems 10-30 cm high, prostrate at the base. Leaves short, narrow, flat or with inrolled margins; uppermost sheath not inflated. Spikelets 4-6 mm long. Anthers 1.5-4 mm. *Salt-marshes and muddy sea-shores; occasional.*

2. P. incurva is very similar to *P. strigosa* but differs in its shorter, stronger, curved flowering stems, inflated upper leaf-sheaths which partly enclose the base of the inflorescence and very small anthers. *Dryish coastal grassland in Cos. Dublin and Cork; very rare.*

40. Phalaris

Phalaris arundinacea. 6-7. Stems stout and reed-like, 70-200 cm high. Leaves hairless, long, 8-15 mm broad, rather harsh; sheaths split; ligule long, obtuse, fraying at the tip. Spikelets 1-flowered, 5-6 mm long, purplish red or pale green, numerous, in a freely branched but compact narrow panicle about 15 cm long. Glumes pointed, equal, longer than the flowers. Lemma and palea shining; between them and the glumes are 2 small hairy scales. *Lake-shores, ditches and riversides; common.*

41. Milium

Milium effusum. Millet-grass. 6. Stems erect, smooth, 60-150 cm high. Leaves flat and thin, 6-12 mm broad, rough on the edges; sheaths split; ligule large, oblong, tip pointed. Spikelets 1-flowered, pale green or purple, ovoid, 3 mm long, in a very open, pyramidal panicle about 20 cm long. Glumes equal, oval, membranous; lemma and palea smaller, hard, smooth and glistening. *Glens and rocky woods, mainly in mountain districts; rare. Sometimes planted in ornamental woodland.*

42. Phragmites

Phragmites australis (*P. communis*). **Reed.** *Giolcach.* **7-8.** Hairless; stems stout and leafy. 125-250 cm high. Leaves 15-25 mm broad; sheaths split; ligule replaced by a line of short hairs. Spikelets very numerous, dark purple-brown, narrow and pointed, 12 mm long, each with 3-5 flowers, in a dense feathery panicle 15-30 cm long. Glumes unequal, shorter than the flowers. Lemmas very narrow, with a short almost awn-like point; at the base of each except the lowest is a tuft of white, silky hairs, which become very conspicuous in fruit. *Lake margins, ditches, canals and marshes; very frequent.*

43. Danthonia

Danthonia decumbens (*Sieglingia decumbens*). **6-7.** Stems tufted, 15-40 cm high. Leaves slightly hairy, mostly basal, 3 mm across or less, often with inrolled margins; sheaths split; ligule replaced by a line of hairs. Spikelets 3 or 4-flowered, green or purplish, ovoid, very obtuse, 10 mm long, few, on long but erect pedicels in a raceme or very narrow panicle. Glumes equal, as long as the flowers. Lemmas convex, with a blunt 3-toothed apex, without awns. *Heaths and pastures; frequent.*

44. Molinia

Molinia caerulea. 7-8. Stems wiry, 30-100 cm high, densely tufted, forming large tussocks, with tough stringy roots. Leaves nearly all basal, flat, 5-8 mm broad, sparsely covered with rather long silky hairs. Ligule replaced by a line of hairs.

Spikelets green or purple, numerous, narrow, 5-8 mm long, usually 3-flowered, in a narrow but open panicle 10-30 cm long. Glumes unequal, much shorter than the flowers; lemmas rather blunt. *Wet heaths, moors and bogs, chiefly in mountain districts; frequent throughout and abundant in most of West half.*

Two subspecies are distinguished in Britain; subsp. *caerulea* , generally found in acid ground is shorter, at no more than 0.6 m tall, and smaller, with a panicle less than 30 cm long, than subsp. *arundinacea*; which is mainly found in fens and by rivers and canals. However confirmation of these distinctions needs to be made for Irish material.

45. Nardus
Nardus stricta. Mat-grass. 6-7. Hairless, with densely tufted, stiff, slender stems 10-30 cm high. Leaves very narrow and bristle-like, basal, except for one on each flowering stem which has a pale split sheath; ligule short. Inflorescence a slender, 1-sided, comb-like spike 5-8 cm long. Spikelets green, later purplish, narrow, 7 mm long, inset singly without any glumes. Lemma tapered to a long awn-like point. Palea slightly shorter. Stigma single. *Heaths and dry moors; chiefly in mountain districts; abundant in the North and West, local elsewhere. Seldom grazed by sheep.*

46. Spartina
Vigorous, large, creeping, rhizomatous perennials. Leaves broad and large. Sheaths split; ligule reduced to a short ring of hairs. Spikelets 1-flowered in long, slender, 1-sided spikes. Glumes narrow, pointed, somewhat downy; the lower ones shorter than the flowers, the upper longer. Lemma unawned.

1. Ligules 1.8-3 mm. Anthers 7-10 mm, producing spherical pollen   **2. S. anglica**
    Ligules less than 1-8 mm. Anthers 4-8 mm, producing misshapen
    pollen   ..   ..   **1. S. x townsendii**

1. * Spartina x townsendii *(S. alterniflora x S. maritima).* **7-8.** Stems 40-100 cm high. Leaves hairless, spreading, 6-10 mm broad, jointed at the junction of blade and sheath. Spikelets 15 mm long. Anthers 4-8 mm, lacking pollen. *Planted on tidal mud-flats and spreading; locally abundant.*

2. * S. anglica. 7-8. Is a fertile derivative of *S. x townsendii*. It has wider leaves, slightly narrower spikelets, and anthers 7-13 mm long, containing pollen. *Planted in similar situations, spreading and often commoner than S.* x *townsendii.*

CXXVII. ARACEAE

Perennial herbs. Hairless. Flowers very small and numerous, in a compact spike (the *spadix*) which is associated with, and often partially enclosed by, a large, leafy bract (the *spathe*). Ovary superior.

The 'Arum' or 'Easter lily' grown in greenhouses and gardens is a member of this family from South Africa *(Zantedeschia aethiopica).*

1. Leaves linear, strap-shaped; spadix apparently lacking a spathe   **1. Acorus**
    Leaves not linear; spadix with a distinct spathe   2

2. Leaves broadly oval; more than 30 cm long; spadix without an
    elongated, fleshy tip   ..   ..   ..   **2. Lysichiton**
    Leaves arrow-shaped; less than 30 cm long; spadix with an
    elongated, fleshy tip   ..   ..   **3. Arum**

1. Acorus

* **Acorus calamus. Sweet flag. 6-7.** An *Iris*-like plant up to 125 cm high. Leaves long, strap-shaped, often transversely wrinkled, fragrant when bruised. Flowers small, numerous, in a crowded spike 7-15 cm long, projecting obliquely from the top of the stem; behind it is a long bract similar to the leaves. Perianth-segments 6, free, membranous; stamens 6; ovary superior; stigma stalkless. Fruit not formed in Ireland. *Rivers, canals and lakes in the East; rare.* Native of eastern Asia.

2. Lysichiton

* **Lysichiton americanus. Skunk-cabbage. 4.** A robust, foul-smelling, rhizomatous, marsh plant with shortly stalked, broadly oval leaves 40-120 cm long. Spathe up to 30 cm, bright yellow. Spadix very stout, entirely covered in small, greenish, bisexual flowers. Perianth of 4 membranous segments; stamens 4. *Marshy ground; rare but scattered throughout and sometimes forming extensive local stands.* Native of western North America.

* *L. camtschatcensis*, native of eastern Asia, differing mainly in its smaller, white spathe, is also, doubtfully, reportedly naturalised.

3. Arum

Shortly rhizomatous herbs with hastate-saggitate, untoothed leaves with a long petiole. Flowering stem short. Spathe with its lower part wrapped around and concealing the basal part of the spadix, its upper part forming a hood. Spadix with a long fleshy tip (*appendage*) projecting into the hood. Below the appendage and concealed within the lower part of the spathe are, succesively, a ring of hairs, a zone of male flowers, another ring of hairs, and a zone of female flowers. Perianth absent. Flowers unisexual; consisting of 4 stalkless anthers or a 1-celled ovary. Fruit a red berry.

1. Appendage usually purple, its top about $1/2$ way up the hood;
   leaves appearing in Spring, often dark spotted   ..   **1. A. maculatum**
   Appendage yellowish, its top about $1/3$ of the way up the hood;
   leaves appearing in early Winter, never dark spotted   **2. A. italicum**

1. Arum maculatum. Lords and Ladies, Cuckoo pint. 4-5. Leaves appearing in early Spring, sometimes spotted with blackish-purple. Spadix with a purplish (rarely yellow) appendage which reaches $1/2$ way up the hood. Fruiting spike 3-6 cm. *Woods and shady hedges; widespread but local.*

2. * A. italicum. 4-5. Leaves appearing in the Winter, never spotted with blackish-purple. Spadix with a yellow appendage which reaches $1/3$ of the way up the hood. Fruiting spike 10-15 cm. *Hedgerows; mainly in Dublin, Meath and West Meath.*

CXXVIII. LEMNACEAE

Minute, floating or submerged perennials, consisting of a green frond, not differentiated into stem and leaves, and one or more roots. Reproduction mainly by budding; flowers rarely produced, occurring in small groups at the edge of the frond, monoecious, lacking a perianth and consisting of 1 or 2 stamens or an ovary.

1. Each frond with a single root   ..   ..   ..   **1. Lemna**
   Each frond with several roots   ..   ..   ..   **2. Spirodela**

1. Lemna

Fronds hairless, with a solitary root and usually no more than 5 veins.

1. Fronds with one end elongated forming a long and tail-like
   structure   ..   ..   ..   **1. L. trisulca**
   Fronds round or broadly oval   2
2. Fronds thick, very swollen on the lower side   ..   **2. L. gibba**
   Fronds thin, nearly flat on the lower side   ..   **3. L. minor**

1. Lemna trisulca. Ivy-leaved duckweed. 5-7. Fronds usually submerged, thin and semi-transparent, oblong-lanceolate, 8-14 mm long, blunt at one end, tapering to a long tail-like stalk at the other; usually cohering in groups, with the young thalli attached by their tail-like stalks to the parent frond from which they project at right-angles. *Still or slowly flowing water; rare in the West, occasional elsewhere.*

2. L. gibba. Fronds floating, thick and opaque, flat above and very swollen beneath, round in outline, 3-5 mm across. *Ponds, ditches, canals and lakes, mainly in the North and East (largely around the South shore of Lough Neagh and near Dublin), rare and decreasing.*

3. L. minor. Duckweed. 6-7. Fronds floating, thin but moderately opaque, round to oval in outline, slightly swollen on both surfaces, 2-4 mm long. *In all types of still water; very frequent.*
   * *L. minuta (L. minuscula)*, which differs from the last species in its much smaller fronds with only one vein (3 in *L. minor*) has been recorded from Dublin.

2. Spirodela

* **Spirodela polyrhiza** (*Lemna polyrhiza*). Fronds floating, fairly thick, opaque, round or broadly oval in outline, 5-8 mm across, each with a tassel of several roots and more than 7 indistinct veins. The base of each tassel of roots is subtended by a small scale bearing minute hairs. *Ditches, pools and lakes, now abundant in the Lough Neagh basin, rare elsewhere.*

CXXIX. SPARGANIACEAE

Sparganium. Bur-reed

Perennials. Stems erect or floating; leaves alternate. Flowers monoecious, in globular heads in a raceme or panicle, the upper heads exclusively male, the lower, larger heads exclusively female. Perianth represented by 3-6 scales.

1. Flower-heads in a branched panicle. Perianth-scales dark-tipped   **1. S. erectum**
   Flower-heads in a simple raceme. Perianth-scales uniformly pale   2
2. Leaves erect, stiff, keeled at base   ..   ..   **2. S. emersum**
   Leaves soft, floating, not keeled at base   3
3. Lowest bract 15-50 cm, much longer than the inflorescence   **3. S. angustifolium**
   Lowest bract 3-8 cm, scarcely longer than the inflorescence   **4. S. minimum**

1. Sparganium erectum (*S. ramosum*). **6-7.** Stem erect, 60-100 cm. Leaves erect, keeled at base. 12-18 mm wide. Flower-heads in a terminal panicle, each branch with several male heads near its tip and 1-3 female heads at its base. Fruiting heads 20-25 mm across. *Ditches, pools, canals, slow streams and marshes; frequent.*
   Four subspecies have been recorded from Ireland. In subsp. *erectum* and subsp. *microcarpum* the mature fruit is dark brown or black above (paler below) and distinctly shouldered. In the former the shoulder is flat-topped, 4-6 mm at its widest

point; the shoulder of the latter is more rounded and narrower (2.5-4.5 mm). The uniformly pale brown fruits of subsp. *neglectum* (2-4.5 mm) taper to the beak. Many of the similar but longer (4-7 mm) pale brown subglobose fruits of subsp. *oocarpum* fail to mature.

2. S. emersum (*S. simplex*). **7-8.** Stem erect, 35-75 cm. Leaves erect, 8-10 mm wide; the lowest keeled at base. Flower-heads in a simple raceme, with 3-7 stalkless male heads above and 3-4 female below, the lowest of which are stalked. Fruiting heads 18-20 mm across. *Ditches, slow streams and lake-margins; occasional.*

3. S. angustifolium (*S. affine*). **7-8.** Stem weak, submerged or floating, 50-100 cm. Leaves long, floating, 6 mm wide; base somewhat inflated, not keeled. Flower - heads in a simple raceme, usually with 2 contiguous male heads above and 2-4 stalked female heads below; lower bracts long and leaf-like. Fruiting heads 15 mm across. *Rivers and lakes, mainly in mountain districts; occasional in the West, rare elsewhere.*

4. S. minimum (*S. natans*). **7-8.** Stem floating or submerged, 10-35 cm. Leaves limp, floating, 4-5 mm wide; the base scarcely inflated. Flower-heads in a simple raceme with 1 male above and 2-4 stalkless or shortly stalked female below. Bracts not or only slightly overtopping the infloresence. Fruiting heads 10 mm across. *Bogs, drains, canals and peaty lakes; occasional.*

CXXX. TYPHACEAE

Typha. Bulrush. *Coigeal na mban sidhe*

Tall, erect, reed-like perennials with linear basal leaves sheathing the lower stem. Flowers very numerous, monoecious, in a dense, cylindrical spike, the upper part consisting of male flowers, the lower of female. Perianth represented by numerous hairs.

1. Male and female flowers not separated from one another by
    a distinct gap   ..   ..   ..   **1. Typha latifolia.**
    Male and female flowers separated from one another by a
    distinct gap   ..   ..   ..   **2. T. angustifolia**

1. Typha latifolia. 7-8. Stem 1-2.5 m high. Leaves as long or longer, 15-20 mm wide, rather pale greyish-green, flat or spirally twisted. Spike continuous, without a gap between the male and female portions; the latter 25 mm across in fruit. Hairs of male flowers white; of female flowers dark brown. *Ditches, marshes, canals, lake-margins and slow streams; frequent but local.*

2. T. angustifolia. 7-8. Similar to *T. latifolia* but smaller; leaves not pale greyish-green, somewhat channelled, 6-8 mm wide; female portion of spike 8-12 mm across in fruit, with reddish brown hairs, separated from male portion by a distinct gap. *Lake-margins and pools, mainly in the North half; rare.*

CXXXI. CYPERACEAE (SEDGES)

Herbs, mostly perennial. Stems usually solid, often 3-angled. Leaves alternate or basal, narrow, the lower part consisting of a sheath, which completely encircles the stem, and is not split down one side as in most grasses; the blade, if present, is linear and not lobed, but in some species the leaf consists entirely of sheath. Flowers small, arranged in *spikelets*, which may be solitary or variously grouped into inflorescences. Each spikelet consists of a number of small, overlapping, usually brownish, scale-like bracts, known as *glumes*; in the axils of some or all of these glumes is a solitary, stalkless flower. Glumes which have no flowers in their axils are known as *sterile glumes*. Flowers hermaphrodite except in *Carex*; perianth absent or represented by a few bristles. Stamens 3, rarely 2. Ovary superior; style single, divided above into 2 or 3 linear stigmas. Fruit a small, seed-like nut.

Most species of this family grow in shallow water or in wet places.

1. Perianth consisting of bristles which enlarge greatly in fruit, forming a conspicuous, cottony head .. **8. Eriophorum**
   Perianth absent, or consisting of bristles which remain inconspicuous in fruit 2

2. Flowers unisexual; ovary in female flowers enclosed in a utricle (a flask-shaped structure usually interpreted as a modified bract) **13. Carex**
   Flowers hermaphrodite; ovary and nut not enclosed in a utricle .. 3

3. Spikelets solitary 4
   At least 2 spikelets present on each stem (though sometimes crowded together into a compact head) 7

4. Plant prostrate, submerged or on very wet soil; stem bearing leaves throughout its length .. .. .. **5. Eleogiton**
   Plant erect, usually not submerged; leaves reduced to sheaths, or confined to the lower part of the stem 5

5. All leaves reduced to sheaths .. .. **9. Eleocharis**
   At least the uppermost stem-leaf with a short, green blade .. 6

6. Spikelet subtended by a green bract appearing like a continuation of the stem .. .. **4. Isolepis**
   All bracts small, brown and glume-like .. **6. Trichophorum**

7. Leaves all reduced to sheaths .. .. **3. Schoenoplectus**
   Some leaves possessing blades 8

8. Leaf-blades not more than 2 mm wide 9
   Some leaf-blades at least 4 mm wide 12

9. Spikelets not more than 3 on each stem .. .. **4. Isolepis**
   Spikelets at least 5 on each stem 10

10. Spikelets black or very dark brown 11
    Spikelets white, green or light brown .. .. **11. Rhynchospora**

11. Spikelets flattened; glumes clearly arranged in 2 opposite rows **12. Schoenus**
    Spikelets more or less cylindrical, with glumes not arranged in 2 opposite rows (though the spikelets themselves are arranged in two rows in the spike) .. .. .. **7. Blysmus**

12. Spikelets very numerous, not more than 4 mm long 13
    At least some of the spikelets more than 5 mm long 14

13. Leaves soft, with smooth margins; inflorescence diffuse, with spikelets clearly stalked .. .. **1. Scirpus**
    Leaves stiff, usually with cutting, toothed margins; spikelets stalkless in heads .. .. .. **10. Cladium**

14. Glumes awned; stem leafy; inflorescence obviously terminal .. .. **2. Bolboschoenus**
    Glumes not awned; stem-leaves mostly reduced to sheaths; inflorescence apparently lateral, being subtended by a bract which looks like a continuation of the stem .. **3. Schoenoplectus**

1. Scirpus

Scirpus sylvaticus. 6-7. A stout perennial with creeping rhizome. Stems bluntly 3-angled, leafy, up to 100 cm high. Leaves flat, soft, up to 20 mm wide. Spikelets numerous, stalked, 3-4 mm long, greenish-brown, in a large, diffuse panicle with leafy bracts at its base. Stamens and stigmas 3. *Wet woods and riversides; occasional in the North-east, very rare elsewhere.*

2. Bolboschoenus

Bolboschoenus maritimus (*Scirpus maritimus*). **6-8.** Rhizomatous perennial. Stems bluntly 3-angled, leafy, up to 100 cm high. Leaves keeled, up to 10 mm wide. Spikelets 10-20 mm long, reddish-brown, in one or more terminal clusters of 3-7. Stamens and stigmas 3. Glumes with a slender, awn-like tip. *Tidal rivers and brackish marshes; very frequent. Also very rarely inland (Lough Neagh).*

3. Schoenoplectus

Stout, reed-like perennials with creeping rhizomes, often forming large stands. Leaves few, and confined to lower part of stem; sometimes with blades, sometimes reduced to sheaths. Spikelets 5-8 mm, brown, in a fairly compact inflorescence which appear to be lateral since the bract at its base looks like a continuation of the stem. Stamens 3; stigmas 2 or 3.

1. Stem sharply 3-angled .. .. .. **2. S. triqueter**
   Stem cylindrical .. .. .. **1. S. lacustris**

1. Schoenoplectus lacustris (*Scirpus lacustris*). *Bois-shithbhín.* **6-7.** Stem cylindrical, smooth, up to 250 cm high. Spikelets in one or more clusters.
   Divisible into two subspecies, which are usually distinct, though intermediates are occasionally found:
   Subsp. *lacustris.* Stems stout, dark green, up to 250 cm high. A few leaves often with floating blades. glumes smooth. Stigmas 3. *Shallow water at the margins of lakes, rivers and canals; very frequent.*
   Subsp. *tabernaemontani* (*Scirpus tabernaemontani, Schoenoplectus tabernaemontani*). Stems more slender, pale bluish-green, not more than 150 cm high. all leaves without blades. Glumes minutely papillose. Stigmas 2. *Brackish waters; frequent around the coasts.*

2. S. triqueter (*Scirpus triqueter*). **8-9.** Like *S. lacustris* subsp. *lacustris*, but stems sharply 3-angled, paler green, not more than 150 cm high; inflorescence usually smaller and more compact; glumes with a green midrib; stigmas 2. *Banks of the Shannon in Limerick city, and for some distance downstream; locally abundant.*

4. Isolepis

Small annuals or short-lived perennials, with very slender, cylindrical stems. Leaves few, similar to stems but rather shorter. Spikelets 1-3, clustered together in an inflorescence which is terminal, but often appears lateral because of a slender, leaf-like bract which seems like a prolongation of the stem. Glumes all fertile, spirally arranged. Perianth absent; stamens 2; stigmas 3.

1. Bract usually distinctly longer than the inflorescence; spikelets
      usually 2; nut shiny, ridged [Fig. CXXXIa] .. .. **1. I. setacea**
   Bract shorter than or equalling the inflorescence; spikelet usually
      single; nut not ridged, not shiny [Fig. CXXXIb] .. .. **2. I. cernua**

1. Isolepis setacea (*Scirpus setaceus*). **6-8.** Stems usually 5-10 cm high. Spikelets 4-5 mm long, brown, usually paired, but sometimes single or 3 together. Bract usually shorter than spikelets, sometimes minute. Nut shiny, longitudinally ridged [Fig. CXXXIa]. *Damp, bare ground, especially on sandy or gravelly soils; frequent.*

Fig. CXXIa   Fig. CXXIb

2. Isolepis cernua (*Scirpus cernuus, S. filiformis*). **6-9.** Like *I. setacea*, but spikelets usually greenish and single, rarely paired; bract usually longer than spikelet; nut smooth and dull, without ridges [Fig. CXXXIb]. *Marshy ground; fairly frequent near the coast, very rare inland.*

5. Eleogiton

Eleogiton fluitans (*Scirpus fluitans*). **6-9.** Perennial, with slender stems, grooved on one side, branched, leafy, floating in water or prostrate on damp ground. Leaves grass-like, very narrow, 7-25 cm long. Spikelets solitary at the ends of the branches, pale green, 3-4 mm long, each with about 6 flowers. All bracts glume-like and fertile. Perianth absent; stamens and stigma 3. *Bog-drains and other peaty waters; fairly frequent but local.*

6. Trichophorum

Trichophorum caespitosum (*Scirpus caespitosus*). **5-6.** Perennial, with slender, stiff, cylindrical, unbranched stems 15-30 cm high, densely tufted and forming large tussocks. Leaves confined to base of stems, mostly reduced to brown, shiny sheaths, but the uppermost furnished with a green, leafy tip about 5 mm long. Spikelets solitary, terminal, brown, 4-8 mm long, each with about 5 flowers. Lowest glume as long as the spikelet, ending in a short, green tip. Perianth consisting of short bristles; stamens and stigmas 3. *Moors and drier parts of bogs; very frequent and locally abundant.*

7. Blysmus

Blysmus rufus (*Scirpus rufus*). **6-7.** Stems slender, cylindrical, up to 30 cm high, arising in small tufts from a creeping rhizome. Leaves very narrow, shorter than the stem. Inflorescence a terminal, oblong spike 10-20 mm long, sometimes overtopped by a long, green bract, consisting of about 6 densely packed spikelets arranged in two rows. Each spikelet has 5-6 black or dark brown glumes, of which the two lowest are empty and about as long as the spikelet. Stamens 3; stigmas 2. *Salt-marshes; frequent in the North; local and rather rare elsewhere.*

8. Eriophorum. Bog-cotton. *Ceannbhán*

Perennials. Leaves mostly with blades. Stems cylindrical or bluntly 3-angled. Spikelets large, with numerous flowers, terminal, rarely solitary, more usually several on long, slender stalks in an umbel-like cyme. Glumes black or grey. Perianth of numerous bristles, which enlarge in fruit to form a conspicuous, white, cotton-like mass. Stamens and stigmas 3.

1.   Spikelets solitary, erect; uppermost cauline leaf consisting
        of a wide, loose-fitting sheath; blade rudimentary or absent   **4. E. vaginatum**
     Spikelets usually several, drooping, on slender peduncles;
        cauline leaves with well-developed blades   2

2. Cottony bristles 40-50 mm in fruit; peduncles quite
        smooth   ..   ..   **1. E. angustifolium**
    Cottony bristles 20-25 mm in fruit; peduncle rough
        (test with tip of tongue)   3
3. Stems tufted; leaves mostly 4-7 mm wide   ..   **2. E. latifolium**
    Stems arising singly from a creeping rhizome;
        leaves 1-2 mm wide   ..   ..   ..   **3. E. gracile**

1. Eriophorum angustifolium. 4-6. Stems 3-angled only in the upper part, arising singly from a far-creeping rhizome. Leaves all with blades 3-5 mm wide, channelled, tapering to a fine, 3-angled tip. Spikelets usually 3-6, rarely solitary, drooping, on long, slender, smooth peduncles. Glumes black, with broad membranous margin. Bristles 40-50 mm in fruit. *Wet bogs, bog-pools and drains; abundant.*

2. E. latifolium. 4-6. Stems bluntly 3-angled throughout, loosely tufted; rhizome short. Leaves with blades 4-8 mm wide, flat. Spikelets 2-12, as in *E. angustifolium*, except for the narrow membranous margin to the glumes, the peduncles rough with very minute teeth (scarcely visible without a microscope) and the less conspicuous cottony bristles (20-25 mm in fruit). *Fens, marshes, and flushes in bogs; widespread but rather rare.*

3. E. gracile. 5-7. Stems 3-angled, arising singly from a far-creeping rhizome. Leaves only on lower part of stem; blades 1-2 mm wide, 3-angled or somewhat channelled. Spikelets 3-6, drooping; glumes without membranous margin; peduncles and bristles as in *E. latifolium*. *Wet bogs and lake-margins; occasional in West Galway, very rare elsewhere.*

4. E. vaginatum. 4-5. Stems densely tufted, 3-angled only in upper part. Lower leaves with blades 1-2 mm wide; those on the middle and upper part of the stem reduced to wide, loose-fitting sheaths. Spikelet solitary, erect. Glumes grey, entirely membranous. Bristles 20-30 mm in fruit. *Bogs and moorland; very frequent in the North, West and Centre, occasional in the South and East.*

9. Eleocharis

Perennials. Stems slender, cylindrical (rarely 4-angled), unbranched. Leaves reduced to brown or whitish, membranous sheaths surrounding the lower part of the stem. Spikelet solitary, terminal; all glumes shorter than the spikelet. Flowers hermaphrodite; perianth-bristles inconspicuous; stamens 3; stigmas 2 or 3.

1. All glumes fertile (subtending a flower in their axils)   **1. E. quinqueflora**
    Lowest glume of spikelet sterile   2
2. Spikelets 2-4 mm long   3
    Most spikelets at least 7 mm long   4
3. Spikelets green   ..   ..   ..   **2. E. parvula**
    Spikelets brown   ..   ..   ..   **3. E. acicularis**
4. Rhizome short; stems densely tufted; uppermost leaf-sheath
        cut off obliquely at the top   ..   ..   **6. E. multicaulis**
    Rhizome creeping; stems single or in small tufts; uppermost
        leaf-sheath cut off transversely at the top   5
5. Lowest two glumes sterile, each embracing only half the
        circumference of the spikelet [Fig. CXXXIc]   ..   **4. E. palustris**
    Only one sterile glume, which embraces the whole of the
        base of the spikelet [Fig. CXXXId] ..   ..   **5. E. uniglumis**

Fig. CXXXIc   Fig. CXXXId

1. Eleocharis quinqueflora (*Scirpus pauciflorus*). **5-8.** Rhizome creeping, bearing small tufts of stems 8-25 cm high. Leaf-sheaths cut off transversely at the top. Spikelet 5-6 mm long, pale brown; all glumes fertile, the lowest about half as long as the spikelet, embracing most of the circumference of the spikelet in its base. *Fens, marshes, lakeshores and damp ground. Very rare in the extreme South; occasional to frequent elsewhere.*

2. E. parvula (*Scirpus nanus*). **8-9.** Rhizome whitish, creeping on the surface of the mud. Leaf-sheaths translucent, inconspicuous. Spikelets 2-4 mm long, pale green, consisting of one sterile glume, nearly as long as the spikelet, and about 4 fertile glumes with flowers. *Tidal mud in estuaries; very rare.*

3. E. acicularis. **7-8.** Rhizome creeping, bearing very slender, almost thread-like stems, often 4-angled, 5-15 cm high, usually forming a dense sward. Leaf-sheaths pale brown, cut off transversely at the top. Spikelets 3-5 mm long, brown, with a single sterile glume and 5-6 fertile glumes with flowers. *Rivers, canals, pools and lake-shores; fairly frequent in the Centre; local and rather rare elsewhere.*

4. E. palustris. **6-7.** Stems fairly stout, loosely tufted or solitary, up to 60 cm high. Leaf-sheaths cut off transversely at the top. Spikelets 8-15 mm long, dark brown, with numerous flowers and two sterile glumes at the base, each encircling about half the circumference of the spikelet [Fig. CXXXIc]. *Shallow water, bogs and marshes; very frequent.*

5. E. uniglumis. **6-8.** Very like *E. palustris*, but rather less robust, and with only one sterile glume, which encircles almost the whole circumference of the base of the spikelet [Fig. CXXXId]. *Brackish or calcareous marshes; occasional near the sea; very rare inland.*

6. E. multicaulis. **6-8.** Like *E. palustris*, but with a short rhizome and densely tufted stems rarely more than 30 cm high; leaf-sheaths cut off obliquely at the top, spikelets 5-10 mm long, with a single sterile glume as in *E. uniglumis*. *Bogs and lake-margins; locally abundant in the West; rare elsewhere.*

10. Cladium
Cladium mariscus. **6-8.** A stout, reed-like plant with far-creeping rhizome, forming extensive, dense stands of stout, hollow stems up to 2 m high. Leaves with usually stiff and erect blades, usually with rigid, cutting edges and keel, about 15 mm wide at the base and tapering to a narrow tip. Spikelets 3-5 mm, acute, brown, very

numerous, grouped in small heads in a long, diffuse inflorescence. Lowest 3 or 4 glumes sterile. *Lake-margins and marshes, mainly in the West, occasional to frequent.*

11. Rhynchospora

Slender perennials with erect, leafy stems. Leaves very narrow, channelled. Spikelets grouped into small heads, each spikelet consisting of 4-6 glumes, but only the uppermost 1 or 2 are fertile.

1. Spikelets white at flowering time; uppermost bract shorter
   than the head of spikelets or overtopping it by 1 cm or less .. **1. R. alba**
   Spikelets brown at flowering time; uppermost bract below the
   head of spikelets overtopping it by 2 cm or more .. .. **2. R. fusca**

1. Rhynchospora alba. 7-8. Rhizome short; stems in small tufts, up to 40 cm high. Spikelets white, in 1-3 heads; uppermost bract shorter than the head, or overtopping it by not more than 1 cm. Stamens 2. *Wet bogs, mainly lowland. Very frequent in the West and Centre; rather rare elsewhere.*

2. R. fusca. 7-8. Like *R. alba*, but with longer rhizome and scattered stems; spikelets orange-brown, the head overtopped by the uppermost bract by at least 2 cm; stamens 3. *Wet bogs; occasional in the West and Centre; very rare elsewhere.*

12. Schoenus

Schoenus nigricans. 5-9. Stems cylindrical, stiff, tufted, 25-50 cm high. Leaves few, with blackish sheath and long, very narrow blade. Spikelets black, shining, flattened, 5-10 mm long, in terminal heads of 5-10 subtended by a leafy bract longer than the head. Glumes 6-8, arranged in two opposite rows, mostly sterile, but the uppermost 2-4 with flowers. *Fens, marshes, bogs and lake-shores; very frequent and locally abundant in the West and Centre; rather rare elsewhere.*

13. Carex

Perennials with erect, usually 3-angled stems. Leaves consisting of blade and sheath (the latter sometimes very short or absent in some leaves); at the base of the leaf, in its axil, is a flap of tissue - the *ligule*. Flowers unisexual, without a perianth, arranged in spikelets, each flower consisting either of 3 stamens or of an ovary, which is contained in a flask-shaped *utricle*, from the mouth of which protrudes the style bearing two or three stigmas [Fig. CXXXIe & f]. The utricle may be prolonged at the tip forming a distinct *beak*. Fruit a small nut, enclosed in the utricle. Each flower is subtended by a *glume*, a small bract which is usually chaffy and never leaf-like. Sterile glumes are few or absent. At the fruiting stage the anthers of male flowers have dropped off, but the presence of a male flower can usually be inferred from the persistent filaments protruding beyond the glumes. Glumes subtending male flowers may be different in appearance from those subtending female flowers; for convenience they are referred to below as male and female glumes respectively.

All species except *C. dioica* are monoecious - *i.e.* each plant bears both male and female flowers. In the monoecious species male and female flowers may either be in separate spikelets or mixed together in the same spikelet. So there are 3 types of inflorescence in Carex [Fig. CXXXIg].

It is often difficult to identify species in flower; well-developed fruit is usually essential. Despite their large number most of the species are quite distinct, but in the species here numbered 44 to 48 intermediates are frequent; some, at least, of these are hybrids. Among the other species hybrids are rare (except for *C. hostiana* x *C. viridula*, which is fairly frequent) and all are sterile.

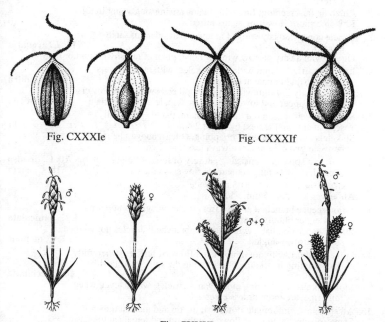

Fig. CXXXIe   Fig. CXXXIf

Fig. CXXXIg

1. Spikelet solitary, terminal ..   2
   Each stem bearing several spikelets, in a raceme-like or
       panicle-like inflorescence   4
2. Plant dioecious; spikelet consisting either of male or of female
       flowers   ..   ..   **1. C. dioica**
   Plant monoecious; each spikelet containing male flowers at the
       top and female flowers at the base   3
3. Utricles 4-6 x 1.5 mm, dark brown, without persistent style;
       stigmas 2; roots reddish brown   ..   **2. C. pulicaris**
   Utricles 5-7 x 0.75 mm, yellowish, with persistent style protruding
       from the mouth; stigmas 3; roots pale brown or yellow   **3. C. pauciflora**
4. Spikelets all similar in general appearance, most of them
       containing both male and female flowers   5
   Spikelets clearly of two kinds, the uppermost one or more entirely
       or principally male, the lower ones entirely or principally female   21
5. Lowest bract exceeding the inflorescence   6
   Lowest bract shorter than or equalling the inflorescence   ..   7
6. Lowest bract stiff, bristle-like; spikelets crowded together in a
       short, compact inflorescence   ..   ..   **13. C. divisa**
   Lowest bract soft, leaf-like; spikelets spaced out in a long,
       interrupted inflorescence   ..   ..   **14. C. remota**

7. Rhizome far-creeping; flowering stems arising singly, not in tufts   8
    Rhizome short; flowering stems tufted   10

8. Utricle conspicuously winged in upper part; plant of sandy
    ground   ..   ..   ..   **11. C. arenaria**
    Utricle with a very narrow wing or none; plant of marshy ground or bog   9

9. Leaves mostly 1-2 mm wide; all spikelets with male flowers
    at the top and female at the base   ..   ..   **6. C. diandra**
    Leaves mostly 2-4 mm wide; middle spikelets with male flowers
    only, the upper and lower with some female and some male   **12. C. disticha**

10. Spikelets well spaced out along the stem, the lowest usually
    separated from the next by about 2 cm   11
    Spikelets crowded, often overlapping, at least above, the interval
    between two neighbours always less than 2 cm   12

11. Uppermost spikelets consisting entirely of female flowers   **10. C. divulsa**
    All spikelets containing some male flowers at the base   ..   **18. C. curta**

12. Some of the leaves at least 5 mm wide   13
    All leaves less than 5 mm wide   14

13. Inflorescence branched at the base; utricles winged in upper part;
    stem rather bluntly 3-angled   ..   ..   **4. C. paniculata**
    Inflorescence compact, cylindrical, unbranched; utricles not winged;
    stem sharply 3-angled   ..   ..   ..   **7. C. otrubae**

14. Spikelets short, with not more than 8 flowers; utricles, when fully
    ripe, pointing in all directions, giving the spikelet a star-like
    appearance ..   ..   **16. C. echinata**
    Most spikelets containing more than 8 utricles, which, even when
    fully ripe, are more or less erect   15

15. All spikelets with female flowers at the tip and male at the base ..   16
    Some spikelets with male flowers at the tip and female at the base
    (some may contain only female flowers)   18

16. Spikelets dark brown   17
    Spikelets pale green   ..   ..   **18. C. curta**

17. Utricles smooth, winged in upper half [Fig. CXXXIh]; leaf-tip
    3-angled; glumes 3-5 mm   ..   ..   **15. C. ovalis**
    Utricles ridged, not winged [Fig. CXXXIi]; leaf-tip flat, though
    very narrow; glumes 2-3 mm   ..   ..   **17. C. elongata**

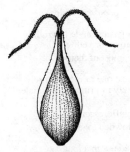   

Fig. CXXXIh   Fig. CXXXIi

18. Spikelets dark brown; plant of wet ground   19
    Spikelets greenish or pale brown; plant of fairly dry ground   ..   20

19. Spikelets at base of inflorescence stalkless; female glumes
    shorter than the utricles; beak of utricle forked at the tip   **6. C. diandra**
    Spikelets at base of inflorescence shortly stalked; female
    glumes about as long as the utricles; beak of utricle not
    forked at tip   ..   ..   ..   **5. C. appropinquata**

20. Roots and leaf-bases often tinged with reddish-purple; utricles
    mostly more than 4 mm long, narrowed gradually to a not
    very distinct beak   ..   **8. C. spicata**
    Plant without reddish-purple colour; utricles mostly less than
    4 mm long, narrowed suddenly to a distinct beak   ..   **9. C. muricata**

21. Utricles downy, or rough with minute papillae   22
    Utricles smooth and hairless   26

22. Leaves and male glumes hairy   ..   ..   ..   **19. C. hirta**
    Leaves and male glumes hairless   23

23. Utricles with a conspicuous, forked beak at least 0.5 mm
    long   ..   ..   **20. C. lasiocarpa**
    Utricles with a very short, scarcely distinct beak, truncate or
    slightly notched at the tip   24

24. Leaves pale bluish-green, at least beneath; most stems with 2-3
    male spikelets   ..   ..   ..   **29. C. flacca**
    Leaves not pale bluish-green; male spikelet single   25

25. Male spikelet usually club-shaped (broadest near the tip),
    up to 3 mm wide; lowest bract with a sheath at least
    2.5 mm long; leaf-sheaths dark brown   **40. C. caryophyllea**
    Male spikelet cylindrical, not more than 1.5 mm wide;
    lowest bract without a sheath; leaf-sheaths reddish   **41. C. pilulifera**

26. Stigmas 2; utricles more or less flattened, green, with a very
    short beak or none; female glumes blackish, with conspicuous
    green midrib   27
    Stigmas 3; utricles 3-angled or inflated, sometimes with a
    conspicuous beak; utricles and female glumes variously coloured   32

27. Lowest bract shorter than the inflorescence   28
    Lowest bract exceeding the inflorescence   30

28. Dwarf mountain plant; leaves seldom more than 20 cm long   **45. C. bigelowii**
    Plant of marshes or lakes; some leaves more than 20 cm long   ..   29

29. Stems usually densely tufted, forming large tussocks;
    leaf-margins rolling outwards on drying   ..   ..   **46. C. elata**
    Stems seldom densely tufted; leaf-margins rolling inwards
    on drying   ..   ..   **47. C. nigra**

30. Male spikelet usually solitary (rarely 2); leaves mostly less than
    3 mm wide   ..   ..   **47. C. nigra**
    Male spikelets 2-4; leaves mostly more than 3 mm wide   ..   31

31. Stem bluntly 3-angled or almost cylindrical, brittle; leaf-margins
    rolling inwards on drying; utricles without veins   ..   **44. C. aquatilis**
    Stem sharply 3-angled, not brittle; leaf-margins rolling outwards
    on drying; utricles with longitudinal veins   ..   ..   **48. C. acuta**

32. Many of the leaves at least 10 mm wide; female spikelets
    8-15 cm long   ..   ..   ..   **26. C. pendula**

Most of the leaves less than 10 mm wide; female spikelets not
more than 10 cm long   33

33. Male spikelet single (rarely 2 on a few stems)   34
Male spikelets 2 or more on most stems   48

34. Leaves hairy, at least on the sheath or the lower surface;
female spikelets whitish-green   ..   ..   **39. C. pallescens**
Leaves hairless; female spikelets often tinged with brown   ..   35

35. Bracts not sheathing, or with a sheath less than 3 mm long   ..   36
At least the lowest bract with a well-developed sheath   ..   37

36. Female spikelets with up to 20 flowers each; utricles slightly
narrower than the female glumes; free portion of ligule
much less than 1 mm long   **42. C. limosa**
Female spikelets with not more than 10 flowers each; utricles
considerably wider than the female glumes; free portion of
ligule about 1 mm long   ..   ..   ..   **43. C. magellanica**

37. Female spikelets with not more than 6 flowers; utricles
7-9 mm long   ..   ..   ..   **31. C. depauperata**
Female spikelets many-flowered; utricles not more than
5.5 mm long   38

38. Lowermost spikelet drooping in fruit   39
Lowermost spikelet more or less erect, even in fruit   42

39. Female spikelets 8-10 mm wide; lowest bract greatly
exceeding the inflorescence   ..   **23. C. pseudocyperus**
Female spikelets not more than 7 mm wide; lowest bract
shorter than the inflorescence, or only slightly longer   ..   40

40. Female spikelets all drooping, very slender, with fruits fairly
widely spaced   ..   ..   ..   **27. C. sylvatica**
Upper female spikelets erect, stout and compact   41

41. Leaves mostly 6-10 mm wide; female glumes drawn out to a
long, slender point   ..   ..   ..   **32. C. laevigata**
Leaves mostly 2-6 mm wide; female glumes obtuse,
sometimes with a short point   ..   ..   **33. C. binervis**

42. Leaves bluish-green to greyish-green   43
Leaves not bluish-green to greyish-green   44

43. Lowest bract shorter than inflorescence; female glumes about
as long as the utricles   ..   ..   ..   **30. C. panicea**
Lowest bract much longer than inflorescence; female glumes
shorter than the utricles   ..   ..   ..   **36. C. extensa**

44. Leaves 6-10 mm wide   ..   ..   ..   **28. C. strigosa**
Leaves 2-5 mm wide   45

45. Female glumes with a membranous, white or translucent
margin   ..   ..   **37. C. hostiana**
Female glumes without a membranous margin   46

46. All bracts shorter than the inflorescence   ..   **34. C. distans**
Some bracts equalling the inflorescence, and many of them
exceeding it   47

47. Female spikelets (except sometimes the lowest) crowded
together immediately below the male spikelet   ..   **38. C. viridula**
All female spikelets well spaced out, not crowded together   **35. C. punctata**

48. Most of the leaves at least 8 mm wide 49
    Leaves not more than 7 mm wide 50
49. Male spikelets often more than 3; male glumes sharply pointed **22. C. riparia**
    Male spikelets not more than 3; male glumes more or less
    obtuse .. .. .. **21. C. acutiformis**
50. Leaves somewhat bluish-green; utricles contracted abruptly to
    a beak, usually standing out at right angles to the axis **24. C. rostrata**
    Leaves not bluish-green; utricles tapered gradually to a beak,
    usually pointing obliquely upwards .. .. **25. C. vesicaria**

I. Spikelet solitary

1. Carex dioica. 5-6. Dioecious. Stems slender, cylindrical, in loose tufts, up to 30 cm high. Leaves very narrow, channelled, shorter than the stem. Spikelet single, terminal, 10-15 mm long. Glumes of both sexes reddish-brown, with membranous margins. Utricles 3 mm, reddish-brown, tapered to a not very distinct, notched beak. *Wet, peaty ground; occasional in the North half, rare in the South.*

2. C. pulicaris. Flea sedge. 5-6. Roots reddish-brown. Stems tufted, slender, stiff, cylindrical, 10-25 cm high. Leaves 1 mm wide or less, shorter than the stem, keeled. Spikelet up to 20 mm long, slender, consisting of about 6 male flowers at the top and the same number of female below. Male glumes 4-5 mm, brown with whitish, membranous margin, subacute. Female glumes 3-4 mm, falling before the fruits are ripe. Utricles 4-6 mm, narrowly ellipsoid, notched at the tip but scarcely beaked, dark, shining brown, standing out at right angles to the axis when ripe. Stigmas 2. *Bogs, heaths, grassy banks and mountain pastures; very frequent.*

3. C. pauciflora. 5-6. Like *C. pulicaris*, but with pale yellow roots; leaves up to 2 mm wide, not keeled; spikelet shorter, with only 2-4 flowers of each sex; utricles longer and narrower, pale brown. Stigmas 3, falling as fruits ripen, but leaving the persistent style protruding from the mouth of the utricle. *Wet bogs; locally abundant on the Garron plateau, County Antrim; also one station in County Down.*

II. Several spikelets on each stem

(a) Spikelets all more or less alike, usually containing both male and female flowers. Stigmas 2.

4. C. paniculata. 5-7. Stems up to 150 cm, densely tufted, often forming large tussocks. Leaves c. 6 mm wide, tapered to a fine, 3-angled tip. Spikelets brown, very numerous, 5-8 mm long, crowded in a dense, compact panicle, usually branched at the base; most spikelets with male flowers above and female below, but some only with female. Bracts short or absent. Utricles brown, almost as long as the glumes, winged in the upper part and tapered to a long, notched beak. *Marshes and ditches; very frequent.*

5. C. appropinquata (*C. paradoxa*). **6.** Like *C. paniculata*, but forming smaller tussocks; stems not more than 80 cm high and leaves only 1-2 mm wide; utricles not winged above. *Marshes and bog-margins; occasional in County Westmeath, very rare elsewhere.*

6. C. diandra. 6-7. Stems slender, sharply 3-angled, not or only loosely tufted and not forming tussocks. Leaves 1-2 mm wide, greyish-green. Spikelets brown, 5-8 mm long, with male flowers above, female below, arranged in a compact, unbranched spike 2-4 cm long. Bracts very small. Utricles not winged; beak forked at the tip. *Lowland bogs, marshes and lake-margins; frequent in the Centre, rather rare elsewhere.*

7. C. otrubae (*C. vulpina*). **6-7.** Stems stout, sharply 3-angled, densely tufted, up to 100 cm high. Leaves erect, bright green, 4-8 mm wide. Spikelets greenish-brown, with male flowers above and female below, arranged in a fairly compact but shaggy spike 3-5 cm long. Female glumes with a slender, sharp point; utricles with a long, forked beak. *Ditches and marshes; frequent near the coast, occasional inland.*

8. C. spicata (*C. contigua*). **6-7.** Stems slender, bluntly 3-angled, in small tufts, up to 70 cm high. Roots purplish-red; this colour often (but not always) extends to the leaf-sheaths and glumes. Leaves 2-4 mm wide. Spikelets with male flowers above and female below, arranged in a slender, compact spike. Bracts very small. Female glumes acutely pointed, brownish; utricles 4-5 mm, green at first, nearly black when ripe, with a poorly defined, shortly notched beak. *Banks and rough grassland; widespread but rare.*

9. C. muricata (*C. pairaei*). **6-7.** Very like *C. spicata*, but without the purplish-red pigment and with smaller utricles (3-4 mm), brown when ripe, and tapered fairly abruptly to a distinct beak. *Dry grassland; rather rare.*

10. C. divulsa. 6-8. Stems slender, 3-angled, fairly densely tufted. Leaves 2-3 mm wide. Spikelets with male flowers above and female below (some of the upper ones sometimes with female flowers only), arranged in a lax spike 5-12 cm long, with the lower spikelets separated from each other by a gap of at least 2 cm. Bracts small, except the lowest, which may be up to 3 cm long. Female glumes pale greenish-brown; utricles 3-5 mm, with forked beak, blackish when ripe. *Hedges, roadsides and open woods, mainly in the South and East; occasional.*

11. C. arenaria. 5-6. Rhizomes far-creeping, sending up widely separated stems and tufts of leaves. Stems sharply 3-angled, 15-75 cm high. Leaves 2-3 mm wide, often with inrolled margins. Spikelets pale yellowish-brown, 8-15 mm long, the uppermost with only male flowers, the lowest with only female, the intermediate with male flowers above, female below; forming a fairly compact spike 4-7 cm long. Utricles 4-6 mm long, broadly winged. *Sand-dunes and sandy shores; very frequent.*

12. C. disticha. 5-6. Like *C. arenaria*, but leaves usually flat; spikelets darker brown, arranged in two ranks in the spike, the uppermost only with female flowers, the intermediate only with male, and the lowest only with female, or mixed; utricle very narrowly winged. *Marshes, drains, lake-shores and wet meadows; rare in the South-West, frequent elsewhere.*

13. C. divisa. 6-7. Stems bluntly 3-angled, up to 75 cm high, arising in small tufts from a short rhizome. Leaves 1-3 mm wide, greyish-green, flat or channelled. Spikelets 3-8, brown, in a compact head or short spike; all with male flowers above and female below. Bracts small, except the lowest, which is longer than the inflorescence. Utricles 3-4 mm, with a short, forked beak. *Estuarine marshes; formerly at the mouth of the River Liffey but long extinct there; still locally frequent in the Barrow estuary below New Ross.*

14. C. remota. 6-7. Stems slender, bluntly 3-angled or 2 ridged, tufted, up to 70 cm high. Leaves 1-2 mm wide, channelled, drooping. Spikelets small, pale brownish-green, very widely separated in a slender spike. Lowest 2 or 3 bracts leaf-like, longer than the inflorescence; the uppermost small and inconspicuous. Spikelets with female flowers above, male below; sometimes only with female. Utricles 3 mm, tapered gradually to a deeply forked beak. *Wet woods, hedges, and other damp, shady places; frequent in most districts.*

15. C. ovalis (*C. leporina*). **6-7.** Stems 3-angled, closely tufted, up to 80 cm high, but often creeping for a short distance at the base. Leaves 1-3 mm wide. Spikelets brown, clustered in a compact head 2-3 cm long, most of them with female flowers above and male below, but some with only female flowers. Female glumes as long as the utricles, which are 4-5 mm long, narrowly winged in the upper part [Fig. CXXXIh], and with a forked beak. *Damp grassland, mostly in hilly districts; frequent.*

16. C. echinata. 5-7. Stems slender, cylindrical or bluntly 3-angled, tufted, up to 40 cm high. Leaves 1-3 mm wide, flat, tapered to a 3-angled tip. Spikelets brownish-green, small, with not more than 8 flowers, fairly widely separated in a slender, lax spike, mostly with female flowers only, but the uppermost with some male flowers at the base. Bracts small. Female glumes 2-3 mm. Utricles 3-4 mm, gradually tapered to a forked beak, spreading in all directions when ripe, so as to give the spikelet a star-like appearance. *Bogs and wet, peaty grassland; frequent and locally abundant.*

17. C. elongata. 5-6. Stems sharply 3-angled, rough, densely tufted, up to 75 cm high. Leaves flat or keeled, about as long as the stem, 2-5 mm wide. Spikelets numerous, reddish-brown, 10 mm long, in a moderately dense spike 3-4 cm long, the lower ones with only female flowers, the upper with some male flowers at the base. Female glumes 2 mm. Utricles 3-4 mm, ribbed; with a slender, truncate beak [Fig. CXXXIi]. *Lake-margins in the North half (Roscommon to Antrim); very local.*

18. C. curta (*C. canescens*). **5-7.** Stems sharply 3-angled, loosely tufted, up to 50 cm high. Leaves about as long, rather pale green, 2-3 mm wide. Spikelets 5-8 mm long, greenish-white, in a dense or fairly lax spike. Each spikelet has female flowers at the tip, male at the base. Female glumes slightly shorter than the utricles, which are 2-3 mm long, with a slightly notched beak. *Bogs and wet grassland; frequent in the North and East, rare elsewhere.*

(b) spikelets plainly of two different types, those above wholly or mainly of male flowers, those below wholly or mainly female

(i) Stigmas 3

19. C. hirta. 5-6. Stems bluntly 3-angled, loosely tufted, 30-70 cm high. Leaves 2-5 mm wide, hairy, at least on the sheaths. Spikelets 4-6, the upper 2-3 male, slender, the lower 2-3 female, stouter, erect, stalked. Lower bracts leaf-like, sheathing, longer than the inflorescence. Male glumes downy. Female glumes 6-8 mm, with a long, awn-like point. Utricles equalling the glumes, downy, with a long, forked beak. *Damp or moderately dry grassland; frequent in most districts.*

20. C. lasiocarpa. 6-8. Rhizomes far-creeping, usually under water. Stems slender, bluntly 3-angled, 50-100 cm high. Leaves about as long as the stems, 1-2 mm wide, greyish-green, usually with inrolled margins. Male spikelets 1-3, slender; glumes purplish-brown, acute. Female spikelets 1-3, stouter; glumes similar. Bracts leaf-like, the lowest about equalling the inflorescence. Utricles greyish-green, downy, with a short, forked beak. *Lake margins and wet fens and bogs. Occasional to frequent in the North, West and Centre; rare in the South and East.*

21. C. acutiformis. 6-8. Rhizome far-creeping, but stems arising in tufts, stout, sharply 3-angled, up to 150 cm high. Leaves about equalling the stems, 7-10 mm wide, keeled. Lower bracts leaf-like, not sheathing, usually overtopping the inflorescence. Male spikelets 3-5, stalkless or shortly stalked, erect; glumes 4-5 mm, reddish-brown, tapered to a fine point. Utricles 3-5 mm, with a short, notched beak. *Marshes, ditches, river-banks and lake-margins; locally frequent in the East half; rare in the West.*

22. C. riparia. 6-8. Like *C. acutiformis*, but often larger and coarser; leaves up to 15 mm wide, rather pale bluish-green; male glumes 7-9 mm, acute; lower female spikelets clearly stalked, sometimes drooping, with glumes 7-10 mm; utricles 5-8 mm, with longer, usually deeply notched beak. *Ditches, marshes and river-banks, mainly near the coast. Occasional in the East; rare elsewhere.*

23. C. pseudocyperus. 6. Stems up to 80 cm, sharply 3-angled, loosely tufted, rough. Leaves bright yellowish-green, longer than the stems, 5-10 mm wide, with rough margins and keel. Bracts leaf-like, mostly overtopping the inflorescence, not sheathing. Male spikelet single; glumes brown, tapered to a fine, hairy tip. Female spikelets 3-5, stalked, stout, shaggy and drooping in fruit; glumes with a hairy, awn-like tip, longer than the utricle but narrower. Utricle 4-8 mm, falling when ripe; beak deeply forked. *Drains, fens and marshes; rather rare.*

24. C. rostrata (*C. inflata*). **6-8.** Stems slender, bluntly 3-angled, up to 100 cm high, arising in small tufts from a far-creeping rhizome and often forming large stands. Leaves about as long as the stem, pale bluish-green, keeled, 2-6 mm wide. Lower bracts leaf-like, equalling the inflorescence, very shortly sheathing. Male spikelets 2-4; glumes obtuse. Female spikelets 2-4, erect, compact, stalkless or shortly stalked; glumes narrow. Utricle 4-6 mm, inflated, narrowed suddenly to a long, notched beak. *Marshes and shallow water; very frequent in most districts.*

25. C. vesicaria. 6-7. Like *C. rostrata* but leaves not pale bluish-green; male glumes acute; female spikelets usually stalked, stouter and shaggier; utricle 6-8 mm, tapered gradually to the beak. *Marshes and shallow water; occasional.*

26. C. pendula. 5-6. Stems stout, densely tufted, up to 150 cm high. Leaves somewhat shorter than the stem, 15-20 mm wide, flat. Bracts leaf-like, sheathing, about equalling the inflorescence. Male spikelets 1-2; glumes 6-8 mm, subacute. Female spikelets 4-5, up to 15 cm long, drooping, stalked, but with the stalk concealed by the bract-sheath; glumes 2-3 mm. Utricle 3-4 mm, with a short, truncate beak. *Damp, shady places, occasional, but in many places planted or escaped from cultivation.*

27. C. sylvatica. 4-7. Stems slender, bluntly 3-angled, tufted, 20-50 cm high. Leaves about equalling the stem, soft, flat, 3-6 mm wide. Bracts sheathing, equalling the inflorescence or shorter. Male spikelet single, slender, pale brown. Female spikelets 3-5, 25-60 mm long, long-stalked, drooping, very slender and lax; glumes membranous with green midrib. Utricles 5 mm, longer than the glume, with a slender, forked beak. *Woods, hedges and other shady places; very frequent.*

28. C. strigosa. 5-8. Like *C. sylvatica*, but with leaves 6-10 mm wide; female spikelets more or less erect, and utricles with a very short, truncate beak. *Damp or shady places; rare.*

29. C. flacca (*C. diversicolor*). **5-8.** Rhizome far-creeping. Stems nearly cylindrical, up to 60 cm high. Leaves pale bluish-green, usually shorter than the stem, 3-4 mm wide, tapered to a slender tip, which is flat or channelled, not prismatic as in *C. panicea*. Bracts shortly sheathing, the lowest equalling or exceeding the inflorescence. Male spikelets usually 2, dark brown. Female spikelets 1-4, erect or nodding; glumes 2-3 mm, purplish-black. Utricle 3 mm, with a very short, truncate beak, blackish when ripe. *Grassland, especially on limestone, sand-dunes and salt-marshes; abundant.*

30. C. panicea. Carnation-grass. 5-8. Stems loosely tufted, up to 50 cm high. Leaves very pale bluish-green, as long as the stem. 2-5 mm wide, very like those of *C. flacca*, but with a solid, 3-angled tip. Bracts shortly sheathing, the lowest about equalling the inflorescence. Male spikelet single. Female spikelets 1-3, erect, stalked, rather lax; glumes purplish-brown with pale midrib, about equalling the utricle. Utricle 3-4 mm, pale green, inflated; beak very short, truncate. *Damp, heathy grassland and disturbed peat; abundant.*

31. C. depauperata. 5-6. Stems cylindrical, loosely tufted, up to 70 cm high. Leaves shorter than the stem, 2-4 mm wide. Bracts leaf-like, sheathing, longer than the spikelets. Male spikelet single, slender, pale brown. Female spikelets 2-4, erect, stalked, short, with not more than 6 flowers. Female glumes brown, shorter than the utricle. Utricle 7-9 mm, with a long, obliquely truncate beak. *Dry woods on limestone; known only from one station in East Cork.*

32. C. laevigata (*C. helodes*). **6-7.** Stems bluntly 3-angled, densely tufted, up to 100 cm high. Leaves shorter than the stem, 5-10 mm wide. Bracts leaf-like, sheathing, shorter than the inflorescence. Male spikelet single, orange-brown. Female spikelets 2-4, widely separated, the lowest usually nodding, the others erect; glumes slightly shorter than the utricle, tapered to a fine point. Utricle 4-6 mm, green, with several longitudinal veins, and often with fine red spots; beak deeply forked. *Open woods and damp grassland; occasional.*

33. C. binervis. 6-8. Stems more or less cylindrical, tufted, up to 130 cm high. Leaves shorter than the stem, 2-6 mm wide. Lower bracts leaf-like, sheathing, shorter than the inflorescence; upper bracts small and bristle-like. Male spikelet single, dark brown. Female spikelets 2-4, widely spaced, 15-45 mm long, stalked, the lowest usually drooping, the others erect; glumes slightly shorter than the utricle, narrowed suddenly to a short point. Utricle 3-5 mm, purplish-brown, not spotted, with two prominent green veins on the margins; beak deeply forked. *Moors and heaths; very frequent.*

34. C. distans. 5-6. Like *C. binervis*, but seldom more than 70 cm high; spikelets all erect, the female not more than 20 mm long; utricles greenish or pale brown, with several, not very prominent veins and a shortly notched beak. *Salt-marshes and rocky ground near the sea; frequent.*

35. C. punctata. 6-7. Stems 3-angled, up to 60 cm high. Leaves 2-5 mm wide, about as long as the stem. Bracts leaf-like, sheathing, usually overtopping the inflorescence. Male spikelet single, orange-brown. Female spikelets 2-4, fairly widely spaced, stalked, erect, 10-25 mm long; glumes acute, shorter than the utricle. Utricle pale, shining green, sometimes finely dotted with red, standing almost at right angles to the axis of the spikelet (in related species such as *C. distans* the utricles are semi-erect). *Rocky or grassy ground near the sea; occasional in the South-West and in West Galway; one station in West Donegal; unknown elsewhere.*

36. C. extensa. 6-7. Stems bluntly 3-angled, tufted, up to 35 cm high. Leaves about as long as the stem, 2-3 mm wide, rather pale bluish-green. Bracts leaf-like, exceeding the inflorescence, sheathing, some or all standing out from the stem at a wide angle. Male spikelet single. Female spikelets 2-4, usually closely crowded together, erect, shortly stalked, 5-15 mm long; glumes shorter than the utricles, very shortly pointed; utricles greyish-green, with a short, slightly notched beak. *Salt-marshes and other muddy or sandy places near the sea; frequent. Also in two stations on Lough Neagh.*

37. C. hostiana (*C. fulva*). **6-7.** Stems arising singly from a creeping rhizome, bluntly 3-angled, up to 50 cm high. Leaves shorter than the stem, 2-5 mm wide, narrowed to a fine, solid, 3-angled tip. Bracts leaf-like, sheathing, shorter than the inflorescence. Male spikelet single (rarely 2); glumes dark brown with a whitish membranous margin. Female spikelets 2-4, fairly widely spaced, stalked, erect, 10-30 mm long; glumes brown, with a fairly conspicuous, whitish, membranous margin. Utricles yellowish-green, 4-5 mm long, with a slender, deeply forked beak. *Damp places in moorland or rough pastures; frequent in the West; occasional elsewhere.*

38. C. viridula (incl. *C. flava*, *C. lepidocarpa*, *C. demissa*, *C. oederi* and *C. serotina*). **5-8.** Stems cylindrical or bluntly 3-angled, tufted, up to 65 cm high, but often much less. Leaves 2-5 mm wide. Bracts leaf-like, exceeding the inflorescence, with very short sheaths or none. Male spikelet single. Female spikelets 2-5, crowded together (except sometimes the lowest), stalkless or very shortly stalked, not more than twice as long as wide; glumes brown with green midrib, equalling the utricle or slightly shorter; utricle 2-5 mm, yellowish-green, beaked. *Lake-shores, bog-margins, fens and damp, peaty places; abundant in the North and West; frequent elsewhere.*

Very variable. The three variants described below as subspecies were until recently regarded as separate species, but although they are easily distinguished in their typical form, intermediates, especially between subsp. (b) on the one hand and (a) or (c) on the other, are so common as to make this separation impracticable.

Subsp. *viridula* (*C. serotina*, *C. oederi*). Stem erect, seldom more than 20 cm and often much less. Leaves usually longer than the stem. Male spikelet usually stalkless. Utricle 2-3.5 mm, narrowed suddenly to a short beak. *Stony or muddy lake-shores; more rarely in fens or damp grassland. Frequent in the West; rather rare elsewhere.*

Subsp. *oedocarpa* (*C. demissa*, *C. flava*). Stem up to 40 cm high, usually curved upwards from a prostrate base. Leaves usually somewhat shorter than the stem, often curved outwards. Male spikelet stalked. Utricle 3-4 mm, suddenly narrowed to a fairly long, forked beak. *Bog-margins, bare peat, acid marshes and damp grassland; very frequent to abundant.*

Subsp. *brachyrhyncha* (*C. lepidocarpa*). Stems straight, up to 65 cm high. Leaves equalling the stem or slightly shorter. Male spikelet usually shortly stalked. Utricles 3-5 mm, narrowed gradually to a beak nearly as long as the rest of the utricle, the lower ones bent downwards and somewhat curved. *Fens, calcareous marshes and lake-margins; very frequent in the West and Centre; rather rare elsewhere.*

39. C. pallescens. 5-6. Stems sharply 3-angled, tufted, up to 50 cm high. Leaves about as long as the stem, downy, at least on the sheaths, 2-5 mm wide. Lower bracts leaf-like, very shortly sheathing, usually overtopping the inflorescence. Male spikelet single. Female spikelets 2-3, close together, stalked; glumes brownish, about as long as the utricle, tapered to a slender point; utricle 2-3 mm green, shining, oblong-ellipsoid, obtuse, without beak. *Damp grassland or moorland and open woods; frequent, though local, in the North and West; rare elsewhere.*

40. C. caryophyllea. 4-6. Stems 3-angled, loosely tufted, up to 25 cm, leafy below. Leaves slightly shorter than the stem, 1-2 mm wide, tapered to a solid, 3 angled point. Lower bracts leaf-like, with a short but distinct sheath. Male spikelet single, often club-shaped (broadest near the tip). Female spikelets 1-3, closely clustered below the male, 5-10 mm long; glumes brown with a short green point; utricle 2-3 mm, green, downy, with a very short beak. *Dry grassland, mainly on base-rich soils; very frequent.*

41. C. pilulifera. 7-8. Like *C. caryophyllea*, but flowering later; stems densely tufted; bracts not sheathing; male spikelet slender, not club-shaped; female glumes without a distinct point. *Heathy grassland and stony ground on acid soils; frequent.*

42. C. limosa. 5-8. Stems slender, 3-angled, up to 40 cm high, arising singly from a far-creeping rhizome. Leaves about as long as the stem, 1-2 mm wide, somewhat pale bluish-green. Bracts leaf-like but short, not or very shortly sheathing. Male spikelet single. Female spikelets 1-3, stalked, drooping, usually with 10-12 flowers; glumes slightly wider and longer than the utricle, brownish, acute. Utricle 3-4 mm, green, with a short, truncate beak. *Wet bogs and margins of lakes and pools; locally frequent in the West, rare elsewhere.*

43. C. magellanica. 7-8. Like *C. limosa*, but stems loosely tufted; leaves 2-4 mm wide; female spikelets short, with fewer than 10 flowers; glumes narrower than the utricle; utricle without a beak. *Mountain bogs in Ulster; rare.*

(ii) Stigmas 2

The five species constituting this group have many features in common, and they hybridize frequently, forming fertile hybrids capable of back-crossing. This obscures the lines of specific difference. All members of the group have one or more slender, brown male spikelets, two or more erect, stalkless or shortly stalked female spikelets, leaf-like bracts without sheaths, female glumes purplish-black with conspicuous green midrib, contrasting with the green (rarely tinged with purple), flattish utricles, which have a very short, truncate beak.

44. C. aquatilis. 6-8. Stems up to 100 cm, very bluntly 3-angled, brittle. Leaves smooth and shiny, about as long as the stem, 3-5 mm wide; margins rolling inwards on drying; sheaths reddish. Lowest bract exceeding the inflorescence. Male spikelets 2-4. Female spikelets 2-5, slender, shortly stalked; glumes obtuse or acute, about as long as the utricle. *Rivers, drains and lake-margins; rare.*

45. C. bigelowii (*C. rigida*). **6-7.** Stems sharply 3-angled, stiff, arising singly from a creeping rhizome, 5-25 cm high. Leaves slightly shorter than the stem, stiff, often curved, 2-6 mm wide. Bracts leaf-like, short. Male spikelet usually single. Female spikelets 2-3, stalkless; glumes subacute, slightly longer than the utricle. *Mountain-summits and ridges, above 600 m; rather rare.*

46. C. elata (*C. hudsonii*). **4-5.** Stems sharply 3-angled, usually densely tufted and often forming large tussocks. Leaves about as long as the stem, rough; margins rolling outwards on drying. Bracts much shorter than the inflorescence. Male spikelet 1-3. Female spikelets 2-3, more or less stalkless; glumes acute to obtuse, narrower than the utricle and usually slightly shorter. *Lake-margins and marshes; locally frequent in the Centre, occasional elsewhere.*

47. C. nigra (*C. goodenowii*). **5-7.** Stems rather bluntly 3-angled, slender, loosely tufted, 10-60 cm high. Leaves shorter than or equalling the stem, pale bluish-green, 1-3 mm wide; margins rolling inwards on drying. Bracts shorter than the inflorescence or equalling it. Male spikelet 1-2. Female spikelets 2-4, the lowest shortly stalked; glumes obtuse to acute, usually shorter than the utricle. *Marshes, wet grassland and riversides; abundant in the North and West; frequent elsewhere.*

48. C. acuta (*C. gracilis*). **5-6.** Stems sharply 3-angled, at least above, stout, up to 120 cm high. Leaves equalling or longer than the stem, rather pale bluish-green, 3-10 mm wide; margins rolling outwards on drying. Bracts overtopping the inflorescence. Male spikelets 2-4. Female spikelets 2-4, up to 50 mm long, the lowest shortly stalked; glumes acute to obtuse, usually longer than the utricle. *Rivers and lake-margins, mainly in the North half; rather rare.*

Index to species of Carex

CXXXII. ORCHIDACEAE

Erect perennials, usually hairless, with irregular flowers in spikes or racemes. Leaves simple and stalkless. Perianth of 6 free segments, all more or less petal-like, but the 3 outer, which differ from the 3 inner in shape and often in colour, are known as sepals, and the 3 inner as petals. The lower petal, known as the *labellum*, always differs from the other 2. Stamen 1, fused with the style to form a central structure called the *column*, at the top of which can be seen the glistening stigma and, behind or above it, 2 *pollinia* (compact masses of pollen). Ovary inferior, 3-celled, often twisted; usually slender and resembling a pedicel. Fruit a capsule; seeds very minute and numerous [Fig. CXXXIIa].

An enormous family, of which many showy, tropical species are cultivated in hot-houses.

1. Leaves reduced to brown scales. Plant with no green parts .. **3. Neottia**
   Green leaves present. Plant with some parts green 2
2. Labellum without any spur or pouch 3
   Labellum drawn out at the back into a spur or pouch .. 8

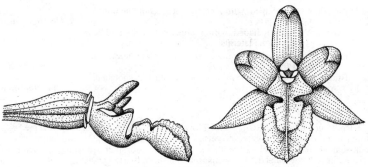

Fig. CXXXIIa

3. Flowers white or cream   4
    Flowers green, brown or multi-coloured, or, if white, tinged
       with red or brown   5
4. Flowers small, arranged in 1 or more spiral lines in a rather
       compact spike   ..   ..   ..   **5. Spiranthes**
    Flowers large, not spirally arranged, in a loose spike   **2. Cephalanthera**
5. Stem bearing only 2, almost basal leaves. Labellum with 2 long,
       narrow lobes   ..   ..   ..   **4. Listera**
    Stem usually with more than 2 leaves. Labellum entire, or with
       broad lobes   6
6. Labellum velvety, resembling the body of an insect or spider,
       central area often distinctively patterned and mutli-coloured   **14. Ophrys**
    Labellum not velvety, not resembling the body of an insect
       or spider; central area not multi-coloured   7
7. Stem 5-12 cm high. Flowers minute, yellowish-green   **15. Hammarbya**
    Stem 15-70 cm high. Flowers large, usually tinged with red
       or brown   ..   .. **1. Epipactis**
8. Flowers pink or purple   9
    Flowers white, green or brown   13
9. Spur slender and pointed, at least as long as the ovary   ..   10
    Spur short and stout, seldom as long as the ovary   11
10. Flowers not fragrant, in a very dense, pyrimidal spike. Labellum
       bearing 2 ridges on its upper surface near the base   **13. Anacamptis**
    Flowers fragrant, in a moderately dense, cylindrical spike.
       Labellum without ridges   ..   ..   **7. Gymnadenia**
11. Spur very short and pouch-like; flowers never opening very widely **11. Neotinea**
    Spur at least as long as the ovary; flowers opening widely   ..   12
12. Spur directed obliquely downwards, tapering to a pointed tip.
       Bracts often exceeding the flowers   ..   **10. Dactylorhiza**
    Spur directed upwards or horizontal, with a stout, blunt tip.
       Bracts usually not exceeding the flowers   ..   .. **12. Orchis**
13. Spur over 5 mm long   14
    Spur not more than 2.5 mm long   15
14. Spur 12-20 mm long; labellum strap-shaped   ..   **6. Platanthera**
    Spur about 6 mm long; labellum 3-lobed   ..   **10. Dactylorhiza**

15. Labellum strap-shaped, with 3 small apical teeth, the middle
the smallest .. .. .. **9. Coeloglossum**
Labellum not strap-shaped, with 3 largish lobes, the middle at
least as large as the laterals 16
16. Bracts longer than ovary; middle lobe of labellum not notched;
spur about $^1/_3$ as long as ovary .. .. **8. Pseudorchis**
Bracts shorter than ovary; middle lobe of labellum notched;
spur very short .. .. .. **11. Neotinea**

1. Epipactis

Roots not tuberous. Stem leafy. Flowers drooping, in a rather lax raceme with
longish, green bracts. Labellum constricted in the middle; upper half more or less
cup-shaped, the cup held beneath the column; lower half spreading or hanging,
triangular or heart-shaped. Ovary tapering to a short, twisted pedicel.
Further investigation of this genus is needed in Ireland.

1. Labellum at least as long as sepals, pinkish-white with yellow
spots .. .. **1. E. palustris**
Labellum barely equalling sepals, green or reddish 2
2. Inflorescence axis hairless. Flowers pendulous .. **3. E. phyllanthes**
Inflorescence axis downy. Flowers spreading or erect .. 3
3. Flowers entirely dark red; ovary hairy. Leaves in 2 ranks **4. E. atrorubens**
Flowers greenish, at least in part (the petals tinged with pink);
ovary nearly hairless. Leaves not in 2 ranks .. **2. E. helleborine**

1. Epipactis palustris. 6-7. Stem 20-60 cm high, thin and wiry, usually hairy
above. Leaves oblong-lanceolate, rather erect, 7-12 cm long. Flowers 17 mm across,
rather few, in a lax, somewhat 1-sided raceme. Sepals deep pink or purplish-red;
upper petals shorter and paler; labellum at least as long as sepals, white, veined with
red and with a yellow spot in the middle. Ovary slender, spindle-shaped, covered
with short down. *Marshes, bogs, lake-shores, and dune slacks; locally frequent, but
declining, in the Centre; rare elsewhere.*

2. E. helleborine (*E. latifolia*). **7-8.** Stem 30-80 cm high, hairy above. Leaves
broadly oval, dull green, strongly ribbed, flat, not in 2 ranks. Flowers 8-12 mm
across, in a long 1-sided raceme. Sepals dull green; upper petals shorter, tinged with
red; labellum reddish-pink, much shorter than sepals, with a sharp, reflexed tip.
Ovary pear-shaped or cylindrical, more or less hairless. *Woods and thickets; frequent
in parts of the North and West, rather rare elsewhere.*
Plants differing from *E. helleborine* in their greyish-green, lilac-tinged leaves and
flowers with a rather long, narrow labellum have been found in County Antrim: those
with the upper leaves in 2 ranks and a hairy ovary apparently correspond to *E.
youngiana*, those with spirally arranged upper leaves and a hairless ovary to *E.
purpurata*. Plants with a hairless ovary and upper leaves in 2 ranks correspond to *E.
leptochila*; however their occurrence in Ireland awaits confirmation.

3. E. phyllanthes. 6-8. Similar to *E. helleborine*, differing in its smaller, folded,
2-ranked leaves, smaller, pendulous, green flowers, and hairless axis to the inflorescence. *Woods and dune-slacks; very rare, known only from the South-east and North.*

4. E. atrorubens (*E. atropurpurea*). **7-8.** Stem 15-30 cm high, hairy, especially
in the upper part. Leaves oval-oblong to lanceolate, concave and keeled, arranged in
2 ranks. Flowers 8-12 mm across, in a stiff, spike-like raceme. Sepals, petals and
labellum dark red; labellum shorter than the sepals. Ovary downy, pear-shaped,

tapering to a very short pedicel. *Bare limestone hills; occasional in Clare and East Galway, unknown elsewhere.*

2. Cephalanthera

Cephalanthera longifolia (*C. ensifolia*). **6-7.** Stem slender, 25-60 cm high, bearing rather numerous, erect, linear-oblong strap-shaped leaves. Flowers pure white, 12 mm long, rather erect, usually few, in a lax, graceful spike. Bracts very small, except for the lowest 1 or 2, which are often leafy. Sepals lanceolate; upper petals shorter and broader. Labellum constricted in the middle as in *Epipactis*; lower half trough-shaped, with a yellow-orange spot near the base *Damp woods and scrub; largely in the South half; very rare.*

3. Neottia

Neottia nidus-avis. Bird's nest orchid. 6-7. Whole plant yellowish-brown. Stem 25-35 cm high, arising from a tangled mass of stout, fleshy fibres. Leaves reduced to brown scales. Flowers 10 mm across, on short, twisted pedicels, in a long, cylindrical, spike-like raceme. Sepals and upper petals oval, entire; labellum twice as wide as long, 2-lobed. *Woods; rare.*

4. Listera

Plants with a single pair of almost opposite, broadly oval, leaves, rather below the middle of the stem. Labellum long, hanging, 2-lobed. Ovary globular, on a distinct pedicel.

1. Labellum about 10 mm long, green .. .. .. **1. L. ovata**
   Labellum about 5 mm long or less, reddish-brown .. .. **2. L. cordata**

1. Listera ovata. Twayblade. 6-7. Stem 20-45 cm high; leaves 6-12 cm long, with sheathing bases, not cordate. Flowers green, rather small, numerous, in a long, slender, rather lax raceme. Sepals oval; upper petals linear-oblong, forming, with the sepals, a hood over the column. Labellum yellowish-green, 10 mm long, deeply divided into 2 linear, obtuse lobes. *Woods and damp pastures; frequent.*

2. L. cordata. Lesser twayblade. 6-8. Similar to *L. ovata*, but shorter (10-20 cm high), with longer, often cordate leaves; much smaller flowers reddish-brown, with the labellum no more than 5 mm long and deeply divided into 2 narrow, pointed lobes. *Usually among moss at the base of heather plants.*

5. Spiranthes

Flowers in a twisted spike, arranged in 1 or more spiral rows. Flowers white, scented; labellum scarcely longer than other petals or sepals, entire, without a spur.

1. Leaves oval. Flowers in a single, spirally twisted row .. **1. S. spiralis**
   Leaves lanceolate. Flowers in 3 spirally twisted rows **2. S. romanzoffiana**

1. Spiranthes spiralis. Lady's tresses. 8-9. Stem slender, 7-15 cm high, leafless, but with a rosette of small, oval, pale bluish-green leaves beside it. Flowers in a single, spirally twisted row, forming a slender spike. Sepals and petals free, the two lateral sepals pointing outwards. *Sandy ground and dry pastures, especially near the sea; locally frequent in the South half, but declining, very rare in the North.*

2. S. romanzoffiana. 7-8. Leaves linear-lanceolate, erect, some of them on the stem. Flowers in 3 spirally twisted rows, forming a short dense spike. Sepals and petals all united in the lower part. *Damp meadows, lake-shores and boggy ground in the South-west, West and North-east (around Lough Neagh); rare and very local inland. Outside of Ireland know only from western Britain and North America.*

6. Platanthera. Butterfly orchid

Stem bearing, near the base, a single pair of almost opposite large, oval leaves, and a few much smaller ones higher-up. Flowers whitish, fragrant, in a rather lax spike. Lateral sepals spreading; upper one erect, forming a hood with the petals. Labellum linear-oblong, entire, longer than the sepals. Spur very long and slender. Ovary curved and twisted, stalkless.

1. Pollinia parallel to one another   ..   ..   .. **1. P. bifolia**
   Pollinia diverging from each other   ..   ..   **2. P. chlorantha**

1. Platanthera bifolia. 6-7. 15-30 cm high; spike slender and almost cylindrical; flowers white or cream, only faintly tinged with green, 12-17 mm across; pollinia vertical and parallel. *Damp pastures and heaths; frequent in the West, Centre, and North; rarer in the East and South.*

2. P. chlorantha. 6-7. Similar to *P. bifolia* but bigger in most of its parts; 27-40 cm high; spike broader and slightly pyramidal; flowers with the labellum tinged with green, 17-25 mm across; pollinia leaning backwards, and diverging downwards. *Similar situations; frequent in most districts, though less so in the South-west.*

7. Gymnadenia

Gymnadenia conopsea. Fragrant orchid. 6-7. Stem leafy, 15-40 cm high. Leaves long and narrow, rather erect. Flowers numerous, 8 mm across, pinkish to reddish-purple, rarely white, fragrant, in a long, moderately lax, cylindrical spike. Bracts narrow, longer than the ovary. Upper sepal and petals forming a hood; labellum broad, with 3 short lobes and a slender, pointed, slightly curved spur longer than the ovary. Ovary slender, stalkless, twisted and curved. *Pastures, heathy grassland, dune slacks and cut-away bog; very frequent in the Centre, local elsewhere.*

Three sub-species are recognised in Britain, further work is needed to confirm their occurrence in Ireland. In subsp. *borealis* the labellum is narrow (4 mm wide) and scarcely lobed; flowers of subsp. *conopsea* have a spur 12-14 mm long and a deeply lobed labellum up to 6.5 mm wide and about the same length; whereas subsp. *densiflora* has a spur 14-16 mm long, a deeply lobed labellum 6.5-7 mm wide which is wider than long.

8. Pseudorchis

Pseudorchis albida (*Leuchorchis albida*). **6-7.** Stem 10-30 cm high, rather stiff, bearing, near the base 3-4 oblong leaves. Flowers white, slightly fragrant, 3-4 mm across, in a moderately dense, slightly 1-sided, cylindrical spike. Bracts slightly longer than ovary. Sepals and petals forming a loose hood. Labellum deeply 3-lobed; lobes nearly equal, entire. Spur obtuse, $1/3$ to $1/2$ as long as ovary. Ovary stalkless, slightly twisted. *Upland pastures and heaths; very rare.*

9. Coeloglossum

Coeloglossum viride. Frog orchid. 6-7. Stem 8-25 cm high, with about 4 bluish-green oval-oblong leaves near the base. Flowers greenish, often edged or suffused with reddish-brown, 8 mm across, in a short, cylindrical spike. Sepals and upper petals forming a hood. Labellum oblong, much longer than sepals, 3-lobed at the apex with the middle lobe much smaller than the laterals. Spur very short and obtuse. Ovary stalkless, twisted. *Heathy or gravelly pastures; fairly rare but easily overlooked.*

10. Dactylorhiza

Flowers pink or purple, in rather dense, usually cylindrical spikes. Sepals and upper petals nearly equal; labellum larger, bearing a pointed spur, directed obliquely downwards, somewhat shorter than ovary. Ovary cylindrical, twisted, stalkless.

A very variable genus, wherein hybridisation between species is common; this often makes individuals very difficult to identify. Our treatment is based on that of T. Curtis.

Dactylorhiza may hybridise with *Gymnadenia*. These hybrids generally resemble *Dactylorhiza* but the flowers are scented, of intermediate shape, with a longer spur and the leaves are only faintly spotted (hybrids between *G. conopsea* and *D. fuschii* or *D. maculata* are the most frequent).

1. Floral bracts short and narrow, 15 x 2.5 mm; flowers white
    or pink .. .. **1. D. maculata**
    Floral bracts long and wide, 20 x 5 mm; flowers purple, pink or red 2
2. Leaves broadest near the base and tapering towards the tip,
    light-green .. .. **2. D. incarnata**
    Leaves broadest near the middle or of the same length throughout,
    dark green .. .. **3. D. majalis**

1. Dactylorhiza maculata (*Dactylorchis maculata, D. fuchsii, Dactylorchis fuchsii, Orchis fuchsii*). **6-8.** Stems solid, 15-60 cm high. Leaves usually less than 7, 2-8 times as long as wide, usually heavily spotted with black, the lowest broadly oval-oblong, obtuse, scarcely keeled, the upper ones narrower, more pointed and keeled, usually not as long as the flowering-spike. Floral bracts about 15 x 2.5 mm. Flowers pink or mauve. Labellum flat, deeply and about equally 3-lobed, about 10 mm wide; the lateral lobes often crenate. Spur conical. *Wood margins, meadows, damp grassy places, moors, heathy pastures and bog-margins; frequent.*

There are 3 subspecies:
Subsp. *fuchsii* (*D. fuchsii, D. maculata*). The above description applies to subsp. *fuchsii* var. *fuchsii;* plants found on limestone grassland in the West with white flowers and unspotted leaves are a distinct variety (*Orchis okellyi, D. fuchsii* subsp. *okellyi*). Rare plants growing in wood and heathland margins in western regions, more than 40 cm tall with more than 7 lightly spotted leaves, are another distinct variety.

Subsp. *ericetorum* (*Orchis ericetorum*). Differs from subsp. *fuchsii* in that the middle lobe of the labellum is usually smaller than the two lateral lobes. *Heaths and bogs; frequent.*

Plants found on machair and cliff-tops, differing from subsp. *fuchsii* in that they are shorter and have darker pink flowers with a rather wide labellum (up to 12 mm) with the lateral lobes themselves lobed and a stout spur constitute a third sub-species (*D. fuchsii* subsp. *hebridensis*).

2. D. incarnata (*Dactylorchis incarnata, Orchis latifolia*). **6-8.** Stems hollow, 15-30 cm high. Leaves 3-5, 5-9 times as long as wide, usually unspotted, linear-lanceolate, broadest near the base, longer than the flowering-spike. Floral bracts about 19-28 x 6 mm. Flowers white, pink or purple. Labellum more or less entire, sometimes with a small apical tooth, about 8 mm wide. Spur tapering to a blunt point. *Marshy meadows, fens and dune slacks; frequent.*

There are 2 subspecies:
Subsp. *incarnata*. The above description applies to subsp. *incarnata* var. *incarnata* ; var. *haematoides* has rather narrower leaves spotted on one side only; var. *hyphamatoides* (sometimes called *D. incarnata* subsp. *cruenta*) from western Ireland also has narrower leaves though they are spotted on both sides.

Subsp. *coccinea* has red flowers and unspotted leaves. *Dune-slacks.*

3. D. majalis (*D. praetermissa*). **6-8.** Stems more or less solid, 10-70 cm high. Leaves 3-11, 2-6 times as long as wide, lanceolate, often spotted with overlapping black spots, broadest near the middle, slightly exceeding the flowering-spike. Floral bracts about 1-4 x 0.8 mm. Flowers mauve to purple. Labellum 3-lobed with the middle lobe by far the longest. Spur cylindrical. *Marshes, wet meadows, sand-dunes and pastures; widespread.*

There are 2 subspecies:

Subsp. *majalis.* The above description applies to subsp. *majalis* var. *majalis; var. brevifolia (D. purpurella)* has simple spots, sometimes confined to the tip, on the leaves, a tapering spur and a more or less unlobed, purple labellum

Subsp. *traunsteinerioides (D. traunsteinerioides, D. traunsteineri)* has faintly spotted or unspotted leaves at least 7 times as long as wide. *Bogs, fens and wet areas in machair.*

11. Neotinea

Neotinea maculata (*N. intacta*). **Irish orchid. 5-6.** Stem 12-25 cm high. Leaves few, oblong, often with purple spots. Flowers 3-4 mm across, never opening very fully, in a dense, narrow, cylindrical spike. Bracts shorter than ovary. Perianth greenish-white, often streaked with a dull purplish-pink. Sepals and upper petals forming a hood. Labellum small, hanging, 3-lobed; middle lobe the largest, slightly notched at the tip. Spur very short and blunt. Ovary twisted, stalkless. *Rocky pastures and hillsides, grassland on sandy or gravelly ground; occasional in parts of the West and Centre, unknown elsewhere.*

12. Orchis

Flowers purple, in spikes. Sepals and petals nearly equal; labellum larger, lobed, bearing a stout, obtuse, upwardly directed spur, slightly shorter than the ovary.

1. Lateral sepals green-veined, converging with the petals to form
   a helmet-like hood above the column. Leaves without spots .. **1. O. morio**
   Lateral sepals not green-veined, at first spreading, later folded
   back, but not forming a hood with the petals. Leaves usually
   spotted .. .. **2. O. mascula**

1. Orchis morio. Green-winged orchid. 5-6. Stem hollow, 7-30 cm high. Leaves lanceolate, more or less basal. Flowers few, 15-20 mm across, in a short and rather lax cylindrical spike. Sepals purple or mauve, veined with green, all joining with the upper petals to form a hood. Labellum purple or mauve, broader than long, convex, shallowly lobed. Spur straight. *Meadows, pastures and sandhills; occasional and declining, in the Centre and parts of the East, rare elsewhere.*

2. O. mascula. Early purple orchid. 4-5. Stem 12-35 cm high, stout, usually solid. Leaves oblong, usually with dark spots. Flowers 20 mm across, reddish-purple, not fragrant, in a long moderately dense, cylindrical spike. Bracts very slender, about as long as ovary. Lateral sepals erect; upper one arched forward over the upper petals. Labellum broad, convex, 3-lobed; middle lobe the longest, often notched, with a pale, dark spotted area in the centre. Spur curved. *Damp pastures, shady banks and thickets; frequent.*

13. Anacamptis

Anacamptis pyramidalis. 6-7. Stem 25-45 cm high, slender or hairless. Leaves linear-lanceolate, mostly basal or nearly so. Flowers bright rose-pink or magenta, numerous, 6-8 mm across, in a short very dense, pyramidal spike. Sepals lanceolate; upper petals similar but smaller, erect; labellum flat, with 3 blunt lobes, drawn out at the base into a very slender pointed spur, usually longer than the ovary. Ovary cylindrical, twisted, stalkless. *Pastures, banks and sandhills; frequent in the Centre, rather rare elsewhere.*

14. Ophrys

Stem leafy. Flowers few, in a slender spike. Labellum convex, velvety, not deeply lobed, without a spur, resembling the body of an insect or spider. Ovary slender, stalkless, not twisted.

1. Labellum distinctly longer than wide, with a blue patch in the centre .. .. **1. O. insectifera**
   Labellum about as long as wide, without a blue patch in the centre .. .. **2. O. apifera**

1. Ophrys insectifera (*O. muscifera*). **Fly orchid. 6.** Stem slender, 20-40 cm high. Leaves oblong-lanceolate. Flowers about 15-20 mm across, 3-6 in a very lax spike. Sepals pale green, spreading, upper petals very narrow, reddish-brown. Labellum slightly convex, longer than the sepals, longer than wide, distinctly 3-lobed, the large middle lobe notched, reddish-brown with a blue patch in the centre. *Fens and limestone pavement in the Centre and West rare.*

2. O. apifera. Bee orchid. 6-7. Similar, but flowers somewhat larger, about 20-25 mm across with pink sepals and stem slightly stouter. Labellum broader than the sepals and almost as long, velvety-brown with yellow markings, lobed, but owing to its convexity appearing entire from in front. *Dry banks, sand dunes and grassland on limestone soils; local and rare.*

15. Hammarbya

Hammarbya paludosa (*Malaxis paludosa*). **7-9.** A very small plant, with a slender stem 5-12 cm high, bulbous near the base, and with 2-5 small, concave, oval leaves, basal or nearly so, often fringed with minute bulbs from which new plants develop. Flowers yellowish-green, 4 mm across, in a rather dense, spike-like raceme; each flower is inverted, so that the labellum, which is flanked by the paired sepals, is uppermost, and the unpaired sepal lowest. Perianth segments entire; petals, including labellum, shorter than the sepals. *Wet spongy bogs, usually in tufts of* Sphagnum; *very rare.*

GLOSSARY OF TECHNICAL TERMS

Achene. A dry, indehiscent, one-seeded fruit with a membranous pericarp.

Alternate. Arising singly, not in pairs or whorls [Glos. Fig. 1].

Annual. A plant which grows from seed, flowers and dies, all within a period of twelve months.

Anther. The upper part of a stamen, in which the pollen is produced [Glos. Fig. 2].

Aril. An extra coat, usually rather fleshy, found on certain seeds, outside the normal seed-coat.

Auricle. One of the projecting lobes at either side of the base of a cordate, sagittate or stem-clasping leaf [Glos. Fig. 3].

Awn. A long, bristle-like point; commonly borne by the glumes of certain grasses, *e.g.*, Barley [Glos. Fig. 4].

Axil. The angle between a leaf and the stem just above its point of attachment. Each axil normally contains a bud.

Axillary. Arising from, or situated in the axil of a leaf.

Basal. Refers to leaves arising from the extreme base of the stem.

Berry. A fleshy fruit, usually rather small, containing one or more seeds in a pericarp which is entirely succulent.

Biennial. A plant which normally lives for about two years, producing leaves and often a stout root the first year, and flowers the second.

Bifid. Deeply divided, usually lengthwise, into two.

Biternate. A ternate leaf in which the divisions are themselves ternate.

Bract. A leaf, usually smaller and often different in shape or texture from the foliage leaves, which is closely associated with a flower or inflorescence. Bracts may be solitary, or grouped together in an involucre. In the Umbelliferae the members of the involucre at the base of the general umbel are called bracts, those at the base of the primary umbels bracteoles.

Bracteole. A small bract at the base of a single flower in a compound inflorescence; and especially one at the base of a partial umbel in a member of the Umbelliferae [Glos. Fig. 5].

Calyx. The sepals, considered as a whole, whether free or united; forming the outermost whorl of floral parts [Glos. Fig. 2].

Capsule. A dry, dehiscent fruit, formed from two or more carpels, usually containing numerous seeds.

Carpel. One of the units of which the pistil is composed, consisting of an ovary, style and stigma. Sometimes each flower has a single carpel: more often there are two or more, which may be quite free from each other or wholly or partly fused together [Glos. Fig. 2].

Catkin. A type of inflorescence characteristic of the families numbered XXI to XXV in this book. It is typically a cylindrical spike, ultimately falling as a whole, made up of numerous, small unisexual flowers, with an inconspicuous perianth or none, arranged singly or in small groups in the axis of usually crowded and overlapping-scale-like bracts.

Cordate. Notched or indented at the base, where the stalk is attached [Glos. Fig. 6].

Corm. A storage organ, found in the *Crocus*, *Gladiolus*, *etc.,* looking superficially like a bulb, but consisting of a swollen stem-base instead of swollen leaves.

Corolla. The petals, considered as a whole, whether free or united; found immediately inside the calyx [Glos. Fig. 2].

Corymb. A raceme or panicle (or cyme) in which the flowers that arise from lower down on the axis have longer stalks than those that arise higher up, so that all the flowers are brought to about the same level and the inflorescence has a flat top [Glos. Fig. 7].

Cotyledon. The first leaf, or one of the first pair of leaves produced by a plant; it is already formed in the seed.

Crenate. Scalloped, *i.e.* with very blunt, rounded teeth [Glos. Fig. 8].

Cyme. An inflorescence in which the terminal or central flower is the first to open, subsequent flowers being produced on branches which arise below it. This flower terminates the main axis, whereas in a raceme the axis continues to grow as long as flowers are being produced. Sometimes the branches of a cyme arise on one side only, so as to produce the appearance of a somewhat coiled raceme [Glos. Fig. 9].

Dehiscent. Splitting when ripe, so as to release the seeds while the fruit remains attached to the plant.

Dicotyledon. A member of the larger of the principal classes into which flowering plants are divided. Dicotyledons are usually characterized by the possession of two seed-leaves (cotyledons) in the seedling, leaves in which the veins branch freely, forming an irregular network without parallel members, and flowers in which the parts are not in threes or sixes.

Dioecious. Having the male and female flowers on different plants (*cv.* monoecious).

Disc-floret. The collective term for the tubular florets found at the centre of the head of a member of the Compositae where the outer florets are ligulate; disc-florets have a tubular corolla, with 5 small, triangular apical teeth (*cv.* ray-floret) [Glos. Fig. 10].

Drupe. A fruit in which the outer part of the pericarp is fleshy and the inner part hard and woody, forming one or more stones to the fruit, in each of which is a single seed.

Entire. With a smooth, continuous margin; neither lobed nor toothed [Glos. Fig. 11].

Epicalyx. A ring of bracts immediately below the calyx and sometimes partly fused with it, looking like a second calyx superimposed on the first.

Filament. The stalk of the stamen, on which the anther is borne [Glos. Fig. 2].

Flexuous. Wavy.

Floret. A single flower in an inflorescence which consists of a large number of small flowers massed together (as in the Compositae).

Follicle. A dry, dehiscent fruit, splitting along one margin, formed from a carpel of an un-united pistil.

Free central. A placenta which has the form of a column in the centre of the cavity of a 1-celled ovary, attached to the base but not to the walls [Glos. Fig. 12].

Fruit. The structure, whether dry or fleshy, into which the ovary is transformed after fertilization; in it are contained the seed or seeds.

General Umbel. A compound inflorescence in the Umbelliferae formed by the meeting together, at one point, of the stalks of the primary umbels.

Glabrous. Hairless.

Glume. The 2 outermost, small, chaffy bracts which enclose the flowers of sedges and grasses [Glos. Fig. 4].

Gymnosperm. A member of one of the principal classes into which flowering plants are divided, represented in Ireland by the Coniferae. They differ from Dicotyledons and Monocotyledons (which together constitute the Angiosperms) in several important respects, particularly in the position of their ovules, which are exposed to the air at the time of fertilization, instead of being inside a closed ovary.

Hastate. Arrow-shaped but with a pair of pointed lobes at the base, directed outwards [Glos. Fig. 13].

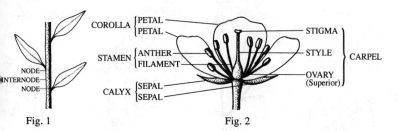

Fig. 1

Fig. 2

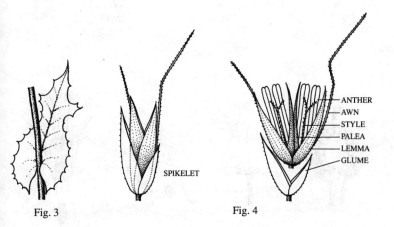

Fig. 3

SPIKELET

Fig. 4

ANTHER
AWN
STYLE
PALEA
LEMMA
GLUME

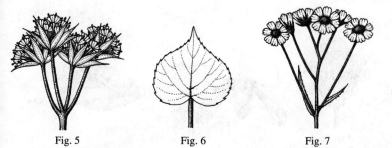

Fig. 5

Fig. 6

Fig. 7

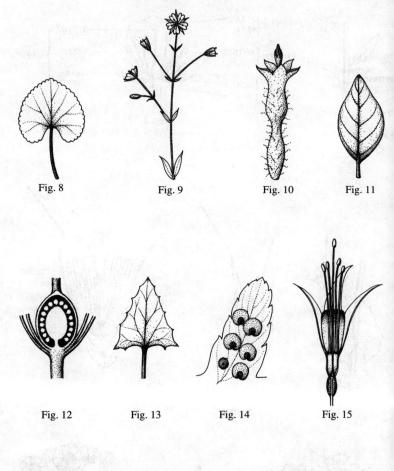

Fig. 8

Fig. 9

Fig. 10

Fig. 11

Fig. 12

Fig. 13

Fig. 14

Fig. 15

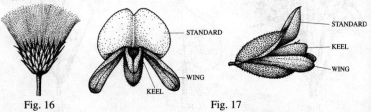

Fig. 16

STANDARD

WING

KEEL

Fig. 17

STANDARD

KEEL

WING

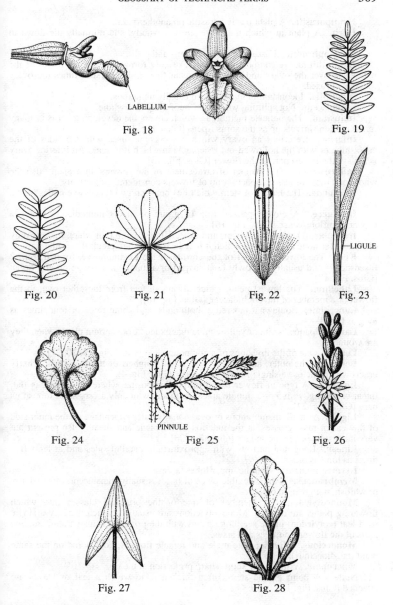

LABELLUM

Fig. 18

Fig. 19

Fig. 20

Fig. 21

Fig. 22

LIGULE

Fig. 23

Fig. 24

PINNULE

Fig. 25

Fig. 26

Fig. 27

Fig. 28

Hemiparasite. A plant partly parasitic on another plant.

Herb. A plant in which the stems are not woody, and normally die down in winter.

Hermaphrodite. Possessing both stamens and pistil.

Hypanthium. A compound structure, usually formed by the upgrowth of the receptacle over the ovary and their subsequent fusion, though sometimes the ovary remains unfused.

Indefinite. Inconstant in number, and usually numerous.

Indehiscent. Not splitting when ripe, but falling as a whole.

Indusium. The delicate membrane which covers the developing sorus in many ferns; it often shrivels up as the sorus ripens [Glos. Fig. 14].

Inferior. Describes an ovary which has become fused with the sides of the calyx-tube or with the hollowed-out receptacle in which it is sunk. An inferior ovary is always the lowest part of the flower [Glos. Fig. 15].

Inflorescence. The manner of arragement of the flowers on a plant; also the whole of a more or less compact group of flowers considered collectively.

Internode. The length of stem which lies between two successive nodes [Glos. Fig. 1].

Involucre. A closely-packed ring or group of bracts immediately below a flower or inflorescence [Glos. Fig. 16].

Irregular. Describes a flower, and especially its corolla, in which there is only one plane (or none at all) along which it may be divided into precisely similar halves.

Keel. The lowest segment of the corolla of the Leguminosae, formed from 2 fused petals and usually narrowly boat-shaped <u>or</u> a longitudinal ridge on any organ [Glos. Fig. 17].

Labellum. The lowest petal, which always differs from the other two, in the flower of a member of the Orchidaceae [Glos. Fig. 18].

Lanceolate. Somewhat tapered at both ends, and about three or four times as long as broad.

Latex. Opaque, white or yellow juice that exudes from certain plants when they are wounded.

Leaflet. One of the divisions of a compound leaf [Glos. Fig. 19, 20, 21]..

Lemma. The outer, and usually larger and tougher, of the two small, chaffy bracts which enclose a single flower of a grass [Glos. Fig. 4].

Ligulate. A type of flower found in the Compositae where the corolla is flat, linear or oblong, with 3 or 5 minute apical teeth and with only a very short tube at its base [Glos. Fig. 22].

Ligule. A small, membranous or occasionally hairy appendage on the inner side of the leaf of most grasses, at the junction of the blade and sheath; also present but very inconspicuous in the sedges [Glos. Fig. 23].

Linear. Long and narrow, with approximately parallel sides and at least five times as long as broad.

Lyrate. Pinnatifid with the upper lobes largest.

Membranous. A thin, flexible piece of tissue, usually translucent, often silvery or whitish, not green in colour.

Monocotyledon. A member of one of the principal classes into which flowering plants are divided. Monocotyledons are usually characterized by a single seed-leaf (cotyledon) in the seedling, leaves with the principal veins parallel, and the parts of the flowers in threes and sixes.

Monoecious. With separate male and female flowers, both borne on the same plant (*cv.* dioecious).

Mucronate. With a very short, sharp projection at the tip.

Node. A point on the stem, often thickened, to which a leaf or leaves are attached [Glos. Fig. 1].

Nut. A dry, indehiscent fruit with a woody pericarp and a single seed.

Nutlet. One of the four small, seed-like portions of which the fruit of members of the Boraginaceae and the Labiatae consists.

Oblong. With sides nearly parallel for most of their length, and with the length two to five times the breadth.

Opposite. Arising in pairs, one on either side of the stem.

Oval. Used in this book in a wide sense, to describe any flat structure which is more or less elliptical and one and a half to three times as long as broad.

Ovary. The principal and lowest part of a carpel, or of a fused pistil; it contains the ovules [Glos. Fig. 2].

Ovoid. Approximately egg-shaped; describes a solid object which, viewed from the side, presents an oval image.

Ovule. A minute, ovoid body, found inside the ovary, which after fertilization develops into a seed.

Palea. The inner, and usually the more delicate, of the two small, chaffy bracts which enclose the flower of a grass [Glos. Fig. 4].

Palmate. Describes a compound leaf or other organ, in which the leaflets or segments radiate outwards from nearly the same point, somewhat like the fingers of an outstretched hand [Glos. Fig. 21].

Panicle. A branched raceme, *i.e.,* an inflorescence in which the branches, themselves racemes, are arranged like the flowers in a simple raceme; also, more loosely, any freely branched inflorescence that is not obviously a cyme or corymb.

Pappus. The hairs or scales (representing the calyx) which crown the fruit of many members of the Compositae and Valerianaceae [Glos. Fig. 22].

Parietal. Describes a placenta where the ovules are attached to the ovary wall; the ovules may be directly attached and obviously peripheral or connected to the ovary wall through an outgrowth of tissue and so held in a more central location in the ovary.

Pedicel. The stalk of a single flower in an inflorescence.

Peduncle. The stalk of an inflorescence, or of a solitary flower.

Peltate. With the stalk attached to the lower surface, and not to the margin [Glos. Fig. 24].

Perennial. Living normally for more than two years. In herbaceous perennials most of the stem dies down each winter, but the rootstock survives.

Perianth. The calyx and corolla together; used especially to describe structures which may be calyx or corolla or both.

Pericarp. The main part of the fruit, excluding the seeds; it is formed from the wall of the ovary.

Petal. One of the individual elements of the corolla; usually conspicuously coloured and forming the most visible part of the flower [Glos. Fig. 2].

Pinna. One of the primary divisions, springing from the rachis, into which the leaves of most ferns is divided [Glos. Fig. 25].

Pinnate. Describes a compound leaf or other organ in which the leaflets or segments are arranged in two ranks on opposite sides of the axis, like the barbs of a feather [Glos. Fig. 19, 20].

Pinnule. One of the secondary divisions of a fern leaf, bearing the same relation to a pinna as the pinna does to the whole leaf [Glos. Fig. 25].

Pistil. The carpel or carpels of a flower, whether free or united.

Placenta. The part of the inner surface of the ovary to which the ovules are attached.

Primary Umbel. In the Umbelliferae one of the number of small umbels whose stalks all meet together at one point forming the general umbel.

Pteridophyta. A primary division of the plant kingdom, to which the ferns, horsetails, club-mosses and a few other plants belong. They differ from the seed-plants in many important features, and especially in that the body which is dispersed for reproductive purpose is a minute spore and not a seed.

Raceme. An inflorescence in which a number of stalked flowers are arranged along a single, unbranched axis, which continues to grow during the development of the flowers, so that the oldest flowers are at the base and the youngest at the tip [Glos. Fig. 26].

Rachis. The axis of a fern-leaf, to which the pinnae are attached.

Ray-floret. The collective term for the ligulate florets found at the periphery of the head of a member of the Compositae where the inner florets are tubular; ray-florets have a flat, linear or oblong, corolla, with 3 or 5 minute apical teeth and with only a very short tube at their base (*cv.* Disc-floret) [Glos. Fig. 22].

Receptacle. The apex of the peduncle, on which the various parts of the flower (or, in flower-heads like those of the Compositae, the florets) are inserted.

Regular. Describes a flower, and especially its corolla, which can be divided along several different planes into precisely similar halves.

Rhizome. A stem which creeps on or below the surface of the ground, usually somewhat root-like in appearance.

Rib. An elevated piece of tissue which runs across the long-axis of an organ.

Ridge. An elevated piece of tissue which runs along the long-axis of an organ (a term often confused with a rib).

Root-stock. That part of the stem of an herbacious perennial, more or less underground, which persists from one year to another ; it varies from a densely tufted mass of stem bases to a long creeping rhizome.

Runner. A branch of the stem which creeps along the surface of the ground, and usually takes root at some distance from the parent plant.

Sagittate. Shaped like an arrow-head, i.e., somewhat triangular with pointed lobes at the base, the lobes directed backwards along the stalk [Glos. Fig. 27].

Sepal. A constituent element of the calyx; found outside of the petals, normally smaller than them and green [Glos. Fig. 2].

Sorus. A compact group of sporangia on the leaf of a fern.

Spike. An inflorescence which resembles a raceme except that the flowers are sessile on the axis.

Spikelet. One of the small, compact spikes in which the flowers of sedges and grasses are arranged, together with glumes [Glos. Fig. 4].

Sporangium. A minute vessel in which the spores of Pteridophytes are developed.

Stamen. The male reproductive structure in the flowering plants; comprising the pollen producing anther and its stalk, the filament.

Staminode. A sterile stamen.

Standard. The upstanding petal in the flowers of the Leguminosae; although comprising a single petal, the standard is often notched in the middle and so falsely appears to be formed from the fusion of 2 petals [Glos. Fig. 17].

Stigma. The uppermost part of the carpel, usually sticky or rough, on which the pollen germinates [Glos. Fig. 2].

Stipule. A small, leaf-like or scale-like appendage found, nearly always in pairs, at the base of the petioles of many plants [Glos. Fig. 28].

Stolon. A creeping stem, above ground and usually leafy, arising from the base of the main stem of the plant, which is erect.

Style. The stalk-like part of a carpel or pistil, which arises from the top of the ovary and supports the stigma [Glos. Fig. 2].

Superior. Describes an ovary which is not fused with the receptacle or calyx-tube, even though it may be deeply sunk in it [Glos. Fig. 2].

Sympetalous. With the petals united, at least at the base.

Ternate. Divided into 3 leaflets or segments, like the leaf of a shamrock.

Tubular. Florets in the Compositae which have a tubular corolla, with 3 or 5 small, triangular apical teeth [Glos. Fig. 10].

Tubercle. A small swelling, usually oval or circular in shape.

Umbel. An inflorescence in which the stalks of all the flowers radiate from a single point. In a compound umbel the stalks of a number of partial umbels meet in a point, forming the general umbel.

Unisexual. Describes a flower which possesses stamens or pistil, but not both.

Vein. A strand of conducting tissue, forming a usually raised line on a leaf.

Viviparous. Bearing leafy buds in place of flowers.

Whorled. Arising in groups of three or more from the same point on the stem.

Wing. One of the 2 lateral petals in the Leguminosae; usually closely appressed to the keel, one on either side [Glos. Fig. 17].

GLOSSARY OF LATIN NAMES

Derivations.

A large proportion of the scientfic names of Irish plants are of classical Latin or Greek origin and are probably obscure to present-day readers. This glossary lists names of species commonly found in Ireland and other names that re-occur in the flora, and gives their botanical meaning.

The full name of a species is a combination of a generic name with a specific name following; usually the generic name is a noun and the specific epithet is a qualifying adjective. When species or genera are first named, the names chosen often relate to some obvious feature of the morphology of the plant, or the geographical location in which it was first found, or the type of habitat it grows in, or some important botanist, or the supposed medical properties of the plant. Many people find that an understanding of the derivation of the name of the species is useful as it helps them to recall, more easily, the plant to which the name refers. Most names of species are combinations of Latin or Greek words and a number of suffixes and prefixes are therefore used again and again in their construction.

Suffixes:

It is common to see names of species ending in *i* or *ii* or *ianum e.g. Fumaria bastardii* or *Epilobium komorovianum.* These endings are used to commemorate well-known botanists, often that botanist responsible for first finding the species (in the first example the person concerned is the Frenchman Toussaint Bastard and in the second, the Russian Alexander Komorov). The choice of ending (*i, ii, ianum etc.*) depends on a complex set of rules.

A common suffix *-alis* - indicates belonging to - *e.g. autumnalis* means Autumnal or belonging to Autumn and *occidentalis* means Western or belonging to the West. Another suffix *-anus* - as in *africanus* for example, has much the same meaning.

Other common endings *-ensis* - as in *pratensis*, *-iana* as in *virginiana* and *-icum* as in *pensylvanicum* indicate a country or place or habitat where the species was originally found.

A number of rather less common suffixes are *-odes* - which means having the form of, or resembling, hence *horminiodes* which indicates resemblance to a related genus *Horminium; -folia* which indicates some quality associated with the leaf - *e.g.*, *latifolia* indicates a broad leaf and *ensifolia* a sword-shaped leaf; *-caulis* - indicates a quality associated with the stem - as in *multicaulis* - many stemmed; *-rhiza* indicates qualities associated with the root - as in *polyrhiza* which means with many roots; *-escens* - which indicates the process of becoming, or not fully achieved resemblance - as in *rubescens* which means to grow red and *senescens* which means becoming old.

Prefixes:

There are a number of prefixes used to indicate quantity: for example, *uni* - means single, hence *uniflora* (single-flowered), *bi* -means two as in *biennis* (two years), *bifolia* (two-leaved), *biflora* (two-flowered) or *binervis* (two-nerved); *di* -also means two and appears in combination as *diandra* (literally 2 men; but used to mean with 2 stamens), similarly *digyna* means having 2 styles and *dioica* literally means with 2 houses but is used to indicate that the male and female flowers appear on separate plants *i.e.* the plant is dioecious; *tri* - is used similarly to indicate three, as in *triandra* (with three stamens), *trifoliata* (literally with three leaves; actually with three leaflets). Another common example is *atro-* (from the Latin ater) which means dark as in *atrocinerea* (dark ashy-grey) or *atropurpurea* (dark red or purple).

315

acaulis	stemless
acris	sharp, pungent
acutum, acutus	sharply pointed
aestivum	flowering or fruiting in summer
agrestis	growing in fields
alata	winged
alba, album, albida	white
alliaria	smelling of garlic
alpina, alpinus, alpinum	alpine; *i.e.,* confined in some countries, but not always in Ireland, to high mountains
altissima	very tall
amphibium	living on land or in water
amplexicaule	with leaves clasping the stem
anglica, anglicum	English
angustifolia, angustifolium	narrow-leaved
annua, annuus	annual
anserina	eaten by geese
apetela	without petals
apifera	bee-bearing
aquatica, aquaticus, aquatilis	growing in water
aquifolium	needle-leaved
arabica	Arabian
arborea	tree-like
arenaria, arenarius	growing in sand
argentea	silver-white
articulatus	jointed
arvense, arvensis	growing in ploughed fields or arable land
ascendens	ascending, *i.e.,* creeping at the base only
asperrough,	harsh
atrocinerea	dark ashy-grey
atropurpurea	dark red or purple
aurita	eared
australe	Southern
auriculata	with ear-like projecting appendages at the base of a leaf
autumnalis	Autumnal
avium	of birds
baccata	with berries
biennis	biennial
biflorus	two-flowered
bifolia	two-leaved
binervis	two-nerved
boreale	Northern
bracteata	having bracts, or modified leaves
bufonius	of toad (refers to the damp habitat)
bulbosus	bulbous
caerulea	dark blue
caesius	blue-grey
caespitosus	tufted
calycinum	with a large calyx
campestre, campestris	common, or growing in fields or plains

canina, caninus	dog-like; a term applied to a useless plant
capreolata	with tendrils
caryophyllea	Carnation-like
catharticus	purging
cernua	nodding
chinensis	Chinese
chlorantha	green-flowered
ciliata, ciliatum, ciliaris	with eye-lash like hairs on the margin
cineraria, cinerea	ashy-grey
circinatus	coiled inwards, with the tip innermost
claviculata	with tendrils
collina	growing on hills
coloratus	coloured
communis	common
commutatus	confused (with another species)
compressa	squeezed together
cordata	heart-shaped
corniculata, corniculatus	horned
crispa, crispus	curled
cristatus	crested
crocata, crocatum	saffron-yellow
cyanus	dark blue
danica	Danish
decumbens	creeping, but with the apex erect
demersum	submerged
denticulata	finely-toothed
diandra	two stamens
digyna	two styles
dioica	dioecious; male and female flowers borne on separate plants
dissectum	cut in pieces
distans	standing apart, not fused
disticha	in two rows
dubia, dubium	doubtful, *i.e.*, likely to be confused with other species
dunense	growing on sand-dunes
dysenterica	curing (or perhaps causing) dysentry
echinata	spiny
effusus	poured-out; hence scattered or loosely spreading
elatior	taller; hence very tall
ensifolia	with sword-shaped leaves
erecta, erectus, erectum	upright
europaea, europaeus	European
excelsior	taller; hence very tall or lofty
exigua	small, petty, weak
extensa	stretched-out
ficaria	Fig-like
filiformis	thread-like
fistulosa	hollow
flammula	a little flame

flava, flavum	golden-yellow
flavescens	becoming golden-yellow
flexilis	pliable, easy to bend
flexuosa, flexuosus	tortuous, zig-zag
fluitans	floating
fluviatile, fluviatilis	growing in rivers
foetidissima	evil-smelling
fontana	growing beside springs
fragilis	brittle
fragrans	with a pleasant smell
fruticosa, fruticosus	shrubby
fulva	tawny
fusca	dark coloured; especially dark brown
gallica, gallicum	French
geniculatus	bent sharply, like a knee
germanica	German
gigantea	very large
glabra	smooth, hairless
glabriuscula	nearly hairless
glandulifera	bearing glands
glauca	silvery or bluish-grey
glomerata	crowded together
glutinosa	sticky
gracilis	slender
gramineus	grass-like
grandiflora	with large flowers
graveolens	strongly smelling
guttatum	spotted
hastata	spear-shaped
hederaceus	Ivy-shaped
hederifolia, hederifolium . . .	Ivy-leaved
herbacea	herb-like, not shrubby
heterophyllus, heterophyllum . .	with leaves of two kinds
hibernica	Irish
hircinum	smelling of goats
hirsuta, hisutum, hirta . . .	hairy
hispidus	hairy, with rough stiff hairs
humile	low-growing
hypnoides	moss-like
incana	hoary, white
incarnata	flesh-coloured
inflata	swollen
inflexus	curved, bent inwards
inodora	without a smell
intermedia	intermediate bewteen two species
interruptus	interrupted
italicum	Italian
japonica	Japanese
junceum	Rush-like

lacustris	growing in or beside lakes
laevigatum	smooth
lanatus	woolly
lanceolatus	spear-shaped, lanceolate
latifolia	broad-leaved
littoralis	growing on the shore
lucens, lucidum	shining, glistening
lutea, luteum, luteola	yellow
maculatum	spotted
majalis	of the month of May
major, majus	larger, greater
marginata	bordered
marina, marinum	growing in the sea
maritima, maritimum, maritimus	growing near the sea
mascula	male
media, medium	intermediate, usually in size, between two other species
micrantha	small-flowered
microphyllus	small-leaves
minima, minimum, minimus	smallest or very small
minor, minus	smaller
mite	soft, not sharp, mild
molle, mollis	soft
montana, montanum, montanus	growing in the mountains
moschata, moschatum, moschatus	smelling of musk
multicaulis	with many stems
multiflorus	with many flowers
murale	growing on walls
nana	dwarf
napa	an old name for a Turnip
napellus	Turnip-rooted
natans	swimming, *i.e.*, floating
neglecta, neglectum	neglected
nemoralis, nemorosa, nemorum	growing in woods and glens
niger, nigra, nigrum	black
nitens	shining
nobilis	stately, excellent
nodosa, nodosum	knotted, with numerous joints
nutans	nodding
obscurum	obscure, hard to distinguish
obtusifolius	with blunt leaves
occidentalis	Western
odorata	sweet-smelling, scented
officinale, officinalis, officinarum	used in pharmacy; *i.e.*, at some time used medicinally and then, but perhaps not now, officially recognised as a drug-plant
oleracea, oleraceum, oleraceus	eaten as a vegetable, cultivated
oppositifolia, oppositifolium	opposite leaved
ovata, ovatus	oval

pallescens	becoming pale
paludosa, paludosum, palustre, palustris	growing in marshes
paniculata, paniculatum	panicled
parviflora, parviflorus	small-flowered
pendula	hanging-down, drooping
perenne, perennis	everlasting, perennial
pilosa	softly hairy
pinnatum	feather-like
plicata	folded
polita	polished
praecox	flowering or fruiting early
praelongus	very long
pratense, pratensis	growing in meadows
procera	tall
procumbens	falling down, *i.e.* creeping or trailing
pubens	exuberant, vigorous, but probably intended or an alternative to pubescens
pubescens	becoming downy
pulchella, pulchellum	small and pretty
pulchra, pulcher, pulchrum	beautiful
pulegium	driving away fleas
pulicaris	to do with fleas
punctata	covered with dots
purpurea, purpureum	crimson or purple
pusillus, pusillum	small or insignificant
pyramidalis	pyramidal
racemosus	with a raceme-like panicle
radicans	taking root (at the nodes of creeping stems)
radicata	with a strong tap-root
ramosus	branching
rapa	an old name for a Turnip
reflexum	bent-back
regalis	royal
remota	distant
repens, reptans	creeping
rigida	stiff
rimosa	fissured
riparia	growing on river-banks
roseum	rosy
ruber, rubrum	red
rufus	reddish-brown
rupestre, rupestris, rupicola	growing in rocky places
salicaria, salicina, salicifolia	Willow-leaved
salina	growing in salt-marshes
sanguinea	blood-red
sativa	cultivated, planted
saxatile, saxatilis	growing among rocks
scabra, scabrum	rough
sceleratus	wicked; hence noxious or poisonous
scordium, scorodonia	smelling of Garlic
scoticus, scoticum	Scottish

segetum	growing in cornfields
sempervirens	everlasting
senescens	becoming old
sepium	growing in hedges
serotina	late, backward
serpyllifolia	Thyme-leaved
sessiflora	with stalkless flowers
setaceus	bristle-like
sibirica	Siberian
simplex	simple, unbranched
somniferum	sleep-inducing
speciosa, speciosum	showy, handsome
spicata	with the flowers in a spike
spinosa	spiny
spiralis	spirally-twisted
squalidus	dirty
squarrosus	rough and scaly
stellata, stellaris	star-like
sterilis	barren
striatum	finely-grooved
stricta	very straight, erect
suaveolens	sweet-smelling
subulata	awl-shaped
sylvatica, sylvaticum, sylvaticus	growing in woods. The name is inapposite in Ireland for a number of species
sylvestris	wild, not cultivated
temulentum	drunken; from the supposedly intoxicating qualities of the grain
tenella	delicate
tenuifolium	fine-leaved
tenuis	fine, slender
tetralix	leaves in fours, forming a cross
tinctoria	used in dying
tomentosa	covered with matted, woolly hairs
trivialis	common, ordinary
tuberosum	tuberous
uliginosum	growing in marshes
ulmaria	Elm-like
uniflora	single flowered
urbanum	growing in the city or town
urens	burning, stinging
vaginatum	sheathed
verna, veris	flowering in spring
versicolor	changing colour
verum	true; the species to which the generic name was first applied
verticillata	whorled
vesca	thin, weak
vesicaria	bladder-like, swollen
villosa	shaggy
vineale	wine-coloured

vivipera, viviperum	bearing live young, *i.e.*, producing plantlets on the inflorescence (a form of vegetative reproduction)
viride	green
virosa	poisonous, stinking
viscosa, viscosum	sticky, gummy
vulgare, vulgaris, vulgatum . .	common, ordinary. In a number of genera in Ireland, the species so called is not the most frequently encountered.
xanthochlora	yellowish-green

INDEX TO IRISH COMMON NAMES

For any entry where more than one page reference is given the primary reference is in **bold-face** type.

INDEX TO LATIN AND ENGLISH NAMES

For any entry where more than one page reference is given the primary reference
is in **bold-face** type.